Strength of N

Strength of Materials

*

G. H. RYDER
M.A.(Cantab.), A.M.I.Mech.E.

Principal Lecturer
Royal Military College of Science, Shrivenham

THIRD EDITION IN SI UNITS

M

First published 1953
Reprinted with amendments 1955
Second Edition 1957
Reprinted with amendments 1958
Third Edition 1961
Reprinted 1963
Reprinted with additions 1965
Third Editions in SI units 1969
Reprinted 1970
Reprinted 1971
Reprinted with corrections 1973
Reprinted 1974, 1975, 1977, 1979, 1980 (twice), 1982, 1983

Demy 8vo, xii + 340 pages
287 line illustrations

Published by
THE MACMILLAN PRESS LTD
London and Basingstoke
Companies and representatives throughout the world

ISBN 0 333 10794 2 (hard cover)
0 333 10928 7 (paper cover)

Printed in Hong Kong

Preface

The principal feature of this edition is the introduction of the Systéme International d'Unités (SI), under which the United Kingdom is adopting the metric system. Also the opportunity has been taken to bring the notation up to date, by the use of sigma and tau for stresses, epsilon for strains, for example.

It sets out to cover in one volume the whole of the work required up to final degree standard in Strength of Materials. The only prior knowledge assumed is of elementary applied mechanics and calculus. Consequently, it should prove of value to students preparing for the Higher National Certificate and professional institution examinations, as well as those following a degree, or diploma course.

The main aim has been to give a clear understanding of the principles underlying engineering design, and a special effort has been made to indicate the shortest analysis of a wide variety of problems. Each chapter, starting with assumptions and theory, is complete in itself and is built up logically to cover all aspects of the particular theory. In this way the student is made aware of the limitations from the start, and, although he may leave sections of a chapter to be digested later, it should enable him to avoid making errors in principle.

Separate paragraph numbers are used for each chapter to enable quick reference to be made, and equation numbers quoted in worked examples are from the current paragraph except where stated. A summary of formulae, methods, and underlying principles is given at the end of each chapter; specialized works of reference have been quoted for the use of readers wishing to extend their knowledge of a particular branch of the work.

Examples worked out in the text, and problems given at the end of each chapter, are typical of National Certificate and Degree standard. The aim has been to present a diversity of problems without undue overlapping. Acknowledgement is made to the Senate of the University of London for permission to use questions from their examination papers, which have been marked U.L. Numerical answers are given to all the problems.

1969 G. H. RYDER

Contents

Chapter		Page
	INTRODUCTION	
	Strength of Materials. Conditions of Equilibrium. Stress-Strain Relations. Compatibility. SI Units	xi
I	DIRECT STRESS	
	Load. Stress. Principle of St. Venant. Strain. Hooke's Law. Modulus of Elasticity (Young's Modulus). Tensile Test. Factor of Safety. Strain Energy, Resilience. Impact Loads. Varying Cross-section and Load. Compound Bars. Temperature Stresses. Elastic Packings. Stress Concentrations	1
II	SHEAR STRESS	
	Shear Stress. Complementary Shear Stress. Shear Strain. Modulus of Rigidity. Strain Energy. Cottered Joints. Riveted Joints. Eccentric Loading	24
III	COMPOUND STRESS AND STRAIN	
	Oblique Stress. Simple Tension. Note on Diagrams. Pure Shear. Pure Normal Stresses on Given Planes. General Two-dimensional Stress System. Principal Planes. Principal Stresses. Shorter Method for Principal Stresses. Maximum Shear Stress. Mohr's Stress Circle. Poisson's Ratio. Two-dimensional Stress System. Principal Strains in Three Dimensions. Principal Stresses Determined from Principal Strains. Analysis of Strain. Mohr's Strain Circle. Volumetric Strain. Strain Energy. Shear Strain Energy. Theories of Failure. Graphical Representation. Conclusions	34
IV	ELASTIC CONSTANTS	
	Elastic Constants. Bulk Modulus. Relation between E and G	65
V	SHEARING FORCE AND BENDING MOMENT	
	Shearing Force. Bending Moment. Types of Load. Types of Support. Relations between w, F and M. Concentrated Loads. Uniformly Distributed Loads. Combined Loads. Varying Distributed Loads. Graphical Method	71
VI	BENDING STRESS	
	Pure Bending. Moments of Inertia. Graphical Determination of Moment of Inertia. Bending Stresses. Stress Concentrations in Bending. Combined Bending and Direct Stress. Middle Third Rule for Rectangular Sections. Middle Quarter Rule for Circular Sections. Composite Beams. Reinforced Concrete Beams. Principal Moments of Inertia. Unsymmetrical Bending	86
VII	SHEAR STRESS IN BEAMS	
	Variation of Shear Stress. Rectangular Section. I-Section. Principal Stresses in I-Beams. Pitch of Rivets in Built-up Girders. Solid Circular Section. Thin Circular Tube. Miscellaneous Sections. Shear Centre	117

Chapter		Page
VIII	TORSION	
	Circular Shafts. Strain Energy in Torsion. Shafts of Varying Diameter. Stress Concentrations in Torsion. Shafts under Action of Varying Torque. Compound Shafts. Torsion Beyond the Yield Point. Combined Bending and Twisting. Rectangular Shafts. Torsion of Thin Tubular Sections. Torsion of Thin-Walled Cellular Sections. Torsion of Thin Rectangular Members. Torsion of Thin Open Sections ..	130
IX	DEFLECTION OF BEAMS	
	Strain Energy due to Bending. Application to Impact. Deflection by Calculus. Macaulay's Method. Moment-Area Method. Method of Deflection Coefficients. Deflection due to Shear. Deflection by Graphical Method	152
X	BUILT-IN AND CONTINUOUS BEAMS	
	Moment-Area Method for Built-in Beams. Macaulay Method. Continuous Beams. Beams on Elastic Foundations. Portal Frames	178
XI	BENDING OF CURVED BARS AND RIGID FRAMES	
	Stresses in Bars of Small Initial Curvature. Stresses in Bars of Large Initial Curvature. Deflection of Curved Bars (Direct Method). Deflection from Strain Energy (Castigliano's Theorem). Portal Frame by Strain Energy	195
XII	PLASTIC THEORY OF BENDING	
	Bending Beyond the Yield Stress. Assumptions in the Plastic Theory. Moment of Resistance at a Plastic Hinge. Collapse Loads. Combined Bending and Direct Stress. Portal Frames—Collapse Loads	209
XIII	SPRINGS	
	Close-coiled Helical Springs. Open-coiled Helical Springs. Leaf Springs. Flat Spiral Springs	225
XIV	STRUTS	
	Definition. Pin-ended (Hinged) Strut Axially Loaded. Direction-fixed at Both Ends. Partial Fixing of the Ends. Direction-fixed at One End and Free at the Other. Direction-fixed at One End and Position-fixed at the Other. Strut with Eccentric Load. Strut with Initial Curvature. Limitations of Euler Theory. Rankine-Gordon Formula. Johnson's Parabolic Formula. Perry-Robertson Formula. Straight-Line Formulae. Strut with Lateral Loading. Tie with Lateral Loading. Struts of Varying Cross-Section—Energy Method	238

Chapter		Page
XV	CYLINDERS AND SPHERES Thin Cylinder under Internal Pressure. Thin Spherical Shell under Internal Pressure. Cylindrical Shell with Hemispherical Ends. Volumetric Strain on Capacity. Tube under Combined Loading. Wire Winding of Thin Cylinders. Rotational Stresses in Thin Cylinders. Thick Cylinders. Internal Pressure only. Plastic Yielding of Thick Tubes. Compound Tubes. Hub Shrunk on Solid Shaft. Thick Spherical Shells	259
XVI	ROTATING DISCS AND CYLINDERS Disc of Uniform Thickness. Solid Disc. Disc with Central Hole. Long Cylinder. Disc of Uniform Strength. Temperature Stresses in Uniform Disc. Plastic Collapse of Rotating Discs	287
XVII	CIRCULAR PLATES Circular Plates Symmetrically Loaded. Solid Circular Plate. Annular Ring, Loaded Round Inner Edge	295
XVIII	VIBRATIONS AND CRITICAL SPEEDS Linear Vibrations. Torsional Oscillations—Single Inertia. Torsional Oscillations—Two Inertias. Torsional Oscillations of Spring. Transverse Vibrations—Single Mass. Transverse Vibrations of Uniform Beam. Transverse Vibrations—Combined Loading. Energy Method for Frequency. Whirling of Shafts. Whirling of Eccentrically Mounted Mass	302
XIX	MATERIAL TESTING AND EXPERIMENTAL METHODS Tensile Tests. Compression Tests. Hardness Tests. Impact Tests. Effect of Carbon Content. Effect of Tempering. Creep. Fatigue. Extensometers. Electrical Resistance Strain Gauges. Photo-Elastic Stress Analysis. Brittle Lacquers	320
Appendix—TABLE OF ELASTIC CONSTANTS		337
Index		338

Notation

A, a	Area, constants
B, b	Width.
D, d	Diameter, depth.
E	Young's Modulus.
e	Eccentricity, extension.
F	Shearing force.
f	Frequency of vibration.
G	Modulus of rigidity.
g	Acceleration due to gravity.
h	Distance, height.
I	Moment of inertia.
J	Polar moment of inertia.
K	Bulk modulus, radius of gyration.
k	Stress concentration factor, stiffness of shaft, spring, or beam
L, l	Length. Load factor.
M	Bending moment, mass.
m	Modular ratio, mass.
P	Load.
p	Pressure or compressive stress.
R, r	Radius, reaction.
S	Shape factor.
T	Torque.
t	Thickness, temperature, time.
U	Strain energy—resilience.
u	Radial shift.
V, v	Volume.
W	Concentrated load
w	Distributed load, weight per unit length.
X, x	Co-ordinate; extension.
Y, y	Co-ordinate; deflection.
Z	Section modulus.
z	Co-ordinate; intercept.
α	Coefficient of thermal expansion, angle.
δ	Deflection.
ε	Direct Strain.
θ	Slope of beam, twist of shaft
ϕ	Shear strain, chord angle.
ρ	Density.
σ	Direct stress.
$\sigma_x, \sigma_y, \sigma_z$	Stresses in Directions OX, OY, OZ
$\sigma_1, \sigma_2, \sigma_3$	Principal stresses.
τ	Shear stress.
ν	Poisson's ratio.
ω	Angular velocity.
$\wedge$	Sign for maximum (e.g., $\widehat{M}$).

Introduction

Strength of Materials is the study of the behaviour of structural and machine members under the action of external loads, taking into account the internal forces created and the resulting deformations. Analysis is directed towards determining the limiting loads which the member can stand before failure of the material or excessive deformation occurs. To this end three basic sets of relations can be obtained, as set out in the following paragraphs.

Throughout the text it will be shown how these conditions are brought into play. It will not always be necessary to apply all the conditions, as simplified analysis may be suggested by symmetry or approximations. In other cases relations will be obtained by indirect methods, e.g. by strain energy or virtual work, which themselves incorporate certain of the basic conditions.

Conditions of Equilibrium. The external forces and reactions on a member (including inertia forces if necessary) must form a system in equilibrium, and are therefore related by a certain number of equations, known as the conditions of equilibrium, depending on the configuration.*

In a general three-dimensional system six such equations are obtained, in a coplanar system three, reducing to two if the forces are parallel or concurrent. These equations can be obtained by resolving or taking moments, and the number of unknown forces or reactions which can thereby be determined is equal to the number of such equations.

Stress-Strain Relations. It will be shown subsequently that for a given material there are relations between the strains (i.e. deformation) in a member and the stresses (i.e. internal forces) producing them. These stresses and strains can be analysed by methods to be developed, and equations connecting them can be obtained. The number of such relations depends on the complication of the system in a similar manner to that of the preceding paragraph.

Compatibility. Sometimes a number of relations can be obtained between the strains or deformations to ensure that the system derived from any assumptions made is compatible, i.e. the deformations can exist concurrently. Such conditions clearly arise where a number of parts have to fit together, as in the analysis of compound bars, beams, and cylinders.

* See author's *Mechanics Applied to Engineering*.

SI Units. In this system the fundamental units of mass, length and time are the kilogramme (kg), metre (m), and second (s).

The derived unit of force is a Newton (N), being that force which produces unit acceleration on unit mass, i.e.

$$1\text{N} = 1 \text{ kg.m/s}^2$$

(note that, where standard gravitational acceleration is 9·81 m/s^2, the force of gravity – weight – on 1 kg is 9·81 N).

Multiples and sub-multiples of the basic units can be used, preferably in steps of 10^3 (e.g. mm length, kN = 1000 N, MN = 10^6 N, etc.). The basic unit of stress or pressure is N/m^2, but since this is very small, a more realistic unit for stress analysis is the MN/m^2 or N/mm^2. It will be seen that these are equal in value, and in the present text the latter has been preferred, giving a clearer interpretation of stress as the force acting on a "point" area.

CHAPTER I

Direct Stress

1.1. Load. Any engineering design which is built up of a number of members is in equilibrium under the action of external forces and the reactions at the points of support.

Each individual member of the design is subjected to external forces which constitute the *load* on the member. Since the member is itself in equilibrium the resultant of all the forces acting on it must be zero, but they produce a tendency for the body to be deformed or torn asunder. This action is resisted by the internal forces of cohesion between particles of the material itself. The external forces may be transmitted through contact with other members, or may be due to fluid pressure, gravity, or inertia effects.

The simplest type of load (P) is a direct pull or push, known technically as ***tension*** or ***compression***, as illustrated in Fig. 1.1.

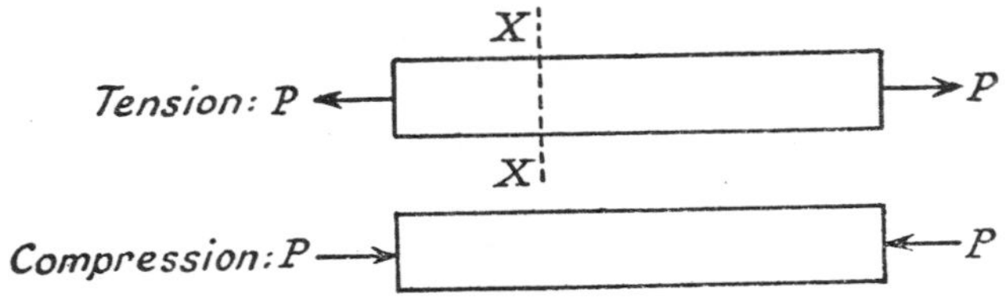

Fig. 1.1

An example of tension is provided by the rope attached to a crane hook, and of compression the leg of a table. In each case the load consists of two equal and opposite forces acting in line and tending to fracture the member. The forces on the crane rope are the load being raised at the one end and the pull of the winding gear at the other, and on the table leg a portion of the table weight on top and the reaction of the ground underneath. In structural frameworks some members will be in tension, some in compression, the load consisting of the reactions through the joints at the ends of the member.

If the member is in motion the load may be caused partly by dynamic or inertia forces. For instance the connecting rod of a reciprocating engine is acted on by inertia forces due to piston acceleration and due to its own acceleration, as well as gas pressure forces on the piston and gravity effects. Again, the load on a flywheel is created by the centrifugal forces on the particles of the rim.

Load will be measured in kg or Newtons (N). The standard gravity force on 1 kg is 9·81 N.

1.2. Stress. Across any section such as XX of the member represented in Fig. 1.1 the total force carried must equal the load P. This is distributed among the internal forces of cohesion, which are called *stresses*.

If the member is imagined cut through the section XX (Fig. 1.2), each portion is in equilibrium under the action of the external load P and the stresses at XX.

Stresses which are normal to the plane on which they act are called *direct* stresses, and are either *tensile* or *compressive*.

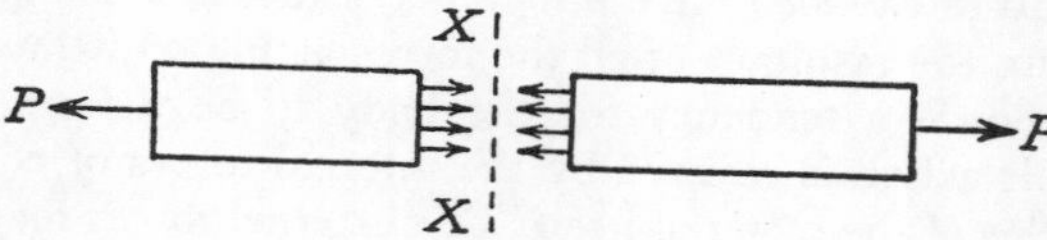

Fig. 1.2

The force transmitted across any section, divided by the area of that section, is called the *intensity of stress*, or, for brevity, the *stress* (σ). If it is assumed that the load is uniformly distributed over the section, then

$$\sigma = P/A$$

where A is the area.

In a great many instances the intensity of stress varies throughout the member, and the stress at any point is defined as the limiting ratio of $\delta P/\delta A$ for a small area enclosing that point.

(Stress is force per unit area, and the S.I. units are N/m^2 or multiples of this).

1.3. Principle of St. Venant. This principle states that the actual distribution of the load over the surface of its application will not affect the distribution of stress or strain on sections of the body which are at an appreciable distance (relative to the dimensions) away from the load. Any convenient statically equivalent loading may therefore be substituted for the actual load distribution, provided that the stress analysis in the region of the load is not required.

For instance, a rod in simple tension may have the end load applied either (a) centrally concentrated, or (b) distributed round the circumference of the rod, or (c) distributed over the end cross-section. All these are statically equivalent, but case (c) is the simplest to deal with analytically, and St. Venant's principle provides the justification for always assuming this distribution to apply. For points in the rod distant more than three times its greatest width from the area of loading no appreciable error will be introduced.

1.4. Strain. Strain is a measure of the deformation produced in the member by the load.

Direct stresses produce a change in length in the direction of the stress. If a rod of length l is in tension and the stretch or elongation produced is x, then the direct strain ε is defined as the ratio

$$\frac{\text{Elongation}}{\text{Original length}}$$

or

$$\varepsilon = x/l$$

Normally, tensile strains will be considered positive and compressive strains (i.e. a decrease in length) negative.

Note that strain is a *ratio*, or change per unit length, and hence *dimensionless*.

1.5. Hooke's Law. Principle of Superposition. This states that *strain is proportional to the stress producing it*, and forms the basis of later analysis in this book. It is obeyed within certain limits of stress by most ferrous alloys (see Para. 1.7), and can usually be assumed to apply with sufficient accuracy to other engineering materials such as timber, concrete, and non-ferrous alloys.

In this chapter only direct stresses and the resultant strains are being considered, but in general a material is said to be *elastic* if all the deformations are proportional to the load. Where a number of loads are acting together on an elastic material, the principle of superposition states that the resultant strain will be the sum of the individual strains caused by each load acting separately.

1.6. Modulus of Elasticity (Young's Modulus). Within the limits for which Hooke's law is obeyed, the ratio of the direct stress to the strain produced is called Young's Modulus or the Modulus of Elasticity (E), i.e.

$$E = \sigma/\varepsilon \tag{1}$$

For a bar of uniform cross-section A and length l this can be written

$$E = Pl/Ax \tag{2}$$

E is therefore a constant for a given material, and is usually assumed to be the same in tension or compression. For those materials mentioned in Para. 1.5 which do not exactly obey Hooke's law it is frequently possible to apply an average value of E over a given range of stress, to satisfy the above equations.

Young's modulus represents the stress required to cause unit strain, i.e. provided Hooke's law continued to be obeyed, a stress numerically equal to the modulus, when applied to a uniform bar, would cause the length to be doubled. In fact, however, for engineering materials the strain will rarely exceed 1/1000, so that the change in length may always be considered small compared with the original length, e.g. mild steel has a value of E approximately 205,000 N/mm^2 and will rarely be stressed higher than 150 N/mm^2. At this value the strain is

$$150/205{,}000 = 0{\cdot}00073 \quad \text{from (1) above,}$$

so that a bar 1 m long will change in length by 0·73 mm.

To sum up, most metals have a high value of E and consequently the strains are always small. On the other hand rubber, though it does not obey Hooke's law very accurately, has a low value of E and will undergo considerable deformation at moderate stress values.

Particular values of E for various materials are given in the Appendix.

Since strain is dimensionless, it follows that the units of E are the same as those of σ.

1.7. Tensile Test. The following remarks apply mainly to the behaviour of ***mild steel***, but other engineering materials show the same phenomena to a varying degree. Further discussion of tensile tests will be found in Chapter XIX.

The test is carried out on a bar of uniform cross-section, usually circular, in a testing machine which indicates the tensile load being applied. For the very small strains involved in the early part of the test, the elongation of a measured length (called the *gauge length*) is recorded

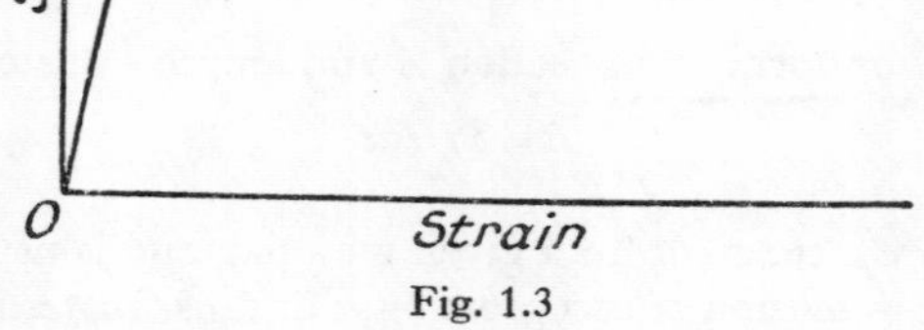

Fig. 1.3

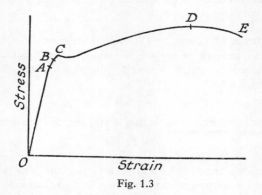

by an "extensometer" or "strain gauge" (for particular types see Paras. 19.9 and 19.10).

The load is increased gradually, and at first the elongation, and hence the strain, is proportional to the load (and hence to the stress). This relation (i.e. Hooke's law) holds up to a value of the stress known as the *limit of proportionality* (point A in Fig. 1.3). Hooke's law ceases to be obeyed beyond this point, although the material may still be in the "elastic" state, in the sense that, if the load were removed, the strain would also return to zero. The point B shows the *elastic limit.*

If the material is stressed beyond this point, some *plastic* deformation will occur, i.e. strain which is not recoverable if the load is removed.

The next important occurrence is the *yield point* C, at which the metal shows an appreciable strain even without further increase in load. In an actual test the extensometer would be removed at or before the yield point, further extension being measurable by dividers and scale. With mild steel careful testing will reveal a drop in load immediately yielding commences, so that there are two values, known as the *upper* and *lower* yield points. For materials showing no definite yield, a *proof stress* is used to determine the onset of plastic strain (Para. 19.1).

After yielding has taken place, further straining can only be achieved by increasing the load, the stress-strain curve continuing to rise up to the point D. The strain in the region from C to D is in the region of 100 times that from O to C, and is partly elastic (i.e. recoverable), but mainly plastic (i.e. permanent strain). At this stage (D) the bar begins to form a local "neck," the load falling off from the maximum until fracture at E. Although in design the material will only be used in the range OA, it is useful to examine the other properties obtained from the test.

The *maximum,* or *ultimate, tensile stress* is calculated by dividing the load at D by the *original* cross-sectional area. Here it should be pointed out that the true stress occurring in the necked portion is much higher than this, and in fact reaches its greatest value at the breaking load, but it is the stress which a member can stand distributed over its original area which interests the designer.

The capacity for being drawn out plastically before breaking is called the *ductility* of the material, and is measured by the following two quantities. If the total increase in the gauge length at fracture is expressed as a percentage of its original length, the figure is called the *percentage elongation.* A similar calculation of the reduction in cross-sectional area at the neck, expressed as a percentage of the original area, gives the *percentage reduction in area or contraction.* The latter is considered to be a better measure of ductility, being independent of the gauge length, but both elongation and contraction are made up of "uniform" and "local" deformations in proportions depending on the material (see Para. 19.1 (e)).

EXAMPLE 1. *The following results were obtained in a tensile test on a mild-steel specimen of original diameter 2 cm. and gauge length 4 cm.*

At the limit of proportionality the load was 80,000N and the extension

0·048 mm. The specimen yielded at a load of 85,000 N, and the maximum load withstood was 150,000 N.

When the two parts were fitted together after being broken, the length between gauge points was found to be 5·56 cm, and the diameter at the neck was 1·58 cm.

Calculate Young's modulus and the stress at the limit of proportionality, the yield stress, and ultimate tensile stress; also the percentage elongation and contraction.

Hooke's law is obeyed up to the limit of proportionality, and Young's modulus is calculated from $E=Pl/Ax$ (Eq. (2), Para. 1.6).

$P=80{,}000$ N. $\qquad l=4$ cm

$A=\pi$ cm^2 $\qquad x=0{\cdot}048$ mm

$$\therefore\ E=\frac{80{,}000\times 4\times 10}{\pi\times 100\times 0{\cdot}048}$$

$$=213{,}000\ \text{N/mm}^2$$

Stress at limit of proportionality $=P/A=255$ N/mm^2

Yield stress $=85{,}000/\pi\times 100=271$ N/mm^2

Ultimate tensile stress $=150{,}000/\pi\times 100=478$ N/mm^2

$$\text{Percentage elongation}=\frac{5{\cdot}56-4}{4}\times 100=39\%$$

$$\text{Percentage contraction}=\frac{2^2-1{\cdot}58^2}{2^2}\times 100=38\%$$

1.8. Factor of Safety. It has been pointed out that stress is calculated from a knowledge of the magnitude and position of application of the load, the dimensions of the member, and the properties of the material. In practice none of these factors is known exactly, and possible errors arise from various sources.

(a) *The type of load* may be described as "dead" load (i.e. static, probably gravity), "live" load (such as vehicles crossing a bridge), "fluctuating" load (e.g. the alternating tension and compression in the connecting rod of a reciprocating engine—see "fatigue"), or "impact" or shock load. The magnitude of the load is frequently subject to uncertainty, and for a given member the permissible load decreases in the order of the types just described. Other approximations are involved when, for simplification of analysis, the load is assumed to be concentrated at a point, or uniformly distributed over an area.

(b) *The dimensions of the member* should be known with accuracy, though any sudden changes of cross-section will cause stress concentrations which cannot easily be analysed (see Paras. 1.15 and 8.4). In this respect methods of manufacture (e.g. cast, forged, or machined surfaces) and standards of workmanship will have their influence.

(c) *The character of the material* is usually assumed to be homogeneous and isotropic. The latter implies that the elastic properties are the same in all directions, which is true for most metals but certainly not so for timber. Steels and most ductile materials can be assumed to have the same strength in tension and compression, but cast iron and concrete are much weaker in tension than compression. Cast materials are always liable to internal flaws and inclusions which may be sources of weakness.

(d) *Hooke's law is assumed to apply*, which will introduce an error when dealing with cast iron, concrete, and non-ferrous alloys.

Other assumptions made in particular parts of the theory will be stated in the appropriate chapter.

In spite of all these approximations and assumptions, a body of theory has been developed which in many cases can be shown to agree with experimental results within a reasonable margin of error, and forms the basis for sound design. When dealing with problems outside the scope of mathematical analysis the engineer must use his experience to suggest simplifications which will enable an estimate of the stresses to be made. Alternatively, an experimental method may be employed, such as photo-elasticity (Para. 19.11).

The maximum permissible stress, or *working stress*, is determined from a consideration of the above factors, taking into account the social and economic consequences of failure, and the *factor of safety* is normally defined as the ratio between the ultimate tensile stress and the working stress, i.e.

$$\text{Factor of safety} = \frac{\text{Ultimate stress}}{\text{Working stress}}$$

Based on this definition, values used in engineering design will vary from about 3 (for dead loads accurately known) to 12 (for shock loads of indefinite magnitude).

It is becoming more frequent practice to define the factor of safety as the ratio of the yield stress (or sometimes the elastic limit) to the working stress, since the member is considered to have "failed" if the stress in any part of it is sufficient to cause plastic deformation. If this interpretation is intended, it should be stated, otherwise the previous definition will be assumed.

A more logical approach, particularly for ductile materials and all problems of instability (e.g. struts), is to work with a *load factor*, being the ratio between the load at failure and the working load. Again, where rigidity is the main criterion, design may be based on a limiting deflection when subjected to the working load.

A more detailed discussion of the cause of failure is reserved until later (Para. 3.21).

1.9. Strain Energy, Resilience. When a tensile or compressive load P is applied to a bar there is a change in length x which, for an elastic material, is proportional to the load (Fig. 1.4). The *strain energy* (U) of the bar is defined as the work done by the load in straining it.

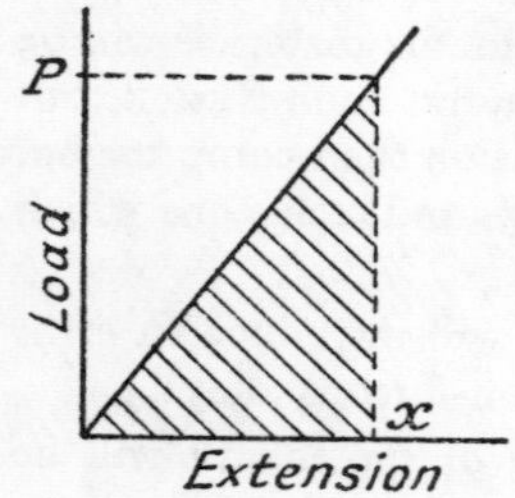

Fig. 1.4

For a gradually applied or "static" load the work done is represented by the shaded area in Fig. 1.4, giving

$$U = \tfrac{1}{2}Px \qquad (1)$$

To express the strain energy in terms of the stress and dimensions, for a bar of uniform section A and length l substitute $P = \sigma A$ (Para. 1.2) and $x = \sigma l/E$ (Para. 1.6), giving

$$U = \tfrac{1}{2}.\sigma A.\sigma l/E$$

$$= (\sigma^2/2E)Al \qquad (2)$$

But Al is the volume of the bar, and hence equation (2) can be stated: "the strain energy per unit volume (usually called the *resilience*) in simple tension or compression is $\sigma^2/2E$."

Proof resilience is the value at the elastic limit, or at the proof stress for non-ferrous materials (see Para. 19.1).

Strain energy is always a positive quantity, and, being work units, will be expressed in $N\,m$ (i.e. Joules).

EXAMPLE 2. *Calculate the strain energy of the bolt shown in Fig. 1·5 under a tensile load of 10 kN.*

Show that the strain energy is increased, for the same maximum stress, by turning down the shank of the bolt to the root diameter of the thread. $E = 205{,}000$ *N/mm²*

It is normal practice to assume that the load is distributed evenly over the core of the screwed portion (i.e. the root diameter 16.6 mm. Area of core $= 217$ mm².

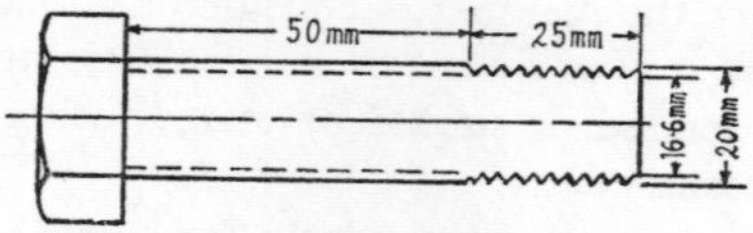

Fig. 1.5

Stress in screwed portion $= 10{,}000/217$
$= 46$ N/mm²

Stress in shank (at 20 mm dia., area 314 mm²)
$= 10{,}000/314$
$= 31{\cdot}8$ N/mm²

Total strain energy, from (2)

$$= \frac{1}{2 \times 205,000}(46^2 \times 217 \times 25 + 31{\cdot}8^2 \times 314 \times 50)$$
$$= 67 \text{ N.mm}$$

If now the shank is turned down to 16·6 mm dia. the stress in the bolt will be 46 N/mm^2 throughout, and the strain energy

$$= 46^2 \times 217 \times 75/(2 \times 205,000)$$
$$= 84 \text{ N.mm.}$$

The reader should check the calculation by using equation (1), in which $P = 10$ kN and x is the total extension of the bolt.

1.10. Impact Loads. Supposing a weight W falls through a height h on to a collar attached to one end of a uniform bar, the other end being fixed. Then an extension will be caused which is greater than that due to the application of the same load gradually applied. (Note that, if the bar does not fail, W will subsequently oscillate about, and come to rest in, the normal equilibrium position.)

In Fig. 1.6, x is the maximum extension set up, and the corresponding stress in the bar is σ.

Let P be the equivalent static or gradually applied load which would produce the same extension x. Then the strain energy in the bar at this instant is $\frac{1}{2}Px$, by Para. 1.9.

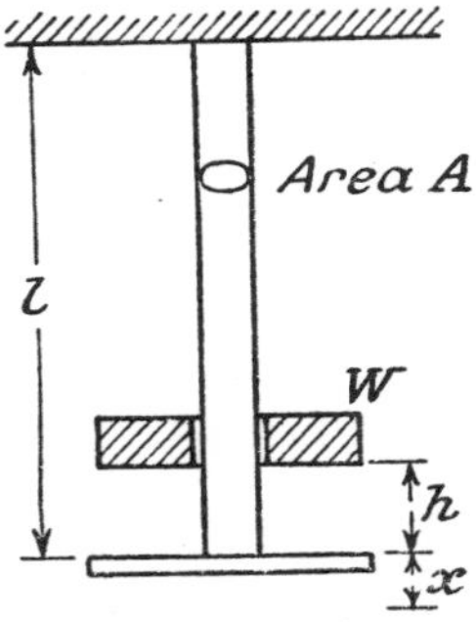

Fig. 1.6

Neglecting loss of energy at impact, the following equation is obtained:

Loss of potential energy of weight = Gain of strain energy of bar

i.e. $$W(h + x) = \tfrac{1}{2}Px$$

Applying the relation $x = Pl/AE$ (Para. 1.6), a quadratic in P is obtained, i.e.

$$W(h + Pl/AE) = \tfrac{1}{2}(P^2l/AE)$$

Rearranging, and multiplying through by AE/l,

$$P^2/2 - WP - WhAE/l = 0$$

Solving, and discarding the negative root,

$$P = W + \sqrt{(W^2 + 2WhAE/l)}$$
$$= W[1 + \sqrt{(1 + 2hAE/Wl)}]$$

From which $x = Pl/AE$ and $\sigma = P/A$ can be found.

The particular case of $h = 0$ (i.e. for a *suddenly applied* load) gives a value $P = 2W$; i.e. ***the stress produced by a suddenly applied load is twice the static stress.***

The above simple analysis assumes that the whole of the rod attains the same value of maximum stress at the same instant. This however is not strictly correct; a wave of stress is set up by the impact and is propagated along the rod. The actual maximum stress set up will then depend on the dimensions of the rod, its density, and the velocity of the load at impact. Usually the approximate analysis gives results on the "safe" side, but this is not always the case.

EXAMPLE 3. *Referring to Fig. 1·6, let a mass of 100 kg fall 4 cm on to a collar attached to a bar of steel 2 cm diameter, 3 m long. Find the maximum stress set up.* $E = 205{,}000\ N/mm^2$.

Applying the result just obtained

$$\sigma = P/A = W[1 + \sqrt{(1 + 2hAE/Wl)}]/A \text{ where } W = 100 \times 9{\cdot}81 \text{ N}$$

$$= \frac{981}{100\pi}\left[1 + \sqrt{\left(1 + \frac{2 \times 40 \times \pi \times 100 \times 205{,}000}{981 \times 3 \times 1{,}000}\right)}\right]$$

$$= 9{\cdot}81(1 + 42{\cdot}8)/\pi \quad \text{(note units are N and mm)}$$

$$= 134 \text{ N/mm}^2$$

i.e. even with only a 4 cm drop the maximum stress is nearly 44 times the "static" stress.

EXAMPLE 4. ***If in the previous problem the bar is turned down to*** **1** ***cm diameter along*** **1·5** ***m of its length, what will be the maximum stress and extension caused by the*** **100** ***kg load falling*** **4** ***cm?***

Let P be the equivalent gradually applied load to cause the same maximum stress. The corresponding extension is made up of two parts

$$x = Pl_1/A_1E + Pl_2/A_2E$$

$$= \frac{P.1500}{(25\pi)E} + \frac{P.1500}{(100\pi)E}$$

$$= \frac{75P}{\pi \times 205{,}000} \qquad \text{(i)}$$

Applying the energy equation

$$W(h + x) = \tfrac{1}{2}Px$$

$$981\left(40 + \frac{75P}{\pi \times 205{,}000}\right) = \tfrac{1}{2}P\frac{75P}{\pi \times 205{,}000} \qquad \text{(from (i))}$$

$$\times\frac{\pi \times 205{,}000}{75}: \qquad \frac{P^2}{2} - 981P - \frac{981 \times 40 \times \pi \times 205{,}000}{75} = 0$$

Solving $$P = 981 + \sqrt{\left(981^2 + \frac{981 \times 80\pi}{75} 205{,}000\right)}$$

$$= 981 + 981\sqrt{(1 + 700)}$$

$$= 27{,}000 \text{ N}$$

The maximum stress will occur in the smallest section, giving

$$\hat{\sigma} = \frac{P}{A} = \frac{27{,}000}{25\pi}$$

$$= 343 \text{ N/mm}^2$$

The maximum extension

$$x = \frac{75P}{\pi \times 205{,}000} \quad \text{from (i)}$$

$$= 3{\cdot}14 \text{ mm}$$

If the bar is already stressed before impact, e.g. if the collar in the previous examples is given a weight value, it would be correct to allow for the loss of potential energy of this weight after impact and equate the total loss of potential energy to the difference between the final and initial strain energies. Let W' be the weight of the collar and LM in Fig. 1.7 represent the further extension after impact, then the area ALMB represents the increase in strain energy. But area ALMC, being W' times the added extension, represents the loss of potential energy of the collar after impact, leaving area ABC to be equated to the loss of energy of the falling weight alone.

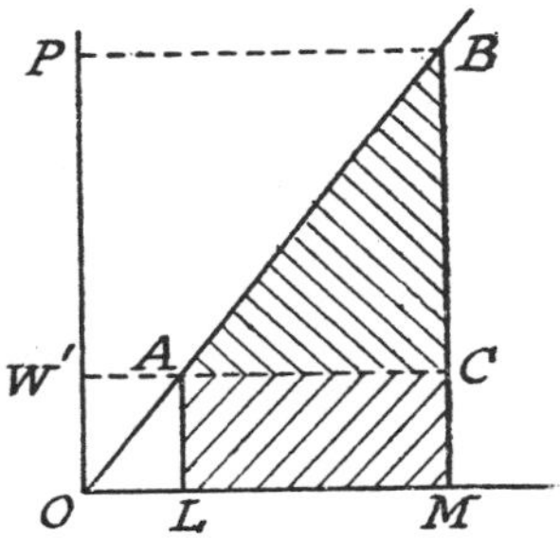

Fig. 1.7

Consequently the stress due to impact may be calculated without consideration of the initial stress, the final total stress being found by adding on the initial stress,

i.e. $$P = P' + W'$$

where P' is calculated on the assumption of zero initial stress (as in Fig. 1.8).

EXAMPLE 5. *The loads to be carried by a lift may be dropped 10 cm on to the floor. The cage itself weighs 100 kg and is supported by 25 m of wire rope weighing 0·9 kg/m, consisting of 49 wires each 1·6 mm diameter. The maximum stress in the wire is limited to 90 N/mm² and E for the rope is 70,000 N/mm². Find the maximum load which can be carried.*

The maximum stress will occur at the top of the wire rope, and the initial stress is found from the weight of cage and rope.

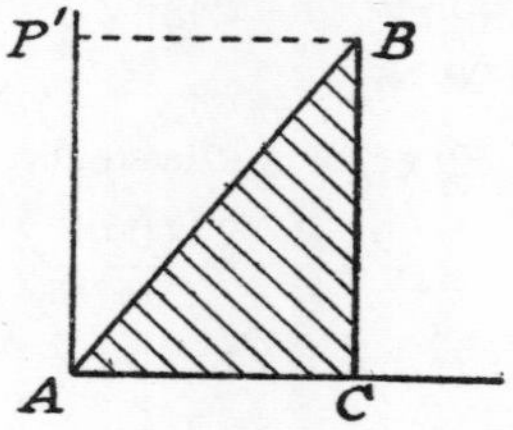

Fig. 1.8

$$\text{Initial stress} = \frac{100 + 25 \times 0{\cdot}9}{49 \times (\pi/4)1{\cdot}6^2}$$

$$= 1{\cdot}24 \text{ kg/mm}^2 = 12{\cdot}2 \text{ N/mm}^2$$

Subtracting this from the permissible stress of 90 N/mm^2 the increased stress due to impact is 77·8 N/mm^2. This would be caused by an equivalent static load of

$$77{\cdot}8 \times 49 \times (\pi/4)(1{\cdot}6)^2 = 7670 \text{ N} = 782 \text{ kg}$$

with an extension of

$$\frac{77{\cdot}8 \times 25 \times 100}{70{,}000} = 2{\cdot}78 \text{ cm.}$$

If W is the load dropped, applying the energy equation gives

$$W(h + x) = \tfrac{1}{2}Px$$

$$W(10 + 2{\cdot}78) = \tfrac{1}{2} \times 782 \times 2{\cdot}78$$

$$W = \frac{782 \times 2{\cdot}78}{2 \times 12{\cdot}78} = 85 \text{ kg}$$

1.11. Varying Cross-section and Load. It is usual to assume that the load is uniformly distributed over the cross-section, and hence the stress will be inversely proportional to the area.

The load also may vary, as in the case of a column where its own weight is to be taken into account, and in the case of inertia loading on members in motion.

EXAMPLE 6. *A rod of length l tapers uniformly from a diameter D at one end to a diameter d at the other. Find the extension caused by an axial load P.*

At a distance x from the small end the diameter is

$$d + (D - d)x/l \quad \text{by proportion (Fig. 1.9).}$$

The extension of a short length dx

$$= \frac{4P\,dx}{\pi[d + (D - d)x/l]^2 E}$$

and for the whole rod:

$$\text{Extension} = \int_0^l \frac{4P\,dx}{\pi[d+(D-d)x/l]^2 E}$$

$$= -\frac{l}{D-d}\cdot\frac{4P}{\pi E}\left\{\frac{1}{d+(D-d)x/l}\right\}_0^l$$

$$= \frac{4Pl}{\pi E(D-d)}\left(\frac{1}{d}-\frac{1}{D}\right)$$

$$= \frac{4Pl}{\pi DdE}$$

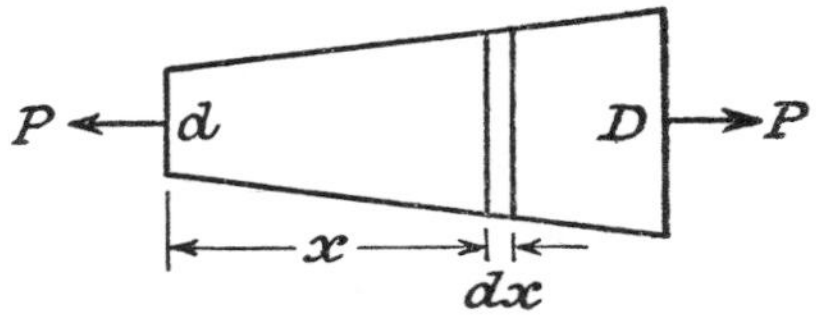

Fig. 1.9

EXAMPLE 7. *What is the condition for a column to have uniform strength (i.e. constant maximum stress) under the action of its own weight when a longitudinal stress σ is applied to the top?*

Let the cross-section at the top be a, and at a distance x from the top be A. Fig. 1.10 shows the forces acting on a slice of thickness dx, where w is the density and σ the uniform stress.

Equating forces

$$\sigma(A+dA)-\sigma A = wA\,dx$$

Separating variables $dA/A = w\,dx/\sigma$

Integrating $\quad \log_e A = (w/\sigma)x + C \qquad$ (i)

When $x=0$, $A=a$

$$\therefore C = \log_e a,$$

giving $\quad \log_e (A/a) = wx/\sigma \quad$ from (i)

or $$A = ae^{wx/\sigma}$$

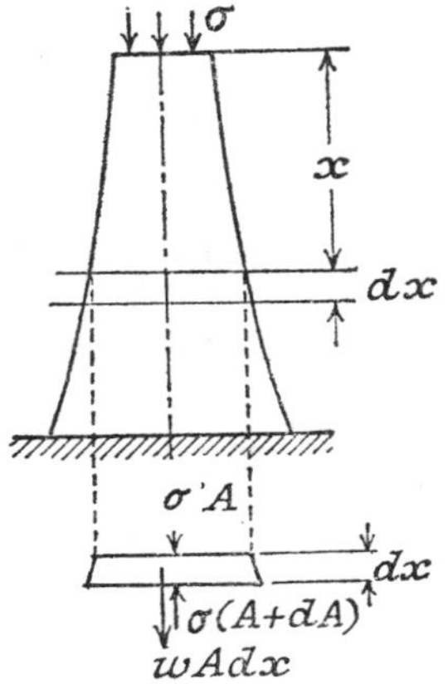

Fig. 1.10

EXAMPLE 8. *A steel rod of uniform section, 1 m long, is rotated about a vertical axis through one end at right angles to its length, at 1000 r.p.m. If the density of the material is 7·8 g/cm³ find the maximum stress.*

Let the stress at a distance x from the axis be σ, in Fig. 1.11, and at $x+dx$, $\sigma+d\sigma$. Writing the area as A, density ρ, and angular velocity ω, the forces acting on an element of length dx are shown in Fig. 1.12, $(\rho\ Adx)x\omega^2$ being the centrifugal force.

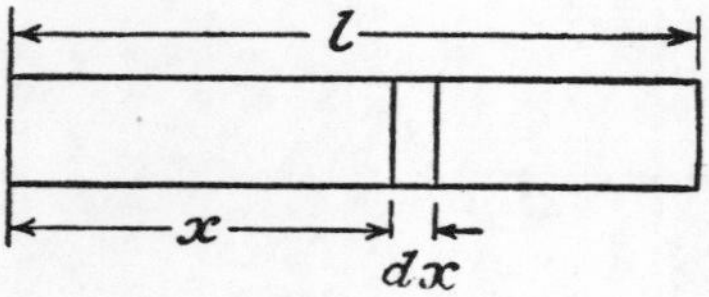

Fig. 1.11

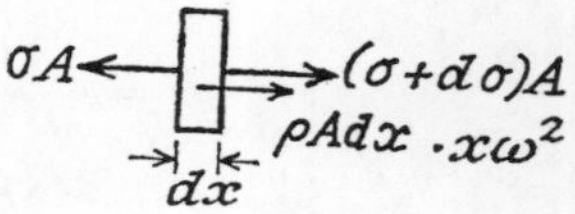

Fig. 1.12

For equilibrium

$$(\sigma + d\sigma)A - \sigma A + (\rho A dx)x\omega^2 = 0$$

or

$$d\sigma = -(\rho x\omega^2)dx$$

Integrating

$$\sigma = -\rho x^2\omega^2/2 + C \qquad \text{(i)}$$

When $x = l$, $\sigma = 0$

$$\therefore C = \rho l^2\omega^2/2$$

and

$$\sigma = (\rho\omega^2/2)(l^2 - x^2) \quad \text{from (i)}$$

The maximum stress occurs at the axis, $x = 0$,

i.e.

$$\sigma = \frac{\rho\omega^2 l^2}{2} = \frac{7{\cdot}8 \times 1000^2 \times (2\pi)^2 \times 1^2}{2 \times 60^2}$$

$$= 42{\cdot}8\ \text{N/mm}^2 \quad (1\ \text{N} = 1\ \text{kg m/s}^2)$$

1.12. Compound Bars. **Any tensile or compressive member which consists of two or more bars or tubes in parallel, usually of different materials, is called a "compound" bar. The method of analysis will be illustrated by two examples.**

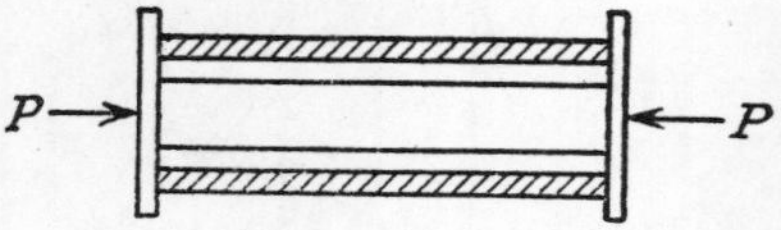

Fig. 1.13

Example 9. ***A compound bar (Fig. 1.13) is made up of a rod of area A_1 and modulus E_1, and a tube of equal length of area A_2 and modulus E_2. If a compressive load P is applied to the compound bar find how the load is shared.***

Since the rod and tube are of the same initial length, and must remain together, then the strain in each part must be the same. The total load carried is P, and let it be shared W_1 and W_2.

Compatibility equation: $\quad W_1/A_1E_1 = W_2/A_2E_2 \qquad$ (i)

Equilibrium equation: $\quad W_1 + W_2 = P \qquad$ (ii)

Substituting $W_2 = \frac{A_2}{A_1}\cdot\frac{E_2}{E_1}\cdot W_1$ from (i) in (ii) gives

$$W_1\left(1+\frac{A_2E_2}{A_1E_1}\right)=P$$

or

$$W_1=\frac{P.A_1E_1}{A_1E_1+A_2E_2}$$

Then

$$W_2=\frac{P.A_2E_2}{A_1E_1+A_2E_2}\quad \text{from (i)}$$

EXAMPLE 10. *A central steel rod 18 mm diameter passes through a copper sleeve 24 mm inside and 39 mm outside diameter. It is provided with nuts and washers at each end, and the nuts are tightened until a stress of 10 N/mm² is set up in the steel. The whole assembly is then placed in a lathe and a cut is taken along half the length of the tube, removing the copper to a depth of 1·5 mm* (a) *Calculate the stress now existing in the steel.* (b) *If an additional end thrust of 5000 N is applied to the ends of the steel bar calculate the final stress in the steel.* $E_s = 2E_c$.

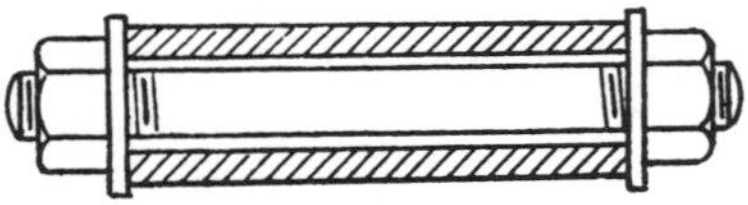

Fig. 1.14

When the nuts are tightened on the tube, the effect is to put the steel rod in tension (stress σ_{s1}), and the copper tube in compression (stress σ_{c1}).

Equilibrium equation:

Pull on rod = Push on tube

i.e.

$$\sigma_{s1}(\pi/4)\ 18^2=\sigma_{c1}(\pi/4)[39^2-24^2]$$

$$10\times 324=\sigma_{c1}(1521-576)$$

$$\text{giving } \sigma_{c1}=3{\cdot}43\ \text{N/mm}^2$$

(a) When the tube is reduced in area for half its length, let the compressive stresses be σ_{c2} in the reduced section and $\sigma_{c2'}$ in the remainder. Let σ_{s2} be the stress in the rod, and l the length of rod and tube.

Equilibrium equation:

Load on tube = Load on rod

i.e.

$$\sigma_{c2}(\pi/4)[36^2-24^2]=\sigma_{c2}'(\pi/4)[39^2-24^2]=\sigma_{s2}(\pi/4)18^2$$

$$\sigma_{c2}{\cdot}720=\sigma_{c2}'{\cdot}945=\sigma_{s2}{\cdot}324$$

From which

$$\sigma_{c2}=(9/20)\sigma_{s2} \quad \text{(i)}$$

and

$$\sigma_{c2}'=(12/35)\sigma_{s2} \quad \text{(ii)}$$

Compatibility equation:

Reduction in length of rod = Reduction in length of tube

i.e.

$$\frac{\sigma_{s1}-\sigma_{s2}}{E_s}\cdot l=\frac{\sigma_{c2}-\sigma_{c1}}{E_c}\cdot\frac{l}{2}+\frac{\sigma_{c2}'-\sigma_{c1}}{E_c}\cdot\frac{l}{2}$$

Note that reduction in length is caused by a decrease of tension in the rod and an increase of compression in the tube. Substituting the known values and solving for σ_{s2}, using (i) and (ii)

$$\frac{10-\sigma_{s2}}{2E_c}=\frac{(9/20)\sigma_{s2}-3{\cdot}43}{E_c}\cdot\frac{1}{2}+\frac{(12/35)\sigma_{s2}-3{\cdot}43}{E_c}\cdot\frac{1}{2}$$

$$10-\sigma_{s2}=(9/20)\,\sigma_{s2}-3{\cdot}43+(12/35)\sigma_{s2}-3{\cdot}43$$

$$(251/140)\sigma_{s2}=16{\cdot}86$$

i.e. $$\sigma_{s2}=9{\cdot}4\ \text{N/mm}^2$$

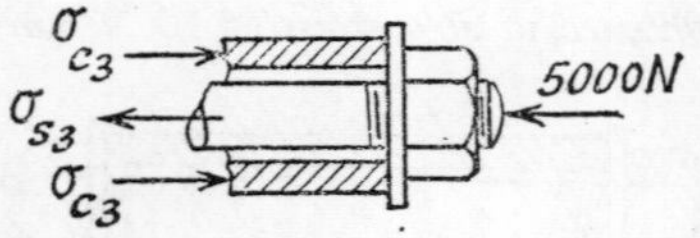

Fig. 1.15

(b) An additional end thrust of 5000 N will cause a further reduction in the tension in the rod and an increase in compression in the tube. Let the corresponding stresses be σ_{s3}, σ_{c3} in the reduced section, and σ_{c3}' in the remainder

Equilibrium equation:

$$5000=\sigma_{c3}(\pi/4)[36^2-24^2]-\sigma_{s3}(\pi/4)18^2$$

giving $$\sigma_{c3}=(9/20)\sigma_{s3}+8{\cdot}85 \qquad \text{(iii)}$$

The load must be constant along the length of the tube, giving

$$\sigma_{c3}'(\pi/4)(945)=\sigma_{c3}(\pi/4)720 \text{ as before}$$

i.e. $$\sigma_{c3}'=(16/21)\sigma_{c3}$$

$$=(12/35)\sigma_{s3}+6{\cdot}75 \quad \text{from (iii)} \qquad \text{(iv)}$$

Compatibility equation referred to initial conditions,

$$\frac{\sigma_{s1}-\sigma_{s3}}{E_s}\cdot l=\frac{\sigma_{c3}-\sigma_{c1}}{E_c}\cdot\frac{l}{2}+\frac{\sigma_{c3}'-\sigma_{c1}}{E_c}\cdot\frac{l}{2}$$

Substituting from (iii) and (iv) and solving for σ_{s3}

$$10-\sigma_{s3}=(9/20)\sigma_{s3}+8{\cdot}85-3{\cdot}43+(12/35)\sigma_{s3}+6{\cdot}75-3{\cdot}43$$

$$(251/140)\sigma_{s3}=1{\cdot}26$$

$$\sigma_{s3}=0{\cdot}7\ \text{N/mm}^2$$

1.13. Temperature Stresses. If a compound bar made up of several materials is subjected to a change in temperature there will be a tendency for the component parts to expand different amounts due to the unequal coefficients of thermal expansion. If the parts are constrained to remain together then the actual change in length must be the same for each. This change is the resultant (taking into account positive and negative strains) of the effects due to temperature and stress conditions.

EXAMPLE 11. *A steel tube 2·4 cm external diameter and 1·8 cm internal diameter encloses a copper rod 1·5 cm diameter to which it is rigidly joined at each end. If, at a temperature of 10°C there is no longitudinal stress calculate the stresses in the rod and tube when the temperature is raised to 200°C.*

$E_s = 210{,}000\ \text{N/mm}^2$ $\qquad\qquad E = 100{,}000\ \text{N/mm}^2$

Coefficients of linear expansion: $\alpha_s = 11 \times 10^{-6}/°C.$, $\alpha_c = 18 \times 10^{-6}/°C.$

From the constants given it is seen that the copper rod would expand more than the steel tube if it were free. Since the two are joined together the copper will be prevented from expanding its full amount and will be put in compression, the steel being put in tension, the compound bar taking up an intermediate position (Fig. 1.16).

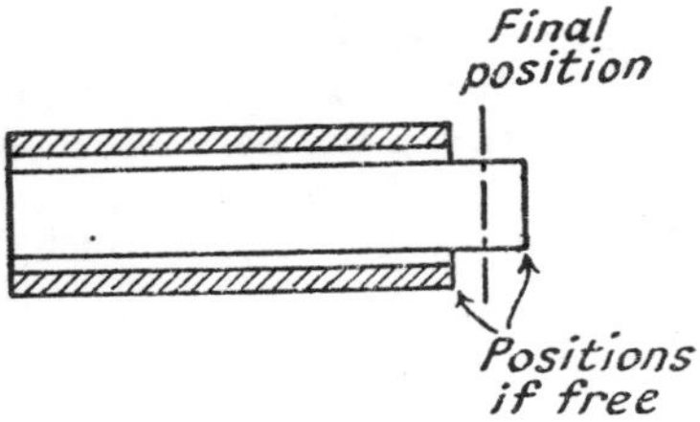

Fig. 1.16

Let σ_c = compressive stress in copper,

and σ_s = tensile stress in steel.

Equilibrium equation:

$$\sigma_c(\pi/4)(1{\cdot}5^2) = \sigma_s(\pi/4)[2{\cdot}4^2 - 1{\cdot}8^2]$$

i.e.
$$\sigma_c = 1{\cdot}12\sigma_s \qquad \text{(i)}$$

Compatibility equation: (it may be assumed that the original lengths are the same).

Temperature strain of rod − Compressive strain

= Temperature strain of tube + tensile strain

$$18 \times 10^{-6}(200 - 10) - \sigma_c/100{,}000 = 11 \times 10^{-6}(200 - 10) + \sigma_s/210{,}000$$

i.e.
$$4{\cdot}76\ \sigma_s + 10\ \sigma_c = 1330$$

Substituting for σ_c from (i) in (ii)

$$\sigma_s = 1330\ /\ 15{\cdot}96 = 83{\cdot}3\ \text{N/mm}^2$$

From (i):
$$\sigma_c = 1{\cdot}12 \times 83{\cdot}3 = 93{\cdot}3\ \text{N/mm}^2$$

1.14. Elastic Packings. This includes a variety of problems in which two parts are held together by bolts which are tightened against elastic washers or sheets of packing. Solution is obtained by a consideration of the statical equilibrium and the elasticity of the bolts and packing.

EXAMPLE 12. *A square rigid base plate of 20 cm. sides bears a column which applies a central load of 5 kN. The base plate is held down to a rigid foundation by 4 bolts placed symmetrically at the corners of a square of 16 cm sides. Between the base plate and the foundation there is a sheet of elastic packing. While the load is carried the bolts are tightened to a tension of 0·5 kN, the extension of the bolts being half the compression of the packing due to the load and the tension in the bolts. If the line of action of the load shifts 2 cm. parallel to a side of the base plate, find the new tensions in the bolts.*

(U.L.)

Since the eccentric load is equivalent to a central load and a couple, it follows that the base plate will rotate about its centre line, the net upthrust of the packing and bolts remaining equal to 5 kN.

Although the packing acts over an area, a "line" diagram can be considered (Fig. 1.17), in which the action of the bolts is shown in pairs

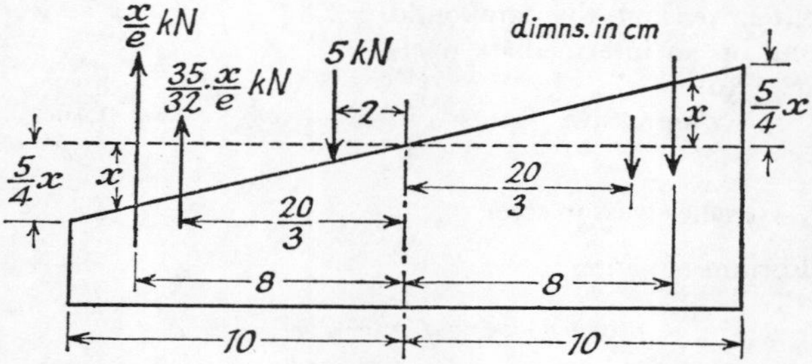

Fig. 1.17

and the upthrust of the packing is treated as a load per unit length of varying intensity.

Let the initial extension of each bolt be *e*. Let one pair of bolts increase in length by *x*, the other pair decreasing by *x*, when the load is shifted.

For two bolts together, the initial load of 1 kN produces an extension e. Hence an extension x will be produced by a load of x/e kN. This implies an increase in tension of x/e kN on one side of the plate, and a decrease of x/e kN on the other side.

The total initial load on the packing is 7 kN, distributed over 20 cm and causing a compression of $2e$. That is to say, a compression of $2e$ is produced by a rate of loading of $\frac{7}{20}$ kN/cm. After the load is shifted the change of compression at the edge of the packing is $\frac{5}{4}x$ by geometry, and the mean change is therefore $\frac{5}{8}x$, which corresponds to a mean rate of loading of

$$\frac{5}{8}\cdot\frac{x}{2e}\cdot\frac{7}{20} \quad \text{or} \quad \frac{7}{64}\cdot\frac{x}{e} \text{ kN/cm.}$$

Multiplying the mean rate of loading and the distance on one side of the centre line gives the change in total force in the packing on one side,

i.e.
$$\frac{7}{64}\cdot\frac{x}{e}10 \quad \text{or} \quad \frac{35}{32}\cdot\frac{x}{e} \text{ kN}$$

upwards on one side and downwards on the other. These forces act through the centroid of the load distribution diagram, which is a triangle representing a rate of loading increasing uniformly from the centre outwards. This centroid is $\frac{2}{3}.10$ or $\frac{20}{3}$ cm from the centre line.

Taking moments about the centre line (Fig. 1.17),

$$2 \times \frac{x}{e} \times 8 + 2 \times \frac{35}{32} \cdot \frac{x}{e} \times \frac{20}{3} = 5 \times 2$$

giving

$$\frac{x}{e} = \frac{5 \times 24}{367}$$
$$= 0{\cdot}328 \text{ kN}$$

But the change in tension in each bolt separately is

$$\tfrac{1}{2}x/e = 0{\cdot}164 \text{ kN}$$

Hence the final tensions in the bolts are

$$0{\cdot}5 + 0{\cdot}164 = 0{\cdot}664 \text{ kN}$$

and

$$0{\cdot}5 - 0{\cdot}164 = 0{\cdot}336 \text{ kN}.$$

1.15. Stress Concentrations in Tensile Members. When a member is subjected to a tensile load, it has so far been assumed that the stress is uniform and is obtained by dividing the load by the corresponding area of transverse cross-section. However, if a rapid change of cross-section occurs along the length of the member, the stress will no longer be uniform, and cannot be calculated by the normal procedure. The ratio

$$k = \frac{\text{Maximum stress}}{\text{Average stress at minimum section}}$$

is called the *stress concentration factor*, and values of this ratio for some important cases are given below.

(1) *Small Elliptic Hole at the Centre* (Fig. 1.18(a)). By theoretical

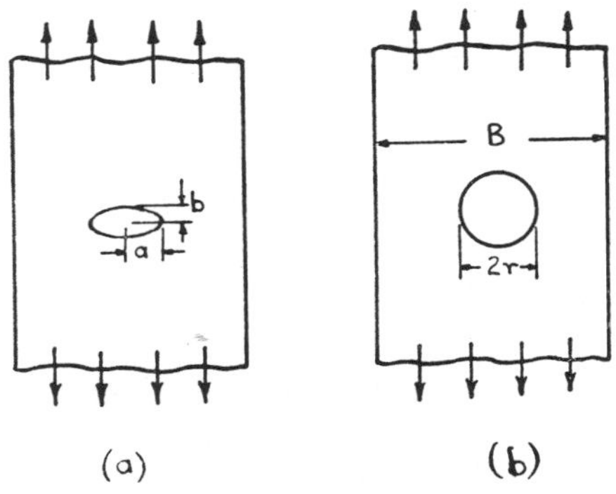

Fig. 1.18

analysis Inglis showed that the maximum stress would occur at the ends of the semi-major axes a, and the stress concentration factor

$$k = 1 + 2a/b$$

the width of the plate being considered large compared with a.

Note that as b becomes small, k increases very rapidly, the limiting case representing a transverse crack in the plate. On the other hand a zero value for a reduces k to unity, i.e. a longitudinal crack has no stress concentration effect. When $a = b$ the hole becomes circular, and $k = 3$.

(2) *Circular Hole at the Centre* (Fig. 1.18(b)). By an approximate analysis Timoshenko obtained the following values for k to be applied to the mean stress at the minimum cross-section.

r/B	0·167	0·1	0·0625	0·05
k	2·25	2·46	2·71	2·97

Similar results over a different range of sizes were obtained photo-elastically (see Para. 19.11) by Frocht. A selection of values is quoted below.

r/B	0·333	0·292	0·222	0·143	0·083
k	2·05	2·1	2·15	2·3	2·5

Note the agreement with paragraph (1) above for small values of r/B.

(3) *Edge Fillets* (Fig. 1.19). These values were also determined photo-elastically, and are as follows.

r/B	0·333	0·292	0·222	0·143	0·083
(a) k	1·25	1·35	1·65	2·05	2·3
(b) k	1·25	1·3	1·5	1·65	1·8

In a ductile material, the full stress concentration factor may not be developed if local yielding has occurred, as the above factors have been determined for the elastic region. When the material becomes plastic at any point a redistribution of stress and strain will occur. However, under rapidly fluctuating loads (see "fatigue") this redistribution may not be able to take place, so that stress concentrations are always a danger under "fatigue" conditions and in brittle materials.

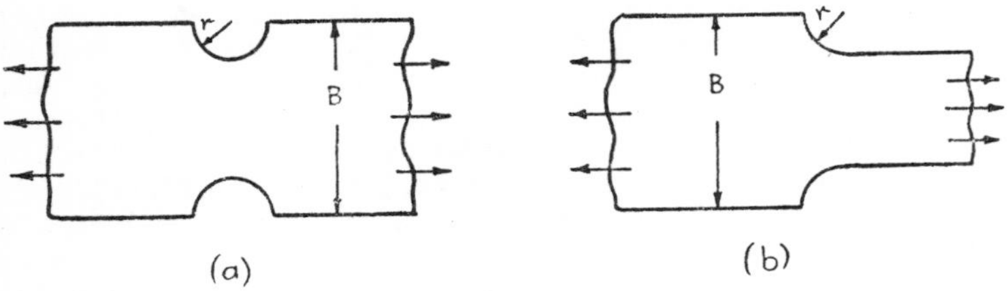

Fig. 1.19

SUMMARY

Stress $\sigma = P/A$ assuming uniform distribution over the cross-section

Strain $\varepsilon = x/l$

Modulus $E = \sigma/\varepsilon = Pl/Ax$ within the limits of Hooke's law.

$$\text{Factor of Safety} = \frac{\text{Ultimate stress}}{\text{Working stress}}$$

$$\text{Load Factor} = \frac{\text{Collapse Load}}{\text{Working Load}}$$

Strain Energy $U = \frac{1}{2}Px = (\sigma^2/2E) \times \text{volume}$.

Impact Loads: Loss of P.E. = Gain of S.E.

Varying cross-section and load: solution by integration.

Compound bars and temperature stresses: apply load equation for equilibrium, and compatibility equation if parts remain together.

Elastic packings: consider elasticity and equilibrium.

$$\text{Stress Concentration Factor} = \frac{\text{Maximum stress}}{\text{Average stress at minimum section}}$$

REFERENCES

Hetenyi, M., and Lui, T. D., *Method of Calculating Stress Concentration Factors.* Jnl. App. Mechs. Vol. 23, 3. Sept. 1956.

Lipson and Juvinall, *Handbook of Stress and Strength,* Macmillan & Co. 1963.

Peterson, R. E., *Stress Concentration Design Factors.* Wiley & Sons. 1953.

Kolsky, H., *Stress Waves in Solids.* O.U.P. 1953.

Walker, P. B., *Fatigue of Nut and Bolt.* Jnl. Roy. Aero. Soc. June 1958.

Svensson, N. L., *Factor of Safety based on Probability.* Engineering, 27 January 1961, p. 154.

PROBLEMS

1. A tie bar on a vertical pressing machine is 2 m long and 4 cm diameter. What is the stress and extension under a load of 100 kN? $E = 205{,}000$ N/mm^2.
(79·6 N/mm^2; 0·78 mm)

2. A brass tube 5 cm outside diameter, 4 cm bore, and 30 cm long, is compressed between two end washers by a load of 25 kN, and the reduction in length measured is 0·2 mm. Assuming Hooke's law to apply, calculate Young's modulus.
(53,200 N/mm^2)

3. A rod 1 m long is 10 cm^2 in area for a portion of its length and 5 cm^2 in area for the remainder. The strain energy of this stepped bar is 40% of that of a bar 10 cm^2 in area 1m long under the same maximum stress. What is the length of the portion 10 cm^2 in area?
(40 cm)

4. A compound bar 90 cm long is made of a rod of steel 30 cm long 3 cm diameter securely fastened to a rod of copper 60 cm long. Under a pull of 50 kN the extensions in each portion are found to be equal. What is (a) the diameter of the copper rod, (b) the stresses in steel and copper, (c) the work done in extending the compound bar? $E_s = 205{,}000$ N/mm^2; $E_c = 110{,}000$ N/mm^2.
((a) 5·8 cm; (b) 70·6, 18·9 N/mm^2; (c) 5·17 Nm)

5. A vertical rod 2 m long, fixed at the upper end, is 13 cm^2 in area for 1 m and 20 cm^2 in area for 1 m. A collar is attached to the free end. Through what height can a load of 100 kg fall on to the collar to cause a maximum stress of 50 N/mm^2? $E = 200{,}000$ N/mm^2.
(1·32 cm)

6. Two rods A and B of equal free length hang vertically 60 cm apart and support a rigid bar horizontally. The bar remains horizontal when carrying a load of 5000 kg at 20 cm from A. If the stress in B is 50 N/mm^2 find the stress in A and the areas of A and B. $E_A = 200{,}000$ N/mm^2; $E_B = 90{,}000$ N/mm^2.
(111 N/mm^2; 295 mm^2; 327 mm^2)

7. The cross-section of a bar is given by $(1 + x^2/100)$ cm^2 where x cm is th distance from one end. Find the extension under a load of 20 kN on a length of 10 cm. $E = 200{,}000$ N/mm^2.
(0·008 cm)

8. Three vertical wires in the same plane are suspended from a horizontal support. They are all of the same length and carry a load by means of a rigid cross bar at their lower ends. One of the wires is of copper and the other two are of steel. The load is increased and the temperature changed so that the stress in each wire is increased by 10 N/mm^2. Find the change of temperature. $E_s = 205{,}000$ N/mm^2; $E_c = 102{,}000$ N/mm^2; $\alpha_s = 11 \times 10^{-6}/°$ C.; $\alpha_c = 18 \times 10^{-6}/°$ C.
($-7·0$ C.)

9. A square rigid plate is hung from a rigid support by means of four steel bars of length L and cross-section A, symmetrically arranged. A load W is then hung from the middle of the plate.

A steel rod of initial length $L - \lambda$ and cross-section a is now attached to the rigid support and heated to a temperature $t°$ above the normal so that it can be connected with the middle of the square plate. The four bars and rod are all vertical and the plate horizontal. At normal temperature it is found that the load in each of the four bars has been reduced by 20%. Show that the values of λ and t are **respectively**

$$(WL/5E)(1/a - 1/A) \quad \text{and} \quad (W/5E\beta)(1/a + 1/4A)$$

where β is the **coefficient of expansion of steel. (U.L.)**

10. A steel tie rod 25 mm diameter is placed concentrically in a brass tube 3 mm thick and 40 mm mean diameter. Nuts and washers are fitted on the tie rod so that the ends of the tube are enclosed by the washers. The nuts are initially tightened to give a compressive stress of 30 N/mm² in the tube and a tensile load of 45 kN is then applied to the tie rod. Find the resultant stresses in tie rod and tube (1) when there is no change of temperature, (2) when the temperature increases by 60° C. $E_s = 205{,}000$ N/mm²; $E_b = 80{,}000$ N/mm²; $\alpha_s = 1{\cdot}1 \times 10^{-5}/°$ C; $\alpha_b = 1{\cdot}89 \times 10^{-5}/°$ C. ((1) 93·7, 2·5 N/mm²; (2) 116, 31·6 N/mm²).

11. An elastic packing piece is bolted between a rigid rectangular plate and a rigid foundation by two bolts pitched 25 cm apart and symmetrically placed on the longer centre line of the plate, which is 37·5 cm long. The tension in each bolt is initially 20,000 N, the extension of each bolt 0·0125 mm, and the compression of the packing piece 0·5 mm. If one bolt is further tightened to a tension of 25,000 N. determine the tension in the other bolt. (20,800 N)

12. Two equal washers 15 cm apart are compressed between a rigid horizontal base and a rigid horizontal plate by two equal bolts. The bolts are 30 cm apart, arranged symmetrically on either side of the washers and collinear with them. Initially each bolt is tightened to a tension of 27 kN with an extension of 0·0045 cm. If the compression of a washer is four times the extension of a bolt for the same load, determine the increase in tension in one bolt when the other one is further tightened to 36 kN. (4900 N)

13. The figure shows a steel bolt 2·5 cm diameter which passes centrally through a brass tube having an outside diameter 3·8 cm and inside diameter 2·84 cm and also through a rigid cast iron body. The screw has 4 threads/cm and the nut is initially just tight. Find the changes in the stresses in the bolt and tube due to (a) tightening the nut by turning it through 30°, (b) an increase in temperature of 25°C.

Assume that there is no change in the thickness of the cast iron body on account of stress. $E_s = 200{,}000$ N/mm², $E_b = 100{,}000$ N/mm², $\alpha_s = 13 \times 10^{-6}/°$C., $\alpha_b = 19 \times 10^{-6}/°$ C., $\alpha_{ci} = 11 \times 10^{-6}/°$ C.
(note difference in length of bolt and tube: (a) 92·5 N/mm² each (b) 6·68 N/mm² each.

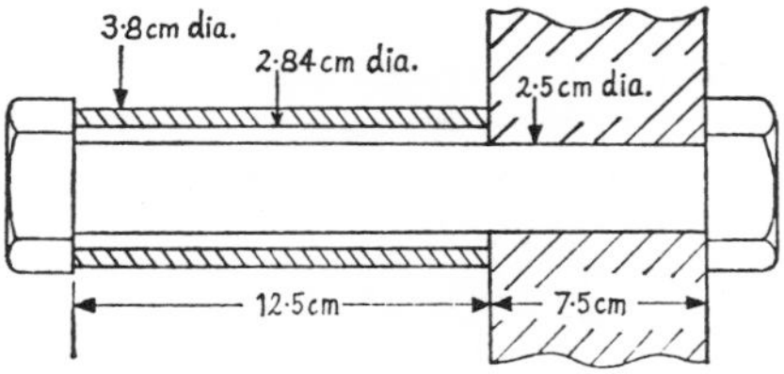

CHAPTER II

Shear Stress

2.1. Shear Stress. If the applied load P consists of two equal and opposite parallel forces not in the same line (as in Fig. 2.1), then there is a tendency for one part of the body to slide over or shear from the other part across any section LM. If the cross-section at LM measured parallel to the load is A, then the average shear stress $\tau = P/A$. If the shear stress varies, then at a point $\tau = \delta P/\delta A$.

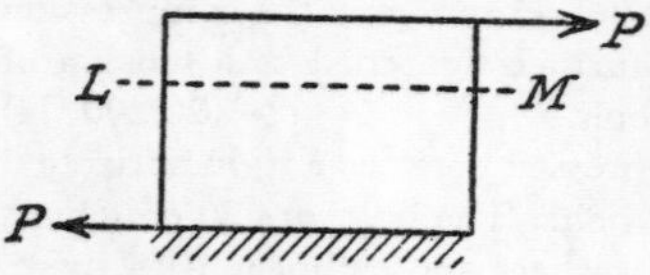

Fig. 2.1

Notice that *shear stress is tangential to the area* over which it acts.

The most common occurrences of pure shear are in riveted and cottered joints, which will be treated later in this chapter.

Shear stress is, of course, expressed in the same units as direct stress, being load per unit area.

2.2. Complementary Shear Stress. Let ABCD (Fig. 2.2), be a small rectangular element of sides x, y, and z perpendicular to the figure. Let there be a shear stress τ acting on planes AB and CD.

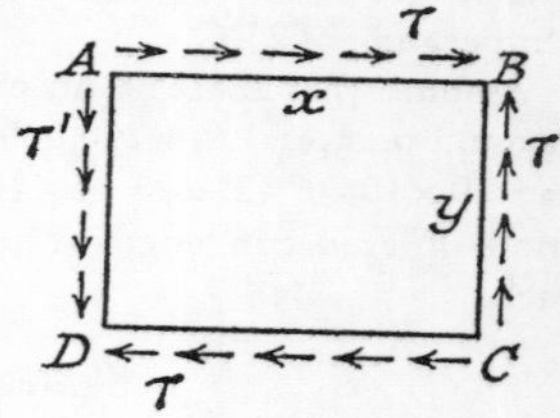

Fig. 2.2

It is clear that these stresses will form a couple $(\tau . xz)y$ which can only be balanced by tangential forces on planes AD and BC (any normal stresses which exist will balance out in pairs). These are known as complementary shear stresses.

Let τ' be the complementary shear stress induced on planes AD and BC. Then for equilibrium

$$(\tau . xz)y = (\tau' . yz)x$$

i.e.

$$\tau' = \tau,$$

showing that **every shear stress is accompanied by an equal complementary shear stress** on planes at right angles. The directions of the shear stresses on an element are either both towards or both away from a corner, to produce balancing couples.

The existence of the complementary shear stress may be an important factor in the failure of anisotropic materials such as timber, which is weak in shear along the grain (see Ex. 1, Chap. VII).

It can now be shown that **near a free boundary** (i.e. no external applied forces) **the shear stress on any cross-section must act in a direction parallel to the boundary.** This is because if there were a component in a direction at right angles to the boundary it would require a complementary shear stress on the boundary plane. For example, the shear stress distribution over a section of a rivet must be as Fig. 2.3(a) and *not* as 2.3(b).

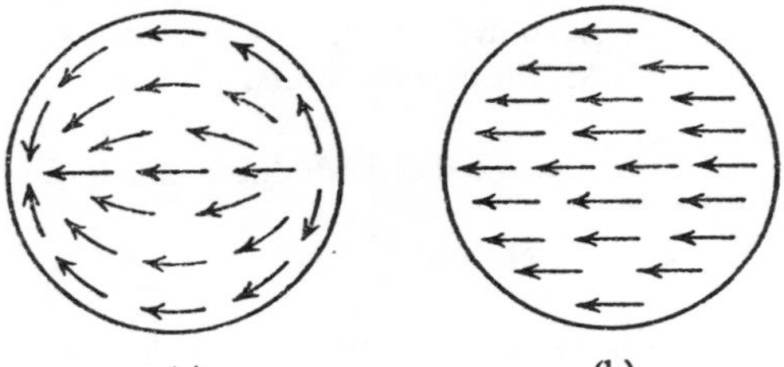

(a) (b)

Fig. 2.3

This causes an obvious complication in that the shear stress varies in magnitude and direction, though in this particular case the variation is not usually allowed for in design. Further important applications of this principle will be found when dealing with shear stress in beams of various cross-sections (Chapter VII).

EXAMPLE 1. *A flange coupling joining two sections of shaft is required to transmit 250 kW at 1000 r.p.m. If six bolts are to be used on a pitch circle diameter of 14 cm, find the diameter of the bolts. Allowable mean shear stress 75 N/mm².*

Torque to be transmitted

$$= \frac{\text{Watts} \times 60}{2\pi N} \text{ Nm}$$

$$= \frac{250 \times 1000 \times 60}{2\pi \times 1000}$$

$$= 2380 \text{ Nm}$$

If d mm is the diameter of a bolt, the load carried by one bolt

$$= 75 \times \pi d^2/4 \text{ N}$$

Multiplying by the number of bolts and the radius arm, the torque carried

$$= 75 \times (\pi d^2/4) \times 6 \times 0{\cdot}07 \text{ Nm}$$

$$= 2380 \text{ from above}$$

$$\therefore \quad d^2 = \frac{2380 \times 4}{75\pi \times 0{\cdot}42} = 96{\cdot}3$$

giving $$d = 9{\cdot}82 \text{ mm, say } 10 \text{ mm}$$

2.3 Shear Strain. The distortion produced by shear stress on an element or rectangular block is shown in Fig. 2.4. The ***shear strain or "slide"*** is ϕ, and can be defined as the change in the right angle. It is measured in radians, and is dimensionless.

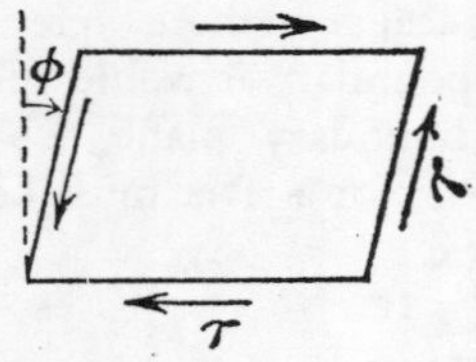

Fig. 2.4

2.4. Modulus of Rigidity. For elastic materials it is found that shear strain is proportional to the shear stress producing it, within certain limits.

The ratio $\dfrac{\text{Shear stress}}{\text{Shear strain}}$ is called the Modulus of Rigidity, i.e.

$$G = \tau/\phi \ \text{N/mm}^2.$$

2.5. Strain Energy. Within the limit of proportionality stress is proportional to strain, and

Strain energy (U) = Work done in straining

$= \frac{1}{2}$(Final couple) × (Angle turned through)

for a gradually applied stress (work done is proportional to shaded area in Fig. 2.5),

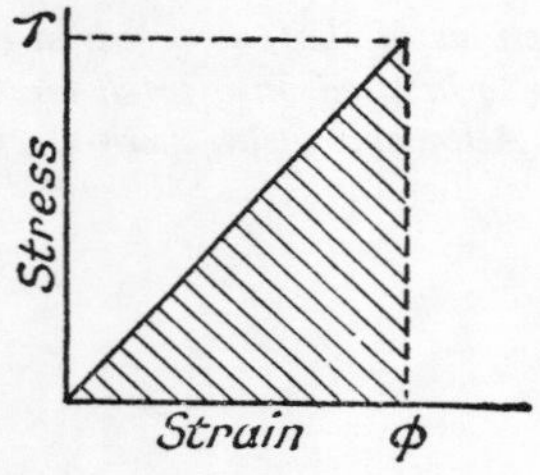

Fig. 2.5

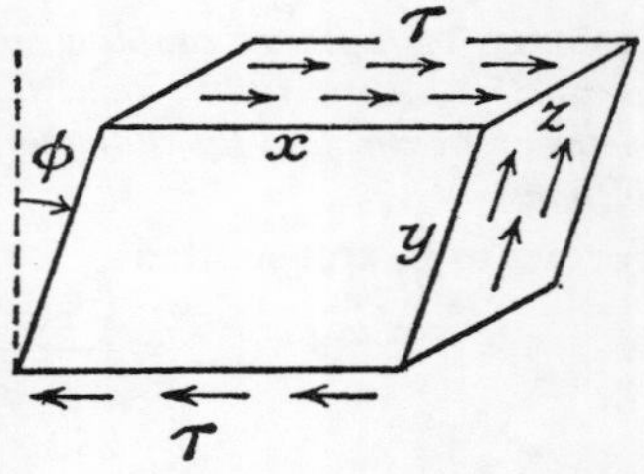

Fig. 2.6

i.e.
$$U = \tfrac{1}{2}(\tau yz.x)\phi \quad \text{from Fig. 2.6}$$
$$= \tfrac{1}{2}.\tau xyz.\tau/G \quad \text{from Para. 2.4}$$
$$= (\tau^2/2G) \times \textbf{volume}$$

(compare with $\sigma^2/2E$ for direct stress). The units are again *Nm*.

For suddenly applied loads the principles of Para. 1.10 may be applied.

2.6. Cottered Joints. A cottered joint is used to join two members by means of a tapered pin or cotter which passes through slots in the ends of the members.

The cottered joint shown in Fig. 2.7 may fail in the following ways:

(1) By tension in the rod: tensile stress $= \dfrac{P}{\pi d^2/4}$.

(2) By shear of the cotter through AB and CD: shear stress $= P/2ef$.

(3) By shear of the right-hand member through EF and GH: shear stress $= P/4ab$.

(4) By shear of the left-hand member through JK and LM: shear stress $= P/2ch$.

(5) By crushing between the right-hand member and the cotter.

If the crushing or bearing pressure p between the two curved surfaces (the side FH of the cotter) is assumed constant (Fig. 2.8), then the total load P is equal to the pressure × the "projected" area on a plane perpendicular to P, i.e.

$$P = p \times 2af$$

or

$$p = P/2af$$

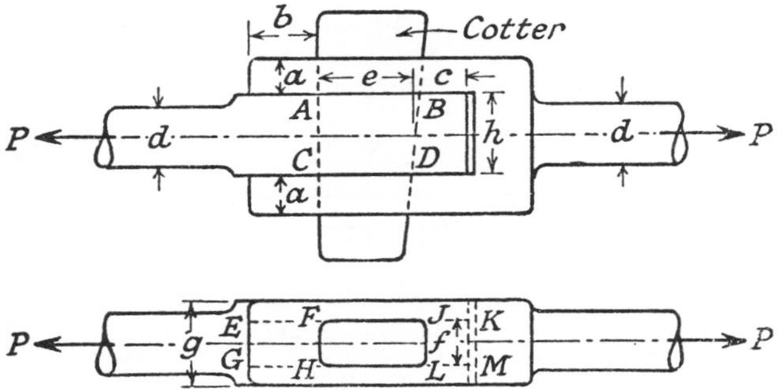

Fig. 2.7

(6) By crushing between the left-hand member and the cotter.

Here the projected area is fh, giving a crushing stress $= P/fh$.

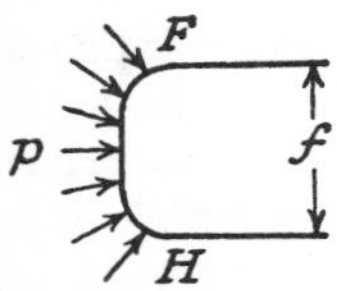

Fig. 2.8

If the joint is designed so that each of the above values is equal to the permissible stress, it is said to be equally strong against all types of failure.

EXAMPLE 2. *In the joint shown in Fig. 2.7, if the diameter of the rod is 5 cm, and the thickness of the cotter 1.25 cm, find the other dimensions required so that the strength shall be the same against all types of failure. Permissible stresses are 300 N/mm² tension, 150 N/mm² shear in the members, 225 N/mm² shear in the cotter, and 450 N/mm² crushing.*

(1) Load

$$P = 300 \times (\pi/4)50^2 = 588 \text{ kN}$$

(2) Shear of cotter

$$225 = 588{,}000/(2e \times 12{\cdot}5)$$
$$e = 105 \text{ mm}$$

(3) Shear of right-hand member

$$150 = 588{,}000/4ab$$
$$ab = 980$$

(4) Shear of left-hand member

$$150 = 588{,}000/2ch$$
$$ch = 1960$$

(5) Crushing between right-hand member and cotter

$$450 = 588{,}000/(2a \times 12{\cdot}5)$$
$$a = 52{\cdot}4 \text{ mm}$$

From (3)

$$b = 18{\cdot}7 \quad \text{mm}$$

(6) Crushing between left-hand member and cotter

$$450 = 558{,}000/(12{\cdot}5 \times h)$$
$$h = 104{\cdot}8 \text{ mm}$$

From (4)

$$c = 18{\cdot}7 \text{ mm}$$

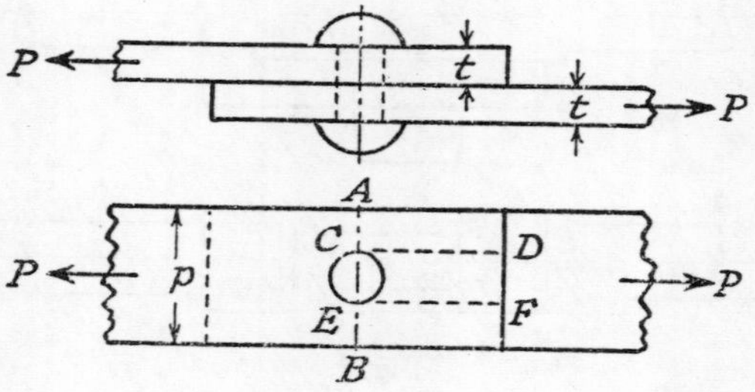

Fig. 2.9

2.7. Riveted Joints. These may be either *lap joints* (Fig. 2.9) or *butt joints* (Fig. 2.10), the latter being usually provided with two cover plates. The ***rivets*** are driven home hot, and hence will shrink away from the holes when cold. They will exert considerable force on the plates, pressing them together, and the friction resulting may be sufficient to carry the load, in which case there is no transverse load on the rivets. However, the amount of friction is a very doubtful factor, depending on the condition of the surfaces in contact and the standard of workmanship in applying the rivets. It is usual, therefore, to neglect friction forces entirely, and consider that slip has taken place between the rivets and the plates and that all the load is carried by the rivets. If the plates are assumed rigid compared with the rivets, then for symmetrically applied loads the deformation of each rivet will be the same, and hence the load will be shared equally by the rivets.

Consider first a lap joint with a single row of rivets of pitch p. Let load per rivet $= P$ (Fig. 2.9).

$t =$ thickness of plates.
$d =$ diameter of rivet or hole (considered equal).
$\sigma =$ permissible tensile stress in plate.
$\tau =$ permissible shear stress in rivet.
$\tau' =$ permissible shear stress in plate.
$\sigma_c =$ permissible bearing pressure on rivet.

There are four principal ways in which the joint may fail:

(1) By tearing the plate; taking the least cross-section AB, the permissible load is

$$P_1 = \sigma(p-d)t$$

(2) By shearing the rivet at the section between the plates

$$P_2 = \tau . \pi d^2/4$$

(3) By crushing between the rivet and one plate

$$P_3 = \sigma_c . dt \quad \text{(see Para. 2.6, (5))}.$$

(4) By shearing the plate along CD and EF

$$P_4 = \tau' . 2CD . t$$

The efficiency of the joint is taken as

$$\frac{\text{Least load to cause failure}}{\text{Load carried by parent plate}} \times 100\%$$

$$= \frac{\text{Least of } P_1 \ldots P_4}{\sigma p t} \times 100\%$$

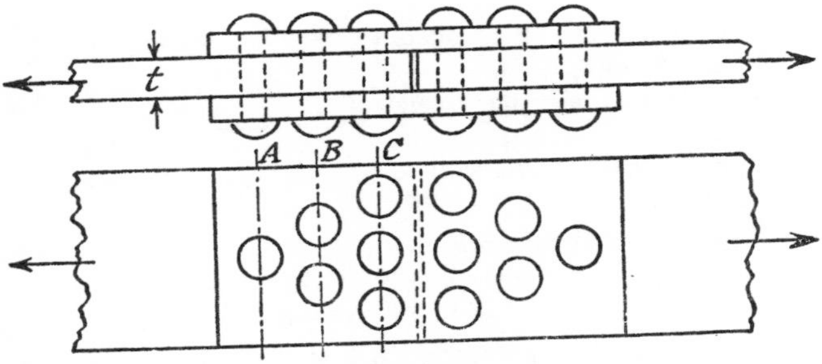

Fig. 2.10

For butt joints the cover plates should be greater than half the thickness of the main plates, and the most efficient way to arrange, say six rivets on either side, is in 3, 2, 1 formation (Fig. 2.10). Then, on the assumption of equal load per rivet, the full load is carried across the plate at A (width reduced by 1 hole), $\frac{5}{6}$ of the load across the plate at B (width reduced by 2 holes), and only $\frac{1}{2}$ the load across the plate at C (width reduced by 3 holes).

EXAMPLE 3. *Design a double cover butt joint to withstand a load of 25,000 kg. The plates to be joined are 20·5 cm wide and 1·25 cm thick; 1·9 cm rivets are to be used, and the permissible stresses are: shear 75 N/mm², bearing pressure 180 N/mm², tension 105 N/mm². What is the efficiency of the joint?*

The cover plates are usually each made $\frac{5}{8}$ of the thickness of the plates joined, i.e. 0·8 cm, so that they will not fail before the main plate.

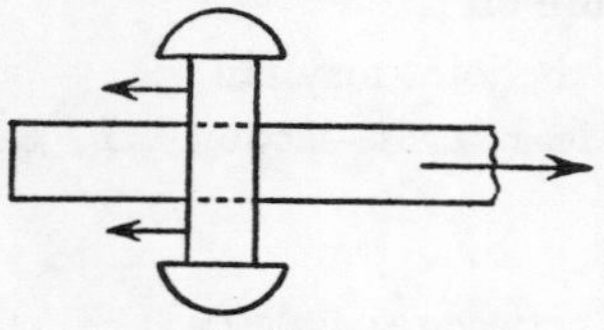

Fig. 2.11

With a double cover joint each rivet is in "*double*" *shear*, since it can only fail by shear along two cross-sections at the same time (shown dotted in Fig. 2.11).

Load to shear one rivet

$$=\tau\ 2\pi d^2/4$$
$$=75\times(2\pi/4)(19)^2$$
$$=42{,}400\text{ N}=4330\text{ kg}$$

Load to crush one rivet

$$=\sigma_c\cdot dt$$
$$=180\times 19\times 12{\cdot}5$$
$$=42{,}700\text{ N}=4350\text{ kg}$$

∴ No. of rivets required 25,000/4330, say 6, arranged as Fig. 2.10.

Load which can be carried by solid plate

$$=\sigma bt$$
$$=105\times 205\times 12{\cdot}5$$
$$=270{,}000\text{ N}=27{,}600\text{ kg}$$

To find the maximum load which can be carried by the riveted joint it is necessary to investigate all possible ways of failure.

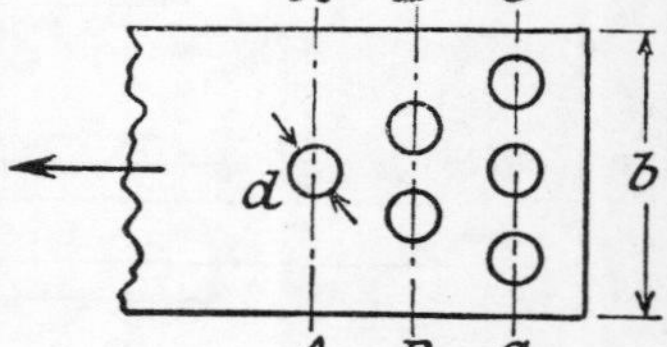

Fig. 2.12

(i) Load to shear all the rivets $=6\times 4330=26{,}000$ kg

(ii) Load to crush all the rivets $=6\times 4350=26{,}200$ kg.

(iii) Plate may tear through section AA (Fig. 2.12),

$$\text{permissible load}=\sigma(b-d)t$$
$$=105\times(205-19)\times 12{\cdot}5$$
$$=244{,}000\text{ N}=25{,}000\text{ kg}$$

(iv) Plate may tear through section BB, at the same time shearing the rivet at AA

$$\text{permissible load}=\sigma(b-2d)t+4330$$
$$=105\times(205-38)\times 12{\cdot}5/9{\cdot}81+4330$$
$$=26{,}200\text{ kg}$$

(v) Plate may tear through section CC, at the same time shearing the 3 rivets at AA and BB,

$$\text{permissible load} = \sigma(b-3d)t + 3 \times 4330$$
$$= 105 \times (205-57) \times 12{\cdot}5/9{\cdot}81 + 13{,}000$$
$$= 31{,}500\text{kg}$$

(vi) Cover plates may tear through section CC,

$$\text{permissible load} = 105(205-57)16/9{\cdot}81 = 25{,}000 \text{ kg}$$

$$\text{Efficiency of joint} = \frac{\text{Least load to cause failure}}{\text{Load carried by solid plate}}$$
$$= \frac{25{,}000}{27{,}600} = 90{\cdot}7\%$$

2.8. Eccentric Loading. If the load is not applied through the centroid of the rivet formation, it will not be equally distributed among the rivets.

Any eccentric load, such as that in Fig. 2.13, may be replaced by an equal parallel load at the centroid G, together with a couple of magnitude equal to the load P times the perpendicular distance h from the centroid on to its line of action. The equivalent loading is shown in

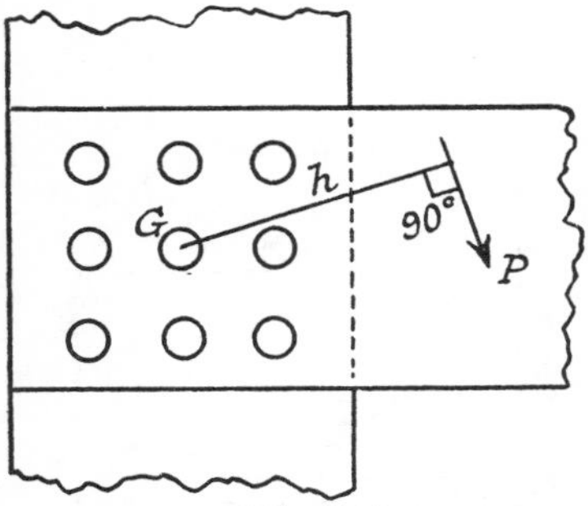

Fig. 2.13

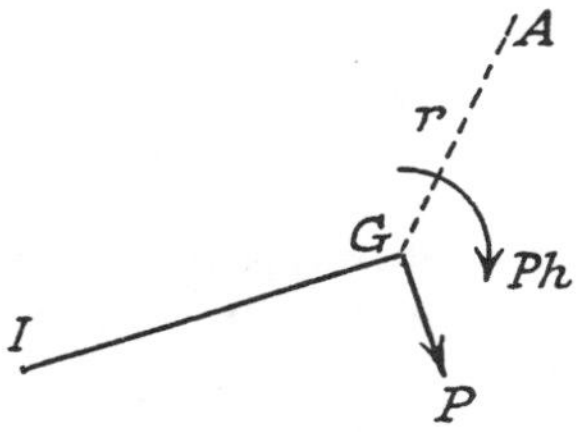

Fig. 2.14

Fig. 2.14, and A represents one of the rivets at a distance r from G. The load on the rivet is then made up of two parts as follows:

(a) *Due to P at G*, each rivet has an equal load P/n, in the direction of P, where n is the total number of rivets.

(b) *Due to the couple Ph*, there will be an angular rotation θ of the joint about G. Assuming the plate "rigid," and the load on a rivet proportional to the relative "slip" at that point between the members joined, the load on the rivet A $= kr\theta$, where k is a constant for a given joint.

By moments about G

$$Ph = \Sigma(kr\theta).r$$

giving

$$k\theta = Ph/\Sigma r^2 \qquad (1)$$

There must be an "instantaneous centre" I about which the joint can be considered to rotate, and since the slip at G is P/nk from (a), IG is given by

$$P/nk = \mathrm{IG}.\theta$$

or

$$\mathrm{IG} = P/nk\theta$$

$$= \Sigma r^2/nh \quad \text{from (1),} \qquad (2)$$

and is perpendicular to the line of action of P. The resultant slip at A is given by the vector sum of P/nk from (a), and $r\theta$ from (b) (Fig. 2.15), being equal to IA.θ and perpendicular to IA. Similarly the load in the rivet A is given by IA.$k\theta$,

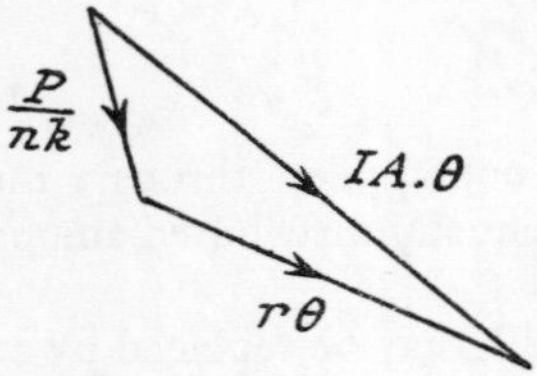

Fig. 2.15

$$= \mathrm{IA}.Ph/\Sigma r^2 \quad \text{from (1)} \qquad (3)$$

In any particular problem the procedure is to calculate IG from (2), and mark the position of I. The factor $k\theta$ is calculated from (1), and the load in each rivet is then found from (3), the distances IA being either calculated or measured. It is clear that the rivet farthest from I takes the maximum load.

EXAMPLE 4. *Fig. 2.16 shows a column to which a bracket is riveted, carrying a load of 10 kN at a distance of 8 cm from the centre line of the column. Examine the distribution of load among the rivets.*

The centroid of the rivet formation is at the centre rivet E, and the instantaneous centre of rotation of the joint I is found from (2) above

$$\mathrm{IE} = \Sigma r^2/nh$$

$$= \frac{4(3\sqrt{2})^2 + 4 \times 3^2}{9 \times 8}$$

$$= 108/72 = 1{\cdot}5 \text{ cm}$$

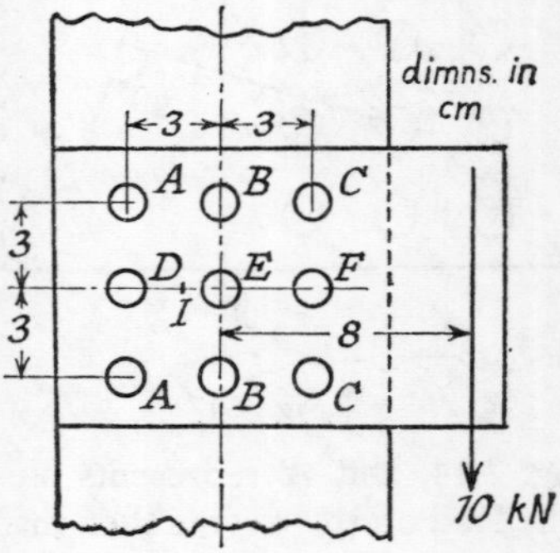

Fig. 2.16

Load in any rivet $= (Ph/\Sigma r^2) \times$ (distance of rivet from I) from (3)

where $Ph/\Sigma r^2 = (10 \times 8)/108 = 0{\cdot}74$ kN/cm.

Load in rivet C $= 0{\cdot}74\sqrt{(3^2 + 4{\cdot}5^2)} = 3{\cdot}95$ kN.

Load in rivet B $= 0{\cdot}74\sqrt{(3^2 + 1{\cdot}5^2)} = 2{\cdot}48$ kN.

Load in rivet A $= 0{\cdot}74\sqrt{(3^2 + 1{\cdot}5^2)} = 2{\cdot}48$ kN.

Load in rivet D $= 0{\cdot}74 \times 1{\cdot}5 = 1{\cdot}11$ kN.

Load in rivet E $= 0{\cdot}74 \times 1{\cdot}5 = 1{\cdot}11$ kN.

Load in rivet F $= 0{\cdot}74 \times 4{\cdot}5 = 3{\cdot}33$ kN.

SUMMARY

Shear Stress $\tau = P/A$. Area tangential to stress.
Modulus of Rigidity $G = \tau/\phi$.
Strain Energy $U = (\tau^2/2G) \times$ volume.

PROBLEMS

1. Estimate the force required to punch out circular blanks 6 cm diameter from plate 2 mm thick. Ultimate shear stress $= 300$ N/mm². (113 kN)

2. A copper tube, external diameter 4 cm, 6 mm thick, fits over a steel rod 2·5 cm diameter. The tube is secured to the bar by two pins 1 cm diameter fitted transversely one at each end. If the temperature after assembly is raised by 50° C. calculate the shear stress in the pins. $E_c = 100{,}000$ N/mm²; $E_s = 200{,}000$ N/mm²; $\alpha_c = 0{\cdot}00002$/° C.; $\alpha_s = 0{\cdot}000012$/°C. (98·5 N/mm²)

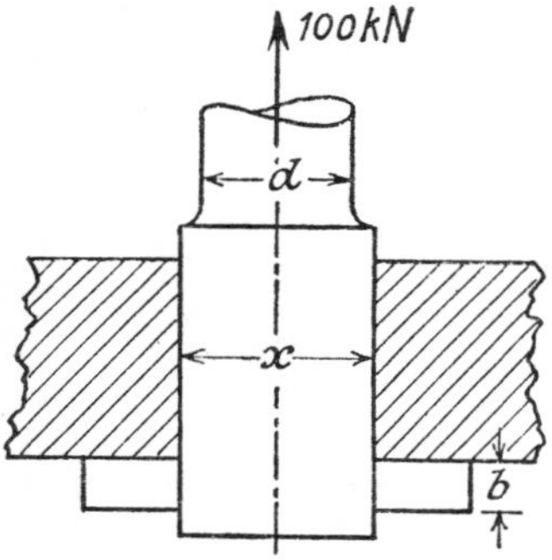

3. The cottered joint shown in the sketch carries a load of 100 kN. The socket is of square section of sides x mm and the cotter is rectangular, b mm by t mm. Find the dimensions d, x, b, and t for the following allowable stresses $\sigma_t = 110$ N/mm²; $\tau = 80$ N/mm²; $\sigma_c = 140$ N/mm². Assume double shear 1·875 times as strong as single shear. (34 mm; 40 mm; 35 mm; 18 mm)

4. A pressure vessel is made from a cylinder with a welded longitudinal joint and dished end plates secured by double-row riveted lap points. Plate thickness 16 mm, diameter of rivets 22 mm, pitch of rivets 60 mm. If the permissible tensile stress in the plates is 100 N/mm² and the shear stress in the rivets 75 N/mm² find the efficiency of the joint. (59%)

5. Two steel plates 30 cm wide, 2.5 cm thick, are connected by a double-strap butt joint. There are ten rivets 2.5 cm diameter on each side. If the allowable tensile stress in the plate is 75 N/mm² and the strengths in tension and shear are the same, what is the maximum shear stress? (52·5 N/mm²)

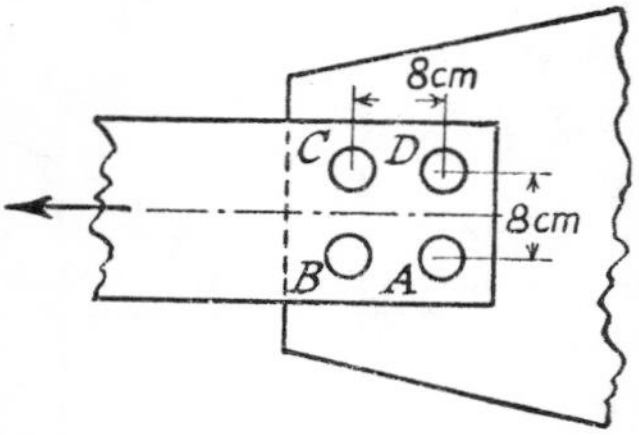

6. A tie bar is attached to a gusset plate by four rivets arranged at the corners of a square, and the pull is applied symmetrically as shown. If the rivet at A is now removed, the load remaining the same, calculate by what percentage the loads on rivets B, C, and D are increased. (68%; 18%; 2%.)

CHAPTER III

Compound Stress and Strain

3.1. Oblique Stress. Previous chapters have dealt with either a pure normal, or direct, stress (i.e. tension or compression), or a pure shear stress. In many instances, however, both direct and shear stresses are brought into play, and the resultant stress across any section will be neither normal nor tangential to the plane. If σ_r is the resultant stress, making an angle ϕ with the normal to the plane on which it acts (Fig. 3.1),

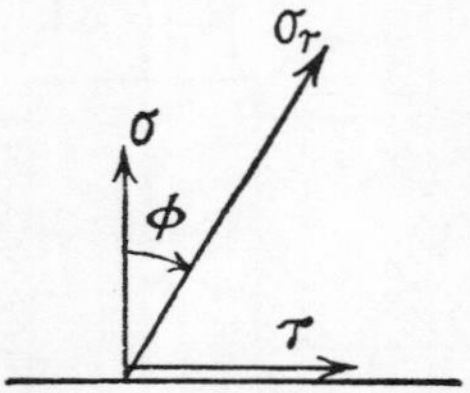

Fig. 3.1

Fig. 3.2

it is usually more convenient to calculate the normal and tangential components σ and τ, then, by equilibrium

$$\phi = \tan^{-1}\tau/\sigma$$

and, from Fig. 3.2,

$$\sigma_r = \sqrt{(\sigma^2 + \tau^2)}$$

Several important particular cases will now be considered, followed by the general stress system in two dimensions.

3.2. Simple Tension. If a bar is under the action of a tensile stress σ along its length then any transverse section such as AB in Fig. 3.3 will have a pure normal stress acting on it. The problem is to find the stress acting on any plane AC at an angle θ to AB. This stress will not be normal to the plane, and may be resolved into two components σ_θ and τ_θ as outlined in Para. 3.1.

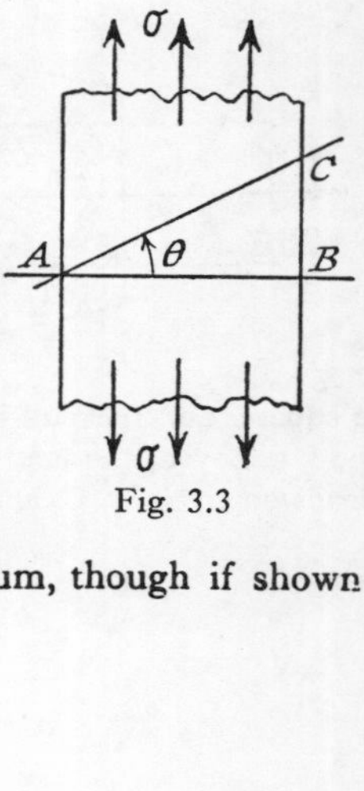

Fig. 3.3

Fig. 3.4(a) shows the *stresses* acting on the three planes of the triangular prism ABC. There can be no stress on the plane BC, which is a longitudinal plane of the bar; the stress component τ_θ must act "up" the plane for equilibrium, though if shown the other way would work out negative in the analysis. Fig. 3.4(b) shows the *forces* acting on the prism, taking a thickness t perpendicular to the figure.

The equations of equilibrium are used to solve for σ_θ and τ_θ.

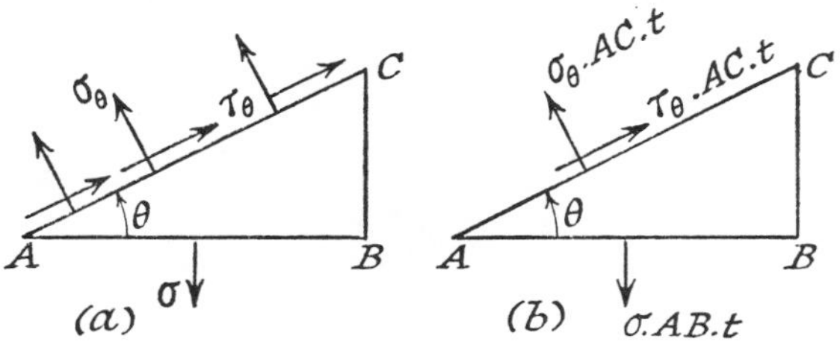

Fig. 3.4

Resolve in the direction of σ_θ:

$$\sigma_\theta.\mathrm{AC}.t=\sigma.\mathrm{AB}.t.\cos\theta$$

i.e.

$$\sigma_\theta=\sigma.(\mathrm{AB}/\mathrm{AC}).\cos\theta$$
$$=\sigma\cos^2\theta \qquad (1)$$

Resolve in the direction of τ_θ:

$$\tau_\theta.\mathrm{AC}.t=\sigma.\mathrm{AB}.t.\sin\theta$$

i.e.

$$\tau_\theta=\sigma.(\mathrm{AB}/\mathrm{AC}).\sin\theta$$
$$=\sigma.\cos\theta.\sin\theta$$
$$=\tfrac{1}{2}\sigma\sin 2\theta \qquad (2)$$

The resultant stress

$$\sigma_r=\sqrt{(\sigma_\theta^2+\tau_\theta^2)}=\sigma\sqrt{(\cos^4\theta+\cos^2\theta.\sin^2\theta)}$$
$$=\sigma\cos\theta \qquad (3)$$

From these results it is seen that the maximum normal stress occurs at $\theta=0$, and is of course equal to the applied stress σ. The maximum shear stress occurs at $\theta=45°$, and its magnitude is $\frac{1}{2}\sigma$; on these planes there is also a normal component $=\frac{1}{2}\sigma$. The variation of stress components with θ is given by the above equations (1), (2), and (3), σ_θ being zero when $\theta=90°$, and τ_θ zero when $\theta=0$ and 90°. The resultant stress is a maximum when $\theta=0$.

The important result here is that **in simple tension (or compression), the maximum shear stress is equal to one-half the applied stress and acts on planes at 45° to it.**

3.3. Note on Diagrams. In most problems the stress is varying from point to point in the member, and it is necessary to consider the equilibrium of an element, which if sufficiently small may be assumed to give the values at a "point."

It is clear that the results are independent of the *thickness* of element considered, and for convenience this will in future be taken as *unity.* Also, as the figures will always be right-angled triangles there will be no loss of generality by assuming the *hypotenuse to be of unit length.* By making use of these simplifications it will be found that the areas on which the stresses act are proportional to 1 (for AC), sin θ (for BC), and cos θ (for AB), and future figures will show the *forces* acting on such an element.

3·4. Pure Shear. Let the stress on a given plane "AB" be a pure shear stress τ, then there is an equal complementary shear stress on the plane "BC" (Para. 2.2). The problem is to find the stress components σ_θ and τ_θ acting on any plane "AC" at an angle θ to AB. For purposes of convention the applied shear stresses will be shown acting towards the "corner" B, and τ_θ acting "up" the plane AC.

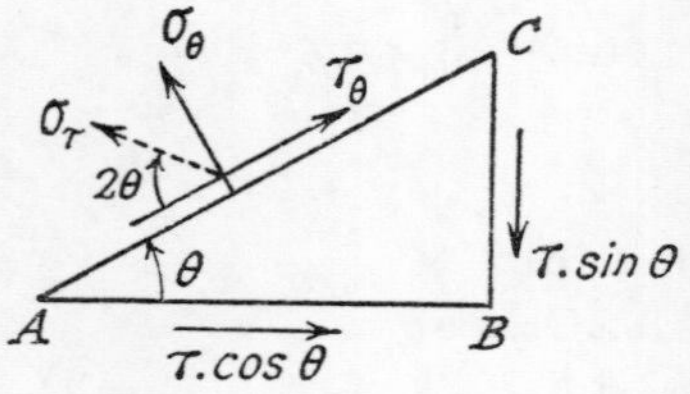

Fig. 3.5

In accordance with the note in Para. 3.3, taking the area of the plane AC as unity, the forces acting on the element are as shown in Fig. 3.5.

Resolving in the direction of σ_θ:

$$\sigma_\theta = (\tau.\cos\theta)\sin\theta + (\tau.\sin\theta)\cos\theta$$
$$= \tau.\sin 2\theta$$

Resolving in the direction of τ_θ:

$$\tau_\theta = (\tau.\sin\theta)\sin\theta - (\tau.\cos\theta)\cos\theta$$
$$= -\tau.\cos 2\theta \text{ (down the plane for } \theta < 45°)$$
$$\sigma_r = \sqrt{(\sigma_\theta^2 + \tau_\theta^2)} = \tau \text{ at } 2\theta \text{ to } \tau_\theta$$

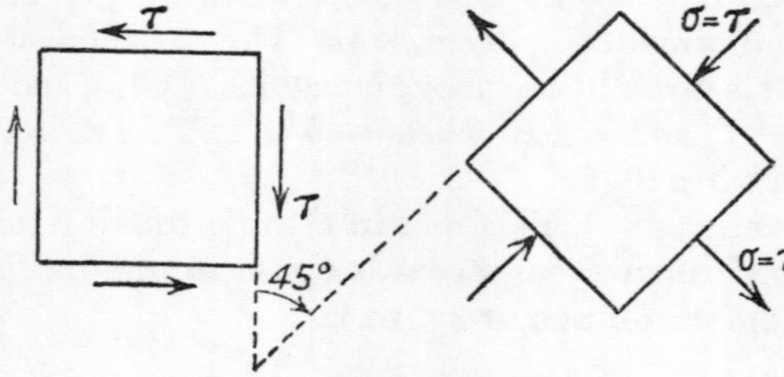

Fig. 3.6

In this system the normal component σ_θ has maximum and minimun values $+\tau$ (tension) and $-\tau$ (compression) on planes at $\pm 45°$ to th applied shear, and on these planes the tangential component τ_θ is zero

This shows that at a point where there is *pure shear stress on two given planes at right angles, the action across the planes of an element taken at 45° to the given planes is one of equal tension and compression.* In fact the two stress systems shown in Fig. 3.6 are identical and interchangeable, a conclusion which will be used later in examining the relation between the elastic constants E and G (Para. 4.3).

3.5. Pure Normal Stresses on Given Planes. Let the known stresses be σ_x on BC and σ_y on AB, then the forces on the element are proportional to those shown in Fig. 3.7.

Resolve in the direction of σ_θ:

$$\sigma_\theta = (\sigma_y . \cos\theta)\cos\theta + (\sigma_x . \sin\theta)\sin\theta$$
$$= \sigma_y \cos^2\theta + \sigma_x \sin^2\theta$$

Resolve in the direction of τ_θ:

$$\tau_\theta = (\sigma_y . \cos\theta)\sin\theta - (\sigma_x . \sin\theta)\cos\theta$$
$$= \tfrac{1}{2}(\sigma_y - \sigma_x)\sin 2\theta$$

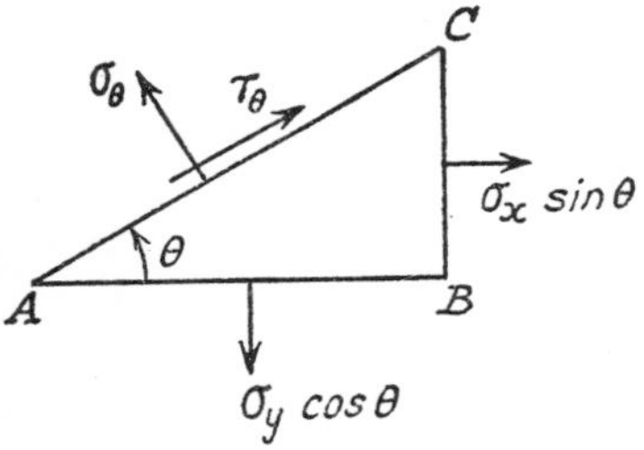

Fig. 3.7

σ_θ can be shown to vary between the limits of σ_x and σ_y, which become its maximum and minimum values; τ_θ, however, *has a maximum value equal numerically to one-half the difference between the given normal stresses and occurring on planes at 45° to the given planes.* This becomes of some significance when calculating the maximum shear stress in any complex stress system, and it will be found that σ_x and σ_y correspond to the Principal Stresses (Para. 3.8).

3.6. General Two-dimensional Stress System. Let the stresses on the planes AB and BC be σ_y, σ_x, and τ, then the forces are as shown in Fig. 3.8.

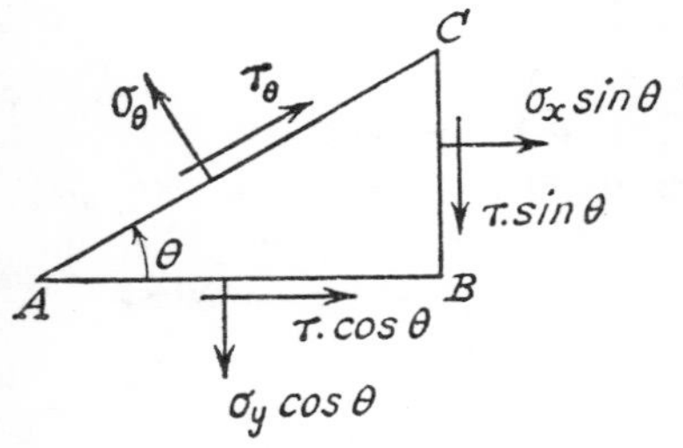

Fig. 3.8

Resolve in the direction of σ_θ:

$$\sigma_\theta = (\sigma_y . \cos\theta)\cos\theta + (\sigma_x . \sin\theta)\sin\theta + (\tau . \cos\theta)\sin\theta + (\tau . \sin\theta)\cos\theta$$
$$= \sigma_y\left(\frac{1+\cos 2\theta}{2}\right) + \sigma_x\left(\frac{1-\cos 2\theta}{2}\right) + \tau . \sin 2\theta$$
$$= \tfrac{1}{2}(\sigma_y + \sigma_x) + \tfrac{1}{2}(\sigma_y - \sigma_x)\cos 2\theta + \tau . \sin 2\theta \qquad (1)$$

Resolve in the direction of τ :

$$\tau_\theta = (\sigma_y . \cos\theta)\sin\theta - (\sigma_x . \sin\theta)\cos\theta + (\tau . \sin\theta)\sin\theta - (\tau . \cos\theta)\cos\theta$$
$$= \tfrac{1}{2}(\sigma_y - \sigma_x)\sin 2\theta - \tau . \cos 2\theta \qquad (2)$$

EXAMPLE 1. *If the stresses on two perpendicular planes through a point are 60 N/mm² tension, 40 N/mm² compression, and 30 N/mm² shear, find the stress components and resultant stress on a plane at 60° to that of the tensile stress.*

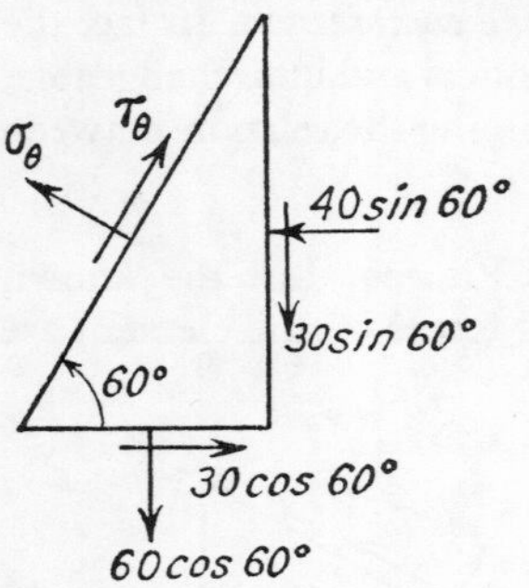

Fig. 3.9

Fig. 3.9 shows the forces on an element.

Resolving

$$\sigma_\theta = (60\cos 60°)\cos 60° - (40\sin 60°)\sin 60° + (30\cos 60°)\sin 60° + (30\sin 60°)\cos 60°$$

$$= 60 \times \frac{1}{2} \times \frac{1}{2} - 40 \times \frac{\sqrt{3}}{2} \times \frac{\sqrt{3}}{2} + 30 \times \frac{1}{2} \times \frac{\sqrt{3}}{2} + 30 \times \frac{\sqrt{3}}{2} \times \frac{1}{2}$$

$$= 15 - 30 + 7{\cdot}5\sqrt{3} + 7{\cdot}5\sqrt{3}$$

$$= 11 \text{ N/mm}^2$$

and

$$\tau_\theta = (60\cos 60°)\sin 60° + (40\sin 60°)\cos 60° - (30\cos 60°)\cos 60° + (30\sin 60°)\sin 60°$$

$$= 15\sqrt{3} + 10\sqrt{3} - 7{\cdot}5 + 22{\cdot}5$$

$$= 58{\cdot}3 \text{ N/mm}^2$$

$$\sigma_r = \sqrt{(11^2 + 58{\cdot}3^2)}$$

$$= 59{\cdot}3 \text{ N/mm}^2$$

at an angle to the

$\phi = \tan^{-1} 58{\cdot}3/1\ 1$ (Fig. 3.10)

$= 80°\ 15'$, (or $20°\ 15'$ to the 60 N/mm² stress).

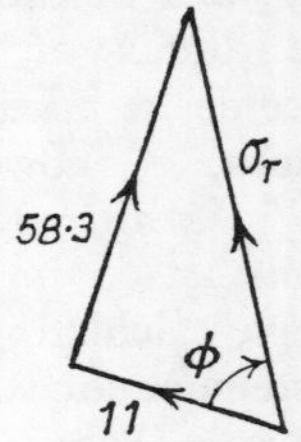

Fig. 3.10

3·7. Principal Planes. It can be seen from equation (2) of Para. 3.6 that there are values of θ for which τ_θ is zero, and the planes on which the shear component is zero are called *Principal Planes.*

From (2)

$$\tan 2\theta = 2\tau/(\sigma_y - \sigma_x) \qquad \text{when } \tau_\theta = 0.$$

This gives two values of 2θ differing by 180°, and hence two values of θ differing by 90°, i.e. the principal planes are two planes at right angles.

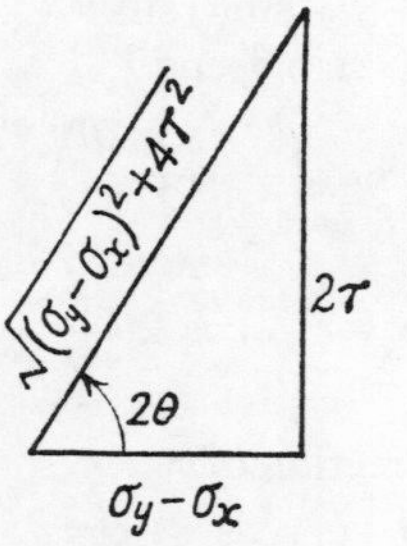

Fig. 3.11

From Fig. 3.11

$$\sin 2\theta = \pm \frac{2\tau}{\sqrt{[(\sigma_y - \sigma_x)^2 + 4\tau^2]}}$$

and

$$\cos 2\theta = \pm \frac{(\sigma_y - \sigma_x)}{\sqrt{[(\sigma_y - \sigma_x)^2 + 4\tau^2]}}$$

where the signs are to be taken both positive or both negative (giving the values for $2\theta+180°$).

3.8. Principal Stresses. The stresses on the principal planes will be pure normal (tension or compression) and their values are called the *Principal Stresses.*

From equation (1) Para. 3.6, using the above values (Para. 3.7)

$$\text{Principal stresses}=\tfrac{1}{2}(\sigma_y+\sigma_x)\pm\frac{\tfrac{1}{2}(\sigma_y-\sigma_x)^2}{\sqrt{[(\sigma_y-\sigma_x)^2+4\tau^2]}}\pm\frac{\tau.2\tau}{\sqrt{[(\sigma_y-\sigma_x)^2+4\tau^2]}}$$

$$=\tfrac{1}{2}(\sigma_y+\sigma_x)\pm\frac{\tfrac{1}{2}[(\sigma_y-\sigma_x)^2+4\tau^2]}{\sqrt{[(\sigma_y-\sigma_x)^2+4\tau^2]}}$$

$$=\tfrac{1}{2}(\sigma_y+\sigma_x)\pm\tfrac{1}{2}\sqrt{[(\sigma_y-\sigma_x)^2+4\tau^2]}$$

The importance of the **principal stresses** lies in the fact that they **are the maximum and minimum values of normal stress** in the two dimensions under consideration, and when they are of opposite type they give the numerical values of the maximum tensile and compressive stresses. This can easily be verified by differentiating equation (1), Para. 3.6,

$$d\sigma_\theta/d\theta=-(\sigma_y-\sigma_x)\sin 2\theta+2\tau.\cos 2\theta$$

Equating to zero for a maximum or minimum gives

$$\tan 2\theta=2\tau/(\sigma_y-\sigma_x)$$

as before for principal planes (Para. 3.7).

3.9 Shorter Method for Principal Stresses. If it is assumed that principal planes, by definition those on which the shear stress is zero, do exist, it is possible to obtain a shorter analysis for their position and the values of the principal stresses. It cannot now be shown that the principal stresses are the maximum values of normal stress, but the method may nevertheless be considered as a treatment from first principles.

Let AC be a principal plane and σ the principal stress acting on it; σ_x, σ_y, and τ are the known stresses on planes BC and AB as before (Fig. 3.12).

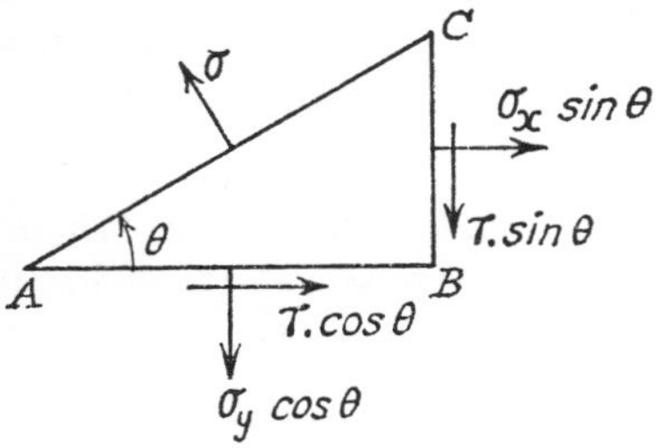

Fig. 3.12

Resolve in the direction of σ_x:

$$\sigma.\sin\theta=\sigma_x.\sin\theta+\tau.\cos\theta$$

or

$$\sigma-\sigma_x=\tau.\cot\theta \qquad (1)$$

Resolve in the direction of σ_y:

$$\sigma . \cos\theta = \sigma_y . \cos\theta + \tau . \sin\theta$$

or

$$\sigma - \sigma_y = \tau . \tan\theta \tag{2}$$

It is now possible to eliminate θ by multiplying corresponding sides of equations (1) and (2), i.e.

$$(\sigma - \sigma_x)(\sigma - \sigma_y) = \tau^2$$

In any numerical problem it is advisable to substitute the values of σ_x, σ_y, and τ at this stage or earlier, and solve the quadratic for the two values of the principal stresses, but it is of interest here to proceed in symbols:

$$\sigma^2 - (\sigma_x + \sigma_y)\sigma + \sigma_x\sigma_y - \tau^2 = 0$$

solving,

$$\sigma = \tfrac{1}{2}(\sigma_x + \sigma_y) \pm \tfrac{1}{2}\sqrt{[(\sigma_x + \sigma_y)^2 - 4\sigma_x\sigma_y + 4\tau^2]}$$
$$= \tfrac{1}{2}(\sigma_x + \sigma_y) \pm \tfrac{1}{2}\sqrt{[(\sigma_x - \sigma_y)^2 + 4\tau^2]}$$

as in Para. 3.8.

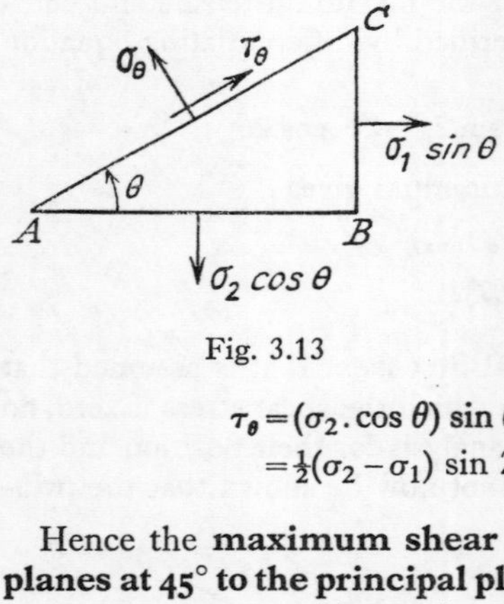

Fig. 3.13

The values of θ for the principal planes are of course found by substitution of the principal stress values in equation (1) or (2).

3.10. Maximum Shear Stress. Let AB and BC be the principal planes and σ_1 and σ_2 the principal stresses (Fig. 3.13).

Then, resolving

$$\tau_\theta = (\sigma_2 . \cos\theta)\sin\theta - (\sigma_1 . \sin\theta)\cos\theta$$
$$= \tfrac{1}{2}(\sigma_2 - \sigma_1)\sin 2\theta \quad \text{(compare Para. 3.5)}$$

Hence the **maximum shear stress occurs** when $2\theta = 90$, i.e. **on planes at 45° to the principal planes** and its magnitude is

$$\tau_{max} = \tfrac{1}{2}(\sigma_2 - \sigma_1)$$
$$= \tfrac{1}{2}\sqrt{[(\sigma_x - \sigma_y)^2 + 4\tau^2]} \quad \text{From Para. 3.8}$$

In words: **the maximum shear stress is one-half the algebraic difference between the principal stresses.**

The same result could be obtained by differentiating equation (2) of Para. 3.6.

It should be mentioned here that, all solids being of three dimensions, there must be three principal stresses, although in many cases the third principal stress is zero. In calculating the maximum shear stress by taking one-half the algebraic difference between the principal stresses the zero principal stress will be of importance if the other two are of the same type. The following figures will clarify this, where σ_1, σ_2, and σ_3 are the principal stresses, compression being shown negative.

σ_1	σ_2	σ_3	Greatest τ
4	2	0	2
4	−2	0	3
4	2	2	1
−4	2	−2	3

EXAMPLE 2. *At a section in a beam the tensile stress due to bending is 50 N/mm² and there is a shear stress of 20 N/mm². Determine from first principles the magnitude and direction of the principal stresses and calculate the maximum shear stress.*

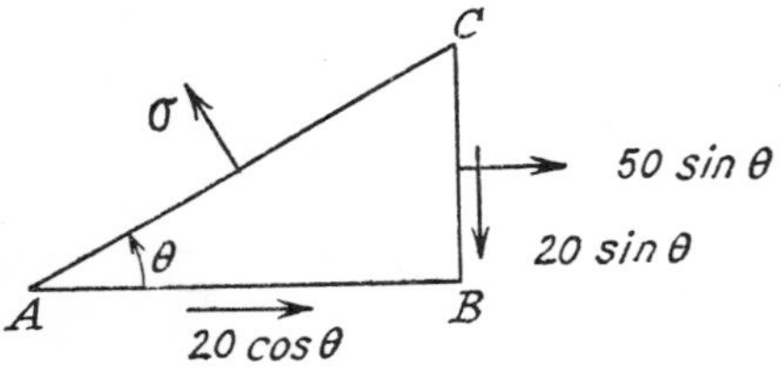

Fig. 3.14

Let AC be a principal plane and BC the plane on which the bending stress acts. There is no normal stress on AB, which is a longitudinal plane of the beam. The forces are shown in Fig. 3.14.

Resolve in the direction AB:

$$\sigma \sin \theta = 50 \sin \theta + 20 \cos \theta$$

$$\sigma - 50 = 20 \cot \theta \qquad \text{(i)}$$

Resolve in the direction BC:

$$\sigma \cos \theta = 20 \sin \theta$$

$$\sigma = 20 \tan \theta \qquad \text{(ii)}$$

Multiply corresponding sides of equations (i) and (ii):

$$\sigma(\sigma - 50) = 20^2$$

or

$$\sigma^2 - 50\sigma - 400 = 0$$

solving,

$$\sigma = \frac{50 \pm 10\sqrt{(25 + 16)}}{2}$$

$$= \frac{50 \pm 64}{2}$$

$$= 57 \text{ or } -7$$

i.e. the principal stresses are 57 N/mm² tension, 7 N/mm² compression, the third being zero.

Substituting in equation (ii)

$$\tan \theta = \sigma/20 = 57/20 \text{ or } -7/20$$

giving $\theta = 70° \ 40'$ and $160° \ 40'$ (differing by 90°), being the directions of the principal planes.

$$\text{Maximum shear stress} = \tfrac{1}{2}(57 - (-7))$$
$$= 32 \text{ N/mm}^2$$

and the planes of maximum shear are at 45° to the principal planes, i.e. $\theta = 25° \ 40'$ and $115° \ 40'$.

3.11. Mohr's Stress Circle. In Fig. 3.15, σ_1 and σ_2 are the principal stresses, on principal planes BC and AB. The stress circle will be developed to find the stress components on any plane AC which makes an angle θ with AB.

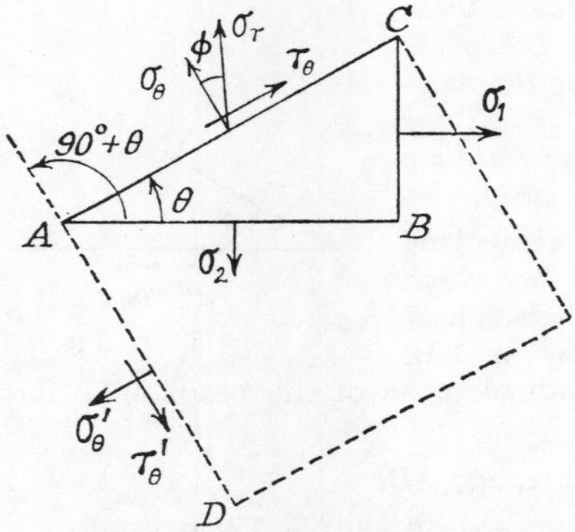

Fig. 3.15

In Fig. 3.16 mark off PL $= \sigma_1$ and PM $= \sigma_2$ (positive direction—tension—to the right). It is shown here for $\sigma_2 > \sigma_1$, but this is not a necessary condition. On LM as diameter describe a circle centre O.

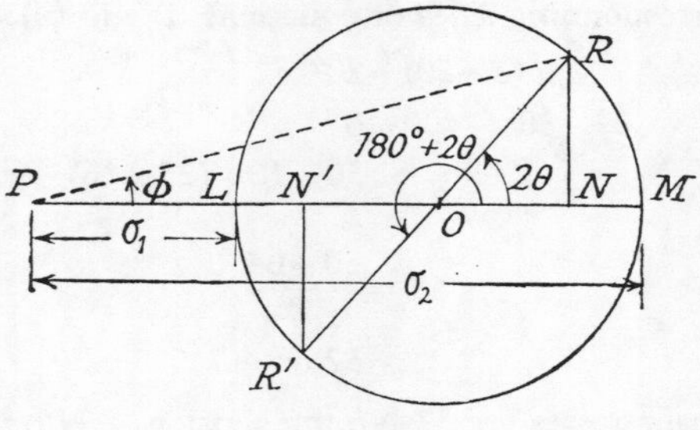

Fig. 3.16

Then the radius OL "represents" the plane of σ_1(BC), and OM "represents" the plane of σ_2 (AB). Plane AC is obtained by rotating

AB through θ anticlockwise, and if OM on the stress circle is rotated through 2θ in the *same* direction, the radius OR is obtained, which will be shown to represent the plane AC. (Note that OR could equally well be obtained by rotating OL clockwise through $180° - 2\theta$, corresponding to rotating BC clockwise through $90° - \theta$.)

Draw RN perpendicular to PM.

$$
\begin{aligned}
\text{Then}\quad \text{PN} &= \text{PO} + \text{ON} \\
&= \tfrac{1}{2}(\sigma_1 + \sigma_2) + \tfrac{1}{2}(\sigma_2 - \sigma_1)\cos 2\theta \\
&= \sigma_1(1 - \cos 2\theta)/2 + \sigma_2(1 + \cos 2\theta)/2 \\
&= \sigma_1 \sin^2\theta + \sigma_2 \cos^2\theta \\
&= \sigma_\theta, \text{ the normal stress component on AC, (Para. 3.5),}
\end{aligned}
$$

$$
\begin{aligned}
\text{and}\quad \text{RN} &= \tfrac{1}{2}(\sigma_2 - \sigma_1)\sin 2\theta \\
&= \tau_\theta, \text{ the shear stress component on AC, (Para. 3.5).}
\end{aligned}
$$

Also the resultant stress

$$
\begin{aligned}
\sigma_r &= \sqrt{(\sigma_\theta^2 + \tau_\theta^2)} \\
&= \text{PR}
\end{aligned}
$$

and its inclination to the normal of the plane is given by $\phi = \angle\text{RPN}$.

σ_θ is found to be a tensile stress in this case, and τ_θ *is considered positive if R is above PM, a positive shear stress being that which will tend to give a clockwise rotation to a rectangular element* (shown dotted in Fig. 3.15).

The stresses on the plane AD, at right angles to AC, are obtained from the radius OR′, at 180° to OR,

i.e. $\sigma_\theta' = \text{PN}'$ and $\tau_\theta' = \text{R}'\text{N}'$

the latter being of the same magnitude as τ_θ but of opposite type, tending to give an anticlockwise rotation to the element dotted in Fig. 3.15.

The maximum shear stress occurs when RN = OR (i.e. $\theta = 45°$) and is equal in magnitude to $\text{OR} = \tfrac{1}{2}(\sigma_2 - \sigma_1)$.

The maximum value of ϕ is obtained when PR is a tangent to the stress circle.

Two particular cases which have previously been treated analytically will be dealt with by this method.

(1) *Pure compression.* If σ is the compressive stress the other principal stress is zero.

Let θ be the angle measured from the plane of zero stress (Fig. 3.17).

In Fig. 3.18, $\text{PL} = \sigma$ numerically, measured to the left for compression, PM = O.

$$
\begin{aligned}
\text{Hence}\quad \text{OR} &= \tfrac{1}{2}\sigma \\
\sigma_\theta &= \text{PN, compressive} \\
\tau_\theta &= \text{RN, positive}
\end{aligned}
$$

Maximum shear stress $=OR=\frac{1}{2}\sigma$, occurring when $\theta=45°$. (Compare Para. 3.2.)

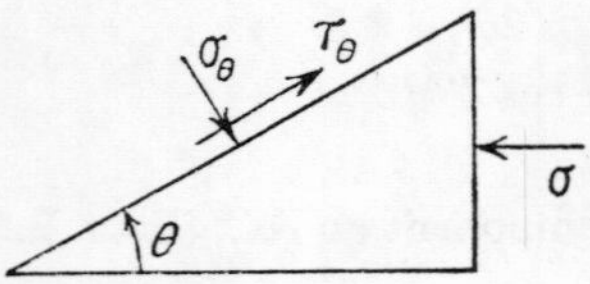

Fig. 3.17

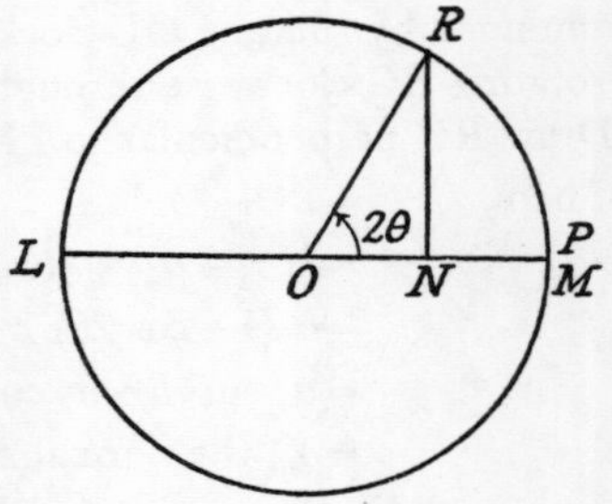

Fig. 3.18

(2) *Principal stresses equal tension and compression.* Let θ be the angle measured anticlockwise from the plane of σ tensile (Fig. 3.19).

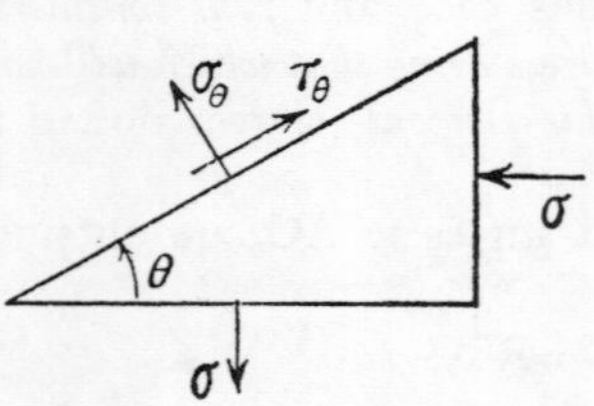

Fig. 3.19

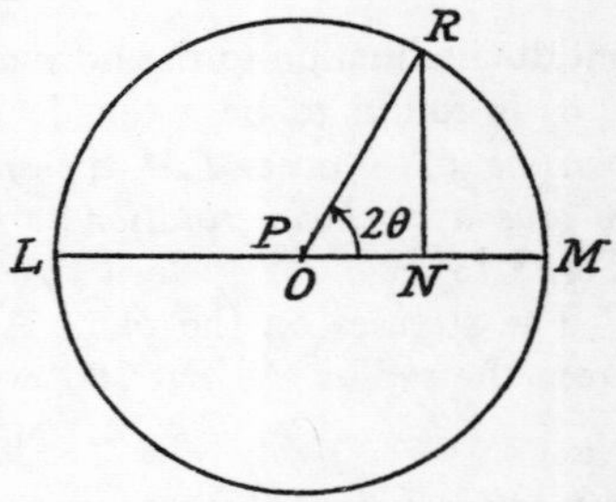

Fig. 3.20

In Fig. 3.20:

$$PM=\sigma \text{ to the right.}$$
$$PL=\sigma \text{ to the left.}$$

Hence O coincides with P.

$\sigma_\theta=PN$ and is tensile for θ between $\pm 45°$, compressive for θ between 45° and 135°.

$\tau_\theta=RN$. When $\theta=45°$, τ_θ reaches its maximum value, numerically equal to σ, on planes where the normal stress is zero (i.e. pure shear). Compare Para. 3.4.

EXAMPLE 3. *A piece of material is subjected to two compressive stresses at right angles, their values being 40 N/mm² and 60 N/mm². Find the position of the plane across which the resultant stress is most inclined to the normal, and determine the value of this resultant stress.*

In Fig. 3.21 the angle θ is inclined to the plane of the 40 tons N/mm² compression.

In Fig. 3.22, PL = 60, PM = 40. The maximum angle ϕ is obtained when PR is a tangent to the stress circle. OR = 10, PO = 50.

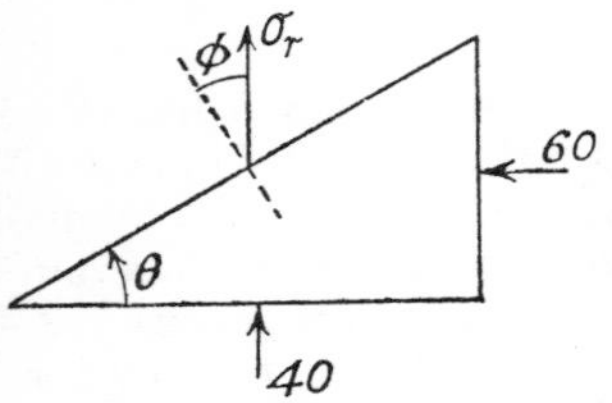

Fig. 3.21

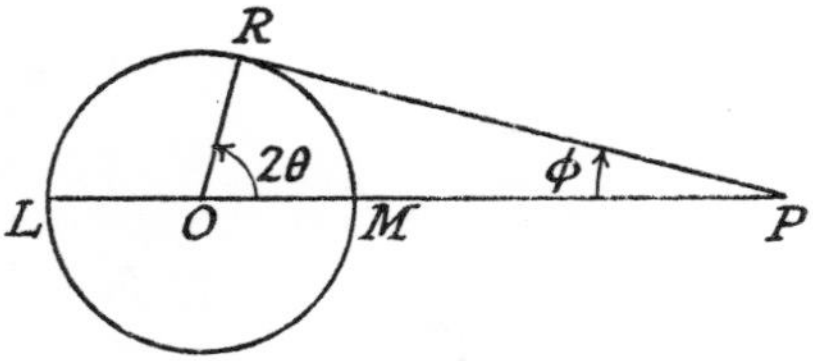

Fig. 3.22

Then
$$\phi = \sin^{-1}\tfrac{1}{5}$$
$$= 11° \ 30'$$
$$\sigma_r = PR = -\sqrt{(50^2 - 10^2)} = -49 \text{ N/mm}^2$$
$$2\theta = 90° - \phi$$
$$\therefore \quad \theta = 39° \ 15'$$

which gives the position of the plane required.

Mohr's stress circle can also be used in the reverse sense, that is, to find the magnitude and direction of the principal stresses in a given stress system, as will be shown below.

EXAMPLE 4. *At a point in a piece of elastic material there are three mutually perpendicular planes on which the stresses are as follows: tensile stress 50 N/mm² and shear stress 40 N/mm² on one plane, compressive stress 35 N/mm² and complementary shear stress 40 N/mm² on the second plane, no stress on the third plane. Find (a) the principal stresses and the positions of the planes on which they act, (b) the positions of planes on which there is no normal stress. (U.L.)*

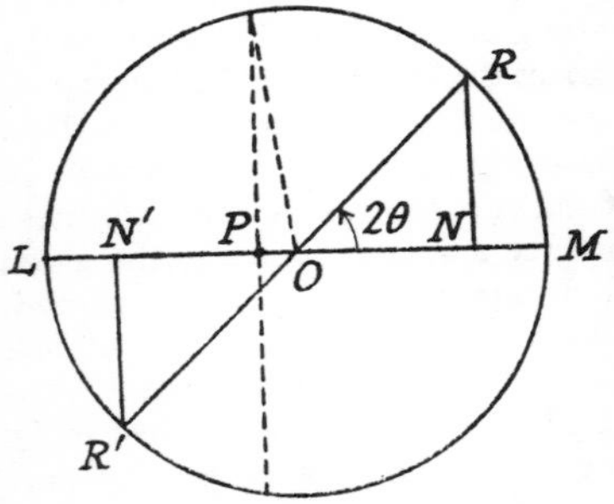

Fig. 3.23

Mark off PN = 50, NR = 40; PN′ = −35, N′R′ = −40. (Fig. 3.23).

Join RR′ cutting NN′ at O. Draw circle centre O, radius OR.

Then
$$ON = \tfrac{1}{2}NN'$$
$$= 42{\cdot}5$$
$$OR = \sqrt{(42{\cdot}5^2 + 40^2)} = 58{\cdot}4$$
$$PO = PN - ON = 7{\cdot}5$$

(a) The principal stresses are

$$PM = PO + OM = 65{\cdot}9 \text{ N/mm}^2, \text{ tensile,}$$

and $$PL = OL - OP = 50{\cdot}9 \text{ N/mm}^2, \text{ compressive.}$$

$$2\theta = \tan^{-1} 40/42{\cdot}5 = 43° \ 20'$$

$$\theta = 21° \ 40'$$

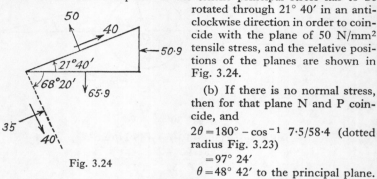

This means that the plane of the tensile principal stress has to be rotated through 21° 40′ in an anti-clockwise direction in order to coincide with the plane of 50 N/mm^2 tensile stress, and the relative positions of the planes are shown in Fig. 3.24.

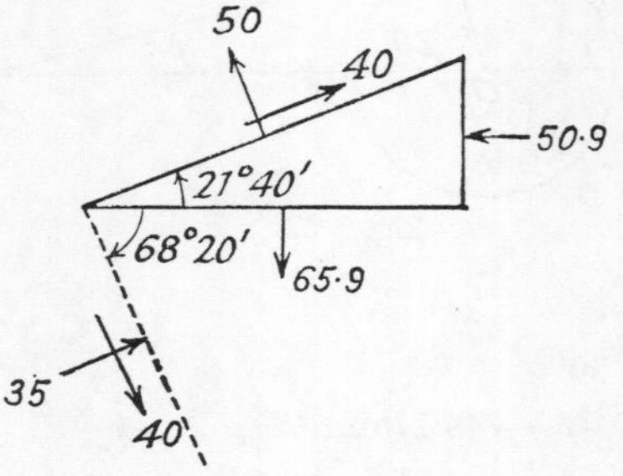

Fig. 3.24

(b) If there is no normal stress, then for that plane N and P coincide, and

$2\theta = 180° - \cos^{-1} 7{\cdot}5/58{\cdot}4$ (dotted radius Fig. 3.23)

$= 97° \ 24'$

$\theta = 48° \ 42'$ to the principal plane.

The following example gives a method of constructing Mohr's circle, and hence finding the principal planes and stresses, when the direct stresses in any three directions are known.

EXAMPLE 5. *Fig. 3.25* (a) *shows the direct stresses in three coplanar directions differing by 60°, at a particular point. It is required to find the magnitude and directions of the principal stresses.*

First draw a vertical line (i.e. the one through P in Fig. 3.25 (b)) and measure off distances proportional to the given stresses (positive to the right, negative to the left). At these distances draw three vertical lines, one for each stress, and starting at an arbitrary point R on the central line draw lines at 60° and 120° to the vertical, cutting the other two verticals in Q and S. In determining which side of the vertical at R to measure these angles, they must be drawn so as to produce a similar figure to the given stress directions, i.e. it must be possible to rotate Fig. 3.25 (a) and place it over R with the 20 N/mm^2 stress in the vertical position. The 60° line from R is produced to cut the 100 N/mm^2 vertical in S, and the 120° is produced (backwards in this case) to cut the −50 N/mm^2 vertical in Q.

The circle passing through QRS (the centre is constructed by perpendicular bisectors on the lines QR and RS) is Mohr's stress circle, the stress conditions on the three given planes being related to the points Q, R′, and S, where R′ is on the vertical through R.

The justification of the construction lies in the fact that the angle at the centre of a circle is twice that at the circumference, and it can be seen that the angles between the radii OQ, OR′, and OS are 120°, which is twice the angle between each pair of given direct stresses.

The principal stresses are then given by

$$PM = \sigma_1 = 112 \text{ N/mm}^2$$

and

$$PL = \sigma_2 = -63 \text{ N/mm}^2$$

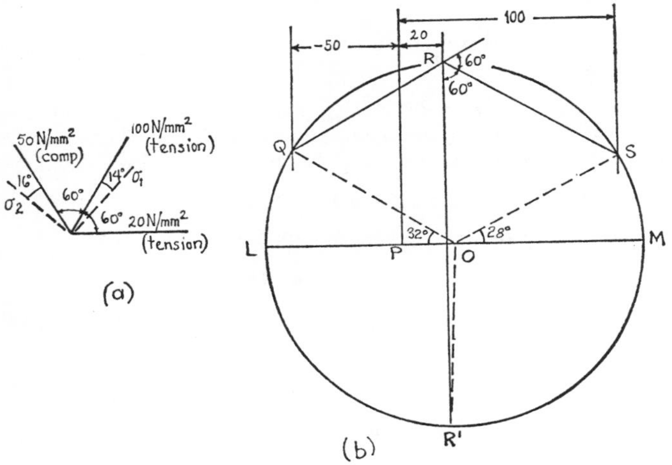

Fig. 3.25

σ_1 being inclined at $\frac{1}{2}\widehat{SOM}$, i.e. 14° to the 100 N/mm² stress and σ_2 being inclined at $\frac{1}{2}\widehat{QOL}$, i.e. 16° to the -50 N/mm² stress.

3.12. Poisson's Ratio. If a bar is subjected to a longitudinal stress there will be a strain in this direction equal to σ/E. There will also be a strain in all directions at right angles to σ, the final shape being dotted in Fig. 3.26.

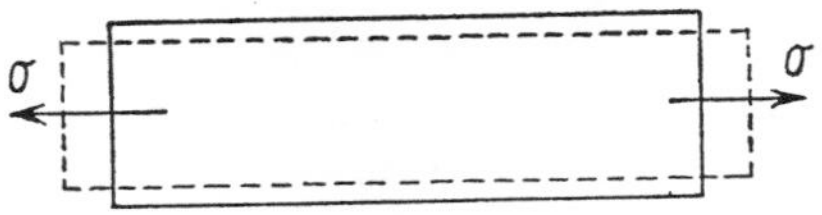

Fig. 3.26

It is found that for an elastic material the lateral strain is proportional to the longitudinal strain, and is of the opposite type. The ratio

$$\frac{\text{lateral strain}}{\text{longitudinal strain}}$$

produced by a single stress is called *Poisson's Ratio*, and the symbol used is ν i.e.

$$\text{Lateral strain} = -\nu . \sigma/E$$

If the stress σ is beyond the elastic limit, and the total longitudinal strain is ε, the "elastic" portion is approximately σ/E and the "plastic" portion is $\varepsilon - \sigma/E$. Poisson's ratio for plastic deformation may be taken as 0·5 (corresponding to no change in density or volume—see Para. 3.18), and hence

$$\text{Total lateral strain} = -\nu\sigma/E - 0{\cdot}5(\varepsilon - \sigma/E)$$

EXAMPLE 6. *A bar of steel 25 cm long, of rectangular cross-section 25 mm by 50 mm is subjected to a uniform tensile stress of 200 N/mm² along its length. Find the changes in dimensions. E = 205,000 N/mm² Poisson's ratio = 0·3.*

$$\text{Longitudinal strain} = \sigma/E = 200/205{,}000$$

$$\therefore \quad \text{Increase in length} = (200/205{,}000) \times 250$$
$$= 0{\cdot}244 \text{ mm}$$

$$\text{Lateral strain} = -\nu\sigma/E = -0{\cdot}3 \times 200/205{,}000$$

$$\therefore \quad \text{Decrease in 25 mm side of section} = (0{\cdot}3 \times 200/205{,}000) \times 25$$
$$= 0{\cdot}0073 \text{ mm.}$$

$$\text{Decrease in 50 mm side of section} = 0{\cdot}0146 \text{ mm.}$$

3·13. Two-dimensional Stress System. It has been proved that every system can be reduced to the action of pure normal stresses on the principal planes, as shown in Fig. 3.27.

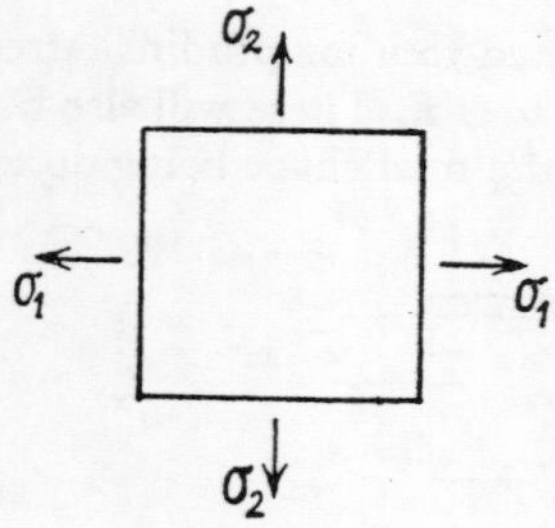

Fig. 3.27

Consider the strains produced by each stress separately.

σ_1 will cause

Strain σ_1/E in the direction of σ_1.
Strain $-\nu\sigma_1/E$ in the direction of σ_2.

σ_2 will cause

Strain σ_2/E in the direction of σ_2.
Strain $-\nu\sigma_2/E$ in the direction of σ_1.

Since the strains are all small, the resultant strains are given by the algebraic sum of those due to each stress separately, i.e.

Strain in the direction of σ_1,

$$\varepsilon_1 = \sigma_1/E - \nu\sigma_2/E$$

Strain in the direction of σ_2,

$$\varepsilon_2 = \sigma_2/E - \nu\sigma_1/E$$

where tensile stress is to be taken positive, and compressive stress negative, a positive strain representing an increase in dimensions in that direction.

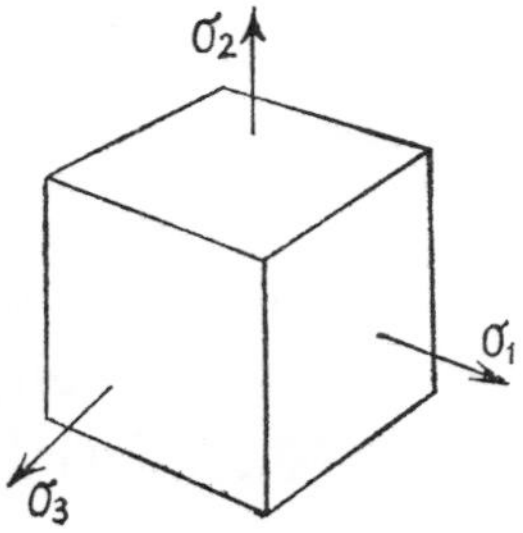

Fig. 3.28

3.14. Principal Strains in Three Dimensions. By a similar derivation to the previous paragraph, it can be shown that the principal strains in the directions of σ_1, σ_2, and σ_3 (Fig. 3.28), are

$$\varepsilon_1 = \sigma_1/E - \nu\sigma_2/E - \nu\sigma_3/E$$
$$\varepsilon_2 = \sigma_2/E - \nu\sigma_3/E - \nu\sigma_1/E$$
$$\varepsilon_3 = \sigma_3/E - \nu\sigma_1/E - \nu\sigma_2/E$$

It should be particularly noted that **stress and strain in any given direction are not proportional where stress exists in more than one dimension.** In fact strain can exist without a stress in the same direction (e.g. if $\sigma_3 = 0$, then $\varepsilon_3 = -\nu\sigma_1/E - \nu\sigma_2/E$), and vice versa.

EXAMPLE 7. *A piece of material is subjected to three perpendicular tensile stresses and the strains in the three directions are in the ratio 3:4:5. If Poisson's ratio is 0·286 find the ratio of the stresses, and their values if the greatest is 60 N/mm²* (*U.L.*)

Let the stresses be σ_1, σ_2, and σ_3, and the corresponding strains $3k$, $4k$, and $5k$.

Then
$$3kE = \sigma_1 - 0{\cdot}286(\sigma_2 + \sigma_3) \quad \text{(i)}$$
$$4kE = \sigma_2 - 0{\cdot}286(\sigma_3 + \sigma_1) \quad \text{(ii)}$$
$$5kE = \sigma_3 - 0{\cdot}286(\sigma_1 + \sigma_2) \quad \text{(iii)}$$

Subtract (i) from (iii):
$$\sigma_3 - \sigma_1 - 0{\cdot}286(\sigma_1 - \sigma_3) = 2kE$$

giving
$$\sigma_3 - \sigma_1 = 2kE/1{\cdot}286 \quad \text{(iv)}$$

Writing (iii):
$$\sigma_3/0{\cdot}286 - \sigma_1 - \sigma_2 = 5kE/0{\cdot}286 \quad \text{(v)}$$

and (ii):
$$\sigma_2 - 0{\cdot}286\sigma_3 - 0{\cdot}286\sigma_1 = 4kE \quad \text{(vi)}$$

Add (v) and (vi):
$$3{\cdot}21\sigma_3 - 1{\cdot}286\sigma_1 = 21{\cdot}5kE \quad \text{(vii)}$$

Writing (iv)
$$1{\cdot}286\sigma_3 - 1{\cdot}286\sigma_1 = 2kE \quad \text{(viii)}$$

Subtract (viii) from (vii): $1{\cdot}924\sigma_3 = 19{\cdot}5kE$

or
$$\sigma_3 = 10{\cdot}14kE$$

From (iv):
$$\sigma_1 = 8{\cdot}58kE$$

From (ii):
$$\sigma_2 = 9{\cdot}34kE$$

Ratio of stresses:
$$\sigma_1;\ \sigma_2:\ \sigma_3 = 0{\cdot}847:0{\cdot}921:1$$

If the greatest $\sigma_3 = 60$ N/mm²
$$\sigma_1 = 50{\cdot}8 \text{ N/mm}^2 \text{ and } \sigma_2 = 55{\cdot}3 \text{ N/mm}^2$$

3.15. Principal Stresses determined from Principal Strains.

(a) *Three-dimensional stress system.* Writing the equations of Para. 3.14.

$$E\varepsilon_1 = \sigma_1 - \nu\sigma_2 - \nu\sigma_3 \tag{1}$$

$$E\varepsilon_2 = \sigma_2 - \nu\sigma_3 - \nu\sigma_1 \tag{2}$$

$$E\varepsilon_3 = \sigma_3 - \nu\sigma_1 - \nu\sigma_2 \tag{3}$$

and subtracting (2) from (1) gives

$$E(\varepsilon_1 - \varepsilon_2) = (\sigma_1 - \sigma_2)(1 + \nu) \tag{4}$$

From (1) and (3), eliminating σ_3

$$E(\varepsilon_1 + \nu\varepsilon_3) = \sigma_1(1 - \nu^2) - \sigma_2(1 + \nu)\nu \tag{5}$$

Multiplying (4) by ν and subtracting from (5)

$$E[(1-\nu)\varepsilon_1 + \nu(\varepsilon_2 + \varepsilon_3)] = \sigma_1(1 - \nu - 2\nu^2)$$
$$= \sigma_1(1+\nu)(1-2\nu)$$

Rearranging,

$$\sigma_1 = \frac{E[(1-\nu)\varepsilon_1 + \nu(\varepsilon_2 + \varepsilon_3)]}{(1+\nu)(1-2\nu)}$$

Similarly

$$\sigma_2 = \frac{E[(1-\nu)\varepsilon_2 + \nu(\varepsilon_3 + \varepsilon_1)]}{(1+\nu)(1-2\nu)}$$

and

$$\sigma_3 = \frac{E[(1-\nu)\varepsilon_3 + \nu(\varepsilon_1 + \varepsilon_2)]}{(1+\nu)(1-2\nu)}$$

(b) *Two-dimensional stress system.* $\sigma_3 = 0$ and

$$E\varepsilon_1 = \sigma_1 - \nu\sigma_2$$
$$E\varepsilon_2 = \sigma_2 - \nu\sigma_1$$

Solving these equations for σ_1 and σ_2 gives

$$\sigma_1 = \frac{E(\varepsilon_1 + \nu\varepsilon_2)}{1-\nu^2}$$

and

$$\sigma_2 = \frac{E(\nu\varepsilon_1 + \varepsilon_2)}{1-\nu^2}$$

3.16. Analysis of Strain. Supposing ε_x, ε_y and ϕ are the linear and shear strains in the plane XOY. It is required to find an expression for ε_θ, the linear strain in a direction inclined at θ to OX, in terms of ε_x, ε_y, ϕ and θ.

In Fig. 3.29 OP, of length r, is the diagonal of a rectangle, which under the given strains distorts into the dotted parallelogram, P moving to P′. Remembering that actual strains are very small,

$$PP' = PQ \cos\theta + QR \sin\theta + RP' \cos\theta \quad \text{approx.}$$
$$= (r\cos\theta . \varepsilon_x)\cos\theta + (r\sin\theta . \varepsilon_y)\sin\theta + (r\sin\theta . \phi)\cos\theta$$
$$= r\varepsilon_x \cos^2\theta + r\varepsilon_y \sin^2\theta + r\phi \sin\theta . \cos\theta$$

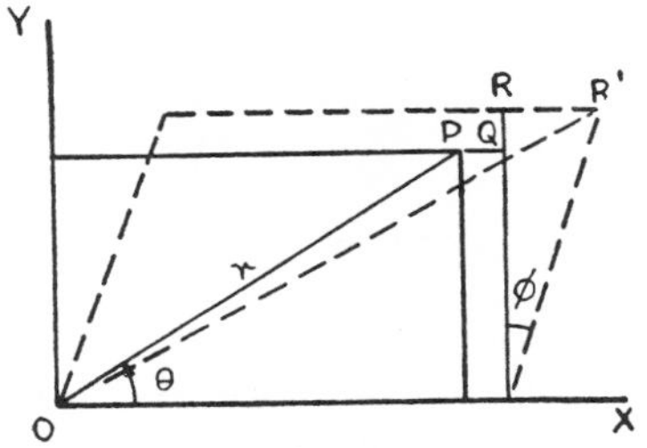

Fig. 3.29

But

$$\varepsilon_\theta = PP'/r \quad \text{by definition}$$
$$= \tfrac{1}{2}\varepsilon_x(1+\cos 2\theta) + \tfrac{1}{2}\varepsilon_y(1-\cos 2\theta) + \tfrac{1}{2}\phi \sin 2\theta \quad \text{from above}$$
$$= \tfrac{1}{2}(\varepsilon_x + \varepsilon_y) + \tfrac{1}{2}(\varepsilon_x - \varepsilon_y)\cos 2\theta + \tfrac{1}{2}\phi \sin 2\theta \qquad (1)$$

This can be compared with equation (1) of Para. 3.6, and the principal strains ε_1 and ε_2, being the maximum and minimum values of strain, occur at values of θ obtained by equating $d\varepsilon_\theta/d\theta$ to zero. i.e.

$$\tan 2\theta = \phi/(\varepsilon_x - \varepsilon_y) \qquad (2)$$

Then, as for principal stresses (Paras. 3.7 and 3.8), ε_1 and ε_2 are given by

$$\tfrac{1}{2}(\varepsilon_x + \varepsilon_y) \pm \tfrac{1}{2}\sqrt{[(\varepsilon_x - \varepsilon_y)^2 + \phi^2]} \qquad (3)$$

In order to evaluate ε_x, ε_y, and ϕ (and hence the principal strains) it is necessary in general to know the linear strains in any three directions at a particular point (if the principal directions are known only two strains are required, since $\phi = 0$ and $\varepsilon_x = \varepsilon_1$, $\varepsilon_y = \varepsilon_2$).

Finally, if these strains are caused by stresses in two dimensions only, the principal stresses can be determined by the method of Para. 3.15 (b).

EXAMPLE 8. *The measured strains in three directions inclined at 60° to one another* (*as in Fig. 3.30*(a)) *are* 550×10^{-6}, -100×10^{-6}, *and* 150×10^{-6}. *Calculate the magnitude and direction of the principal strains in this plane.*

If there is no stress perpendicular to the given plane, determine the principal stresses at the point. E = 200,000 N/mm². *v* = *0·3.*

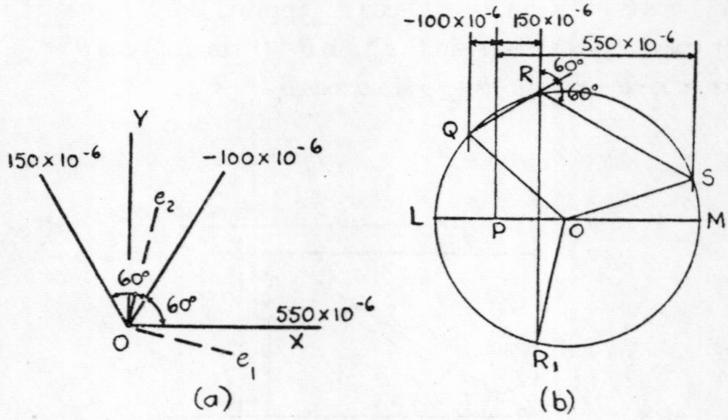

Fig. 3.30

Taking the X-axis in the direction of the 550×10^{-6} strain, ε_x, ε_y and ϕ are determined from equation (1), with $\theta = 0$, 60°, and 120° for the three measured strains, i.e.

$$\begin{aligned}\varepsilon_0 &= 550 \times 10^{-6}\\ &= \tfrac{1}{2}(\varepsilon_x + \varepsilon_y) + \tfrac{1}{2}(\varepsilon_x - \varepsilon_y)\\ &= \varepsilon_x \qquad \text{(i)}\end{aligned}$$

$$\begin{aligned}\varepsilon_{60} &= -100 \times 10^{-6}\\ &= \tfrac{1}{2}(\varepsilon_x + \varepsilon_y) - \tfrac{1}{4}(\varepsilon_x - \varepsilon_y) + \tfrac{1}{2}\phi\sqrt{3}/2\\ &= \tfrac{1}{4}(\varepsilon_x + 3\varepsilon_y) + \tfrac{1}{4}\phi\sqrt{3} \qquad \text{(ii)}\end{aligned}$$

and

$$\begin{aligned}\varepsilon_{120} &= 150 \times 10^{-6}\\ &= \tfrac{1}{2}(\varepsilon_x + \varepsilon_y) - \tfrac{1}{4}(\varepsilon_x - \varepsilon_y) - \tfrac{1}{2}\phi\sqrt{3}/2\\ &= \tfrac{1}{4}(\varepsilon_x + 3\varepsilon_y) - \tfrac{1}{4}\phi\sqrt{3} \qquad \text{(iii)}\end{aligned}$$

Adding (ii) and (iii)

$$\tfrac{1}{2}(\varepsilon_x + 3\varepsilon_y) = 50 \times 10^{-6}$$

or

$$\begin{aligned}\varepsilon_y &= \tfrac{1}{3}(100 \times 10^{-6} - \varepsilon_x)\\ &= -150 \times 10^{-6} \quad \text{from (i)} \qquad \text{(iv)}\end{aligned}$$

From (ii), (i), and (iv) $\tfrac{1}{4}\phi\sqrt{3} = [-100 - \tfrac{1}{4}(550 - 450)]10^{-6}$

giving $\phi = -(500/\sqrt{3})10^{-6}$ (v)

The direction of the principal strains ε_1 and ε_2 (to the X-axis) are given by (2)

$$\begin{aligned}\tan 2\theta &= \phi/(\varepsilon_x - \varepsilon_y)\\ &= -500/700\sqrt{3} \qquad \text{from above}\\ &= -0{\cdot}4125\\ 2\theta &= -22{\cdot}4° \text{ or } 180° - 22{\cdot}4°\\ \theta &= -11{\cdot}2° \text{ or } 78{\cdot}8°\end{aligned}$$

The principal strains, from (3), are

$$\tfrac{1}{2}(\varepsilon_x+\varepsilon_y)\pm\tfrac{1}{2}\sqrt{[(\varepsilon_x-\varepsilon_y)^2+\phi^2]}=200\times10^{-6}\pm\tfrac{1}{2}\sqrt{[700^2+500^2/3]}\,.\,10^{-6}$$
$$=(200\pm379)10^{-6}$$

i.e. $\varepsilon_1=579\times10^{-6}$

and $\varepsilon_2=-179\times10^{-6}$

For a two-dimensional stress system, using the derivation of Para. 3.15 (b), the principal stresses are

$$\sigma_2=\frac{0{\cdot}2(579-0{\cdot}3\times179)}{1-0{\cdot}3^2}$$
$$=115\ \text{N/mm}^2$$

and
$$\sigma_2=\frac{0{\cdot}2(0{\cdot}3\times579-179)}{1-0{\cdot}3^2}$$
$$=-1{\cdot}2\ \text{N/mm}^2$$

3.17. Mohr's Strain Circle. By comparison of Paras. 3.6, 3.8, and 3.16, it will be seen that Mohr's Circle can be used equally to represent strains, the horizontal axis for linear strains ε_x and ε_y, and the vertical axis for half the shear strain, $\tfrac{1}{2}\phi$. Fig. 3.31 shows the relations between

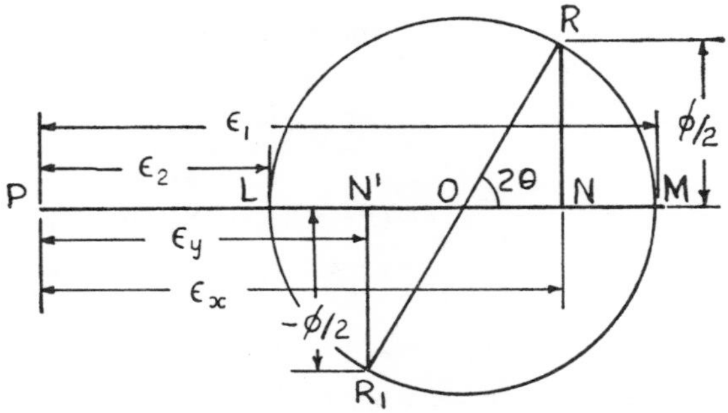

Fig. 3.31

ε_x, ε_y, ϕ and θ, and the principal strains ε_1 and ε_2 as given by eqns. (2) and (3) of Para. 3.16. Note that $PO=\tfrac{1}{2}(\varepsilon_x+\varepsilon_y)$ and $OR=\tfrac{1}{2}\sqrt{[(\varepsilon_x-\varepsilon_y)^2+\phi^2]}$.

The strain circle can be constructed if the linear strains in three directions at a point and in the same plane, are known. The problem of Ex. 8 will now be solved graphically. The given strains are ε_0, ε_{60}, and ε_{120} in Fig. 3.30 (a), and the construction is similar to that of Ex. 5 for the stress circle.

Vertical lines are set off relative to a datum through P (Fig. 3.30 (b)). and at distances on either side proportional to the given strains. From R on the central line (i.e. ε_{120} in this case) lines are set off at 60° and 120° to the vertical, to cut the corresponding strain verticals in Q and S. The strain circle then passes through QRS, the principal strains being

$$\varepsilon_1 = PM = 580 \times 10^{-6}$$

and

$$\varepsilon_2 = PL = -180 \times 10^{-6}$$

The radius OS gives the strain conditions in the X direction, and the angle SOM = 22°. The direction of ε_1 is then $\frac{1}{2}.22 = 11°$ clockwise from the X-axis, and ε_2 is at right angles to ε_1.

Principal stresses can best be obtained from the principal strains by calculation, as in Ex. 8.

3.18. Volumetric Strain. Consider a rectangular solid of sides x, y, and z, under the action of principal stresses σ_1, σ_2, and σ_3 respectively (Fig. 3.32). Then if ε_1, ε_2, and ε_3 are the corresponding linear strains, the dimensions become $x+\varepsilon_1 x$, $y+\varepsilon_2 y$, $z+\varepsilon_3 z$.

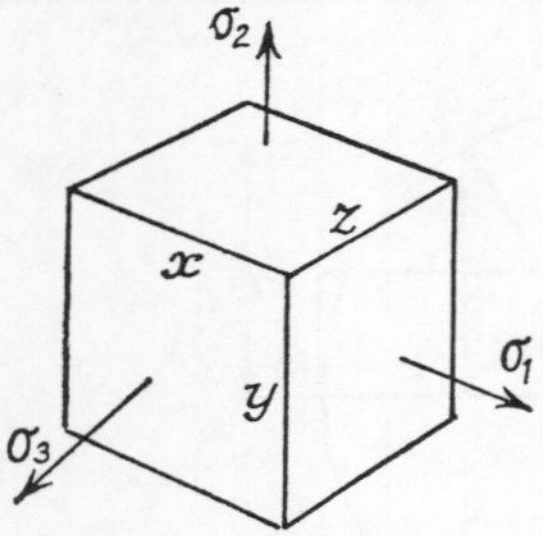

Fig. 3.32

Volumetric strain

$$= \frac{\text{Increase in volume}}{\text{Original volume}}$$

$$= \frac{x(1+\varepsilon_1)y(1+\varepsilon_2)z(1+\varepsilon_3) - xyz}{xyz}$$

$$= (1+\varepsilon_1)(1+\varepsilon_2)(1+\varepsilon_3) - 1$$

$$= 1 + \varepsilon_1 + \varepsilon_2 + \varepsilon_3 + \varepsilon_1\varepsilon_2 + \varepsilon_2\varepsilon_3 + \varepsilon_3\varepsilon_1 + \varepsilon_1\varepsilon_2\varepsilon_3 - 1$$

$$= \varepsilon_1 + \varepsilon_2 + \varepsilon_3$$

to sufficient accuracy, since the strains are small.

Expressing this in words, the **volumetric strain is the algebraic sum of the three principal strains.**

Substituting for the strains in terms of the principal stresses (Para. 3.14) it is found that

$$\text{Volumetric strain} = \frac{(\sigma_1+\sigma_2+\sigma_3)(1-2\nu)}{E}$$

3.19. Strain Energy. Strain energy U is the work done by the stresses in straining the material. It is sufficiently general to consider a unit cube acted on by the principal stresses σ_1, σ_2, and σ_3. If the corresponding strains are ε_1, ε_2, and ε_3, then the total work done $=\Sigma\frac{1}{2}\sigma\varepsilon$, since the stresses are gradually applied from zero, i.e.

$$U=\tfrac{1}{2}\sigma_1\varepsilon_1+\tfrac{1}{2}\sigma_2\varepsilon_2+\tfrac{1}{2}\sigma_3\varepsilon_3$$

$$=(1/2E)[\sigma_1(\sigma_1-\nu\sigma_2-\nu\sigma_3)+\sigma_2(\sigma_2-\nu\sigma_3-\nu\sigma_1)+\sigma_3(\sigma_3-\nu\sigma_1-\nu\sigma_2)]$$ by Para. 3.14

$$=(1/2E)[\sigma_1^2+\sigma_2^2+\sigma_3^2-2\nu(\sigma_1\sigma_2+\sigma_2\sigma_3+\sigma_3\sigma_1)]$$ per unit volume.

For a two-dimensional stress system $\sigma_3=0$

and $U=(1/2E)[\sigma_1^2+\sigma_2^2-2\nu\sigma_1\sigma_2]$ per unit volume.

EXAMPLE 9. *The principal stresses at a point in an elastic material are 60 N/mm² tensile, 20 N/mm² tensile, and 50 N/mm² compressive. Calculate the volumetric strain and the resilience.* $E=100{,}000$ *N/mm²;* $\nu=0{\cdot}35$

$\sigma_1=60$, $\sigma_2=20$, $\sigma_3=-50$.

$$\text{Volumetric strain}=(\sigma_1+\sigma_2+\sigma_3)\frac{1-2\nu}{E} \quad \text{(Para. 3.18)}$$

$$=(60+20-50)\frac{1-0{\cdot}7}{100{,}000}$$

$$=9\times10^{-5}$$

$$\text{Resilience}=[1/(2\times100{,}000)]\,[60^2+20^2+(-50)^2-2\times0{\cdot}35\,(60\times20-20\times50-50\times60)]$$

$$=8460/200{,}000$$

$$=0{\cdot}0423\ \text{N mm/mm}^3$$

3.20. Shear Strain Energy.

Writing

$$\sigma_1=\tfrac{1}{3}(\sigma_1+\sigma_2+\sigma_3)+\tfrac{1}{3}(\sigma_1-\sigma_2)+\tfrac{1}{3}(\sigma_1-\sigma_3)$$

$$\sigma_2=\tfrac{1}{3}(\sigma_1+\sigma_2+\sigma_3)+\tfrac{1}{3}(\sigma_2-\sigma_1)+\tfrac{1}{3}(\sigma_2-\sigma_3)$$

$$\sigma_3=\tfrac{1}{3}(\sigma_1+\sigma_2+\sigma_3)+\tfrac{1}{3}(\sigma_3-\sigma_1)+\tfrac{1}{3}(\sigma_3-\sigma_2),$$

then under the action of the mean stress $\frac{1}{3}(\sigma_1+\sigma_2+\sigma_3)$ there will be volumetric strain with no distortion of shape (i.e. no shear stress anywhere). The strain energy under this mean stress acting in each direction is obtained from the general formula (Para. 3.19), and may be called *volumetric strain energy*,

$$=(3/2E)[(\sigma_1+\sigma_2+\sigma_3)/3]^2(1-2\nu)$$

The other terms in the rearrangement of σ_1, σ_2, and σ_3 are proportional to the maximum shear stress values in the three planes, and will cause a distortion of the shape.

Define Shear strain energy U_s as the difference between Total strain energy and Volumetric strain energy, i.e.

$$U_s = (1/2E)[\sigma_1^2 + \sigma_2^2 + \sigma_3^2 - 2\nu(\sigma_1\sigma_2 + \sigma_2\sigma_3 + \sigma_3\sigma_1)] - [(\sigma_1 + \sigma_2 + \sigma_3)^2(1 - 2\nu)]/6E$$

$$= (1/6E)[(\sigma_1^2 + \sigma_2^2 + \sigma_3^2)(3 - 1 + 2\nu) - (\sigma_1\sigma_2 + \sigma_2\sigma_3 + \sigma_3\sigma_1)(6\nu + 2 - 4\nu)]$$

$$= [(1 + \nu)/6E][2(\sigma_1^2 + \sigma_2^2 + \sigma_3^2) - 2(\sigma_1\sigma_2 + \sigma_2\sigma_3 + \sigma_3\sigma_1)]$$

$$= (1/12G)[(\sigma_1 - \sigma_2)^2 + (\sigma_2 - \sigma_3)^2 + (\sigma_3 - \sigma_1)^2]$$

(See Para. 4.3 for relation between E and G.) The quantities in brackets are each twice the maximum shear stress in their respective planes (Para. 3.10).

In a pure shear system (stress τ), the principal stresses are $\pm\tau$, 0 (Para. 3.4 or 3.8), and by substitution

$$\text{shear strain energy} = (1/12G)[(2\tau)^2 + (-\tau)^2 + (-\tau)^2]$$

$$= \tau^2/2G \quad \text{(compare Para. 2.5)}$$

3.21. Theories of Failure. The theory of elasticity and formulae derived are based on the assumption that the material obeys Hooke's law. Consequently no information can be derived from them if the material has passed beyond its elastic limit at any point in the member. In fact, when "permanent" (non-recoverable) deformations occur the material is said to have "failed." Note that failure does *not* imply rupture.

It is natural to consider that, in a simple tensile test, the elastic limit is associated with a certain value of the tensile stress; but at this stage other quantities, such as shear stress and strain energy, also attain definite values, and any one of these may be the deciding factor in the physical cause of failure.

In a complex stress system these quantities can be calculated from the known stresses and material constants, and the problem is to decide which quantity is the criterion of failure, i.e. the cause of the material passing beyond its elastic limit and taking up a permanent set. Having decided, the actual value of that particular factor which corresponds to the onset of failure is usually taken to be the value it reaches in the simple tension case at the elastic limit.

The principal theories of failure are outlined in detail below, in which σ is the tensile stress at the elastic limit in simple tension, and σ_1, σ_2, σ_3 the principal stresses in any complex system.

(1) *Maximum Principal Stress Theory* (due to Rankine). According to this theory failure will occur when the maximum principal stress in

the complex system reaches the value of the maximum stress at the elastic limit in simple tension, i.e.

$$\sigma_1 = \tfrac{1}{2}(\sigma_x + \sigma_y) + \tfrac{1}{2}\sqrt{[(\sigma_x - \sigma_y)^2 + 4\tau^2]} \quad \text{(Para. 3.8)}$$
$$= \sigma \text{ in simple tension}$$

where σ_x, σ_y, and τ are the stresses on given planes in the complex system.

(2) *Maximum Shear Stress or Stress Difference Theory* (due to Guest and Tresca). This implies that failure will occur when the maximum shear stress in the complex system reaches the value of the maximum shear stress in simple tension at the elastic limit, i.e.

$$\tfrac{1}{2}(\sigma_2 - \sigma_1) = \tfrac{1}{2}\sqrt{[(\sigma_x - \sigma_y)^2 + 4\tau^2]} \quad \text{(Para. 3.10)}$$

on the assumption that the maximum shear is greatest in the XY plane.

$$= \tfrac{1}{2}\sigma \text{ in simple tension (Para. 3.2)}$$

or

$$\sigma_2 - \sigma_1 = \sigma$$

(3) *Strain Energy Theory* (due to Haigh). This theory is based on the argument that as the strains are reversible up to the elastic limit, the energy absorbed by the material should be a single-valued function at failure, independent of the stress system causing it, i.e. strain energy per unit volume causing failure is equal to the strain energy at the elastic limit in simple tension.

$$(1/2E)[\sigma_1^2 + \sigma_2^2 + \sigma_3^2 - 2\nu(\sigma_1\sigma_2 + \sigma_2\sigma_3 + \sigma_3\sigma_1)] = \sigma^2/2E \quad \text{(Para. 3.19)}$$

or

$$\sigma_1^2 + \sigma_2^2 + \sigma_3^2 - 2\nu(\sigma_1\sigma_2 + \sigma_2\sigma_3 + \sigma_3\sigma_1) = \sigma^2$$

(4) *Shear Strain Energy Theory* (due to Mises and Hencky). At failure the shear strain energy in the complex system and in simple tension are equal, i.e.

$$(1/12G)[(\sigma_1 - \sigma_2)^2 + (\sigma_2 - \sigma_3)^2 + (\sigma_3 - \sigma_1)^2] = \sigma^2/6G \quad \text{Para. 3.20)}$$

or

$$(\sigma_1 - \sigma_2)^2 + (\sigma_2 - \sigma_3)^2 + (\sigma_3 - \sigma_1)^2 = 2\sigma^2$$

(The value in the simple tension case is found by putting the principal stresses equal to σ, 0, 0.)

(5) *Maximum Principal Strain Theory* (due to St. Venant). If ε_1 is the maximum strain in the complex stress system, then according to this theory

$$\varepsilon_1 = (1/E)(\sigma_1 - \nu\sigma_2 - \nu\sigma_3) \quad \text{(Para. 3.14)}$$
$$= \sigma/E \text{ in simple tension}$$

or

$$\sigma_1 - \nu\sigma_2 - \nu\sigma_3 = \sigma$$

Other theories have been put forward, but have not proved to be nearer the truth except perhaps for particular types of loading, and discussion will be confined to the theories already outlined.

3.22. Graphical Representation. Where only a two-dimensional stress system is under consideration the limits of principal stress can be shown graphically according to the different theories (Fig. 3.33).

The axes OX and OY show the values of the principal stresses σ_1 and σ_2, σ_3 being zero. Positive directions are to the right for σ_1 and upwards for σ_2. Using the number references attached to the theories in Para. 3.21 values are derived within which the principal stresses must lie for the material to be below the elastic limit. That is to say, according to whichever theory is adopted, failure will occur when the point determined by the principal stresses lies on or outside the boundary of the corresponding figure.

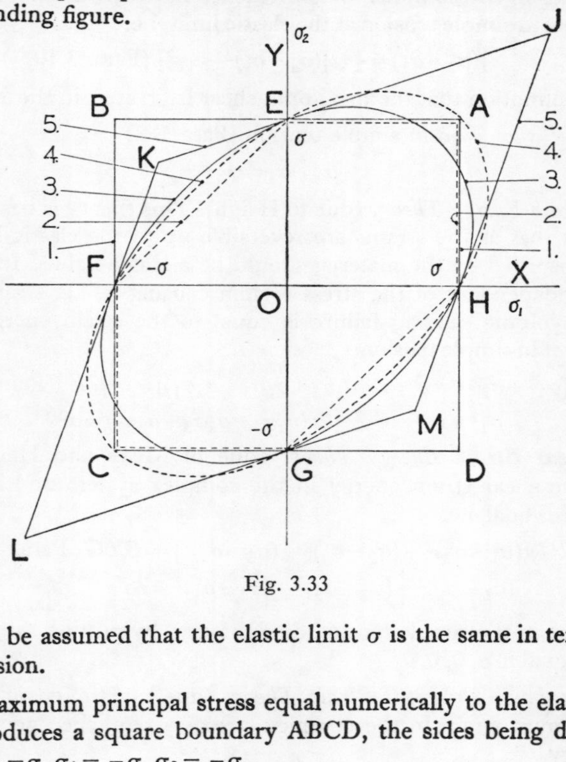

Fig. 3.33

It will be assumed that the elastic limit σ is the same in tension and compression.

(1) Maximum principal stress equal numerically to the elastic limit. This produces a square boundary ABCD, the sides being defined by $\sigma_1 = \sigma$, $\sigma_2 = \sigma$, $\sigma_1 = -\sigma$, $\sigma_2 = -\sigma$.

(2) Maximum shear stress equal numerically to the value in simple tension ($\frac{1}{2}\sigma$). Where the principal stresses are alike, the greatest maximum shear stress is $\frac{1}{2}\sigma_1$ (or $\frac{1}{2}\sigma_2$), obtained by taking half the difference between the principal stresses σ_1 and 0, or σ_2 and 0. This produces lines

$$\tfrac{1}{2}\sigma_1 = \tfrac{1}{2}\sigma, \quad \tfrac{1}{2}\sigma_2 = \tfrac{1}{2}\sigma, \quad \tfrac{1}{2}\sigma_1 = -\tfrac{1}{2}\sigma \text{ and } \tfrac{1}{2}\sigma_2 = -\tfrac{1}{2}\sigma$$

in the first and third quadrants (HA, AE, FC, CG). When the principal stresses are of opposite type, maximum shear stress is

$$\tfrac{1}{2}(\sigma_1 - \sigma_2) = \pm\tfrac{1}{2}\sigma$$

completing the figure in the second and fourth quadrants with the lines EF and GH. The boundary is then AEFCGHA.

(3) In the two-dimensional case, the strain energy theory is defined by an ellipse with axes at 45° to OX and OY; the equation is

$$\sigma_1^2 + \sigma_2^2 - 2\nu\sigma_1\sigma_2 = \sigma^2.$$

It passes through the points E, F, G, and H.

(4) The shear strain energy theory results in an ellipse similar to (3), defined by

$$\sigma_1^2 - \sigma_1\sigma_2 + \sigma_2^2 = \sigma^2$$

(5) The principal strains are

$$(1/E)(\sigma_1 - \nu\sigma_2) \quad \text{and} \quad (1/E)(\sigma_2 - \nu\sigma_1)$$

and failure is assumed to occur when either of these values reaches $\pm\sigma/E$. For like principal stresses the lines HJ, JE, FL, and LG are produced by the equations

$$\sigma_1 - \nu\sigma_2 = \sigma, \quad \sigma_2 - \nu\sigma_1 = \sigma, \quad \sigma_1 - \nu\sigma_2 = -\sigma, \quad \text{and} \quad \sigma_2 - \nu\sigma_1 = -\sigma$$

respectively. For unlike stresses EK, KF, GM, and MH complete the figure.

3.23. Conclusions. Considerable experimental work has been done on various stress systems, such as tubes under the action of internal pressure, end loads, and torsion; also on different materials. So far, however, no conclusive evidence has been produced in favour of any one theory.

It must be admitted that the cause of failure depends not only on the properties of the material but also on the stress system to which it is subjected, and it may not be possible to embody the results for all cases in one comprehensive formula. The following general conclusions may be used as a guide to design.

In the case of brittle materials such as cast iron the maximum principal stress theory should be used. For ductile materials the maximum shear stress or strain energy theories give a good approximation, but the shear strain energy theory is to be preferred, particularly when the mean principal stress is compressive. The maximum strain theory should not be used in general, as it only gives reliable results in particular cases.

It should be noted that, since the shear stress and shear strain energy theories depend only on stress differences, they are independent of the value of the mean stress and imply that a material will not fail under a "hydrostatic" stress system (i.e. $\sigma_1 = \sigma_2 = \sigma_3$). In practice the effect of such a stress system, if tensile, is to produce a brittle type fracture in a normally ductile material, no plastic deformation having taken place. Conversely, a triaxial compressive system will produce a ductile type failure in a normally brittle material. In general the tendency to ductility is increased as the ratio of max. shear to max. tensile stress under load increases.

EXAMPLE 10. *If the principal stresses at a point in an elastic material are 2f tensile, f tensile, and ½f compressive, calculate the value of f at failure according to five different theories.*

The elastic limit in simple tension is 200 N/mm² and Poisson's ratio = 0·3.

(1) *Maximum principal stress theory*

In the complex system, maximum stress $= 2f$

In simple tension, maximum stress $= 200$ N/mm²

Equating gives $f = 100$ N/mm²

(2) *Maximum shear stress theory*

Maximum shear stress = Half difference between principal stresses

$$= \tfrac{1}{2}[2f - (-\tfrac{1}{2}f)]$$
$$= \tfrac{5}{4}f$$

In simple tension, principal stresses are 200, 0, 0, and

$$\text{maximum shear stress} = \tfrac{1}{2} \times 200$$
$$= 100 \text{ N/mm}^2 \quad \text{(See also Para. 3.2.)}$$

Equating gives $f = 80$ N/mm²

(3) *Strain energy theory*

In the complex system

$$U = (1/2E)[(2f)^2 + f^2 + (-\tfrac{1}{2}f)^2 - 2 \times 0{\cdot}3(2f.f - f.f/2 - f/2.2f)] \quad \text{(Para. 3.19)}$$
$$= 4{\cdot}95 f^2/2E$$

In simple tension: $U = 200^2/2\text{E}$

Equating gives $f = 200/\sqrt{4{\cdot}95}$

$$= 89{\cdot}8 \text{ N/mm}^2$$

(4) *Shear strain energy theory*

In the complex system

$$U_s = (1/12G)[(2f - f)^2 + (f + \tfrac{1}{2}f)^2 + (-\tfrac{1}{2}f - 2f)^2] \quad \text{(Para 3.20.)}$$
$$= 9{\cdot}5 f^2/12G$$

In simple tension (principal stress 200, 0, 0)

$$U_s = 200^2/6G$$

Equating gives $f = 200/\sqrt{4{\cdot}75}$

$$= 91{\cdot}7 \text{ N/mm}^2$$

(5) *Maximum strain theory*

Equating the maximum strain in the complex and simple tension cases

$$(1/E)(2f - 0{\cdot}3f + 0{\cdot}3f/2) = 200/E$$

or

$$f = 200/1{\cdot}85$$
$$= 108 \text{ N/mm}^2$$

EXAMPLE 11. *The load on a bolt consists of an axial pull of 10 kN together with a transverse shear force of 5 kN. Estimate the diameter of bolt required according to* (1) *maximum principal stress theory,* (2) *maximum shear stress theory,* (3) *strain energy theory,* (4) *shear strain energy theory. Elastic limit in tension is 270 N/mm², and a factor of safety of 3 is to be applied. Poisson's ratio = 0·3.*

The permissible simple tensile stress is 270/(Factor of safety) = 90N/mm².

Let required diameter be d mm, then the applied stresses are

$$\sigma = \frac{10{,}000}{\pi d^2/4} = \frac{40{,}000}{\pi d^2} \text{ N/mm}^2$$

and

$$\tau = \frac{5000}{\pi d^2/4} = \frac{20{,}000}{\pi d^2} \text{ N/mm}^2 \text{ shear (Fig. 3·34),}$$

assuming uniform distribution over the cross-section.

(1) Maximum principal stress in bolt

$= \tfrac{1}{2}\sigma + \tfrac{1}{2}\sqrt{(\sigma^2 + 4\tau^2)}$ (Para. 3.8: $\sigma_x = \sigma$, $\sigma_y = 0$)

$= \tfrac{1}{2}\cdot 40{,}000/\pi d^2 + \tfrac{1}{2}\sqrt{[(40{,}000/\pi d^2)^2 + 4(20{,}000/\pi d^2)^2]}$

$= (20{,}000/\pi d^2)[1 + \sqrt{(1+1)}]$

$= 48{,}290/\pi d^2$

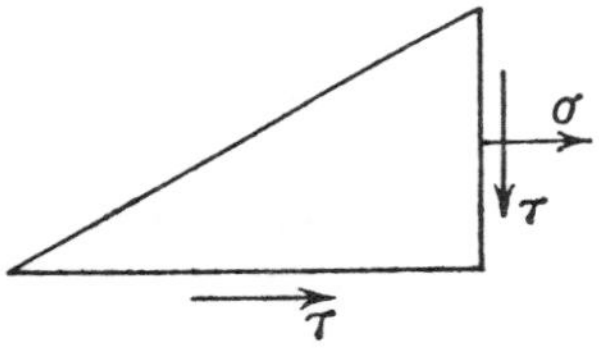

Fig. 3.34

Maximum stress in simple tension = 90

Equating to above gives

$$d = \sqrt{(48{,}290/90\pi)}$$
$$= 13{\cdot}1 \text{ mm.}$$

(2) Maximum shear stress $= \tfrac{1}{2}\sqrt{(\sigma^2 + 4\tau^2)}$ (Para. 3.10)

$$= 28{,}290/\pi d^2$$
$$= 45 \text{ in simple tension}$$
$$\therefore \quad d = \sqrt{(28{,}290/45\pi)}$$
$$= 14{\cdot}2 \text{ mm.}$$

(3) Principal stresses are $\tfrac{1}{2}\sigma \pm \tfrac{1}{2}\sqrt{(\sigma^2 + 4\tau^2)}$, 0, i.e.

$$48{,}290/\pi d^2, \; -8290/\pi d^2, \quad 0$$

Strain energy $= (1/2E)(48{,}290^2 + 8290^2 + 2 \times 0{\cdot}3 \times 48{,}290 \times 8290)/\pi^2 d^4$

$= 26{\cdot}4 \times 10^8/(2E\ \pi^2 d^4)$

$= 90^2/2E$ in simple tension

$$\therefore \quad d = \sqrt[4]{(26{\cdot}4 \times 10^6/81\pi^2)}$$
$$= 13{\cdot}5 \text{ mm.}$$

(4) Shear strain energy

$$=(1/12G)[(48{,}290+8290)^2+8290^2+48{,}290^2]/\pi^2 d^4$$
$$=90^2/6G \text{ in simple tension}$$
$$\therefore\quad d=\sqrt[4]{[(56{\cdot}0\times 10^6\times 6)/(81\pi^2\times 12)]}$$
$$=13{\cdot}7 \text{ mm.}$$

SUMMARY

Resultant Stress $\sigma=\sqrt{(\sigma^2+\tau^2)}$ at angle to normal $\phi=\tan^{-1}\tau/\sigma$.

Pure Shear equivalent to equal tension and compression on planes at 45°.

Principal Planes—zero shear.

Principal Stresses $\sigma_1, \sigma_2=\frac{1}{2}(\sigma_x+\sigma_y)\pm\frac{1}{2}\sqrt{[(\sigma_x-\sigma_y)^2+4\tau^2]}$

Maximum Shear Stress $=\frac{1}{2}\sqrt{[(\sigma_x-\sigma_y)^2+4\tau^2]}$

$$=\tfrac{1}{2}(\sigma_1-\sigma_2)$$

Mohr's Stress Circle.

Poisson's Ratio $\nu=\dfrac{\text{lateral}}{\text{longitudinal}}$ strain due to a single stress.

Principal Strains, $\varepsilon_1=(1/E)(\sigma_1-\nu\sigma_2-\nu\sigma_3)$, etc.

Volumetric Strain $=\varepsilon_1+\varepsilon_2+\varepsilon_3$

$$=\frac{(\sigma_1+\sigma_2+\sigma_3)(1-2\nu)}{E}$$

Mohr's Strain Circle.

Strain Energy $U=(1/2E)[\sigma_1{}^2+\sigma_2{}^2+\sigma_3{}^2-2\nu(\sigma_1\sigma_2+\sigma_2\sigma_3+\sigma_3\sigma_1)]$

Shear Strain Energy $U_s=(1/12G)[(\sigma_1-\sigma_2)^2+(\sigma_2-\sigma_3)^2+(\sigma_3-\sigma_1)^2]$

Theories of Failure. Brittle material: maximum stress. Ductile material: maximum shear stress or shear strain energy.

PROBLEMS

1. At a cross-section of a beam there is a longitudinal bending stress of 120 N/mm² tension, and a transverse shear stress of 50 N/mm². Find from first principles the resultant stress in magnitude and direction on a plane inclined at 30° to the longitudinal axis. (Note: there is no normal stress on longitudinal planes.) (106 N/mm² at 13° 40′ to the axis).

2. In a piece of material a tensile stress f_1 and a shearing stress q act on a given plane. Show that the principal stresses are always of opposite sign. If an additional tensile stress f_2 acts on a plane perpendicular to that of f_1 find the condition that both principal stresses may be of the same sign. (U.L.) $(f_1 f_2>q^2)$

3. Direct stresses of 120 N/mm² tension and 90 N/mm² compression are applied to an elastic material at a certain point, on planes at right angles.

The greater principal stress is limited to 150 N/mm². What shearing stress may be applied to the given planes, and what will be the maximum shearing stress at the point? Work from first principles. (85 N/mm²; 135 N/mm²)

4. A column rests on a foundation block, the top of the latter being horizontal. The column transmits to the block a compressive stress of 174 N/mm^2 together with a shear stress of 46·6 N/mm^2. Find the magnitude and direction of the principal stresses at a point just below the top face of the block.
(185 N/mm^2 compression, 14°; 11·7 N/mm^2 tension, 104°)

5. Show that the sum of the normal components of the stresses on any two planes at right angles is constant in a material subjected to a two-dimensional stress system.

At a point in a material there are normal stresses of 30 N/mm^2 and 60 N/mm^2 tensile, together with a shearing stress of 22·5 N/mm^2. Find the value of the principal stresses and the inclination of the principal planes to the direction of the 60 N/mm^2 stress. (72 N/mm^2; 18 N/mm^2; 61° 48′, 151° 48′.)

6. Draw and describe Mohr's stress circle.

If, at a point in a material, the minimum and maximum principal stresses are 30 N/mm^2 and 90 N/mm^2, both tension, find the shear stress and normal stress on a plane through this point making an angle of $\tan^{-1}$ 0·25 with the plane on which the maximum principal stress acts. (14·1; 86·5 N/mm^2)

7. The principal stresses at a point are 45 N/mm^2 tension and 75 N/mm^2 tension. Working from first principles, determine for a plane at 40° to that of the latter stress: (a) the magnitude and angle of obliquity of the resultant stress, (b) the normal and tangential component stresses.
(64·5 N/mm^2, 13·5°; 62·7, 14·8 N/mm^2)

8. A bar of rectangular cross-section is in tension under an axial stress of 100 N/mm^2. If $\nu = \frac{1}{3}$ for the material, what stresses must be applied to the side faces to prevent any change in cross-sectional dimensions? Show that, by the introduction of these lateral stresses, the axial strain has been reduced in the ratio 2/3. (50 N/mm^2)

9. An axial tensile force of 100 kN is applied to a steel rod 4 cm diameter 50 cm long. Deduce the change in volume if $E = 210{,}000$ N/mm^2 and the ratio of longitudinal to lateral strain is 3·8. (0·113 cm^3)

10. A rectangular block of steel is subjected to normal stresses 75 N/mm^2 tensile, 90 N/mm^2 compressive, and 60 N/mm^2 tensile, on each of its three pairs of faces. What are the strains in each of the three directions if Poisson's ratio is 1/3·5 and E is 202,000 N/mm^2. (0·000412; −0·000635; 0·000318.)

11. A cylindrical bar 1 cm diameter is subjected to an end thrust of 4000 N and is encased in a closely fitting sheath which reduces lateral expansion by one-half of its value if free. Determine (a) the longitudinal strain in the bar, (b) the pressure exerted by the sheath, and (c) the strain energy per unit volume. $E = 210{,}000$ N/mm^2; $\nu = 0{\cdot}283$. (0·00021; 10 N/mm^2; 0·00515 N/mm^2)

12. A piece of material is subjected to two perpendicular stresses, σ_1 tensile and σ_2 compressive. Find an expression for the strain energy per unit volume.

If a stress of 120 N/mm^2 acting alone gives the same value of strain energy as the expression already found, find the value of σ_2 when σ_1 is 105 N/mm^2 Poisson's ratio $= 0{\cdot}32$. (33·75 N/mm^2)

13. A flat brass plate was stretched by tensile forces acting in directions x and y at right angles. Strain gauges showed that the strain in the x direction was 0·00072 and in the y direction 0·00016. Find (a) the stresses acting in the x and y directions and (b) the normal and shear stresses on a plane inclined at 30° to the x direction. E =80,000 N/mm². Poisson's ratio =0·3.

(I.Mech.E.)

((a) 67·5 N/mm². 33 N/mm². (b) 41·5 N/mm². 15 N/mm².)

14. In a certain material the maximum strain must not exceed that produced by a simple tensile stress of 90 N/mm². Show that the maximum permissible pure shear stress is $90/(1+\nu)$, where ν is Poisson's ratio.

With the same limitation of strain, calculate the energy stored per kg of material, (1) when subjected to a simple tensile stress, (2) when subjected to a pure shear stress.

E=205,000 N/mm²; ν=0·3; density 7600 kg/m³. (2.6 Nm; 4 Nm)

15. A rectangular rosette strain gauge records the following values for the linear strain at a point in a two-dimensional stress system: $e_x = 400 \times 10^{-6}$, $e_y = -100 \times 10^{-6}$, and $e_{45} = 200 \times 10^{-6}$, the latter being at 45° to the X and Y axes. Determine the principal strains and stresses by analysis and by Mohr's strain circle. E=207,000 N/mm², ν=0·3.

(405×10^{-6}, -105×10^{-6}, 85, 3·7 N/mm²
Principal stresses at 5°40′ to XY axes.)

16. A strain gauge rosette has the axes of the three gauges OA, OB and OC at 120° to each other. The observed strains are +0·000554, −0·000456 and +0·000064 along OA, OB and OC respectively.

Determine the inclinations of the principal planes at O relative to OA and the magnitudes of the principal stresses. Determine also the strain at right angles to OA. E=200,000 N/mm². Poisson's ratio =0·3. (U.L.)

(−15° 30′, 74° 30′; 105, 74·5 N/mm²; −0·000446)

CHAPTER IV

Elastic Constants

4.1. Elastic Constants. These are the relations which determine the deformations produced by a given stress system acting on a particular material. Within the limits for which Hooke's law is obeyed, these factors are constant, and those already defined are the modulus of elasticity E, the modulus of rigidity G, and Poisson's ratio ν. A fourth constant is now to be introduced, which has applications mainly to fluids, being the relation between pressure and change in volume.

4.2. Bulk Modulus. If a "hydrostatic" pressure p (i.e. equal in all directions), acting on a body of initial volume V, causes a reduction in volume equal numerically to δV, then the bulk modulus K is defined as the ratio between fluid pressure and volumetric strain, i.e.

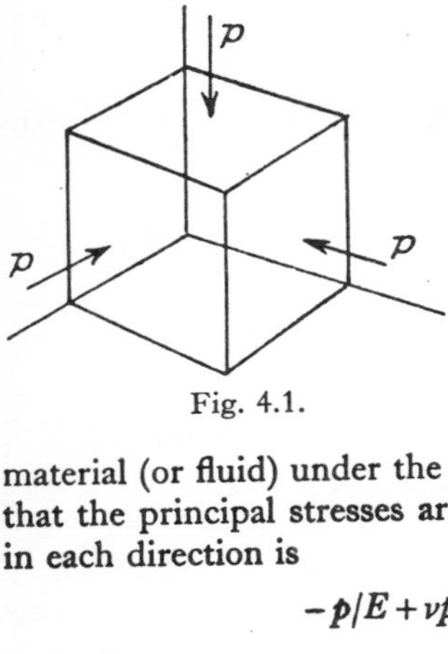

Fig. 4.1.

$$K = \frac{-p}{\delta V/V}$$

the negative sign taking account of the reduction in volume.

Fig. 4.1 represents a unit cube of material (or fluid) under the action of a uniform pressure p. It is clear that the principal stresses are $-p$, $-p$, and $-p$, and the linear strain in each direction is

$$-p/E + \nu p/E + \nu p/E \quad \text{(Para. 3.14.)}$$
$$= -(1-2\nu)p/E$$

But, by Para. 3.18,

$$\text{volumetric strain} = \text{sum of linear strains}$$
$$= -3(1-2\nu)p/E$$

Hence, by definition,

$$K = \frac{-p}{-3(1-2\nu)p/E}$$

$$E = 3K(1-2\nu)$$

Strain energy per unit volume (U), in terms of the principal stresses,

$$=(1/2E)[p^2+p^2+p^2-2\nu(p^2+p^2+p^2)] \quad \text{(Para. 3.19)}$$
$$=3(1-2\nu)p^2/2E$$

i.e. $\boldsymbol{U= p^2/2K}$ from above.

EXAMPLE 1. *A frictionless plunger 6 mm diameter, weighing 1 kg, compresses oil in a steel container. A weight of 1·5 kg is dropped from a height of 5 cm on to the plunger. Calculate the maximum pressure set up in the oil if its volume is 5000 cm³ and the container is assumed rigid. $K=2800$ N/mm² for oil.*

Let p N/mm² be the *additional* momentary maximum pressure set up by the falling weight. Then, neglecting loss of energy at impact:
Loss of potential energy of falling weight = Gain of strain energy of oil.

The volumetric strain produced by p is $-p/K$, and hence the decrease in volume of the oil is $(p/K)\times 5000$ cm³, and this is taken up by the plunger which will therefore sink a further distance

$$=(p/K)\times 5000\times 10^3\times 4/\pi(6)^2 \text{ mm}$$
$$=p\times 5\times 10^6/9\pi K$$

$$\therefore \quad \text{Loss of potential energy} = 1{\cdot}5\times 9{\cdot}81\left(50+\frac{p\times 5\times 10^6}{9\pi K}\right)\text{N mm}$$
$$\text{Gain of strain energy} = (p^2/2K)\times 5\times 10^6 \text{ N.mm}$$

Equating these last two quantities, and multiplying through by $K/5\times 10^6$ produces the quadratic

$$p^2/2=\frac{14{\cdot}7K}{5\times 10^6}\left(50+\frac{p\times 5\times 10^6}{9\pi K}\right)$$

or
$$p^2/2-0{\cdot}52p-0{\cdot}412=0$$

Solving
$$p=0{\cdot}52+\sqrt{(0{\cdot}52^2+2\times 0{\cdot}412)}$$
$$=1{\cdot}56 \text{ N/mm}^2$$

Adding the initial pressure due to the 1 kg weight gives the final maximum pressure of

$$1{\cdot}56+9{\cdot}81/9\pi \text{ or } 1{\cdot}91 \text{ N/mm}^2$$

4·3. Relation between *E* and *G*. It is necessary first of all to establish the relation between a pure shear stress and a pure normal stress system at a point in an elastic material. This was discussed in Para. 3.4, and may also be deduced from the principal stress formulae, but for completeness it will be treated here from first principles.

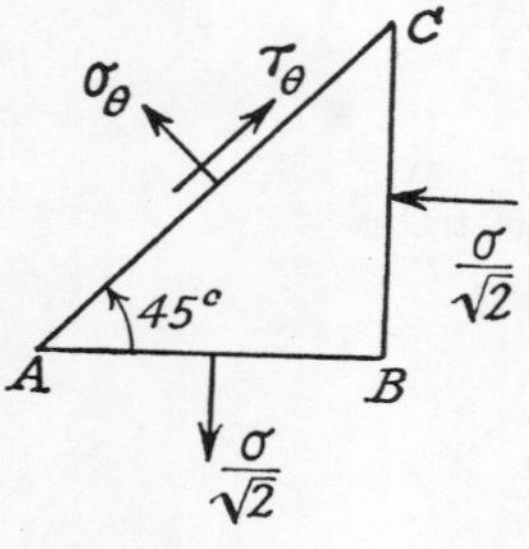

Fig. 4.2

In Fig. 4.2 the applied stresses are σ tensile on AB and σ compressive on BC. If the stress components on a plane AC at 45° to AB are σ_θ and τ_θ, then the forces acting are as shown, taking the area on AC as unity.

Resolving along and at right angles to AC,

$$\tau_\theta = (\sigma/\sqrt{2}) \sin 45° + (\sigma/\sqrt{2}) \cos 45°$$
$$= \sigma$$

and
$$\sigma_\theta = (\sigma/\sqrt{2}) \cos 45° - (\sigma/\sqrt{2}) \sin 45° = 0$$

i.e. there is pure shear on planes at 45° to AB and BC, of magnitude equal to the applied normal stresses.

Fig. 4.3 shows a square element ABCD, sides of unstrained length 2 units under the action of equal normal stresses σ, tension and compression. Then it has been shown that the element EFGH is in pure shear of equal magnitude σ.

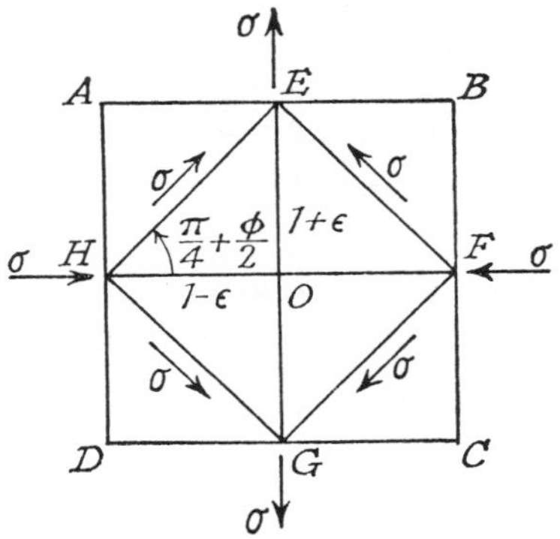

Fig. 4.3

Linear strain in direction EG $= \sigma/E + \nu\sigma/E$

say
$$\varepsilon = (1+\nu)\sigma/E \quad (1)$$

Linear strain in direction HF $= -\sigma/E - \nu\sigma/E$
$$= -\varepsilon$$

Hence the strained lengths of EO and HO are $1+\varepsilon$ and $1-\varepsilon$ respectively.

The shear strain
$$\phi = \sigma/G \text{ (Para 2.4)} \quad (2)$$

on the element EFGH, and the angle EHG will increase to $\pi/2 + \phi$. Angle EHO is half this value, i.e. $\pi/4 + \phi/2$.

Considering the triangle EOH,

$$\tan \text{EHO} = \text{EO/HO}$$

i.e.
$$\tan\left(\frac{\pi}{4} + \frac{\phi}{2}\right) = \frac{1+\varepsilon}{1-\varepsilon}$$

Expanding

$$\frac{1+\varepsilon}{1-\varepsilon}=\frac{\tan \pi/4+\tan \phi/2}{1-\tan \pi/4 . \tan \phi/2}$$

$$=\frac{1+\phi/2}{1-\phi/2} \text{ approx.}$$

since $\tan \pi/4=1$ and $\tan \phi/2 \doteqdot \phi/2$ for small angles.

Clearly $\varepsilon=\phi/2$

and by substitution for ε and ϕ from (1) and (2):

$$(1+\nu)\sigma/E=\sigma/2G$$

Rearranging $E=2G(1+\nu)$

By elimination of Poisson's ratio between the above and $E=3K(1-2\nu)$ of Para. 4.2, it can be shown that $E=9GK/(G+3K)$, and in fact if any two elastic constants are known, the other two may be calculated. Experimentally, however, it is not satisfactory to calculate Poisson's ratio by determining E and G separately, as will be illustrated by the following example.

Example 2. *Show that if E is assumed correct, an error of 1% in the determination of G will involve an error of about 5% in the calculation of Poisson's ratio when its correct value is 0·25.*

Let the correct values be E, G, and ν

Then $$E=2G(1+\nu) \qquad \text{(i)}$$

If G is increased to $1{\cdot}01G$, let the calculated value of Poisson's ratio be ν', then

$$E=2\times 1{\cdot}01G(1+\nu') \qquad \text{(ii)}$$

Eliminating E between (i) and (ii)

$$G(1+\nu)=1{\cdot}01G(1+\nu')$$

i.e. $$1+\nu=1{\cdot}01+1{\cdot}01\nu'$$

or $$\nu'-\nu=-0{\cdot}01-0{\cdot}01\nu' \qquad \text{(iii)}$$

The percentage error in ν is

$$\frac{\nu'-\nu}{\nu}\times 100=-0{\cdot}01\frac{1+\nu'}{\nu}\times 100 \text{ from (iii)}$$

$$=-(1+0{\cdot}25)/0{\cdot}25 \text{ approx.}$$

$$=-5\%$$

Alternatively, the problem may be solved by calculus, differentiating the equation

$$E=2G(1+\nu)$$

remembering that $\delta E=0$ since E does not vary.

$$\therefore \quad 0=2\delta G(1+\nu)+2G\ \delta\nu$$

or $$\delta\nu=-\frac{\delta G}{G}(1+\nu) \qquad \text{(iv)}$$

Percentage error $= \frac{\delta\nu}{\nu} \times 100$

$$= -\frac{\delta G}{G} \cdot \frac{(1+\nu)}{\nu} \times 100 \quad \text{from (iv)}$$

$$= -\frac{1}{100} \cdot \frac{1+0{\cdot}25}{0{\cdot}25} \times 100$$

$$= -5\%.$$

SUMMARY

Bulk Modulus $K = \dfrac{\text{Fluid pressure}}{\text{Volumetric strain}}$.

$E = 3K(1-2\nu)$
$U = p^2/2K$ per unit volume.
$E = 2G(1+\nu)$
$E = 9GK/(G+3K)$

PROBLEMS

1. A small light piston 1·29 cm² in area compresses oil in a rigid container of 16,400 cm³ capacity. When a weight of 10 kg is gradually applied to the piston its movement is observed to be 3·5 cm. If a weight of 4 kg falls from a height of 16·8 cm on to the 10-kg load, determine the maximum pressure developed in the oil container, neglecting the effects of friction and loss of energy.

(2·59 N/mm²)

2. Prove from first principles the relation between E, G, and K.

If two pieces of material A and B have the same bulk modulus, but the value of E for B is 1% greater than that for A, find the value of G for the material B in terms of E and G for the material A. (U.L.) ($101E\,G_a/(101E_a - 3G_a)$.)

3. Express Poisson's ratio in terms of G and K, and prove the derivation.

Determine the percentage change in volume of a steel bar 7·6 cm square section 1 m long when subjected to an axial compressive load of 20 kN. What change in volume would a 10 cm cube of steel suffer at a depth of 4.8 km in sea water? $E = 205{,}000$ N/mm²; $G = 82{,}000$ N/mm².

($(3K-2G)/2(G+3K)$; 0·00085; 0·35 cm³)

4. The principal stresses in an elastic material are σ_1 tensile and σ_2 compressive. Derive an expression for the strain energy per unit volume.

If these principal stresses are caused by a tensile stress σ and a shearing stress τ on a certain plane find, from the energy equation, the relation between E, G, and ν. (U.L.)

5. A determination of E and G gives values of 205,000 N/mm² and 80,700 N/mm². Calculate Poisson's ratio and the bulk modulus.

Find the change in diameter produced in a bar of this material 5 cm diameter acted on by an axial tensile load of 150 kN.

If both moduli are liable to an error of ±2% find the maximum percentage error in the derived value of Poisson's ratio.

(0·27; 148,000 N/mm²; 0·00505 mm ± 19%.)

6. An element of elastic material is acted upon by three principal stresses and the three principal strains s_{xx}, s_{yy}, and s_{zz} are measured. Show that the principal stress in the direction xx is given by

$$\alpha\Delta + 2Gs_{xx}$$

where $\alpha = mE/[(m+1)(m-2)]$, Δ is the volumetric strain, G is the modulus of rigidity, and $1/m$ is Poisson's ratio.

In a certain test the principal strains were found to be 0·00071, 0·00140, and −0·00185. Determine the three principal stresses. Take $E = 207{,}000$ N/mm^2 and Poisson's ratio $= 0{\cdot}35$. (U.L.)

(155, 261, −237 N/mm^2, see Para. 3.15.)

CHAPTER V

Shearing Force and Bending Moment

5.1. Shearing Force. The shearing force at any section of a beam represents the tendency for the portion of beam to one side of the section to slide or shear laterally relative to the other portion.

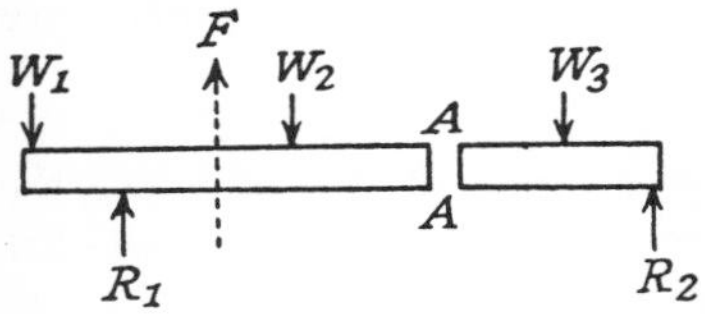

Fig. 5.1

Consider the case shown in Fig. 5.1, in which a beam carrying loads W_1, W_2, and W_3 is simply supported at two points, the reactions at the supports being R_1 and R_2. Now imagine the beam to be divided into two portions by a section at AA. The resultant of the loads and reactions to the left of AA is F vertically upwards, and since the whole beam is in equilibrium, the resultant of the forces to the right of AA must also be F, acting downwards. F is called the *Shearing Force* (abbrev. S.F.) at the section AA and may be defined as follows: *the shearing force at any section of a beam is the algebraic sum of the lateral components of the forces acting on either side of the section.*

Where a force is in neither the axial nor lateral direction it must be resolved in the usual way, the lateral component being taken into account in the shearing force.

Shearing force will be considered positive when the resultant of the forces to the left is upwards, or to the right is downwards.

A *shearing force diagram* is one which shows the variation of shearing force along the length of the beam.

5.2. Bending Moment. In a similar manner it can be argued that if the moment about the section AA of the forces to the left is M clockwise (Fig. 5.2), then the moment of the forces to the right of AA must be M anticlockwise. M is called the *Bending Moment* (abbrev. B.M.) *at* AA, and *is defined as: the algebraic sum of the moments about the section of all the forces acting on either side of the section.*

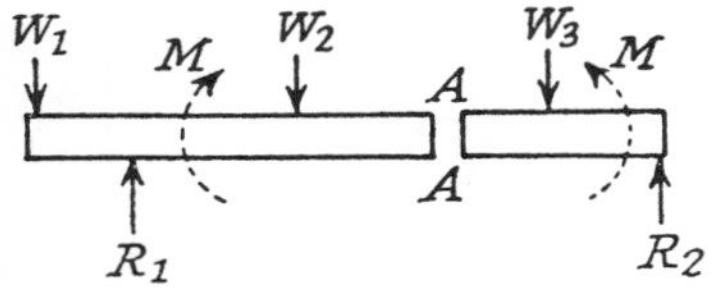

Fig. 5.2

Bending moment will be considered positive when the moment on the left portion is clockwise, and on the right portion anticlockwise. This is referred to as *sagging* bending moment since it tends to make the beam concave upwards at AA. Negative bending moment is termed *hogging*.

A *bending moment diagram* is one which shows the variation of bending moment along the length of the beam.

5·3. Types of Load. A beam is normally horizontal, the loads being vertical, other cases which occur being looked upon as exceptions.

A *concentrated* load is one which is considered to act at a point, although in practice it must really be distributed over a small area.

A *distributed* load is one which is spread in some manner over the length of the beam. The rate of loading w may be uniform, or may vary from point to point along the beam.

5·4. Types of Support. A *simple* or *free* support is one on which the beam is rested, and which exerts a reaction on the beam. Normally the reaction will be considered as acting at a point, though it may be distributed along a length of beam in a similar manner to a distributed load.

A *built-in* or *encastré* support is frequently met with, the effect being to fix the direction of the beam at the support. In order to do this the support must exert a "fixing" moment M and a reaction R on the beam (Fig. 5.3). A beam thus fixed at one end is called a *cantilever*; when fixed at both ends the reactions are not statically determinate, and this case will be dealt with later (Chapter X).

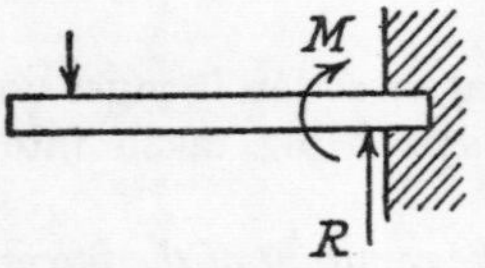

Fig. 5.3

In practice it is not usually possible to obtain perfect fixing, and the "fixing" moment applied will be related to the angular movement at the support. When in doubt about the rigidity (e.g. a riveted joint), it is "safer" to assume that the beam is freely supported.

5·5. Relations between w, F, and M. Fig. 5.4 shows a short length

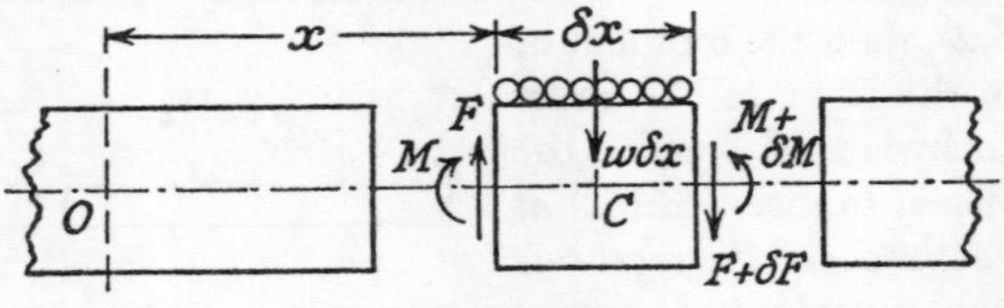

Fig. 5·4

δx imagined to be a "slice" cut out from a loaded beam at a distance x from a fixed origin O.

Let the shearing force at the section x be F, and at $x+\delta x$ be $F+\delta F$. Similarly, the bending moment is M at x, and $M+\delta M$ at $x+\delta x$. If w is the mean rate of loading on the length δx, the total load is $w\delta x$, acting approximately (exactly, if uniformly distributed) through the centre C. The element must be in equilibrium under the action of these forces and couples, and the following equations are obtained.

Taking moments about C:

$$M+F.\delta x/2+(F+\delta F)\delta x/2=M+\delta M$$

Neglecting the product $\delta F.\delta x$, and taking the limit, gives

$$F=dM/dx \quad (1)$$

Resolving vertically

$$w\delta x+F+\delta F=F$$

or

$$w=-dF/dx \quad (2)$$

$$=-d^2M/dx^2 \quad \text{from (1)} \quad (3)$$

From equation (1) it can be seen that, if M is varying continuously, zero shearing force corresponds to maximum or minimum bending moment, the latter usually indicating the greatest value of negative bending moment. It will be seen later, however, that "peaks" in the bending moment diagram frequently occur at concentrated loads or reactions, and are not then given by $F=dM/dx=0$, although they may represent the greatest bending moment on the beam. Consequently it is not always sufficient to investigate the points of zero shearing force when determining the maximum bending moment.

At a point on the beam where the type of bending is changing from sagging to hogging, the bending moment must be zero, and this is called a point of *inflection* or *contraflexure*.

By integrating equation (1) between two values of $x=a$ and b, then

$$M_b-M_a=\int_a^b F dx$$

showing that the increase in bending moment between two sections is given by the area under the shearing force diagram.

Similarly, integrating equation (2)

$$F_a-F_b=\int_a^b w dx$$

= the area under the load distribution diagram.

Integrating equation (3) gives

$$M_a-M_b=\int\int_a^b w dx.dx$$

These relations prove very valuable when the rate of loading cannot be expressed in an algebraic form, and provide a means of graphical solution.

5.6. Concentrated Loads

EXAMPLE 1. *A cantilever of length l carries a concentrated load W at its free end. Draw the S.F. and B.M. diagrams.*

At a section a distance x from the free end, consider the forces to the left.

Then $F = -W$ and is constant along the whole beam (i.e. for all values of x).

Taking moments about the section gives $M = -Wx$, so that the maximum bending moment occurs at the fixed end, i.e.

$$\hat{M} = Wl \text{ (hogging)}$$

From equilibrium considerations, the fixing moment applied at the built-in end is Wl, and the reaction is W.

The S.F. and B.M. diagrams are therefore as shown in Fig. 5.5.

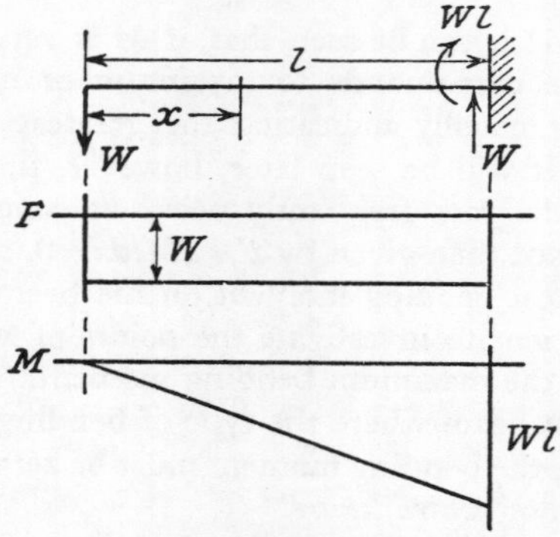

Fig. 5.5

EXAMPLE 2. *A beam 10 m long is simply supported at its ends and carries concentrated loads of 30 kN and 50 kN at distances of 3 m. from each end. Draw the S.F. and B.M. diagrams.*

First calculate the reactions R_1 and R_2 at the supports (Fig. 5.6).

By moments about R_2:

$$R_1 \times 10 = 30 \times 7 + 50 \times 3$$

$$\therefore \quad R_1 = 36 \text{ kN}$$

and

$$R_2 = 30 + 50 - R_1 = 44 \text{ kN}$$

Let x be the distance of the section from the left-hand end.

Shearing Force:

$$0 < x < 3, \quad F = R_1 = 36 \text{ kN}$$

$$3 < x < 7, \quad F = R_1 - 30 = 6 \text{ kN}$$

$$7 < x < 10, \quad F = R_1 - 30 - 50 = -44 \text{ kN}$$

Note that the last value $= -R_2$, which provides a check on the working.

Bending Moment:

$$0<x<3, \quad M=R_1x=36x \text{ kNm}$$
$$3<x<7, \quad M=R_1x-30(x-3)=6x+90 \text{ kNm}$$
$$7<x<10, \quad M=R_1x-30(x-3)-50(x-7)$$
$$= -44x+440 \text{ kNm}$$

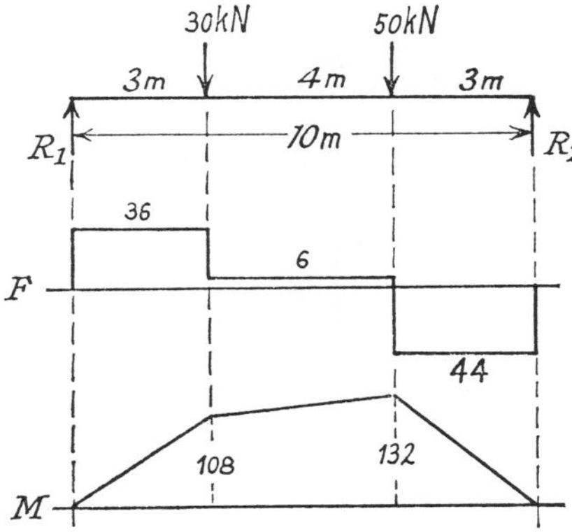

Fig. 5.6

Principal values of M are: at $x=3$ m, $M=108$ kNm, at $x=7$ m, $M=132$ kNm. Note that the latter value can be checked by taking $R_2 \times 3$ as calculated for the right-hand portion.

The following general conclusions can be drawn when only concentrated loads and reactions are concerned:

(1) *The shearing force suffers a sudden change when passing through a load point, the change being numerically equal to the load.*

(2) *The bending moment diagram is a series of straight lines between the loads, the slope of the lines being equal to the shearing force between those points.*

5·7. Uniformly Distributed Loads

EXAMPLE 3. *Draw the S.F. and B.M. diagrams for a simply supported beam of length l carrying a uniformly distributed load w/unit length across the whole span.*

The total load carried $= wl$, and by symmetry the reactions at the end supports are each $wl/2$ (Fig. 5.7).

If x is the distance of the section considered from the left-hand end

$$F=wl/2-wx$$
$$=w(l/2-x)$$

giving *a straight line of slope equal to the rate of loading* (compare

$w = -dF/dx$ of Para. 5.5). End values of S.F. are $\pm wl/2$, with a zero value at the centre.

The B.M. at the section x is found by treating the distributed load as acting at its centre of gravity, which is $x/2$ from the section (Fig. 5.8), giving

$$M = (wl/2)x - (wx)x/2$$
$$= (wx/2)(l - x)$$

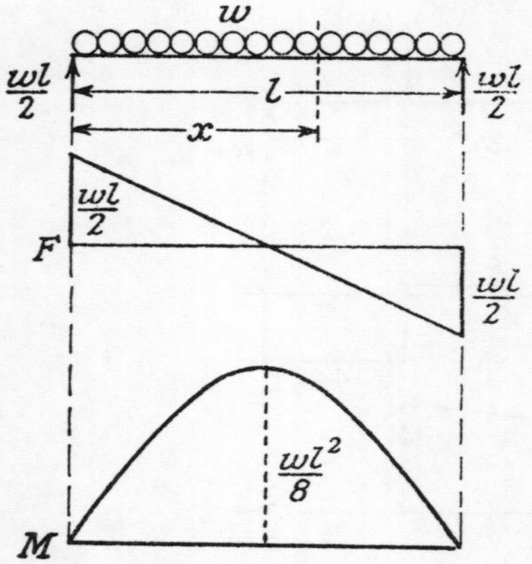

Fig. 5.7

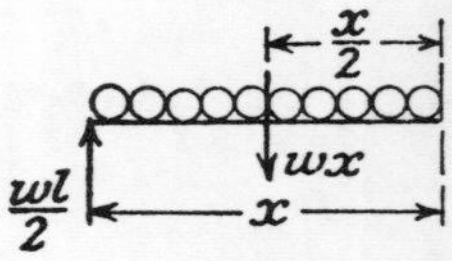

Fig. 5.8

This is *a parabolic curve*, having zero values at each end and a maximum at the centre (corresponding to zero shear, from $F = dM/dx$, Para. 5.5)

$$\hat{M} = (wl/4)(l - l/2) \quad \text{putting } x = l/2$$
$$= wl^2/8$$

5.8. Combined Loads

EXAMPLE 4. *A beam 25 m long is supported at A and B and loaded as shown in Fig. 5.9. Sketch the S.F. and B.M. diagrams and find* (a) *the position and magnitude of maximum B.M. and* (b) *the position of the point of contraflexure.*

By moments about B:

$$20R_a = 10{,}000 \times 15 + 2000 \times 5 - 3000 \times 5$$

(all loads are taken into account for equilibrium, the distributed load acting as its centre of gravity).

$$\therefore \quad R_a = 7250 \text{ kg} \equiv 71{\cdot}1 \text{ kN}$$
$$\therefore \quad R_b = \text{Total load} - R_a$$
$$= 7750 \text{ kg} \equiv 76 \text{ kN}$$

Shearing Force. Starting at the left-hand end, $F = 71{\cdot}1$ kN at A. As the section moves away from A, F decreases at a uniform rate $= w$ (i.e. $F = 71{\cdot}1 - wx$), reaching a value -27 kN at E.

Between E and D, F is constant (no load on ED), and at D it suffers a sudden decrease of 19·6 kN (i.e. the load at D). Similarly there is an increase of 76 kN at B (the reaction at B), making the value of $F = 29{\cdot}4$ kN between B and C (checking with the end load at C).

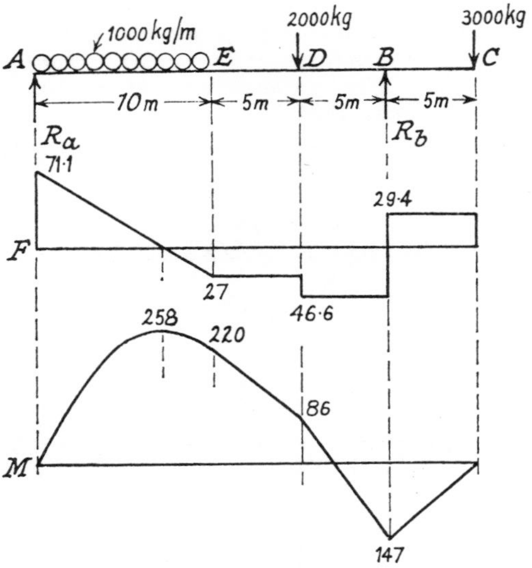

Fig. 5.9

Bending Moment. From A to E:

$$M = R_a x - wx^2/2$$
$$= 71{\cdot}1x - 4{\cdot}9x^2 \text{ kNm}$$

a parabola which can be sketched by evaluating for several values of x.

For x beyond E the distributed load may be treated as a single load of 98·1 kN acting at 5 m from A.

Between E and D:

$$M = 71{\cdot}1x - 98{\cdot}1(x - 5)$$
$$= -27x + 490$$

producing a straight line between E and D, similar equations applying for sections DB and BC.

However, it is only necessary to evaluate M at the points D and B (it is zero at C), and draw straight lines between these values.

At D: $M = -27 \times 15 + 490 = 86$ kNm

At B: $M = -29{\cdot}4 \times 5$
$= -147$ kNm. (calculated for the portion BC).

(a) The maximum B.M. between A and E is where the shearing force is zero, i.e. 7·25 m from A.

$$\therefore \quad \hat{M} = 71{\cdot}1 \times 7{\cdot}25 - 4{\cdot}9 \times 7{\cdot}25^2 = 258 \text{ kNm}$$

(b) The point of contraflexure (zero B.M.) occurs between D and B at

$$\left(\frac{147}{147+86}\right)\times 5=3{\cdot}16 \text{ m from B.}$$

EXAMPLE 5. *A girder 30 m long carrying a uniformly distributed load of w kN/m is to be supported on two piers 18 m apart so that the greatest B.M. shall be as small as possible. Find the distances of the piers from the ends of the girder and the maximum B.M.*

Let the distance of one pier from the end be d m, the other being $12-d$ m. (Fig. 5.10).

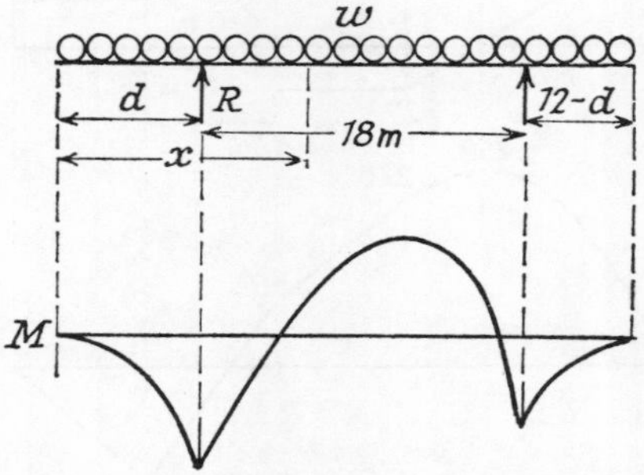

Fig. 5.10

By moments about the right-hand support

$$18R=30w(3+d)$$
$$R=(5w/3)(3+d)$$

where $(3+d)$ m is the distance from the centre of the beam to the right-hand pier.

For the overhanging end, $M=-wx^2/2$, giving a maximum value at the support

$$=-wd^2/2 \qquad \text{(i)}$$

For the portion between the supports

$$M=-wx^2/2+R(x-d)$$

(x from left-hand end), which is a maximum when

$$dM/dx=0=-wx+R$$

i.e. $x=R/w=(5/3)(3+d)$ from above,

and

$$\hat{M}=-(25/18)w(3+d)^2+(5w/3)(3+d)[(5/3)(3+d)-d]$$
$$=-(25w/18)(3+d)^2+(5w/9)(3+d)(15+2d)$$
$$=(5w/18)(45+12d-d^2) \qquad \text{(ii)}$$

For the greatest B.M. to be as small as possible it is necessary to make the two possible values equal (numerically), since it is clear that if the supports are moved to the right from this position the value at the left pier will be increased, and if moved to the left the value between the piers will be increased.

Equating ***numerical*** values (i) and (ii):

$$wd^2/2 = (5w/18)(45 + 12d - d^2)$$

$\times 18$: $$9d^2 = 225 + 60d - 5d^2$$

or $$14d^2 - 60d - 225 = 0.$$

Solving $$d = \frac{60 \pm \sqrt{(3600 + 4 \times 14 \times 225)}}{28}$$

$$= 6{\cdot}7 \text{ m. (one pier)}$$

and $$12 - d = 5{\cdot}3 \text{ m. (other pier)}$$

$$\hat{M} = wd^2/2 \text{ from (i), numerically}$$

$$= 22{\cdot}4w \text{ kNm}$$

EXAMPLE 6. *Draw the S.F. and B.M. diagrams for a beam 8 m long simply supported at its ends, carrying a load of 20 kN which is applied through a bracket. The bracket is fixed to the beam at a distance of 6 m from one support, the length of bracket in the direction of the beam being 1 m. (Fig. 5.11.)*

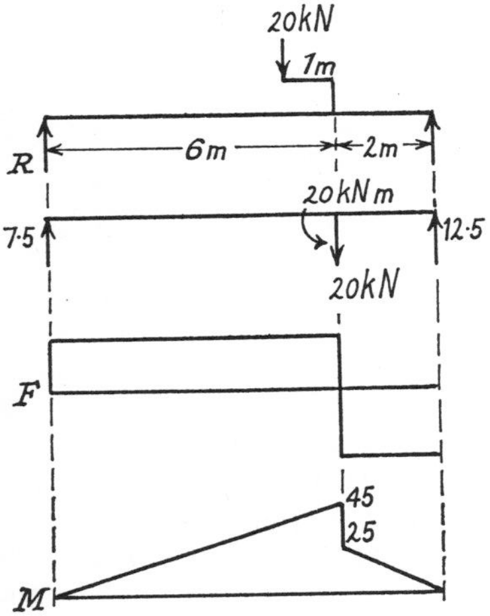

Fig. 5.11

By moments about the right-hand end

$$R = (20 \times 3)/8 = 7{\cdot}5 \text{ kN}$$

The effect of the bracket is to apply a load of 20 kN, and a B.M. of 20 kNm, at a point 6 m from the left-hand end.

Thus F has a value of 7·5 kN along 6 m of the beam and $-12{\cdot}5$ kN along the other 2 m.

M increases from zero to $7{\cdot}5 \times 6 =$ 45 kNm at the bracket on one side, and from zero to $12{\cdot}5 \times 2 = 25$ kNm at the bracket on the other side. There is a sudden change in the B.M. at the bracket, equal to 20 kNm.

5.9. Varying Distributed Loads

EXAMPLE 7. *A beam ABC, 27 m long, is simply supported at A and B, 18 m apart, and carries a load of 20 kN at 6 m from A together with a distributed load whose intensity varies in linear fashion from zero at A and C to 10 kN/m at B.*

Draw the S.F. and B.M. diagrams and calculate the position and magnitude of the maximum B.M.

The total load on the beam

$$=20+\tfrac{1}{2}\times 270=155\text{ kN}$$

since the mean rate of loading is $\frac{1}{2}\times 10$ kN/m.

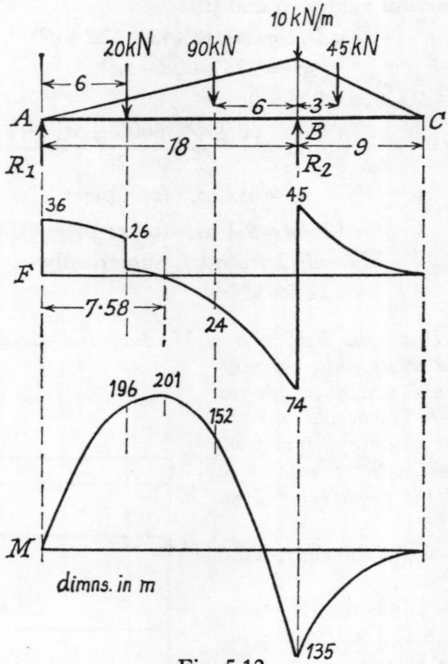

Fig. 5.12

The total distributed load on AB $=\frac{1}{2}\times 18\times 10=90$ kN, and on BC $=\frac{1}{2}\times 9\times 10=45$ kN, each acting through its centre of gravity, which is $\frac{2}{3}\times 18=12$ m from A in one case, and $\frac{2}{3}\times 9=6$ m from C in the other case (these are the centroids of triangles representing the load distribution).

Then by moments about B for the whole beam

$$R_1=(20\times 12+90\times 6-45\times 3)/18=36\text{ kN}$$

hence $\quad R_2=155-36=119$ kN

At a distance $x(<18)$ from A, the rate of loading $=10x/18$ kN/m.

The distributed load on this length is

$$(\text{mean rate of loading})\times x=\tfrac{1}{2}(10x/18)x$$
$$=10x^2/36\text{ kN}$$

and its centre of gravity is $2x/3$ m from A.

For $0<x<6$, $\quad F=36-10x^2/36$

at $x=6$ m, $\quad F=26$ kN

$$M=36x-(10x^2/36)x/3$$
$$=36x-10x^3/108$$

at $x=6$ m, $\quad M=196$ kNm

For $6<x<18$ $F=36-20-10x^2/36$

at $x=12$ m, $F=-24$ kN

at $x=18$ m, $F=-74$ kN

$$F=0 \text{ when } x=6\sqrt{1\cdot6}=7\cdot58 \text{ m}$$

$$M=36x-20(x-6)-10x^3/108$$

$$=16x+120-10x^3/108$$

at $x=12$ m, $M=152$ kNm

at $x=18$ m, $M=-135$ kNm

Maximum bending moment occurs at zero shearing force, i.e. $x=7\cdot58$m

$$M=201 \text{ kNm}$$

The portion BC may be dealt with more conveniently by using a variable X measured from C. Then, by a similar argument

$$F=\tfrac{1}{2}(10X/9)X=10X^2/18 \text{ kN}$$

at $X=9$ m, $F=45$ kN

$$M=-\tfrac{1}{2}(10X/9)X(X/3)=-10X^3/54 \text{ kNm}$$

at $X=9$ m, $M=-135$ kNm (check $x=18$ m)

The complete diagrams are sketched in Fig. 5.12, and it is seen that, for a uniformly varying distributed load, the shearing force diagram consists of a series of parabolic curves, and the bending moment diagram is made up of "cubics," discontinuities occurring at concentrated loads or reactions. It was, of course, shown in Para. 5.5 that shearing force can be obtained by integrating the loading function, and bending moment by integrating the shearing force, from which it follows that the curves produced will be of a successively "higher order" in x.

5.10. Graphical Method. In Para. 5.5 it was shown that the change of bending moment was given by the double integral of the rate of loading. This integration can be carried out conveniently by means of a funicular polygon, as illustrated in Fig. 5.13

Suppose the loads carried on a simply supported beam are W_1, W_2, W_3, and W_4. R_1 and R_2 are the reactions at the supports. Letter the spaces between the loads and reactions A, B, C, D, E, and F.

Draw to scale ab $=W_1$, bc $=W_2$, cd $=W_3$, and de $=W_4$. Take any pole O to the left of this line and join O to a, b, c, d, and e. This is called the polar diagram.

Commencing at any point p on the line of action of R_1, draw pq parallel to Oa in the space "A," qr parallel to Ob in the space "B," and similarly rs, st, and tu. Draw Of parallel to pu.

It will now be shown that fa represents R_1 and ef represents R_2. Also that pqrstu is the bending moment diagram on a base pu, M being proportional to the vertical ordinates.

W_1 is represented by ab, and acts through the point q; it can be replaced by forces aO along qp and Ob along qr. Similarly W_2 can be replaced by forces represented by bO along rq and Oc along rs, W_3 by cO along sr and Od along st, etc. All these forces cancel each other out, except aO along qp and Oe along tu; and these two forces must be in equilibrium with R_1 and R_2. This can only be so if R_1 is equivalent to a force Oa along pq and fO along up, R_2 being equivalent to eO along ut and Of along pu. Hence R_1 is represented by fa, and R_2 by ef.

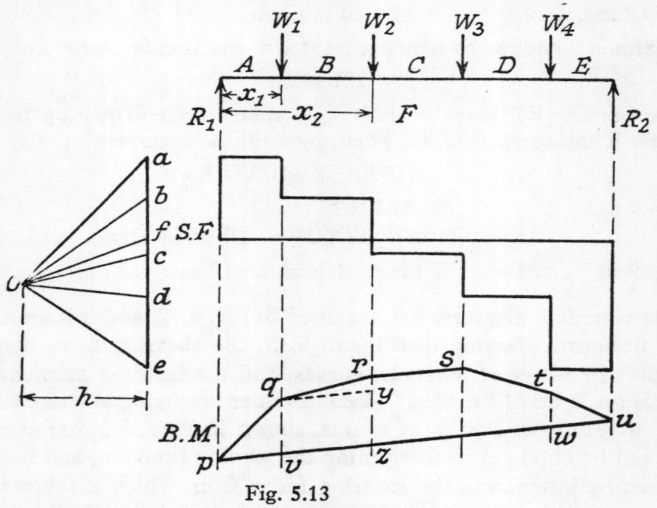

Fig. 5.13

Triangles pqv and Oaf are similar, hence

$$qv = af . pv/Of$$

or $$\propto af . x_1/h$$

where x_1 is the distance of W_1 from the left-hand end of the beam and h is the length of the perpendicular from O on to ae.

But af. $x_1 \propto R_1 x_1$, i.e. the B.M. at x_1.

Hence, for a given position of the pole O, qv represents the B.M. at x_1 to a certain scale.

If qy is drawn parallel to pu, then the triangle qry is similar to Obf and

$$ry = bf . qy/Of$$
$$= bf . (x_2 - x_1)/h$$

$$\therefore \quad rz = qv + ry$$
$$= af . x_1/h + bf(x_2 - x_1)/h$$

which is $$\propto R_1 x_1 + (R_1 - W_1)(x_2 - x_1)$$
$$= R_1 x_2 - W_1(x_2 - x_1)$$

i.e. the B.M. at x_2.

Similarly the ordinates at the other load points give the bending moments at those points, the scale being determined as follows:

If the load scale of the polar diagram is 1 cm $= s_1$ N, the length scale (along the beam) is 1 cm $= s_2$ m, and the bending moment scale required is 1 cm $= s_3$ Nm, then the length

$$\text{qv} \propto \text{caf}.x_1/h \quad \text{as shown above}$$
$$= R_1x_1/s_1s_2h = M_1/s_1s_2h$$

But $\quad \text{qv} = M_1/s_3$

$$\therefore \quad h = s_3/s_1s_2 \text{ cm}$$

If a base on the same level as f is drawn and the points a, b, c, d, and e are projected across from the polar diagram the shearing force diagram is obtained.

This method can equally well be used for distributed loads by dividing the loading diagram into "strips" and taking the load on a strip to act as concentrated at its centre of gravity.

For cantilevers, if the pole O is taken on the same horizontal level as the point a, the base of the bending moment diagram will be horizontal.

SUMMARY

Shearing Force F.
Bending Moment M. Positive senses:
Rate of Loading w.
$F = dM/dx$.
$w = -dF/dx = -d^2M/dx^2$.

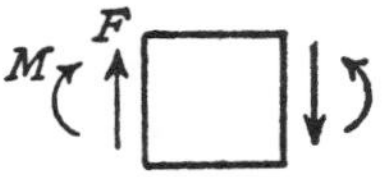

The following table of maximum shearing force and bending moment in standard cases is given for reference.

Loading	$\hat{F}$	$\hat{M}$
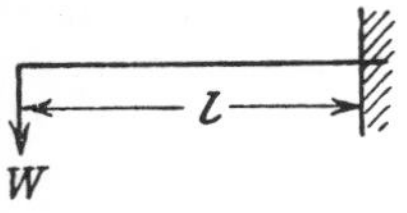	W	Wl (fixed end)
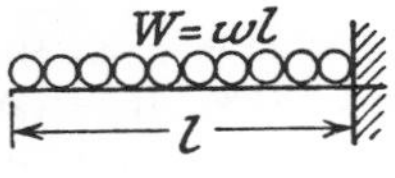	W (fixed end)	$Wl/2$ (fixed end)
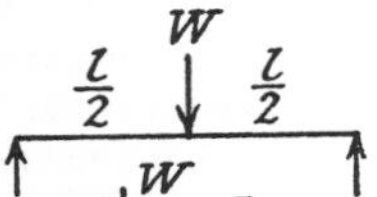	$W/2$	$Wl/4$ (centre)
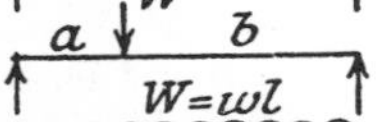	Wb/l	Wab/l(load)
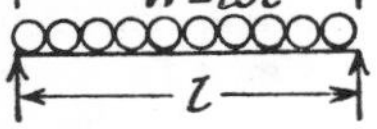	$W/2$ (support)	$Wl/8$ (centre)

PROBLEMS

1. A beam ABCDEF, in which AB = 2m, BC = 2 m, CD = 2·33 m, DE = 2 m and EF = 2 m, carries loads of 50 kN, 50 kN, 40 kN, and 40 kN at A, C, D, and F respectively, and is supported at B and E.

Draw the S.F. and B.M. diagrams and find (a) maximum S.F., (b) maximum B.M., (c) point of inflection. (50 kN; 100 kNm; none.)

2. Sketch the B.M. and S.F. diagrams for the beam shown and state (a) the position and magnitude of the maximum bending moment, (b) the position of the point of contraflexure. (3·63 m; 238 kNm; 2·66 m.)

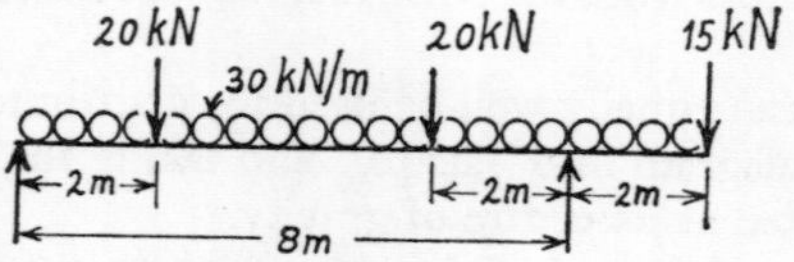

3. Draw the S.F. and B.M. diagrams for the propped cantilever shown and find the position and magnitude of the maximum B.M. (8 m; 240 kNm.)

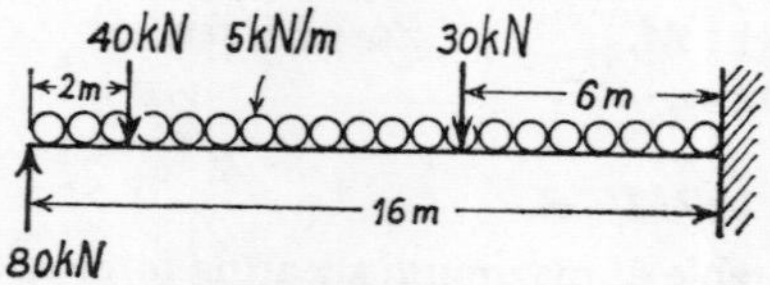

4. A horizontal beam AD, 10 m long, carries a uniformly distributed load of 360 N/m run, together with a concentrated load of 900 N at the left-hand end A. The beam is supported at B, 1 m from A, and at C, which is in the right-hand half of the beam, x m from D. Determine the value of x if the mid-point of the beam is a point of inflexion, and plot the B.M. diagram. Locate any other points of inflexion. (3 m)

5. A horizontal beam, simply supported on a span of 10 m, carries a total load of 1000 kg. The load distribution varies parabolically from zero at each end to a maximum at mid-span. Calculate the values of the B.M. at intervals of 1 m and plot the B.M. diagram. State the values of (a) maximum B.M., (b) shearing force at quarter span. (U.L.) (15,400 Nm; 3380 N)

6. A beam ABC is simply supported at B and C and AB is a cantilevered portion. AB = 5 m, BC = 15 m. The loading consists of 2000 kg concentrated at A, 3000 kg concentrated at D, 11 m from C, and 4000 kg concentrated at 5 m from C. In addition the beam carries a uniformly distributed load of 2000 kg/m over the length DC. Draw dimensioned sketches of the S.F. and B.M. diagrams.

7. A beam ABCD is 24 m long and is simply supported at B and D, 18 m apart. A concentrated load of 20 kN at A and a total distributed load of 120 kN, which varies linearly from p kN/m at the centre C to q kN/m at D, is spread from C to D. Find the values of p and q for the reactions at B and D to be equal.

Find also the point of contraflexure and the position and magnitude of the maximum bending moment.

(12·5 kN/m; 7·5 kN/m; 2·4 m B; 7·7 m D; 285 kNm)

8. A horizontal beam is simply supported at its ends and carries a uniformly distributed load of 40 kN/m between the supports, which are 7·5 m apart. Counter-clockwise moments of 100 and 80 kNm are applied to the two ends. Draw the B.M. diagram and find (1) the reactions at the supports, and (2) the position and magnitude of the greatest B.M.

(174, 126 kN; 4·35 m, 280 kNm)

CHAPTER VI

Bending Stress

6.1. Pure Bending. If a length of beam is acted upon by a constant bending moment (zero shearing force), the stresses set up on any cross-section must constitute a pure couple equal in magnitude to the bending moment. Hence it can be deduced that one part of the cross-section is in compression and the other part in tension. Referring to Fig. 6.1(a), subject to the condition that the end sections remain plane, it is clear that for an initially straight beam the inside or concave edge will be in compression and the outside or convex edge will be in tension. There will be an intermediate surface at which the stress is zero ("*neutral*" surface); the neutral surface cuts any cross-section in the *neutral axis*.

The following theory will not be strictly correct when the cross-section is subjected to a shearing force, as this will cause a distortion of transverse planes. However, this will be dealt with separately in

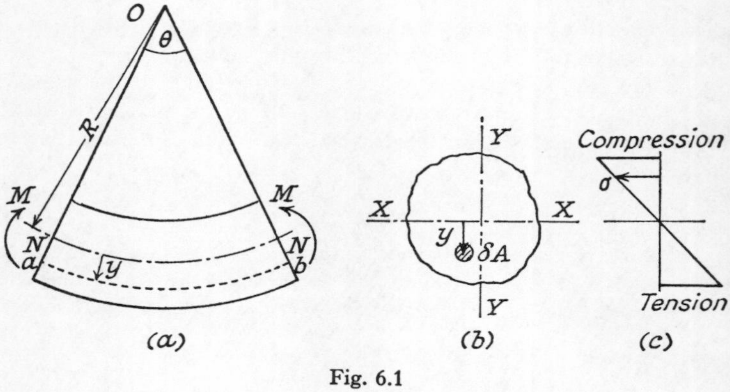

Fig. 6.1

Chapter VII, and the theory of pure bending is accepted as being sufficiently accurate even when the bending moment is varying.

The problem will be treated as one of one-dimensional stress, lateral stresses being neglected. There must, however, be lateral strains, which will cause a distortion of the cross-sectional shape known as *anti-clastic* curvature, but the effect of this on the dimensions will be neglected.

A summary of the assumptions is as follows:

(1) The material is homogeneous, isotropic, and has the same value of Young's modulus in tension and compression.
(2) The beam is initially straight and all longitudinal filaments bend into circular arcs with a common centre of curvature.
(3) Transverse cross-sections remain plane and perpendicular to the neutral surface after bending.
(4) The radius of curvature is large compared with the dimensions of the cross-section.
(5) The stress is purely longitudinal and local effects near concentrated loads will be neglected.

Fig. 6.1(a) shows a length of beam under the action of a bending moment M. O is the centre of curvature, and R is the radius of curvature of the neutral surface NN. The beam subtends an angle θ at O.

Let σ be the longitudinal stress in a filament ab at a distance y from NN. Then the strain in ab is

$$\sigma/E = (\text{ab} - \text{NN})/\text{NN}$$

(since originally all filaments were of the same length NN)

$$= [(R+y)\theta - R\theta]/R\theta$$

$$= y/R$$

or

$$\sigma/y = E/R \qquad (1)$$

It is apparent at this stage that, since E/R is constant, **the stress is proportional to the distance from the neutral axis XX** (Fig. 6.1(c)) and that for purposes of economy and weight reduction the material should be concentrated as much as possible at the greatest distance from the neutral axis. Hence the universal adoption of the I-section for steel beams.

Three equilibrium equations can be obtained for the system of parallel stresses on any cross-section.

If δA is an element of cross-sectional area at a distance y from the neutral axis XX (Fig. 6.1(b)) then for pure bending the net normal force on the cross-section must be zero, i.e.

$$\int \sigma . dA = 0$$

or

$$(E/R)\int y dA = 0 \quad \text{from (1)}$$

This is the condition that **XX passes through the centroid of the section.**

The bending moment is balanced by the moment of the normal forces about XX, i.e.

$$M = \int \sigma y . dA$$

$$= (E/R)\int y^2 . dA \quad \text{from (1)}$$

$$= EI/R$$

where I ($\int y^2 . dA$) is a property of the cross-section known as the moment of inertia or second moment of area (Para. 6.2) or

$$M/I = E/R \tag{2}$$

Equations (1) and (2) may now be combined and written in the convenient form

$$\sigma/y = M/I = E/R \tag{3}$$

In order to satisfy the convention of signs, y should be taken as positive when measured outwards from the centre of curvature, and negative when inwards.

The ratio $I/\hat{y}$ is called the *section modulus* Z, so that $\hat{\sigma} = M/Z$. The bending moment which can be carried by a given section for a limiting maximum stress is called the *moment of resistance.*

A further condition which should not be overlooked is obtained by integrating the moments about the axis YY, perpendicular to the neutral axis and through the centroid. For pure bending about the neutral axis this moment must be zero, i.e.

$$\int \sigma x dA = 0$$

or

$$\int xy dA = 0 \quad \text{from (1)}$$

This integral is referred to as the *product of inertia*, and the axes for which it is zero are called the *Principal Axes* of the cross-section. The limitation on **the above theory** is that it **shall only be applied for bending about a principal axis.** A bending moment in any other plane must be resolved into components about the two principal axes, the resulting stresses being calculated separately. If the cross-section has an axis of symmetry (as is normally the case), then it is easy to show that this satisfies the condition for a principal axis, the other principal axis being at right angles through the centroid. The subject will be dealt with more fuily in Paras. 6.11 and 6.12.

It is important to use consistent units in the bending formula, e.g.

σ N/mm^2

y mm

M Nmm

I mm^4

E N/mm^2

R mm

6.2. Moments of Inertia. Readers may be familiar with the moment of inertia of a rigid body, which is a property obtained by summing the products of particle mass and the square of its distance from a given axis, for all the particles in the body. This function is involved in all problems of angular motion.

By analogy with mass moment of inertia the summation of areas times distance squared from a fixed axis, which arose in the proof of the previous paragraph, is called the *moment of inertia* (I) of the cross-section about that axis. An alternative name is *second moment of area*, the first moment being the sum of the areas times their distance from a given axis.

By definition $I_X = \int y^2 . dA$ about the XX′ axis (Fig. 6.2), and $I_Y = \int x^2 . dA$. The moment of inertia about an axis through O perpendicular to the figure is called the *Polar Moment of Inertia*

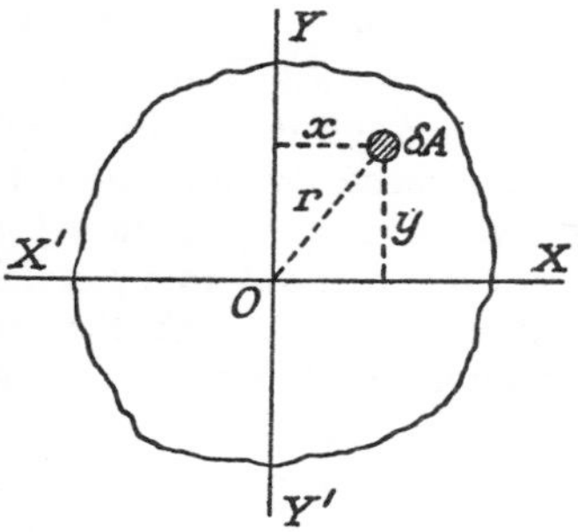

Fig. 6.2

$$J = \int r^2 . dA$$
$$= \int (x^2 + y^2) dA$$
$$= I_x + I_y \qquad (1)$$

This relation is referred to as the *perpendicular axes theorem*, and may be stated as follows: *the sum of the moments of inertia about any two axes in the plane is equal to the moment of inertia about the axis perpendicular to the plane, the three axes being concurrent.*

It follows as a corollary that the *sum of the moments of inertia about any two perpendicular axes through a given point in the plane is constant.*

Circular Section. To calculate the polar moment of inertia about O (Fig. 6.3), $\delta A = 2\pi r . \delta r$.

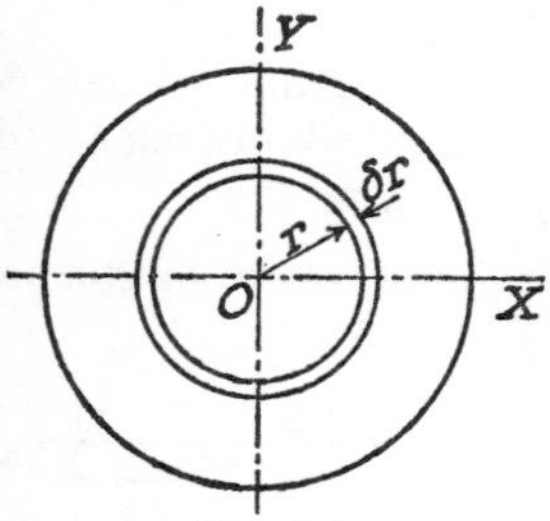

Fig. 6.3

$$\therefore \quad J = \int_0^{d/2} r^2 . 2\pi r . dr$$
$$= 2\pi [r^4/4]_0^{d/2}$$
$$= \pi d^4/32$$

But $J = I_x + I_y$, by the perpendicular axes theorem, and since I_x and I_y are both equal, being moments of inertia about a diameter

$$I_{\text{dia.}} = \tfrac{1}{2} J = \pi d^4/64$$

For a hollow circular section of diameters D, d

$$J = (\pi/32)(D^4 - d^4) \quad \text{and} \quad I = (\pi/64)(D^4 - d^4)$$

The *parallel axes theorem* will now be proved. If ZZ is any axis in the plane of the cross-section and XX is a parallel axis through the centroid G (Fig. 6.4), then

$$I_z = \int (y + h)^2 dA \quad \text{by definition}$$
$$= \int y^2 . dA + 2h \int y . dA + h^2 \int dA$$
$$= I_x + Ah^2 \qquad (2)$$

since $\int y.dA=0$ for an axis through the centroid and A = total area. Stating in words, *the moment of inertia about any axis is equal to the moment of inertia about a parallel axis through the centroid plus the area times the square of the distance between the axes.*

It should be noted from the above that **the moment of inertia about the axis through the centroid is the minimum value** for an axis in that particular direction. If it is required to transfer from one axis ZZ to a parallel axis UU, neither being through the centroid, the operation must be done in two stages, i.e.

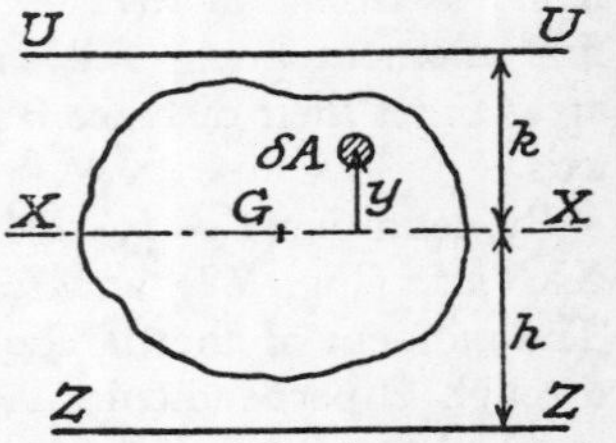

Fig. 6.4

$$I_Z = I_G + Ah^2$$

and
$$I_U = I_G + Ak^2$$

where k = distance between axes XX and UU.

From which
$$I_U = I_Z - Ah^2 + Ak^2 \quad (3)$$

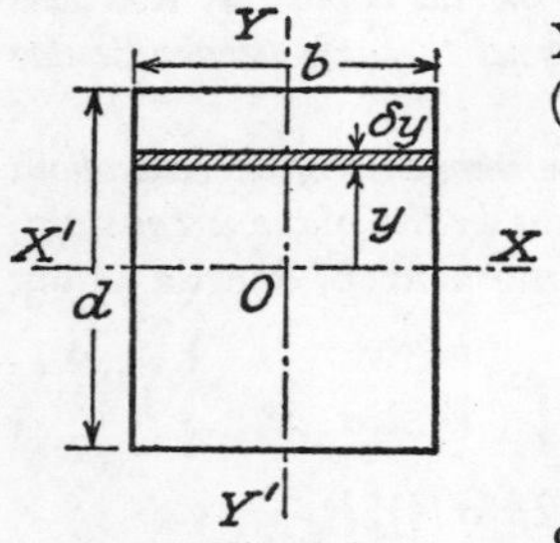

Fig. 6.5

Rectangular Section. For bending about the XX′ axis, let the width be b and the depth d (Fig. 6.5).

Then
$$I_X = \int_{-d/2}^{d/2} y^2.bdy = b\left[\frac{y^3}{3}\right]_{-d/2}^{d/2} = bd^3/12$$

For a hollow rectangular section, of outside dimensions B, D, and inside dimensions b, d,

$$I_X = \tfrac{1}{12}(BD^3 - bd^3).$$

I-*section.* In the case of standard sections the moments of inertia are computed graphically from the actual shape of the cross-section as rolled (see Para. 6.3), but a reasonable approximation may be obtained by estimating a mean flange thickness and working from a series of rectangles as shown in Fig. 6.6.

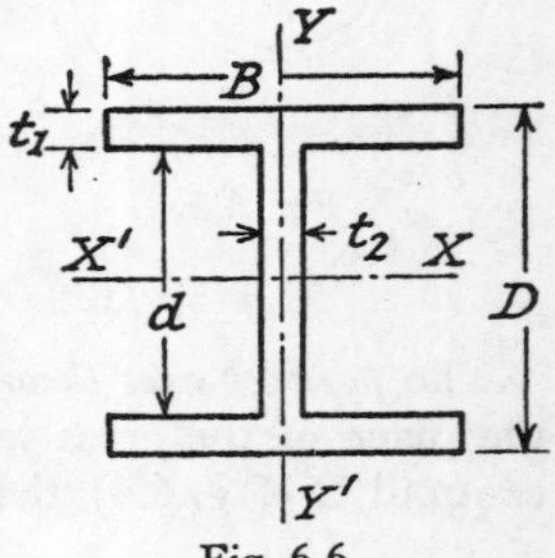

Fig. 6.6

Using the dimensions shown, the moment of inertia about XX′ may be obtained by subtracting that for rectangles $(B-t_2)$ wide and d deep from the overall figure B by D, i.e.

$$I_X = \tfrac{1}{12}[BD^3 - (B-t_2)d^3]$$

Alternatively, and for greater accuracy of computing, the web and flange areas may be treated separately, using the parallel axis theorem for the flanges.

Then $$I_X = 2\{(Bt_1^3/12) + Bt_1[(d+t_1)/2]^2\} + (t_2 d^3/12)$$

where $(d+t_1)/2$ is the distance between the centroid axis of the flange itself and the principal axis of the whole cross-section XX′. The term $Bt_1^3/12$ is very small and can usually be neglected.

$$I_Y = \tfrac{1}{12}(2t_1B^3 + dt_2^3)$$

the "width" being the dimension parallel to YY′, and the "depth" parallel to XX′.

A table of moments of inertia for standard sections is given in the summary at the end of this chapter.

6.3. Graphical Determination of Moment of Inertia. Suppose it is required to find the moment of inertia about the centroid axis XX of the irregular figure shown in Fig. 6.7. Let ZZ be any convenient axis outside the section parallel to XX.

Divide the figure into strips of area δA parallel to ZZ and at a distance y from it. If each strip is the same thickness δy then the areas δA will be proportional to their widths x.

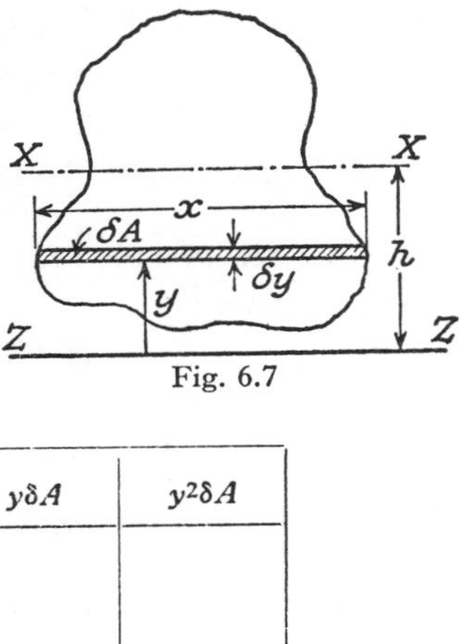

Fig. 6.7

Tabulate the values as follows:

	x	δA	y	$y\delta A$	$y^2\delta A$
Totals		$\Sigma\delta A = A$		$\Sigma y\delta A$	$\Sigma y^2\delta A = I_Z$

If h is the distance of the centroid axis from ZZ, then

$$Ah = \Sigma y\delta A \quad \text{by moments}$$

i.e. $$h = \Sigma y\delta A/A$$

and $I = I_Z - Ah^2$ by the parallel axes theorem (Para. 6.2, Eq. (2)), I_Z being given by $\Sigma y^2\delta A$.

6.4. Bending Stresses

EXAMPLE 1. *The beam of symmetrical I-section shown in Fig. 6.8 is simply supported over a span of 9 m. If the maximum permissible stress is 75 N/mm² what concentrated load can be carried at a distance of 3 m from one support?*

It is understood that XX is the axis of bending, the bending moment being in the plane YY.

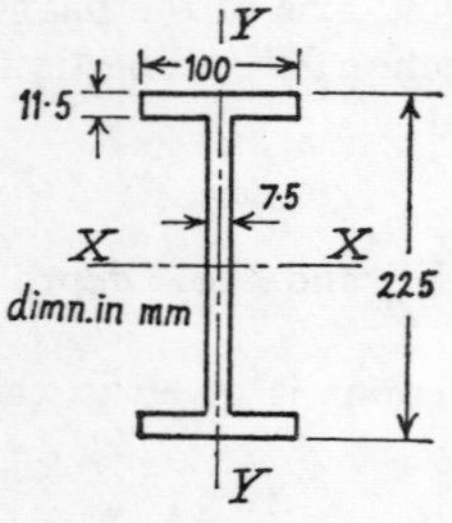

Fig. 6.8

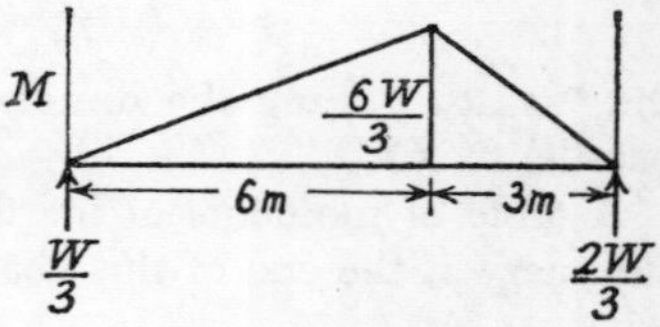

Fig. 6.9

If W kN is the load, the maximum bending moment is

$$M = 6W/3 \text{ kNm. (see Chap. V)}$$
$$= 2 \times 10^6 \, W \text{ Nmm}$$

$$I = 2[100 \times 11{\cdot}5^3/12 + 100 \times 11{\cdot}5(112{\cdot}5 - 11{\cdot}5/2)^2] + 7{\cdot}5 \times 202{\cdot}200^3/12$$

(compare Para. 6.2)

$$= 2[1{\cdot}25 + 1300] \times 10^4 + 515 \times 10^4$$
$$= 31 \times 10^6 \text{ mm}^4$$

$$\hat{\sigma}/\hat{y} = \hat{M}/I \quad \text{(Eq. (3) Para. 6.1) gives}$$
$$75/112{\cdot}5 = 2 \times 10^6 W/31 \times 10^6$$
$$\therefore \quad W = 10{\cdot}3 \text{ kN}$$

EXAMPLE 2. *The cross-section of a cast-iron beam is shown in Fig. 6·10, the loading being in the plane of the web, the upper portion of the section being in compression. If the maximum permissible stresses are 2000 kg/cm² tension and 3000 kg/cm² compression, find the moment of resistance of the section and the actual maximum stresses*

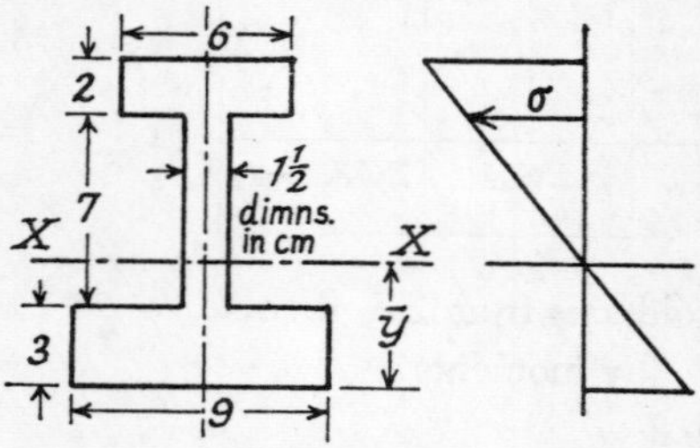

Fig. 6.10

Since the neutral axis XX passes through the centroid it is necessary first to find its position. This and the total moment of inertia about XX can be evaluated conveniently by tabulating as follows, in which y is the distance of the centroid of each area from the bottom edge of the section, I_G the moment of inertia of each area about its own centroid axis parallel to XX, and h the distance between each centroid axis and XX.

Part	A cm^2	y cm	Ay cm^3	I_G cm^4	h cm	Ah^2 cm^4	I_G+Ah^2 cm^4
Top flange .	12	11	132	$(6\times 2^3)/12$	6·13	452	**456**
Web . .	10·5	6·5	68·25	$(1{\cdot}5\times 7^3)/12$	1·63	27·8	70·7
Bottom flange	27	1·5	40·5	$(9\times 3^3)/12$	3·37	306	326·2
Totals . .	$\Sigma A = 49{\cdot}5$		$\Sigma Ay = 240{\cdot}75$	**67·1**		**785·8**	**852·9**

By moments

$$\bar{y} = \Sigma Ay/\Sigma A = 240{\cdot}75/49{\cdot}5$$
$$= 4{\cdot}87 \text{ cm.}$$

For the whole section about the neutral axis $I = 853$ cm^4. The maximum distances from the neutral axis are 4·87 cm on the tension side and 7·13 cm on the compression side. Working out the moment of resistance for each limiting stress individually:

for tension, $M = (2000 \times 853)/4{\cdot}87 = 351{,}000$ kg cm

for compression, $M = (3000 \times 853)/7{\cdot}13 = 359{,}000$ kg cm

The limiting value is therefore 351,000 kg cm, corresponding to a maximum tensile stress of 2000 kg/cm^2 and a maximum compressive stress $= 2000 \times 7{\cdot}13/4{\cdot}87 = 2930$ kg/cm^2 by proportion of distances from the neutral axis.

Alternatively, it may be argued that the actual maximum stress ratio must be determined by the distances from the neutral axis, i.e. 7·13/4·87, from which it can be deduced that the tensile stress is the limiting one, the maximum compressive stress being less than the permissible value. The moment of resistance is then calculated on the basis of 2000 kg/cm^2 tensile stress.

Unsymmetrical sections are used for cast-iron beams because the material is stronger in compression than in tension. The beam must be placed so that the larger flange is on the tension side.

EXAMPLE 3. *A 300 mm by 125 mm I-beam is to be used as a cantilever 3 m long. If the permissible stress is 120 N/mm^2 what uniformly distributed load can be carried? $I = 80 \times 10^6$ mm^4.*

If the cantilever is to be strengthened by steel plates 12·5 mm thick, welded to the top and bottom flanges, find the width of plates required to withstand an increase of 50% in the load, and the length over which the plates should extend, the maximum stress remaining the same.

$$\hat{M} = Wl/2$$

(where W N = total load)

$$= 1500W \text{ Nmm}$$
$$\hat{y} = 150 \text{ mm}$$

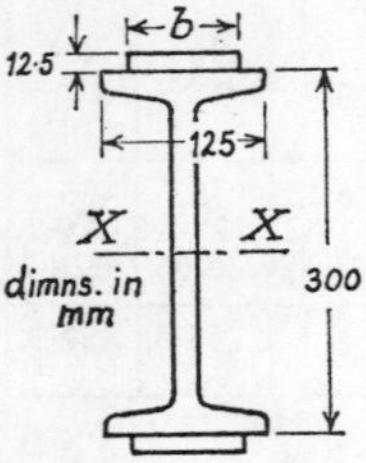

Fig. 6.11

applying $\sigma/\hat{y} = \hat{M}/I$

$$\therefore \quad \frac{120}{150} = \frac{1500W}{80 \times 10^6}$$

$$W = 42{\cdot}7 \text{ kN}$$

or $= 14{\cdot}3$ kN/m

If the load is increased by 50%, $\hat{M}$ becomes $2250W = 96 \times 10^6$ N mm; $\hat{y}$ increases to 162·5 mm

$$\therefore \quad I = 96 \times 10^6 \times 162{\cdot}5/120 = 130 \times 10^6 \text{ mm}^4$$

The increase in moment of inertia is 50×10^6 mm^4, and is the moment of inertia about XX of the two flange plates. If their width is b mm, then

$$2[\tfrac{1}{12}b \times (12{\cdot}5)^3 + (b \times 12{\cdot}5)156^2] = 50 \times 10^6 \text{ mm}^4$$

or
$$b = 50 \times 10^6/(2 \times 30{\cdot}4 \times 10^4) = 82{\cdot}5 \text{ mm.}$$

The length over which the plates must extend is determined by the position at which the maximum stress in the beam itself is equal to 120 N/mm^2 under the increased loading.

If x m is the distance from the free end

$$M = wx^2/2 = 21{\cdot}45 \times x^2/2 \text{ kNm}$$
$$= 10{\cdot}72 \times 10^6 x^2 \text{ N mm}$$

Substituting in the bending stress equation

$$120/150 = 10{\cdot}72 \times 10^6 x^2/80 \times 10^6$$

giving
$$x = 2{\cdot}45 \text{ m.}$$

The maximum bending moment is at the fixed end, and the plates should extend a distance of 0·55 m from this end.

EXAMPLE 4. *The I-beam shown in Fig. 6.12 is simply supported at its ends over a 2 m span and carries a central load of 500 kg which acts through the centroid, the line of action being as shown. Calculate the maximum stress.*

The section being symmetrical, the centroid is at the centre of the web, and the principal axes are XX′ and YY′.

$I_X = 2[\tfrac{1}{12} \times 6 \times 1^3 + 6 \times 1 \times 5{\cdot}5^2]$ for the flanges
$+ \tfrac{1}{12} \cdot \tfrac{3}{4} \cdot 10^3$ for the web
$= 426{\cdot}5$ cm^4

$I_Y = 2 \times \tfrac{1}{12} \cdot 1 \times 6^3 + \tfrac{1}{12} \cdot 10 \times (\tfrac{3}{4})^3$
$= 36{\cdot}35$ cm^4

The maximum bending moment $= Wl/4$
$= 500 \times 200/4 = 25{,}000$ kg cm.

This must be resolved into

$$M_X = 25{,}000 \sin 60°$$
$$= 21{,}700 \text{ kg. cm in the plane YY}'$$

and
$$M_Y = 25{,}000 \cos 60°$$
$$= 12{,}500 \text{ kg cm in the plane XX}'$$

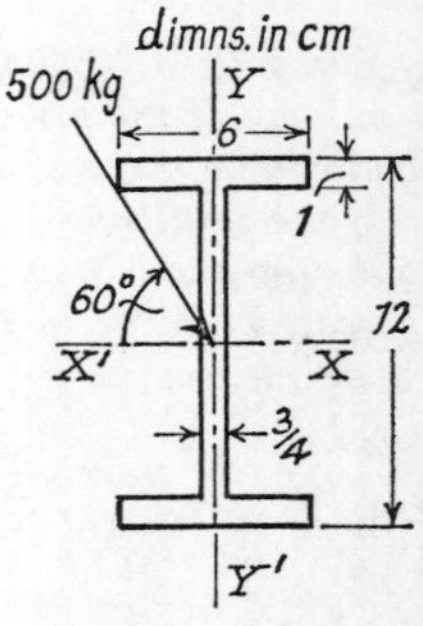

Fig. 6.12

Then the bending stress at any point (x, y) in the section is made up of two parts, one due to bending about axis XX′ and the other due to bending about YY′, i.e.

$$\sigma = M_X . y/I_X + M_Y . x/I_Y$$

where x and y are to be reckoned positive to the right of YY′ and below XX′ respectively. This will ensure tensile stresses positive and compressive stresses negative.

It is clear, then, that the maximum tensile stress occurs at the bottom right-hand tip of the lower flange, where $x = 3$ cm, $y = 6$ cm.

$$= 21{,}700 \times 6/426{\cdot}5 + 12{,}500 \times 3/36{\cdot}35$$
$$= 305 + 1030$$
$$= 1335 \text{ kg/cm}^2 = 131 \text{ N/mm}^2$$

6.5. Stress Concentrations in Bending. The following is a selection of values obtained by Frocht by photo-elastic analysis (Para. 19.11) for

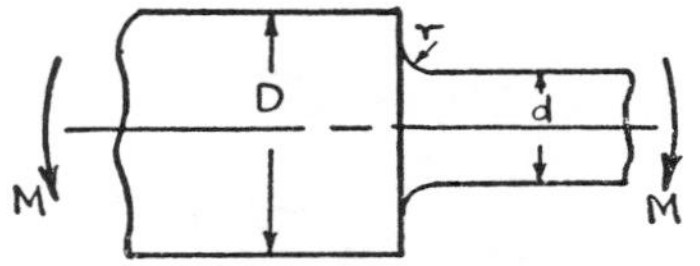

Fig. 6.13

the stress concentration factor k at a change in cross-section in a round or flat bar subjected to a bending moment. In all cases the ratio D/d (Fig. 6.13) was 1·5.

r/d	0·1	0·2	0·4	0·7
k	1·77	1·48	1·27	1·15

6.6. Combined Bending and Direct Stress. Consider the case of a column acted on by a thrust P whose line of action cuts the cross-section at a point on the XX axis at a distance h from the centroid O (Fig. 6.14).

Then P is equivalent to an equal load at O, which produces a uniform direct stress, together with a bending moment Ph about YY, which produces a varying bending stress.

The combined stress, at any point at a distance x from YY, is given by

$$\sigma = P/A + Ph.x/I_Y$$

where A is the cross-sectional area.

If x *is reckoned positive on the same side of YY as the load*, so that the bending stress is of the same type as the direct stress, the equation for compressive loads will give a positive value for compressive stress. The same notation used for tensile loads will produce a positive value for tensile stresses.

Proceeding with the case under consideration, it is clear that the

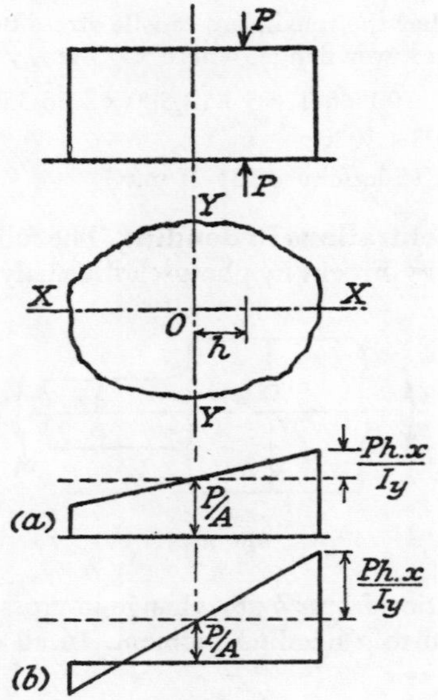

Fig. 6.14

maximum compressive stress will occur at the right-hand edge of the section. At the left-hand edge of the section x is negative, and if $P/A > Ph.x/I_Y$ the stress will remain of the same type, i.e. compressive (Fig. 6.14(a)). If the bending stress is greater than the direct stress, then the tensile stress at the left-hand edge may be written $Ph.x/I_y - P/A$ (Fig. 6.14(b)).

Other points to note from the stress variation diagrams are that the stress at the centroid is P/A, and the usual bending stress diagram is then plotted about this base. Whether there is a reversal of stress depends on the magnitude of the eccentricity h (see Paras. 6.7 and 6.8).

EXAMPLE 5. *A cast-iron column of 8 cm outside diameter and $6\frac{1}{2}$ cm inside diameter carries a central axial load of 10,000 kg and a load of W kg at 13 cm from the axis. If the allowable stresses are 1200 kg/cm² compressive and 300 kg/cm² tensile, find the value of W.*

All diameters being principal axes, assume W lies on XX (Fig. 6.15).

$$A = (\pi/4)(8^2 - 6{\cdot}5^2) = 17{\cdot}1 \text{ cm}^2$$

$$I_Y = (\pi/64)(8^4 - 6{\cdot}5^4)$$
$$= (\pi/64)(8^2 - 6{\cdot}5^2)(8^2 + 6{\cdot}5^2)$$
$$= 113 \text{ cm}^4$$

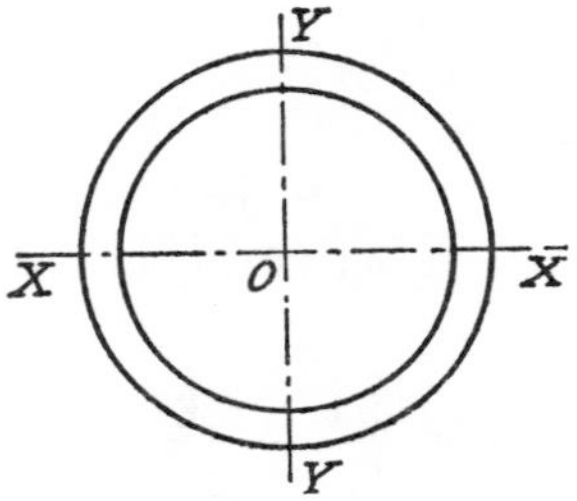

Fig. 6.15

Bending moment $= 13W$ kg cm
Maximum bending stress $= \pm(13W \times 4)/113$ kg/cm^2
Total "direct" stress $= (10{,}000 + W)/17{\cdot}1$ kg/cm^2
Allowable compressive stress $1200 = (10{,}000 + W)/17{\cdot}1 + 52W/113$

giving $$W = 1190 \text{ kg}$$

Allowable tensile stress $300 = -(10{,}000 + W)/17{\cdot}1 + 52W/113$, changing the sign giving

$$W = 2200 \text{ kg}$$

Taking the smaller value, $W = 1190$ kg, and the stress varies from 1200 kg/cm^2 compressive to

$$11{,}190/17{\cdot}1 - (52 \times 1190)/113 = 106 \text{ kg/cm}^2 \text{ compressive}$$

(i.e. there is no tensile stress).

EXAMPLE 6. *The tie bar shown in Fig. 6.16 is 3 m long and of rectangular section 25 mm thick. The longitudinal section is tapered from a depth of 150 mm to 50 mm at the ends. A load of 50 kN acts through the centroid of the smaller end and parallel to the edge AB. Find the position and magnitude of the maximum tensile stress.*

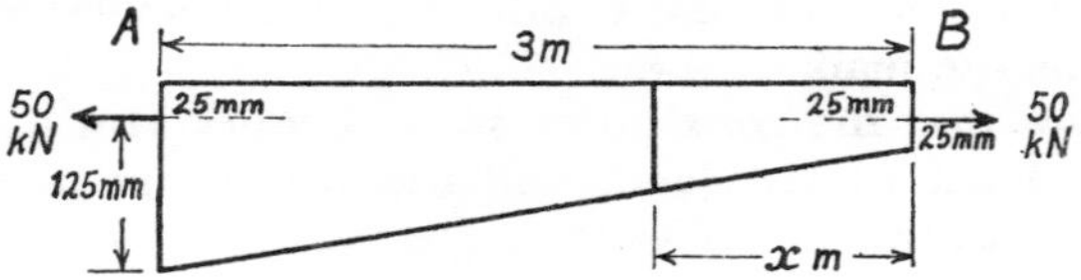

Fig. 6.16

At x m from the smaller end of the depth of the section is

$$50 + 100 \cdot x/3 = 50(1 + 2x/3) \text{ mm}$$

The centroid is at half the depth, i.e. $25+50x/3$ mm from the top edge, so that the line of action of the load is at an eccentricity of $50x/3$ mm.

Area of section $=25\times 50(1+2x/3)$ mm^2

Moment of inertia $=25\times 50^3\dfrac{(1+2x/3)^3}{12}=26\times 10^4(1+2x/3)^3$ mm^4

Tensile stress $\sigma=\dfrac{50\times 10^3}{25\times 50(1+2x/3)}+50\times 10^3\times 50x/3\dfrac{(25+50x/3)}{26\times 10^4(1+2x/3)^3}$
at top edge

$$=\frac{40}{(1+2x/3)}+\frac{80\cdot 3x}{(1+2x/3)^2}$$

For a maximum, $d\sigma/dx=0$.

i.e. $$-\frac{40}{(1+2x/3)^2}\cdot\frac{2}{3}+\frac{80\cdot 3[(1+2x/3)^2-x\cdot 2(1+2x/3)\frac{2}{3}]}{(1+2x/3)^4}=0$$

$\times 3(1+2x/3)^3$: $$-80(1+2x/3)+80\cdot 3[3+2x-4x]=0$$

$$\therefore\quad x=0\cdot 75\text{ m}$$

$$\sigma=\frac{50\times 10^3}{25\times 50\times 1\cdot 5}+\frac{50\times 10^3\times 50\times 0\cdot 25\times 37\cdot 5}{26\times 10^4\times 1\cdot 5^3}$$
$$=53\cdot 5\text{ N/mm}^2$$

Load Eccentric to both Axes. Let the line of action of the load P be at distances of h and k from the principal axes OY and OX (Fig. 6.17).

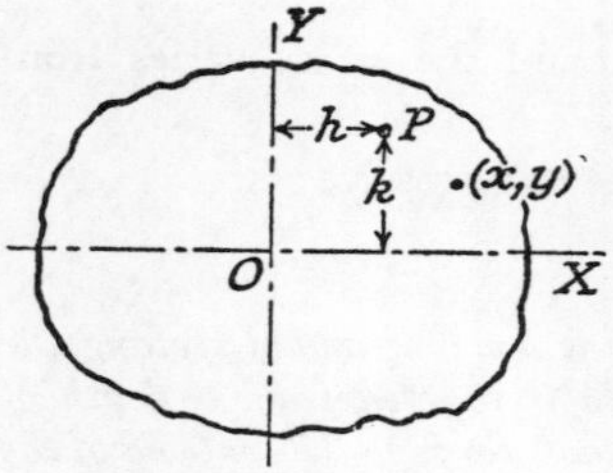

Fig. 6.17

Then the eccentric load is equivalent to a central load P, together with a bending moment Ph about OY and a bending moment Pk about OX.

The stress σ at any point in the section defined by the co-ordinates x, y is made up of three parts, i.e.

$$\sigma=P/A+Ph.x/I_y+Pk.y/I_x$$

where x and y are to be reckoned positive when on the same side of their respective axes OY and OX as the load.

It follows that the maximum stress occurs at a point in the same quadrant as the load, and the minimum stress in the opposite quadrant.

EXAMPLE 7. *A short column of rectangular cross-section 8 cm by 6 cm carries a load of 40 kN at a point 2 cm from the longer side and 3·5 cm from the shorter side. What are the maximum compressive and tensile stresses in the section?*

The eccentricities of the load are $\frac{1}{2}$ cm from OY and 1 cm from OX (Fig. 6.18).

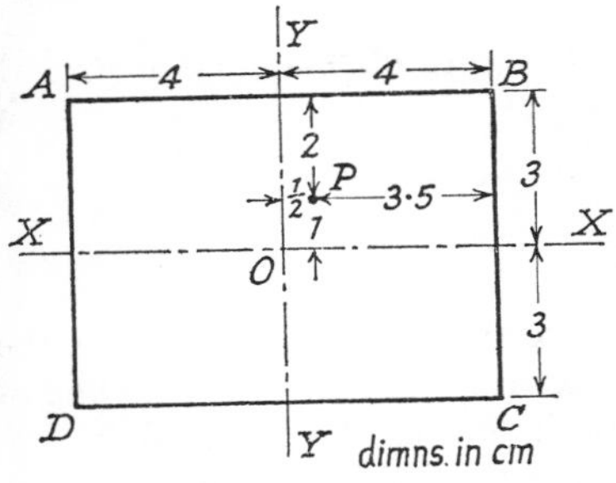

Fig. 6.18

$A = 48\ \text{cm}^2$

$I_X = (8 \times 6^3)/12 = 144\ \text{cm}^4$

$I_Y = (6 \times 8^3)/12 = 256\ \text{cm}^4$

Maximum bending stress due to bending about OX

$= (40{,}000 \times 1)3/144 \times 100$

$= 8{\cdot}33\text{N/mm}^2$

being compressive along the edge AB and tensile along the edge CD.

Maximum bending stress due to bending about OY

$= (40{,}000 \times \frac{1}{2})4/256 \times 100 =$ $3{\cdot}13\ \text{N/mm}^2$

being compressive along the edge BC and tensile along the edge AD.

Direct stress $= 40{,}000/48 \times 100 =\ 8{\cdot}33\ \text{N/mm}^2$ compressive

The maximum compressive stress occurs at B, of magnitude

$$8{\cdot}33 + 8{\cdot}33 + 3{\cdot}13 = 19{\cdot}8\ \text{N/mm}^2$$

The maximum tensile stress occurs at D, of magnitude

$$-8{\cdot}33 + 8{\cdot}33 + 3{\cdot}13 = 3{\cdot}13\ \text{N/mm}^2$$

6.7. Middle Third Rule for Rectangular Sections. In the case of masonry columns it is usual to design so that no tensile stresses will be set up. It will now be shown that for an axial load on a rectangular section the line of action must lie within a central area of the section.

Referring to Fig. 6.19, let the eccentricity of the load be h from OY and k from OX.

Then the combined stress at any point x, y in the section is given by

$$\sigma = P/A + Ph.x/I_Y + Pk.y/I_X \quad \text{(Para. 6.6)}$$
$$= P/bd + 12Ph.x/b^3d + 12Pk.y/bd^3$$

The limiting condition for no tensile stress to be set up is obtained by taking extreme negative values of x and y, i.e. $x = -b/2$, $y = -d/2$ (compare Example 7), and equating the stress to zero, i.e.

$$P/bd - (6Ph.b)/b^3d - (6Pk.d)/bd^3 = 0$$

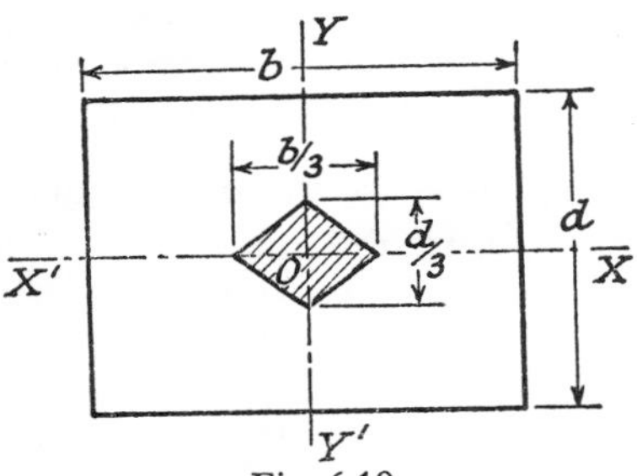

Fig. 6.19

Simplifying and rearranging

$$dh + bk = bd/6$$

gives the limiting values of h and k. In each quadrant the load must lie within the line produced by this equation. When $k = 0$ (load on OX),

$h = b/6$, and when $h = 0$ (load on OY), $k = d/6$, so that *when the load is on either axis it must lie within the "middle third" for the stress to be everywhere compressive.*

For intermediate positions it must lie within the diamond area.

Note that for given values of h and k

$$1 - 12h.x/b^2 - 12k.y/d^2 = 0$$

is the equation of the neutral axis (zero stress).

6.8. Middle Quarter Rule for Circular Sections. Let d be the diameter of the circle, and OX the diameter through which the line of action of the load passes at an eccentricity e from the centre O.

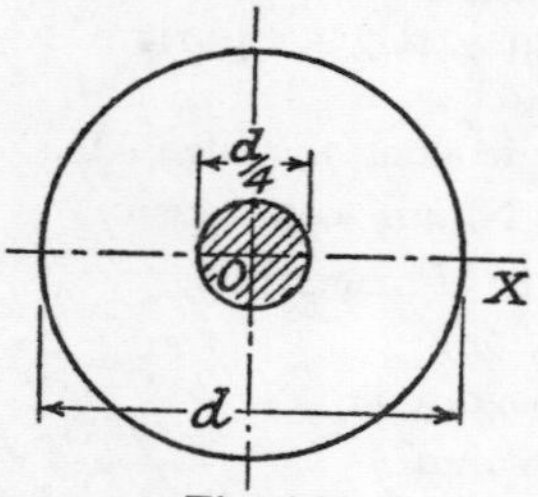

Fig. 6.20

The limiting condition for no tensile stress to be set up is when the maximum tensile bending stress is just equal to the direct compressive stress, i.e.

$$\frac{Pe}{\pi d^4/64} \cdot \frac{d}{2} = \frac{P}{\pi d^2/4}$$

or

$$e = d/8$$

For all possible positions of the load this produces a circle of diameter $d/4$ with centre O ("middle quarter"), within which the load must lie for no tensile stress to be set up (Fig. 6.20).

6.9. Composite Beams. In the case of beams made up of two different materials, such as timber beams reinforced by steel plates, if the parts are assumed to be rigidly connected together the strain at the common surfaces will be the same for both.

Then, if transverse sections remain plane after bending, strain will be proportional to the distance from the common neutral axis.

Denoting the two materials by suffixes 1 and 2, the following equations are obtained from these assumptions.

$$\text{Strain} = \sigma_1/E_1 = \sigma_2/E_2 \text{ at any common surface} \qquad (1)$$

In general, as stress $= E \times$ strain, and strain is proportional to distance from neutral axis

$$\sigma'_1/\sigma'_2 = E_1 y_1/E_2 y_2 \qquad (2)$$

where σ'_1 is the stress in material 1 at a distance y_1 from the neutral axis, and σ'_2 is the stress in material 2 at y_2 from the neutral axis.

$$M_1 = \sigma_1 I_1/y \text{ (Eq. (3), Para. 6.1)} \qquad (3)$$

and

$$M_2 = \sigma_2 I_2/y \qquad (4)$$

where y is the distance from the neutral axis to the common surface and σ_1 and σ_2 are as equation (1).

The total moment of resistance

$$M = M_1 + M_2 = (\sigma_1 I_1 + \sigma_2 I_2)/y \quad \text{from (3) and (4)}$$
$$= (\sigma_1/y)[I_1 + (E_2/E_1)I_2] \quad \text{from (1)}$$
$$= (\sigma_1/y)(I_1 + mI_2) \qquad (5)$$

where m = modular ratio E_2/E_1

$I_1 + mI_2$ can be treated as the *equivalent moment of inertia* of the cross-section, as if all made of material 1, which will give the same moment of resistance as the composite beam. It is frequently convenient to produce an *equivalent section* with $I = I_1 + mI_2$, which can be achieved by *multiplying by m the dimensions of material 2 in the direction parallel to the neutral axis.*

The equivalent figure can be used for finding the position of the neutral axis and the equivalent moment of inertia, but equation (2) should be used for the stresses, taking care to relate corresponding σ and y values for the separate materials.

EXAMPLE 8. *A timber beam 6 cm wide by 8 cm deep is to be reinforced by bolting on two steel flitches, each 6 cm by ½ cm in section. Calculate the moment of resistance in the following cases: (a) flitches attached symmetrically at top and bottom; (b) flitches attached symmetrically at the sides. Allowable timber stress 8 N/mm²*

What is the maximum stress in the steel in each case? $E_s = 210{,}000 \text{N/mm}^2$ $E_t = 14{,}000 \text{ N/mm}^2$

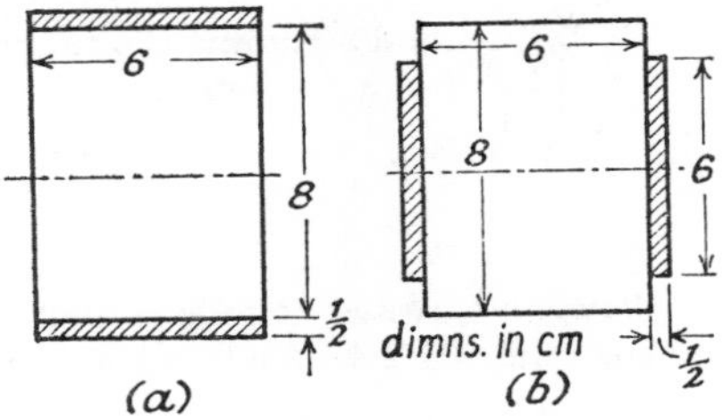

Fig. 6.21

Since the allowable stress in the timber is given, it is convenient to calculate on a basis of equivalent timber section.

(a) $I = I_t + mI_s$

$$= \frac{6 \times 8^3}{12} + 15\left[2 \times \frac{6 \times (\frac{1}{2})^3}{12} + 2 \times (6 \times \tfrac{1}{2}) \times 4{\cdot}25^2\right], \text{ Fig. 6.21(a)}$$
$$= 1884 \text{ cm}^4$$

$$M = \sigma_t I/y_t, \text{ from (5)}$$
$$= 8 \times 1884 \times 10^4/40$$
$$= 3{,}768{,}000 \text{ N.mm} = 3768 \text{ N.m}$$

Maximum stress in steel

$$\sigma_s = \frac{E_s}{E_t}\,\frac{y_s}{y_t}\,.\,\sigma_t \text{ from (2)}$$
$$= 15 \times (4{\cdot}5/4) \times 8$$
$$= 135 \text{ N/mm}^2$$

(b) Again working on equivalent timber

$$I = 6 \times 8^3/12 + 15 \times 2 \times \tfrac{1}{2} \times 6^3/12, \text{ Fig 6.21(b)}$$
$$= 526 \text{ cm}^4$$
$$M = 8 \times 526 \times 10^4/40$$
$$= 1{,}052{,}000 \text{ N.mm} = 1052 \text{ N.m}$$
$$\sigma_s = 15 \times \tfrac{3}{4} \times 8$$
$$= 90 \text{ N/mm}^2$$

EXAMPLE 9. *Two rectangular bars, one steel and one brass, each 38 mm by 9·5 mm are placed together to form a beam 38 mm wide by 19 mm deep, on two supports 760 mm apart, the brass on top of the steel. Determine the maximum central load if the bars are (a) separate and can bend independently, or (b) firmly secured throughout their length. Maximum allowable stress in the brass = 70 N/mm². Maximum allowable stress in the steel = 105 N/mm²; E_b = 87,500 N/mm²; E_s = 210,000 N/mm²* (U.L.)

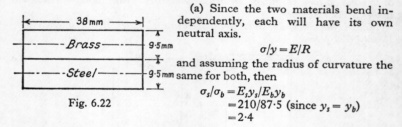

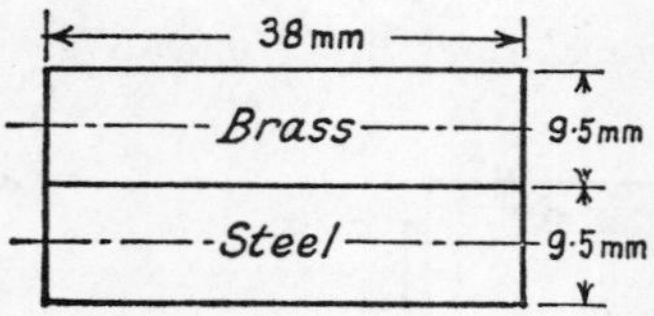

Fig. 6.22

(a) Since the two materials bend independently, each will have its own neutral axis.

$$\sigma/y = E/R$$

and assuming the radius of curvature the same for both, then

$$\sigma_s/\sigma_b = E_s y_s/E_b y_b$$
$$= 210/87{\cdot}5 \text{ (since } y_s = y_b)$$
$$= 2{\cdot}4$$

Referring to the allowable stresses, it follows that the actual stresses must be 105 N/mm² steel and 105/2·4 = 43·75 N/mm² brass.

Moment of resistance of brass

$$M_b = \sigma_b\, I_b/y_b$$
$$= 43{\cdot}75 \times \tfrac{1}{12} \times 38(9{\cdot}5)^3/4{\cdot}75$$
$$= 25{,}000 \text{ N mm}$$

Moment of resistance of steel

$$M_s = 105 \times \tfrac{1}{12} \times 38(9{\cdot}5)^3/4{\cdot}75$$
$$= 60{,}000 \text{ N mm}$$

Total moment of resistance

$$= 85{,}000 \text{ N mm}$$
$$= Wl/4 \text{ for a central load}$$
$$\therefore \quad W = 85{,}000 \times 4/760 = 450 \text{ N}$$

Note that the section could be treated as equivalent brass with a total moment of inertia

$$=I_b+mI_s=\tfrac{1}{12}\times 38(9{\cdot}5)^3(1+2{\cdot}4)$$

The stress variation is as shown in Fig. 6.23.

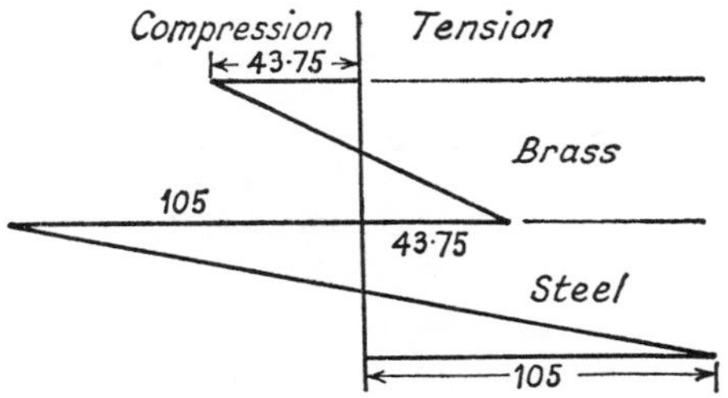

Fig. 6.23

(b) Fig. 6.24 is the equivalent section, as of all brass, and if the parts are rigidly fixed together along their length they will bend about a common neutral axis XX. The dimension of the steel parallel to the neutral axis has been increased in the modular ratio 2·4, and the position of XX is found by moments in the usual way, i.e.

$$\bar{y}=\frac{(38\times 9{\cdot}5)\ 14{\cdot}25+(91\times 9{\cdot}5)\ 4{\cdot}75}{38\times 9{\cdot}5+91\times 9{\cdot}5}$$

$$=7{\cdot}6\ \text{mm}$$

$$I=\tfrac{1}{12}\times 38(9{\cdot}5)^3+(38\times 9{\cdot}5)6{\cdot}65^2+\tfrac{1}{12}\times 91(9{\cdot}5)^3+(91\times 9{\cdot}5)2{\cdot}85^2$$

$$=2750+16{,}000+6{,}700+7000$$

$$=32{,}500\ \text{mm}^4$$

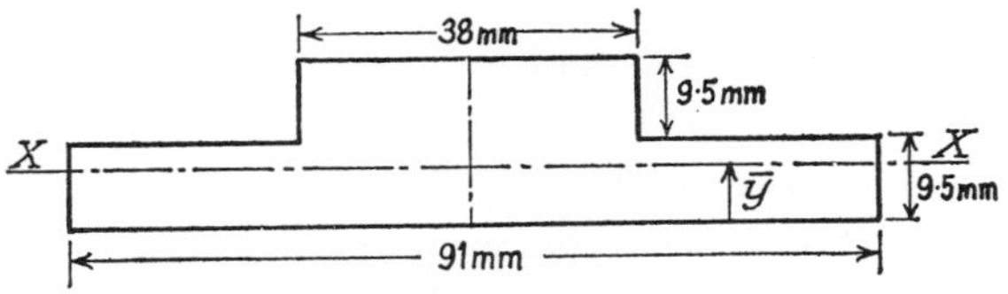

Fig. 6.24

The maximum stress ratio is again determined by the modular ratio and the maximum distances from the neutral axis (Eq. (2)), i.e.

$$\sigma_s/\sigma_b=2{\cdot}4\times 7{\cdot}6/11{\cdot}4$$

$$=1{\cdot}6$$

from which it follows that the allowable steel stress is still the limiting factor, and the maximum stress in the brass is $105/1{\cdot}6=65{\cdot}5$ N/mm².

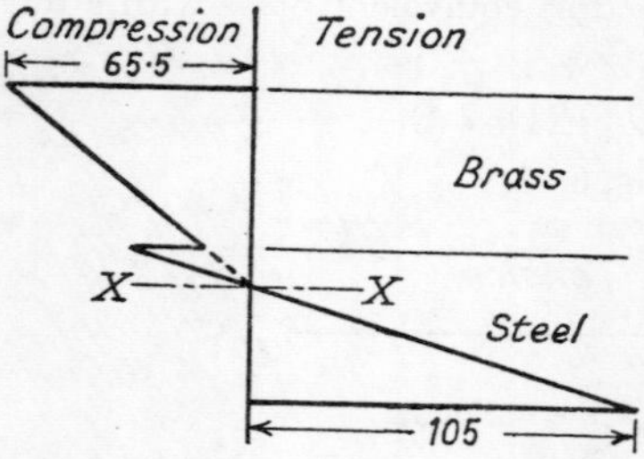

Fig. 6.25

Total moment of resistance

$= (65\cdot5 \times 32{,}500)/11\cdot4 \times 1000$ (Eq. (5))

$= 187$ Nm

Central load $= (187 \times 4)/0\cdot76$

$= 985$ N

The stress variation is shown in Fig. 6.25, the brass being all in compression, the steel being mainly in tension, but in compression above XX. At the common surface the stress ratio is 2·4.

EXAMPLE 10. *A steel rod, 3 cm diameter, is placed inside a brass tube having outside and inside diameters of 6 cm and 5 cm. The rod and tube have the same length and their axes are parallel and ½ cm apart. The ends are covered by rigid plates through which a compressive force of 60 kN is applied, acting along the axis of the tube. Determine the maximum and minimum longitudinal stresses in the rod and tube.* $E_s = 205{,}000$ *N/mm²* $E_b = 95{,}000$ *N/mm².*

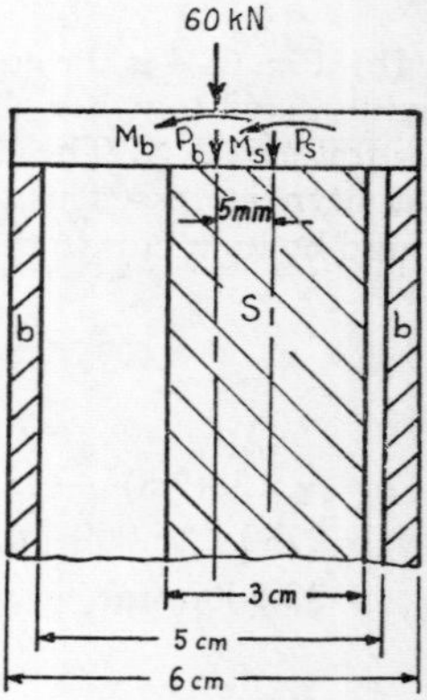

Fig. 6.26

Let P_s and P_b be the direct loads at the axis of the steel rod and brass tube respectively, and M_s and M_b the corresponding bending moments on each (Fig. 6.26).

Then for equilibrium,

$$P_s + P_b = 60{,}000 \quad \text{(i)}$$

and

$$M_s + M_b = P_s \times 5 \quad \text{(ii)}$$

The area of steel

$$A_s = (\pi/4)30^2 = 707 \text{ mm}^2$$

and the area of brass

$$A_b = (\pi/4)(60^2 - 50^2) = 864 \text{ mm}^2$$

The corresponding moments of inertia are

$$I_s = \pi \times 30^4/64 = 39{,}700 \text{ mm}^4$$

and

$$I_b = \pi(60^4 - 50^4)/64 = 329{,}000 \text{ mm}^4$$

Since the end plates are rigid, the rod and tube may be assumed to bend together with the same radius of curvature,

$$M_s/E_sI_s = M_b/E_bI_b$$

i.e.

$$3\cdot84M_s = M_b \quad \text{(iii)}$$

Equating the linear strains for rod and tube at the centre-line of the tube, the compatibility equation is

$$P_s/E_sA_s + M_s \times y/E_sI_s = P_b/E_bA_b \quad \text{(iv)}$$

From (ii) and (iii)

$$M_s = (5/4{\cdot}84)P_s = 1{\cdot}03\ P_s \tag{v}$$

Substituting from (i) and (v) in (iv),

$$\frac{P_s}{205{,}000 \times 707} + \frac{1{\cdot}03\ P_s \times 5}{205{,}000 \times 39{,}700} = \frac{60{,}000 - P_s}{95{,}000 \times 864}$$

$\times 205{,}000 \times 707$: $\quad P_s + 0{\cdot}0917\ P_s = 106{,}000 - 1{\cdot}765 P_s$

giving $\quad P_s = 37{,}100$ N

From (i) $\quad P_b = 22{,}900$ N

From (v) and (iii)

$$M_s = 38{,}200 \text{ N.mm and } M_b = 147{,}000 \text{ N.mm}$$

The maximum and minimum stresses in the steel rod are given by

$$P_s/A_s \pm M_s d/2I_s$$
$$= 37{,}100/707 \pm 38{,}200 \times 30/2 \times 39{,}700$$
$$= 52{\cdot}5 \pm 14{\cdot}4$$
$$= 66{\cdot}9 \text{ and } 38{\cdot}1 \text{ N/mm}^2 \text{ compression.}$$

Similarly, the maximum and minimum stresses in the brass tube are

$$22{,}900/864 \pm 147{,}000 \times 60/2 \times 329{,}000$$
$$= 26{\cdot}5 \pm 13{\cdot}4$$
$$= 39{\cdot}9 \text{ and } 13{\cdot}1 \text{ N/mm}^2 \text{ compression.}$$

EXAMPLE 11. *A straight bimetallic strip consists of a strip of brass of rectangular section of width b and thickness t joined along its length by a strip of steel of the same dimensions, thus forming a composite bar of width b and thickness 2t. If the bar is uniformly heated and is quite free to bend, show that it will bend to a radius*

$$R = \frac{E_B^2 + E_S^2 + 14E_BE_S}{12E_BE_S(\alpha_B - \alpha_S)} \cdot \frac{t}{T}$$

where α_B and α_S are the coefficients of linear expansion and T is the rise in temperature.

Such a strip 200 mm long with the steel and brass each 1·5 mm thick rests on a level surface with the brass uppermost. If the strip is initially straight, find the maximum clearance between it and the surface due to a rise in temperature of 100° C. $\alpha_B = 19 \times 10^{-6}$ per °C. $\alpha_S = 11 \times 10^{-6}$per °C. $E_B = 95{,}000$ N/mm². $E_S = 205{,}000$ N/mm² (U.L.)

The interaction between the two strips produces a force at the common surface tending to compress the brass and extend the steel. If this internal force is P, it gives rise to a "direct" load P at the centre of each section, together with a bending moment in each strip (as in Fig. 6.27). Assuming R is the same for both strips (i.e. large compared with t)

$$M_B = (E_B/R)I_B = bt^3E_B/12R \tag{i}$$

and

$$M_S = (E_S/R)I_S = bt^3E_S/12R \tag{ii}$$

For equilibrium of the cross-section,

$$M_B + M_S = Pt \tag{iii}$$

i.e. $Pt = (bt^3/12R)(E_B + E_S)$ from (i), (ii) and (iii) (iv)

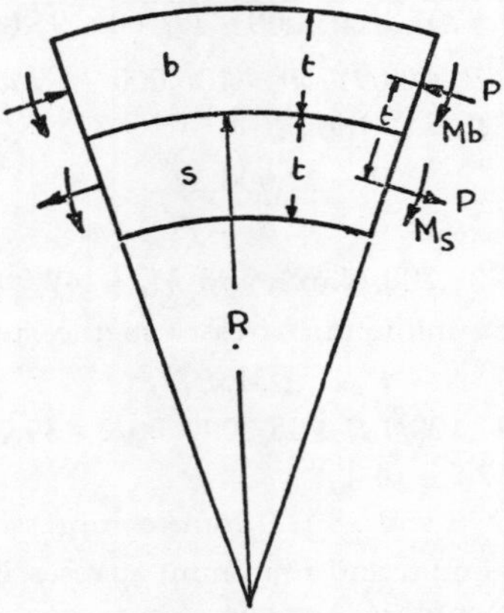

Fig. 6.27

The difference in linear strains at the central axis of each strip is t/R, and allowing for load and temperature, the compatibility equation is

$$t/R = -P/btE_B + \alpha_B T - (P/btE_S + \alpha_S T)$$

i.e.

$$(\alpha_B - \alpha_S)T = \frac{P}{bt}\left(\frac{1}{E_B} + \frac{1}{E_S}\right) + \frac{t}{R}$$

$$= \frac{t}{12R}\,\frac{(E_B + E_S)^2}{E_B E_S} + \frac{t}{R} \quad \text{from (iv)}$$

$$= \frac{t}{12R}\,\frac{E_B{}^2 + E_S{}^2 + 14E_B E_S}{E_B E_S}$$

Re-arranging,

$$R = \frac{E_B{}^2 + E_S{}^2 + 14E_B E_S}{12E_B E_S(\alpha_B - \alpha_S)} \cdot \frac{t}{T}$$

$$= \frac{(95{,}000^2 + 205{,}000^2 + 14 \times 95{,}000 \times 205{,}000) \times 1{\cdot}5}{12 \times 95{,}000 \times 205{,}000 \times 8 \times 10^{-6} \times 100}$$

$= 2740$ mm

The clearance h is given by

$$(2R - h)h = 100 \times 100 \text{ for a circular arc}$$

or

$$h = 10{,}000/2 \times 2740 \text{ approx.}$$

$$= 1{\cdot}83 \text{ mm}$$

6.10. Reinforced Concrete Beams. Concrete is a material which has a useful compressive strength, but is weak in tension, and in fact may develop minute cracks which reduce its tensile strength to zero. Steel reinforcement is therefore placed on the tension side of the beam, and by concentrating this at the greatest distance from the neutral axis the material is used to the best advantage.

It must be determined prior to erection which will be the tension side, but as the concrete is usually poured on site this is no disadvantage. Also, apart from being economical in the use of steel, concrete is useful as a protection against corrosion and in case of fire.

The following assumptions are made in the theory:

(1) The stress in the concrete is zero on the tension side.
(2) The stress in the steel is uniform.
(3) Strain is proportional to distance from neutral axis.
(4) Stress is proportional to strain in the concrete.

Assumption (3) has been found to be true for pure bending, and implies also that there is no relative slip between steel and concrete. The last assumption is not true, since concrete does not obey Hooke's law, but it is possible to take a mean value of the modulus over the range of stress used. Values to be used, and also for allowable stresses, depend on the type and mix of concrete used.

Rectangular Section

In Fig. 6.28 d is the depth of reinforcement measured from the compression face.

Let h be the distance of the neutral axis from the compression face, σ_c the maximum stress in the concrete, and σ_s the stress in the steel.

On the assumption of strains proportional to distance from neutral axis

$$\sigma_s/\sigma_c = (E_s \times \text{strain})/(E_c \times \text{strain})$$
$$= m(d-h)/h \quad \text{where } m = E_s/E_c \tag{1}$$

If the beam is under the action of a pure bending moment M, then the resultant forces P in the steel and concrete must be equal and opposite, i.e.

$$P = \sigma_s A_s = \tfrac{1}{2}\sigma_c . bh \tag{2}$$

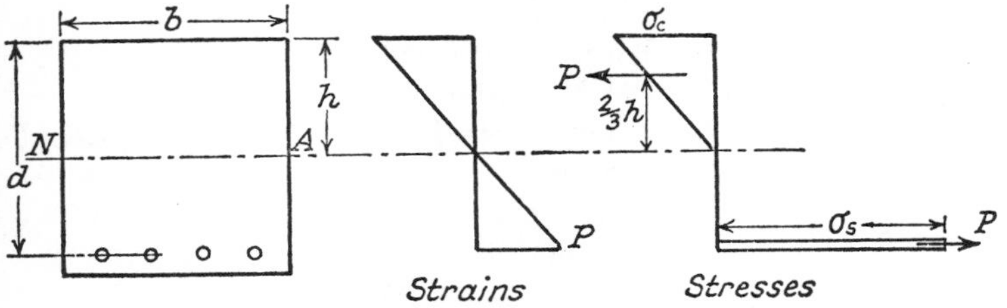

Fig. 6.28

where A_s is the area of steel reinforcement and $\frac{1}{2}\sigma_c$ is the mean stress in the concrete.

The moment of resistance is given by the force P times the couple arm, and noting that the force in the concrete acts at the centroid of the area on the stress diagram

$$\begin{aligned} M &= P(d-h/3), \quad \text{which from (2)} \\ &= \sigma_s A_s(d-h/3) \\ &= \tfrac{1}{2}\sigma_c . bh(d-h/3) \qquad (3) \end{aligned}$$

If the ratio σ_s/σ_c is known, then h can be determined, for a beam of given dimensions, from equation (1). The area of steel reinforcement is then found from equation (2), and the moment of resistance from (3). This is known as the "*economic*" *section*, the limiting values of stress being realised. Any increase in reinforcement above this amount, although resulting in an increase in M, will restrict the stresses attainable.

If the dimensions and A are given, then by eliminating σ_s/σ_c between equations (1) and (2) a quadratic in h is obtained. The actual stresses are then determined from the bending moment equation.

EXAMPLE 12. *A reinforced concrete beam of rectangular section is 12 cm wide and 18 cm deep, with the steel placed 2 cm above the tension face. Find the position of the neutral axis if the area of the steel is 2 cm² and the modular ratio 16.*

Find the maximum stresses produced in the steel and concrete when such a beam 2 m long is simply supported at its ends and carries a central load of 1000 kg.

Strain equation: $$\begin{aligned} \sigma_s/\sigma_c &= m \times (d-h)/h \\ &= 16 \times (16-h)/h \qquad (1) \end{aligned}$$

Load equation $$\sigma_s A_s = \tfrac{1}{2}\sigma_c \cdot bh$$

$$\therefore \quad \sigma_s/\sigma_c = 12h/(2 \times 2) \qquad (2)$$

Eliminating σ_s/σ_c between (1) and (2),

$$16 \times (16-h)/h = 3h$$

or $$3h^2 + 16h - 256 = 0$$

solving $$\begin{aligned} h &= [-16 + \sqrt{(256+3072)}]/6 \\ &= 6{\cdot}95 \text{ cm} \end{aligned}$$

$$\begin{aligned} M &= Wl/4 = (1000 \times 200)/4 \\ &= 50{,}000 \text{ kg. cm.} \end{aligned}$$

But $$M = \sigma_s A_s(d-h/3) = \tfrac{1}{2}\sigma_c\, bh(d-h/3) \qquad \text{from (3)}$$

$$\therefore \quad \sigma_s = \frac{50{,}000}{2(16-2{\cdot}32)} = 1830 \text{ kg/cm}^2$$

and $$\sigma_c = \frac{50{,}000}{\frac{1}{2} \times 12 \times 6{\cdot}95(16-2{\cdot}32)} = 88 \text{ kg/cm}^2$$

Frequently reinforced concrete beams are of T-section, such as occurs where floor slabs are integral with rectangular sections which are parallel and at fixed distances apart. The same basic equations can be applied as above, with modification to the area of concrete in compression.

Cases where the beam is further strengthened by reinforcement on the compression side will be found in the reference book quoted at the end of this chapter.

6.11. Principal Moments of Inertia. It was pointed out in Para. 6.1 that the principal axes of any area are those about which the product of inertia is zero. Axes of symmetry through the centroid are automatically principal axes, the product moments for opposite quadrants cancelling each other out.

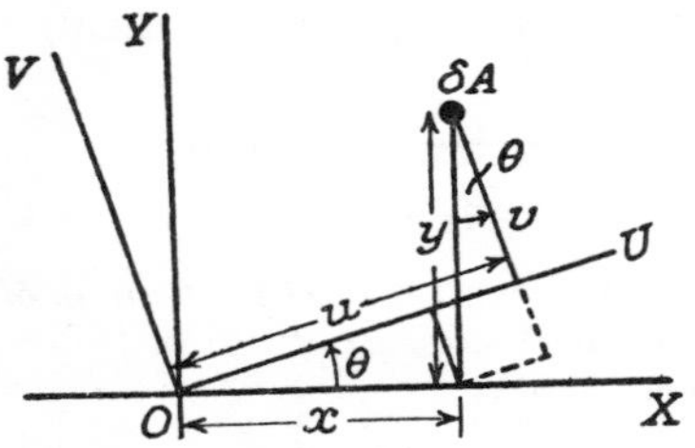

Fig. 6.29

When the direction of the principal axes is unknown, let OX and OY be any two perpendicular axes through the centroid, and OU, OV the principal axes (Fig. 6.29).

Let δA be an element of area with co-ordinates u, v relative to OU, OV, and x, y relative to OX, OY. $\angle$ UOX $=\theta$.

Then $$u = x\cos\theta + y\sin\theta$$
and $$v = y\cos\theta - x\sin\theta$$

The product of inertia

$$\begin{aligned} I_{UV} &= \int uv\,dA \\ &= \int(x\cos\theta + y\sin\theta)(y\cos\theta - x\sin\theta)dA \\ &= \sin\theta.\cos\theta[\int y^2 dA - \int x^2 dA] + (\cos^2\theta - \sin^2\theta)\int xy\,dA \\ &= (\tfrac{1}{2}\sin 2\theta)(I_X - I_Y) + \cos 2\theta.I_{XY} \qquad (1) \end{aligned}$$

Condition for principal axes is $I_{UV}=0$, i.e.

$$\tan 2\theta = 2I_{XY}/(I_Y - I_X) \quad \text{from (1)} \qquad (2)$$

$$\begin{aligned} I_U &= \int v^2.dA \\ &= \cos^2\theta.I_X + \sin^2\theta.I_Y - \sin 2\theta.I_{XY} \end{aligned}$$

and substituting for I_{XY} from (2)

$$\begin{aligned} &= \tfrac{1}{2}(I_X + I_Y) + \tfrac{1}{2}\cos 2\theta(I_X - I_Y) + \tfrac{1}{2}(\sin^2 2\theta/\cos 2\theta)(I_X - I_Y) \\ &= \tfrac{1}{2}(I_X + I_Y) + \tfrac{1}{2}(I_X - I_Y)\sec 2\theta \qquad (3) \end{aligned}$$

$$\begin{aligned} I_V &= \int u^2.dA \\ &= \cos^2\theta.I_Y + \sin^2\theta.I_X + \sin 2\theta.I_{XY} \\ &= \tfrac{1}{2}(I_X + I_Y) - \tfrac{1}{2}(I_X - I_Y)\sec 2\theta \qquad (4) \end{aligned}$$

Adding (3) and (4)

$$I_U + I_V = I_X + I_Y \tag{5}$$

If I_X, I_Y, and I_{XY} are calculated or determined graphically, θ can be found from equation (2), I_U from (3), and I_V from (5).

For a rectangle of dimensions b and d with sides parallel to the axes OX and OY (Fig. 6.30)

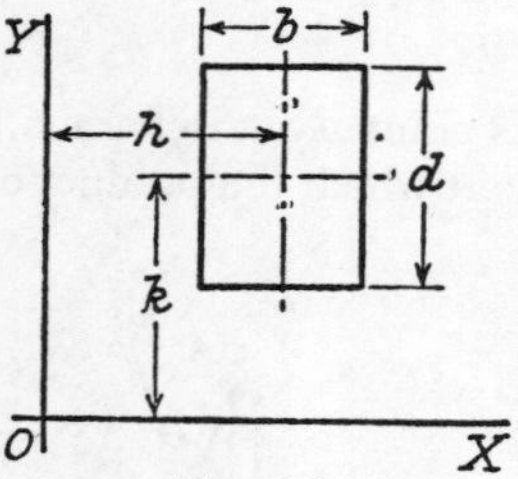

Fig. 6.30

$$I_{XY} = \iint xy\,.\,dy\,.\,dx$$

$$= \left[\frac{x^2}{2}\right]_{h-b/2}^{h+b/2} \times \left[\frac{y^2}{2}\right]_{k-d/2}^{k+d/2}$$

(where h, k are the co-ordinates of the centroid)

$$= hb \times kd$$

$$= bd \times hk$$

$$= Ahk \tag{6}$$

EXAMPLE 13. *Find the position of the principal axes and the values of the principal moments of inertia for an unequal angle 5 cm by 3 cm by 0·5 cm (Fig. 6.31).*

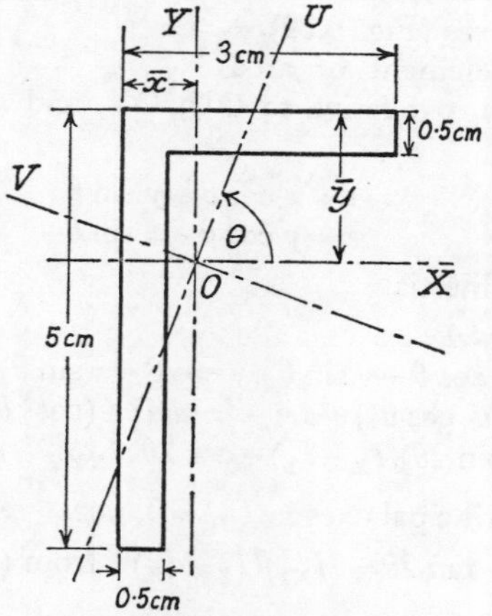

Fig. 6.31

To find the centroid O, by moments:

$$\bar{x} = \frac{(4{\cdot}5 \times 0{\cdot}5) \times 0{\cdot}25 + (3 \times 0{\cdot}5) \times 1{\cdot}5}{(4{\cdot}5 + 3) \times 0{\cdot}5}$$

$$= 0{\cdot}75 \text{ cm}$$

$$\bar{y} = \frac{(4{\cdot}5 \times 0{\cdot}5) \times 2{\cdot}75 + (3 \times 0{\cdot}5) \times 0{\cdot}25}{(4{\cdot}5 + 3) \times 0{\cdot}5}$$

$$= 1{\cdot}75 \text{ cm}$$

$$I_X = \frac{0\cdot5 \times 4\cdot5^3}{12} + (0\cdot5 \times 4\cdot5) \times 1^2 + \frac{3 \times 0\cdot5^3}{12} + (3 \times 0\cdot5) \times 1\cdot5^2$$
$$= 9\cdot44 \text{ cm}^4$$

$$I_Y = \frac{4\cdot5 \times 0\cdot5^3}{12} + (4\cdot5 \times 0\cdot5) \times 0\cdot5^2 + \frac{0\cdot5 \times 3^3}{12} + (0\cdot5 \times 3) \times 0\cdot75^2$$
$$= 2\cdot58 \text{ cm}^4$$

$$I_{XY} = (4\cdot5 \times 0\cdot5) \times (-0\cdot5) \times (-1) + (3 \times 0\cdot5) \times (0\cdot75) \times (1\cdot5) \quad \text{from (6)}$$
$$= 2\cdot813 \text{ cm}^4$$

From (2) $\tan 2\theta = \dfrac{2 \times 2\cdot813}{2\cdot58 - 9\cdot44} = -0\cdot820$

giving $2\theta = 140° \ 40'$

or $\theta = 70° \ 20'$

From (3) $I_U = \frac{1}{2}(9\cdot44 + 2\cdot58) + \frac{1}{2}(9\cdot44 - 2\cdot58) \sec 140° \ 40'$

$= 1\cdot59 \text{ cm}^4$

$I_V = I_X + I_Y - I_U$ from (5)

$= 10\cdot43 \text{ cm}^4$

6.12. Unsymmetrical Bending. The following is a further example of an applied bending moment not in a principal plane, being a more general case than Example 4, where the cross-section was symmetrical.

EXAMPLE 14. *A 5 cm by 3 cm by 0·5 cm angle is used as a cantilever of length 50 cm with the 3 cm leg horizontal. A load of 1000 N is applied at the free end. Determine the position of the neutral axis and the maximum stress set up.*

The position of the centroid O and the inclination of the principal axes UU′ and VV′ (Fig. 6.32) have been determined in Example 13.

The maximum bending moment about XX′ is 1000 × 500 N mm.

Resolving about VV′ and UU′ respectively, gives

$$M_V = 500{,}000 \sin 70° \ 20' = 470{,}080 \text{ N mm}$$

and $$M_U = 500{,}000 \cos 70° \ 20' = 160{,}830 \text{ N mm}$$

The combined bending stress at any point defined by co-ordinates u, v mm is

$$\sigma = M_V . u/I_V + M_U . v/I_U$$

(where u and v are both positive in the quadrant UOV)

$= (470{,}080/104{,}300)u + (160{,}830/15{,}900)v$ (values from Ex. 13)

$= 4\cdot51u + 10\cdot6v$

The equation of the neutral axis is $\sigma = 0$, which reduces to $0\cdot426u + v = 0$. This is a line through O inclined at $\tan^{-1}(-0\cdot426)$, or $-23° \ 4'$ to UU′.

The stress will be tensile "above" the N.A., and compressive "below".

The maximum tensile stress is at the outside of the corner of the angle, where u and v are both positive, and is given by

$$4{\cdot}51(17{\cdot}5 \sin 70^\circ\, 20' - 7{\cdot}5 \cos 70^\circ 20') + 10{\cdot}6(17{\cdot}5 \cos 70^\circ\, 20' + 7{\cdot}5 \sin 70^\circ\, 20') \quad \text{from (i)}$$

$$= 4{\cdot}51 \times 13{\cdot}9 + 10{\cdot}6 \times 13 = 203 \text{ N/mm}^2$$

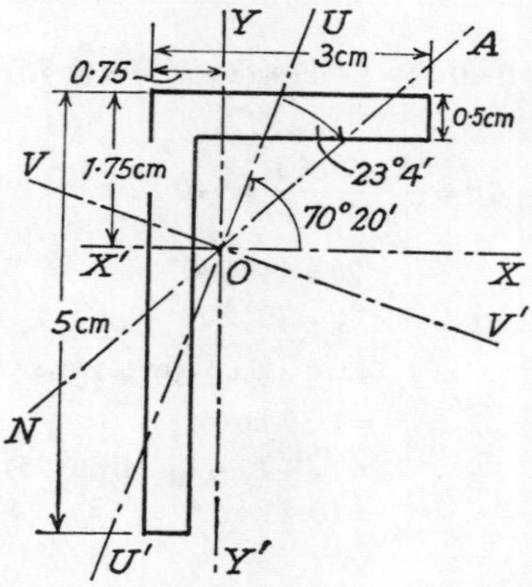

Fig. 6.32

The maximum compressive stress occurs at the inside bottom edge of the vertical leg, where u and v are both negative, and is given by

$$-4{\cdot}51(32{\cdot}5 \sin 70^\circ\, 20' + 2{\cdot}5 \cos 70^\circ\, 20') - 10{\cdot}6\,(32{\cdot}5 \cos 70^\circ\, 20' - 2{\cdot}5 \sin 70^\circ\, 20')$$

$$= -4{\cdot}51 \times 31{\cdot}4 - 10{\cdot}6 \times 8{\cdot}62$$

$$= 233 \text{ N/mm}^2$$

(For deflection of this beam, see Chapter IX, Problem 20.)

SUMMARY

Bending Stress Formula: $\sigma/y = M/I = E/R$

Moments of Inertia:

Section	Axis	I	Z
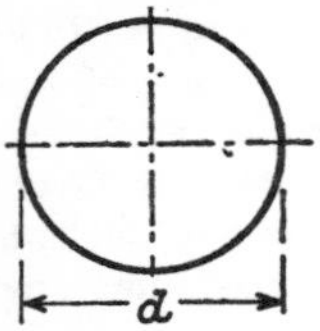	Diameter	$\pi d^4/64$	$\pi d^3/32$
	Polar	$\pi d^4/32$	$\pi d^3/16$
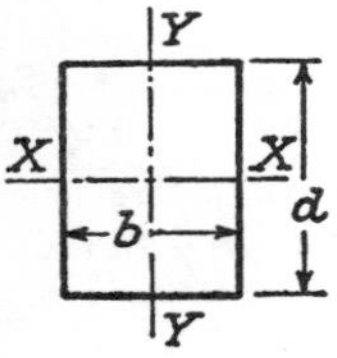	XX	$bd^3/12$	$bd^2/6$
	YY	$db^3/12$	$db^2/6$
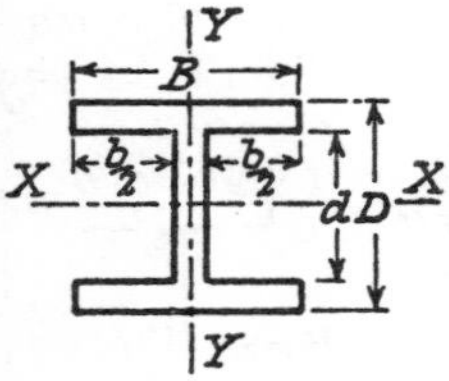	XX	$\frac{1}{12}(BD^3-bd^3)$	$(BD^3-bd^3)/6D$
	YY	$\frac{1}{12}[(D-d)B^3+d(B-b)^3]$	$\frac{(D-d)B^3+d(B-b)^3}{6B}$
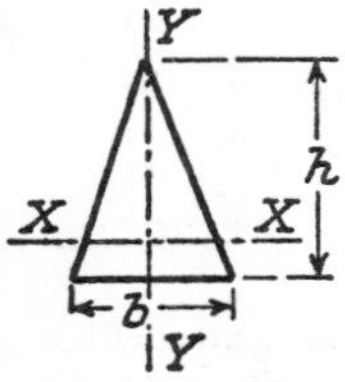	XX	$bh^3/36$	$bh^2/24$
	YY	$hb^3/48$	$hb^2/24$

Combined Bending and Direct Stress $\sigma = P/A + M_X y/I_X + M_Y x/I_Y$

Composite Beams.—Equivalent Section.

Reinforced Concrete Beams.—Strain and Load Equations.

REFERENCES

ERIKSSEN, B., *Theory and Practice of Structural Design applied to Reinforced Concrete*. Concrete Publications Limited. 1953.

SCOTT, W. L., GLANVILLE, W. H., and THOMAS, F. G., *B.S. Code of Practice for Reinforced Concrete*. Concrete Publications Limited. 1950.

RAO, K. L., *Calculation, Design and Testing of Reinforced Concrete*. Pitman. 1953.

PROBLEMS

1. A long rod of uniform rectangular section and thickness t, originally straight, is bent into the form of a circular arc and the displacement d of the mid-point of a length L is measured by means of a dial gauge. If d is regarded as small compared with L, show that the longitudinal surface strain e in the rod is given by $e = 4td/L^2$. (note that $e = t/2R$ by Para. 6.1) (U.L.)

2. Calculate the moments of inertia about XX and YY for the built-up section shown. (738 cm^4; 790 cm^4)

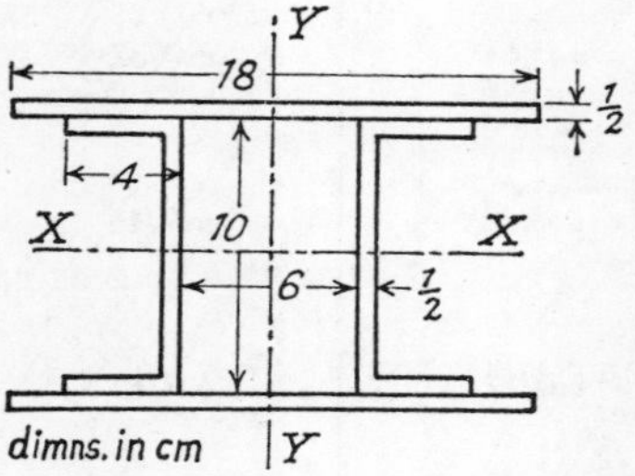

3. A beam of I-section of moment of inertia 954 cm^4 and depth 14 cm is freely supported at its ends. Over what span can a uniform load of 500 kg/m run be carried if the maximum stress is 60 N/mm^2.?

What additional central load can be carried when the maximum stress is 90 N/mm^2? (3·65 m; 456 kg.)

4. A cantilever has a free length of 2·5 m. It is of T-section with the flange 100 mm by 19 mm, web 200 mm by 12·7 mm, the flange being in tension. What load per m run can be applied if the maximum tensile stress is 30 N/mm^2? What is the maximum compressive stress? (310 kg/m; 61 N/mm^2.)

5. A welded girder, of cross-section shown, is to span 9 m, being simply supported at its ends.

A uniformly distributed load of 120 kN/m is to be carried with a maximum bending stress of 120 N/mm^2, the beam being strengthened where necessary by the addition of flange plates 12·7 mm thick. Find the length of plates and their width. (4 m; 0·24 m)

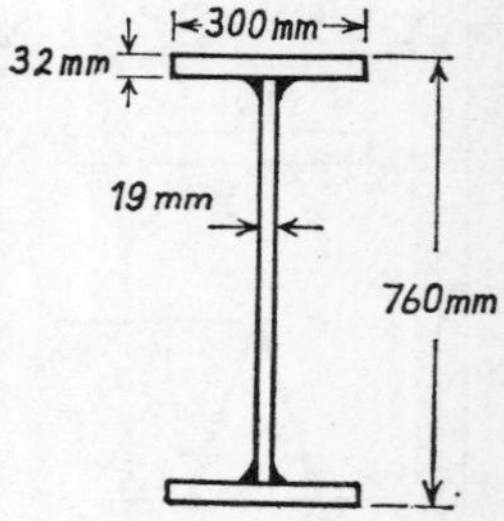

6. A vertical flag staff 9 m high is of square section 150 mm by 150 mm at the ground, tapering to 75 mm by 75 mm at the top. A horizontal pull of 1000 N is applied at the top in the direction of a diagonal of the section. Calculate the maximum stress due to bending (27 N/mm^2 at 4·5 m down.)

7. A short cast-iron column is of hollow section, 200 mm external diameter, 38 mm thick. A vertical compressive load acts at an eccentricity of 63 mm from the axis. If the maximum permitted stresses are 75 N/mm^2 compression and 20 N/mm^2 tension find the greatest load.

Plot a diagram of stress variation. (U.L.) (5×10^4 kg)

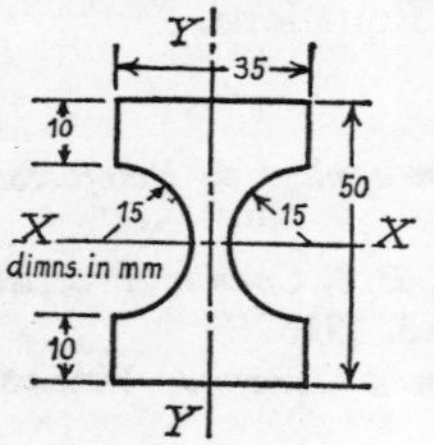

8. The figure shows the section of a beam. What is the ratio of its moment of resistance to bending in the plane YY to that for bending in the plane XX, if the maximum stress due to bending is the same in both cases? For a semicircle of radius r the centroid is at a distance $4r/3\pi$ from the centre. (U.L.)
($I_x = 32{\cdot}5$ cm, $I_y = 8{\cdot}0$ cm^4, 2·85)

9. A 50 mm by 12·5 mm flat steel bar was placed in a testing machine and subjected to a 60 kN load acting as shown. An extensometer placed in line with the load recorded an extension of 0·16 mm on a gauge length of 200 mm. Calculate the maximum and minimum stresses set up, and the value of Young's modulus. (U.L.)

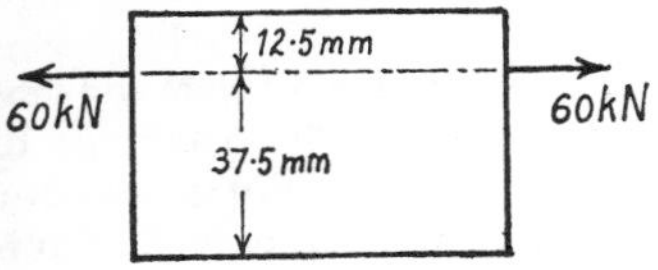

(240 N/mm²; 48 N/mm²;
210,000 N/mm²

10. A short column is of hollow circular section, the centre of the inside hole being 6 mm eccentric to that of the outside. The outside diameter is 96 mm and the inside 48 mm. The line of action of the load intersects the cross-section at a point in line with the two centres. What are the limiting positions of the load for there to be no tensile stress set up? (15·2 mm; 14·0 mm)

11. The cross-section of a masonry column is an equilateral triangle ABC of 2 m sides. The column is subjected to a vertical load of 2×10^5 kg, the resultant of which cuts the cross-section at a point on the median AD, distant $\frac{1}{4}\sqrt{3}$ m from BC. Find the stress at each corner of the cross-section.

(A = 0; B = C = 1·7 N/mm²)

12. A tie bar of rectangular section, originally 75 mm by 25 mm, has these dimensions reduced by $1/n$th of their original values by removal of material from two adjacent faces. If an axial load of 100 kN is applied through the centre of the original section find the value of $1/n$ for a maximum tensile stress of 128 N/mm².

Determine also the magnitude of the last stress. (U.L.)

0·123; 10·2 N/mm²

13. A timber beam, simply supported over a span of 6 m, is to be strengthened by the addition of steel flitches fixed as shown.

With the original timber beam a load of 3500 N/m gave a maximum stress of 4 N/mm². If the flitched beam is to carry an additional load of 900 N/m with a maximum stress in the steel of 55 N/mm², the timber stress remaining the same, find the dimensions. $E_s/E_t = 20$.

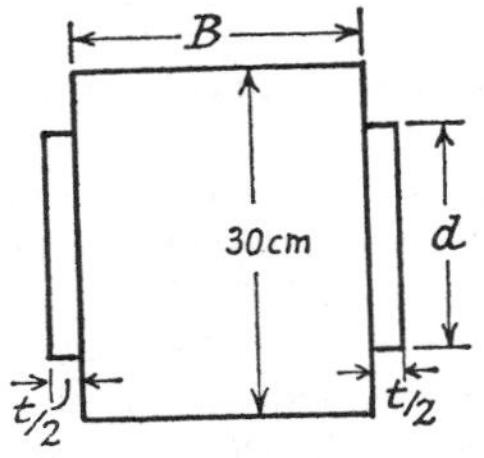

(B = 262 mm; t = 10·3 mm; d = 207 mm)

14. A timber beam 72 mm wide by 144 mm deep is to be reinforced by bonding strips of aluminium alloy 72 mm wide on to the top and bottom faces, over the whole length of the beam. If the moment of resistance of the composite beam is to be 4 times that of the timber alone with the same value of maximum stress in the timber, determine the thickness of alloy strip and the ratio of maximum stresses in alloy and timber. $E_a = 7{\cdot}15 E_t$. (U.L.) (9 mm; 8·04).

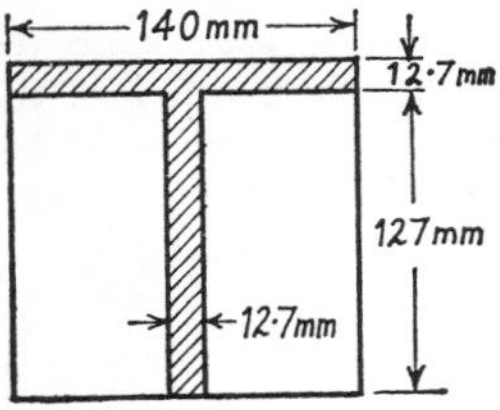

15. The composite beam of steel and timber shown is supported over a span of 6 m and carries a load W at its mid-point. If the maximum stresses in steel and timber are not to exceed 128 N/mm² and 12 N/mm² respectively, find the greatest value of W. $E_s/E_t = 20$. (770 kg)

16. A compound beam is formed by joining two

bars rigidly together, one of steel and the other of brass, each 50 mm wide. The bars are of thickness t_1 and t_2 respectively, so that the total depth of the beam is $t_1 + t_2$. If $E_s = 2E_b$ find the ratio t_1/t_2 so that the neutral axis is at the dividing line of the two bars.

If the total depth of the section is 25 mm and the stresses in the steel and brass are not to exceed 114 N/mm² and 42·5 N/mm² respectively, determine the maximum moment of resistance. (U.L.) (0·707; 260 Nm)

17. A compound beam consists of a steel and a copper bar, each 75 mm by 25 mm section, one resting on the other with the 75 mm sides in contact. They are securely fastened together at the ends so that no relative movement or rotation can take place. The beam is now heated through 100° C. Assuming that both bars bend into an arc of the same radius, but that stresses are only transmitted through the end connections, find the radius of this arc and the maximum tensile and compressive stresses in both materials. For steel, $E = 208{,}000$ N/mm², $\alpha = 11 \times 10^{-6}$ per °C. For copper, $E = 104{,}000$ N/mm², $\alpha = 18 \times 10^{-6}$ per °C. (U.L.)

(Compare Ex. 11. 49·5 m. Steel 66, 40 N/mm². Copper 13·2, 40/mm²)

18. A reinforced concrete beam is to be 225 mm wide and 400 mm deep. The maximum allowable stresses are 7 N/mm² concrete, 126 N/mm² steel. What area of reinforcement is required if both these stresses are developed and the steel is 50 mm above the tension face? Modular ratio 15.

What uniformly distributed load may be carried over a span of 6 m. Concrete weighs 2400 kg/m³, neglect weight of steel. (1000 mm²; 620 kg/m)

19. A reinforced concrete beam of rectangular section is 25 cm wide and 50 cm deep. Steel reinforcement of 11 cm² is placed at 5 cm above the tension face. The maximum compressive stress in the concrete is 4·2 N/mm². The modular ratio is 15. Calculate the moment of resistance and the stress in the steel. (38 kNm; 89 N/mm²)

20. The reinforced concrete beam shown in the figure has maximum stresses of 4·2 N/mm² in the concrete and 112 N/mm² in the steel. Modular ratio 15. Assuming the neutral axis to be inside the full width of the section, find its position and the sectional area of the steel. Calculate also the moment of resistance.

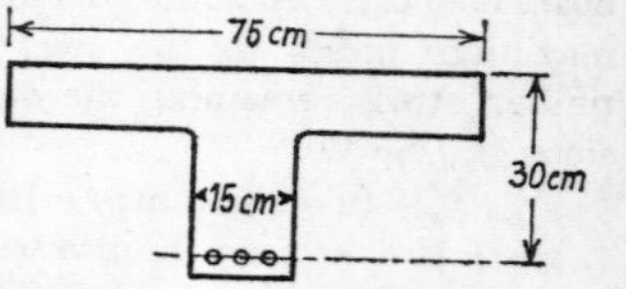

(10·8 cm; 15·2 cm²; 45 kNm)

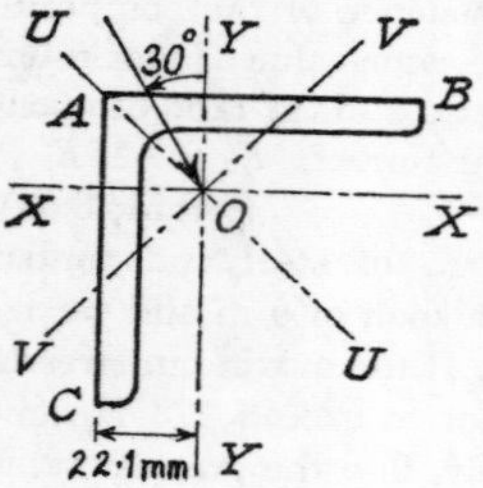

21. A cantilever consists of a 72 mm by 72 mm by 12 mm angle with the top face AB horizontal. It carries a load of 1 kN at 1 m from the fixed end, the line of action passing through the centroid and is inclined at 30° to the vertical. Determine the stresses at A, B, and C, and the position of the neutral axis. $A = 1590$ mm²; $I_X = I_Y = 72{\cdot}3 \times 10^4$ mm⁴, $I_U = 114 \times 10^4$ mm⁴; $I_V = 30{\cdot}5 \times 10^4$ mm⁴ (100; −51; −75 N/mm²; $v/u = -14{\cdot}0$.)

CHAPTER VII

Shear Stress in Beams

7.1. Variation of Shear Stress. The shearing force at any cross-section of a beam will set up a shear stress on transverse sections which in general will vary across the section. In the following analysis it will be assumed that the stress is uniform across the width (i.e. parallel to the neutral axis), and also that the presence of shear stress does not affect the distribution of bending stress. The latter assumption cannot be strictly true, as the existence of shear stress will cause a distortion of transverse planes, which will no longer remain plane (see Para. 9.7).

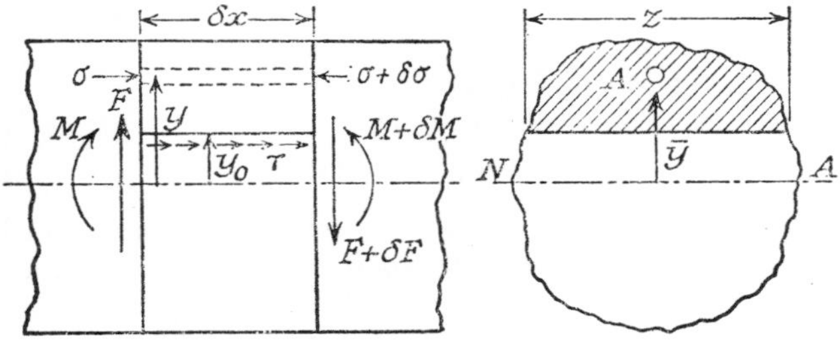

Fig. 7.1

Due to the shear stress on transverse planes there will be a complementary shear stress on longitudinal planes parallel to the neutral axis. In Fig. 7.1 two transverse sections are shown, at a distance δx apart, the shearing forces and bending moments being F, $F+\delta F$, and M, $M+\delta M$ respectively.

Let τ be the value of the complementary shear stress (and hence the transverse shear stress—Para. 2.2), at a distance y_0 from the neutral axis. z is the width of the cross-section at this position, and A the area of cross-section cut off by a line parallel to the neutral axis. $\bar{y}$ is the distance of the centroid of A from the neutral axis.

If σ, $\sigma+\delta\sigma$ are the normal stresses on an element of area δA at the two transverse sections (Fig. 7.2), then there is a difference of longitudinal forces equal to $\delta\sigma.\delta A$, and this quantity summed over the area A is in equilibrium with the transverse shear stress τ on the longitudinal plane of area $z\delta x$, i.e.

$$\tau . z\delta x = \int d\sigma . dA \qquad (1)$$

but $\sigma = My/I$

and $\sigma + \delta\sigma = (M + \delta M)y/I$

$\therefore \quad \delta\sigma = \delta M . y/I$

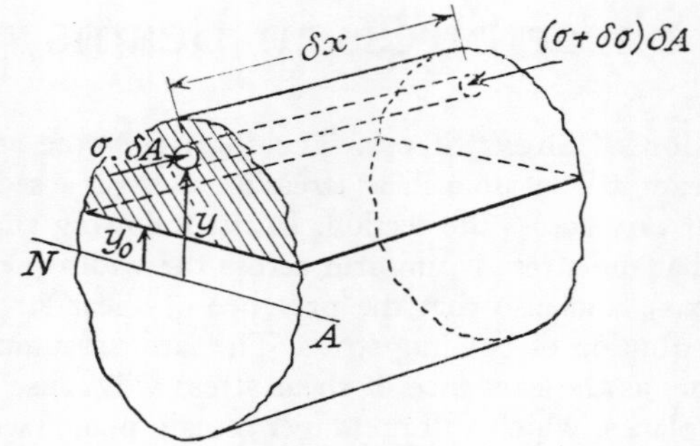

Fig. 7.2

Substituting in (1)

$$\tau . z . \delta x = (\delta M/I)\int y dA$$

or

$$\tau = (\delta M/\delta x) A\bar{y}/zI$$

$$= F \ A\bar{y}/zI \quad (F = dM/dx, \text{ Para. 5.5}) \qquad (2)$$

Note that *z is the actual width of the section at the position where τ is being calculated, and I is the total moment of inertia about the neutral axis.* In many cases it will be convenient to determine $A\bar{y}$ as several parts.

7.2. Rectangular Section. At a distance y from the neutral axis (Fig. 7.3), $A = b(d/2 - y)$, $\bar{y} = \frac{1}{2}(d/2 + y)$, and $z = b$.

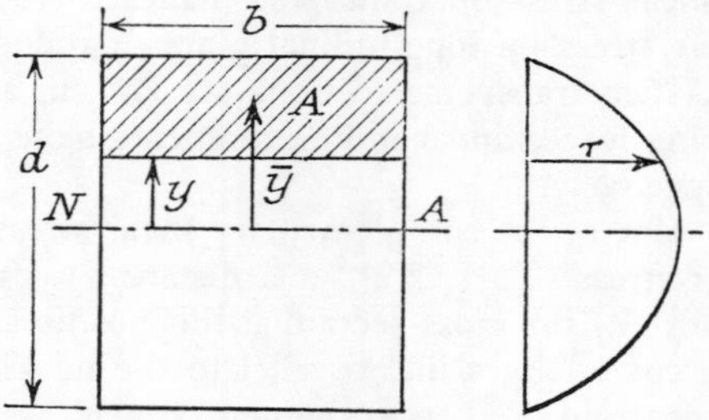

Fig. 7.3

$I = bd^3/12$, hence from (2), Para. 7.1

$$\tau = \frac{F \times b(d/2 - y)(d/2 + y)}{b \times (bd^3/12) \times 2}$$

$$= (6F/bd^3)(d^2/4 - y^2)$$

This shows that there is a parabolic variation of shear stress with y, the maximum shear stress being $\tau = 3F/2bd$, at the neutral axis. If F/bd is called the mean stress, then

$$\tau = 1{\cdot}5 \times \tau_{\text{mean}}$$

EXAMPLE 1. *A timber beam 10 cm wide by 15 cm deep carries a uniformly distributed load over a span of 2 m. If the permissible stresses are 28 N/mm² longitudinally and 2 N/mm² transverse shear, calculate the maximum load which can be carried.*

If W kg is the total load,

$$\hat{M} = Wl/8 = 9{\cdot}81W \times 2/8 \text{ N.m}$$
$$= 2450W \text{ N.mm at the entre,}$$

and $$\hat{F} = 9{\cdot}81W/2 \text{ N at the supports.}$$

Maximum bending stress

$$= 2450W \times 6/100 \times 150^2$$
$$= 28 \text{ N/mm}^2$$

from which

$$W = 4290 \text{ kg}$$

Maximum shear stress

$$= 1{\cdot}5\hat{F}/bd \quad \text{from above}$$

i.e. $$2 = 1{\cdot}5 \times 9{\cdot}81W/(2 \times 100 \times 150)$$

giving $$W = 4080 \text{ kg}$$

The permissible load is therefore 4080 kg total, or 2040 kg/m.

7.3. I-Section. Using the dimensions shown in Fig. 7.4, to find an expression for the *shear stress in the web*, $A\bar{y}$ is made up of two parts, i.e.

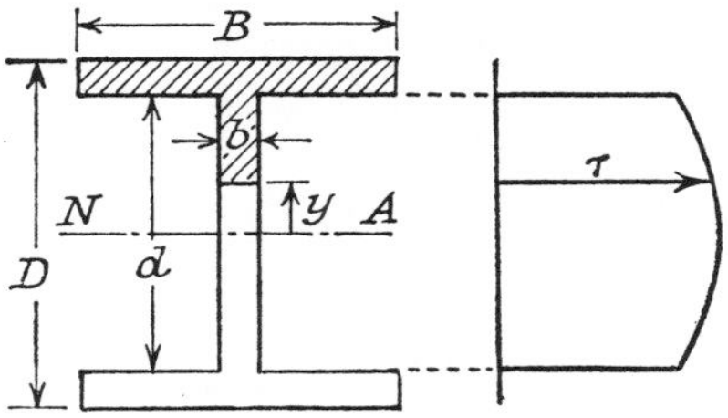

Fig. 7.4

$$A\bar{y} = B\left(\frac{D-d}{2}\right)\left(\frac{D+d}{4}\right) \quad \text{for the flange area}$$

$$+ b(d/2 - y)\frac{d/2 + y}{2} \quad \text{for part of the web.}$$

$z = b$, giving

$$\tau = (F/bI)[B(D^2 - d^2)/8 + (b/2)(d^2/4 - y^2)]$$

As with the rectangular section, the maximum transverse shear stress is at the neutral axis

$$\tau = (F/8bI)[B(D^2 - d^2) + bd^2]$$

At the top of the web

$$\tau = (F/8bI)B(D^2 - d^2)$$

Since the shear stress has to follow the direction of the boundary (Para. 2.2), the distribution must be of the form shown in Fig. 7.5, becoming *horizontal in the flanges*. Consequently the complementary shear stress in the flanges is on longitudinal planes perpendicular to the neutral axis, and the "width z" is replaced by the flange thickness $(D - d)/2$.

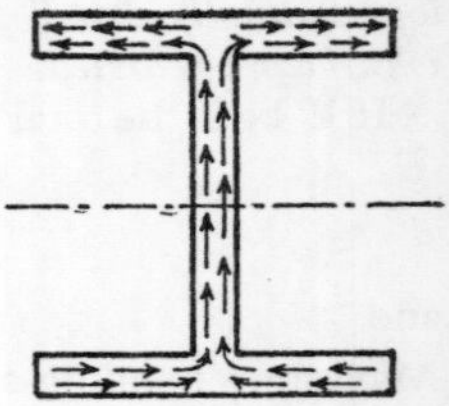

Fig. 7.5

Then

$$\tau = \frac{F.A\bar{y}}{[(D-d)/2]I} \text{ (Fig. 7.6)}$$

showing that the shear stress in the flanges varies from a maximum at the top of the web to zero at the outer tips.

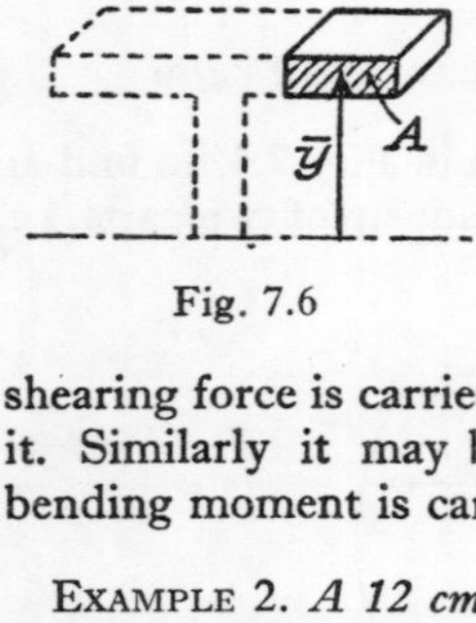

Fig. 7.6

In practice, however, it will be found that most of the shearing force (about 95%) is carried by the web (see Example 2), and the shear stress in the flanges is negligible. As the variation over the web is comparatively small (about 25%), it is convenient for design purposes, and also in calculating deflection due to shear (Para. 9.7), to assume that all the shearing force is carried by the web and is uniformly distributed over it. Similarly it may be assumed as a first approximation that the bending moment is carried wholly by the flanges.

EXAMPLE 2. *A 12 cm by 5 cm I-beam is subjected to a shearing force of 10 kN. Calculate the value of the transverse shear stress at the neutral axis and at the top of the web, and compare with the mean stress on the assumption of uniform distribution over the web. What percentage of shearing force is carried by the web? $I = 220$ cm^4; area $= 9{\cdot}4$ cm^2; web thickness $= 0{\cdot}35$ cm; flange thickness $0{\cdot}55$ cm.*

$$\begin{aligned} A\bar{y} &= (5 \times 0{\cdot}55)5{\cdot}725 + (5{\cdot}45 - y)0{\cdot}35[(5{\cdot}45 + y)/2] \quad \text{(Fig. 7.7)} \\ &= 15{\cdot}75 + (5{\cdot}45^2 - y^2)0{\cdot}35/2 \\ &= 20{\cdot}95 - 0{\cdot}175y^2 \text{ cm}^3 \end{aligned}$$

$$\tau = F.\ A\bar{y}/zI = \frac{10{,}000(20{\cdot}95 - 0{\cdot}175y^2)}{0{\cdot}35 \times 220} \text{ N/cm}^2$$

At the neutral axis

$$\tau = \frac{10{,}000 \times 20{\cdot}95}{0{\cdot}35 \times 220 \times 100}$$
$$= 27{\cdot}2 \text{ N/mm}^2$$

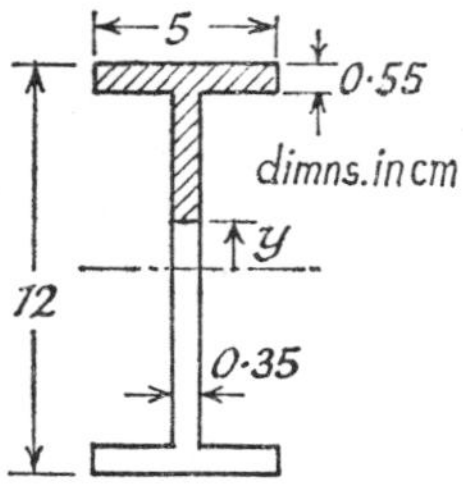

Fig. 7.7

At the top of the web

$$\tau = \frac{100 \times 15{\cdot}75}{0{\cdot}35 \times 220} \quad (y = 5{\cdot}45 \text{ cm})$$
$$= 20{\cdot}1 \text{ N/mm}^2$$

Assuming all the shearing force carried uniformly by the web

$$\tau_{\text{mean}} = \frac{10{,}000}{0{\cdot}35 \times 10{\cdot}9 \times 100}$$
$$= 26{\cdot}2 \text{ N/mm}^2$$

The total shearing force carried by the web is given by

$$\int_{-d/2}^{d/2} \tau . b dy = \int_{-5\cdot45}^{5\cdot45} \frac{0{\cdot}35 \times 10(20{\cdot}95 - 0.175y^2)dy}{0{\cdot}35 \times 220} \quad \text{kN}$$
$$= \frac{1}{22}\left[20{\cdot}95y - \frac{0{\cdot}175y^3}{3}\right]_{-5\cdot45}^{5\cdot45}$$
$$= (228 - 18{\cdot}9)/22$$
$$= 9{\cdot}5 \text{ kN}, \quad \text{i.e. } 95\% \text{ of the total.}$$

The remaining 5% of vertical shearing force is presumably accounted for by the component of shear stress at the junction of the flange and web.

Failure due to shear stress in the web usually takes the form of buckling brought about by the compression stresses on planes at 45° to the transverse section (see Para. 3.4). For this reason deep webs are often supported by vertical stiffeners.

7.4. Principal Stresses in I-Beams. **When an I-section beam is subjected to bending and shear stresses it will usually be found that the maximum principal stress is at the top of the web, the other possible value being the maximum bending stress, which occurs at the outer edge of the flange.**

EXAMPLE 3. *A short vertical column is firmly fixed at the base and projects a distance of 30 cm from the base. The column is of* I-*section 20 cm by 10 cm, flanges 1 cm thick, web 0·7 cm thick.* $I = 2150$ *cm*^{4} *and area* $= 33$ *cm*^{2}.

An inclined load of 80 kN acts on the top of the column in the centre of the section and in the plane containing the centre line of the web. The line of action is at 30° to the vertical. Determine the position and magnitude of the greatest principal stress on the base of the column.

The inclined load will intersect the base cross-section at a distance of 30 tan 30° = 17·3 cm from the centroid.

Resolving the load into vertical and horizontal components, there is a direct load = 80 cos 30° = 69·2 kN, a shearing force = 80 sin 30° = 40 kN, and a bending moment = 69·2 × 0·173 = 12 kNm.

At the top of the web

$$\tau = F\cdot A\bar{y}/zI = \frac{40{,}000\times(10\times1)\times9{\cdot}5}{0{\cdot}7\times2150\times100}$$

$$= 25{\cdot}3\ \text{N/mm}^2$$

$$\text{Bending stress} = 12{,}000\times9/2150 = 50{\cdot}2\ \text{N/mm}^2$$

$$\text{Direct stress} = 692/33 = 21\ \text{N/mm}^2$$

$$\text{Total normal stress } \sigma = 71{\cdot}2\ \text{N/mm}^2$$

$$\text{Maximum principal stress} = \sigma/2 + \tfrac{1}{2}\sqrt{(\sigma^2+4\tau^2)} \quad \text{(Para. 3.8)}$$

$$= 35{\cdot}6 + \tfrac{1}{2}\sqrt{(5070+2570)}$$

$$= 79{\cdot}3\ \text{N/mm}^2 \text{ compression,}$$

at the top of the web

Check also the value of the maximum bending stress, which is

$$12{,}000\times10/2150 = 55{\cdot}8\ \text{N/mm}^2$$

which together with the direct stress gives a maximum stress of 76·8 N/mm² at the outside of the flange, less than the value at the top of the web.

7·5. Pitch of Rivets in Built-up Girders. The load to be carried by one rivet in a beam section built up as in Fig. 7.8(a), is determined

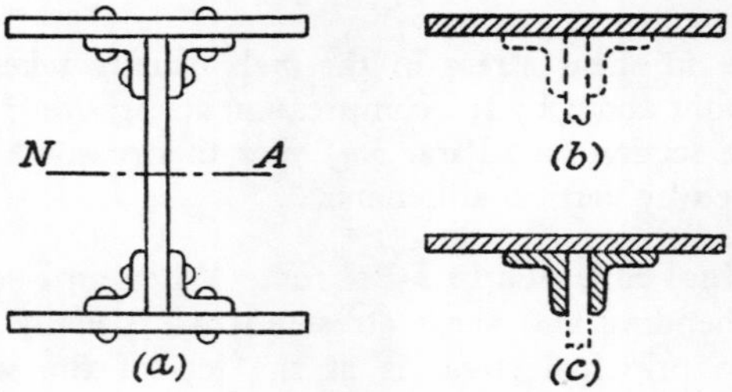

Fig. 7.8

by the difference of normal stresses on certain areas of two transverse sections at a distance apart equal to the pitch of the rivets.

The area to be used is that part of the cross-section which "comes away" when the particular set of rivets is removed. Hence in the case of the rivets holding the flange to the angle sections the area is as shaded in (b), and for the rivets holding the angles to the web the area is shown in (c).

If p is the pitch of the rivets and R the force on the rivets over a length p of beam, then proceeding as in Para. 7.1

$$\begin{aligned} R &= \Sigma\delta\sigma\cdot\delta A \\ &= \Sigma(\delta M.y/I)\delta A \\ &= (\delta M/I)\Sigma y\delta A \\ &= FpA\bar{y}/I \quad \text{approx.} \end{aligned}$$

(compare $F = dM/dx$, and let $dx = p$).

Note that for the flanges there are two rivets to a pitch length, usually staggered so as not to occur together in one cross-section. Also, the web rivets are in double shear.

EXAMPLE 4. *An **I**-section beam is built up of a web plate 240 mm by 12 mm with flange plates 144 mm by 24 mm secured by rivets through angle sections 48 mm by 48 mm by 6 mm, as in Fig. 7·8.*

If the bending stress is limited to 100 N/mm² estimate the maximum uniformly distributed load which can be carried over a span of 12 m.

Assuming 12 mm diameter rivets, calculate their pitch if the allowable shearing stress is 75 N/mm² and bearing pressure 150 N/mm².

$$M = wl^2/8 = \frac{w \times 12^2}{8} \text{ for } w \text{ N/m}$$

$$= 18w \text{ Nm}$$

$I = 12 \times 216^3/12$ for the web, allowing for two rivet holes

$+4[36 \times (6)^3/12 + (36 \times 6)117^2 + 6 \times 30^3/12 + (6 \times 30)93^2]$ for the angles

$+2[132 \times 24^3/12 + (132 \times 24)132^2]$ for the flanges, allowing for one rivet

$= (10{\cdot}1 + 0{\cdot}003 + 11{\cdot}8 + 0{\cdot}053 + 6{\cdot}23 + 0{\cdot}3 + 110) \times 10^6$

$= 138 \times 10^6 \text{ mm}^4$

$$\hat{\sigma} = 100 = \frac{\hat{M}\hat{y}}{I} = \frac{18 \times 10^3 w \times 144}{138 \times 10^6}$$

$$\therefore \quad w = 5340 \text{ N/m}$$

Permissible load per pitch length:

For one rivet in double shear in the web, or two rivets in single shear in the flange

$$= 2 \times (\pi/4) \times (12)^2 \times 75 = 17{,}000 \text{ N} \qquad \text{(i)}$$

Crushing of the rivets (one in web, or two in flange)

$$\begin{aligned} &= (dt) \times 150 \\ &= (12 \times 12) \times 150 = 21{,}600 \text{ N} \qquad \text{(ii)} \end{aligned}$$

For the flange rivets: $A\bar{y} = 132 \times 24 \times 132$ (Fig. 7·8(b))

$= 41{\cdot}7 \times 10^4 \text{ mm}^3$

Load per pitch length = 17,000, smaller of (i) and (ii)

$$\begin{aligned} &= FpA\bar{y}/I \\ &= (5340 \times 12/2)\ p\ 41{\cdot}7 \times 10^4/138 \times 10^6 \end{aligned}$$

$$\therefore \quad p = 176 \text{ mm}$$

For the web rivets:

$$A\bar{y} = 41{\cdot}7 \times 10^4 + 2 \times (36 \times 6)117 + 2 \times (30 \times 6)93 \quad \text{(Fig. 7.8 (c))}$$

$$= 50 \times 10^4 \text{ mm}^3$$

$$\therefore \quad p = RI/FA\bar{y} = \frac{17{,}000 \times 138 \times 10^6}{32{,}000 \times 50 \times 10^4}$$

$$= 147 \text{ mm}$$

7.6. Solid Circular Section. Let τ be the average shear stress across a chord parallel to XX, defined by the angle θ (Fig. 7.9).

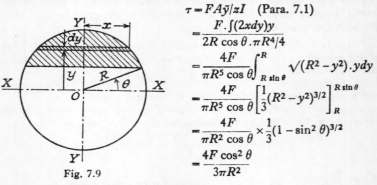

$$\tau = FA\bar{y}/zI \quad \text{(Para. 7.1)}$$

$$= \frac{F.\int(2xdy)y}{2R\cos\theta.\pi R^4/4}$$

$$= \frac{4F}{\pi R^5 \cos\theta}\int_{R\sin\theta}^{R} \sqrt{(R^2 - y^2)}.ydy$$

$$= \frac{4F}{\pi R^5\cos\theta}\left[\frac{1}{3}(R^2 - y^2)^{3/2}\right]_R^{R\sin\theta}$$

$$= \frac{4F}{\pi R^2\cos\theta} \times \frac{1}{3}(1 - \sin^2\theta)^{3/2}$$

$$= \frac{4F\cos^2\theta}{3\pi R^2}$$

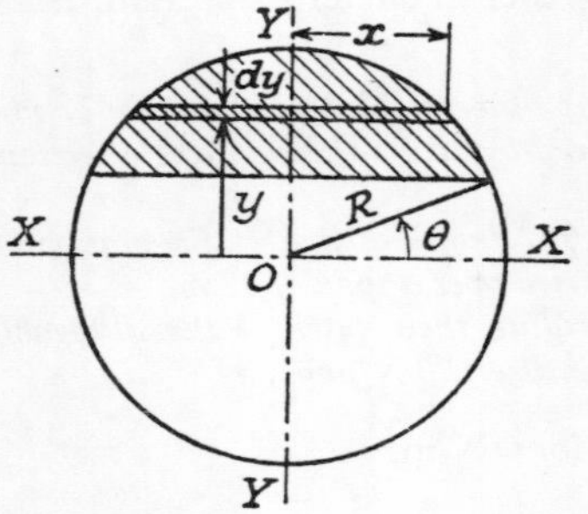

Fig. 7.9

$\hat{\tau} = 4F/3\pi R^2$ at the neutral axis

$= (4/3) \times$ mean shear stress

The directional distribution of shear stress must be as indicated in Fig. 7.10, though this does not affect the magnitude of the greatest shear stress, which is usually the value required.

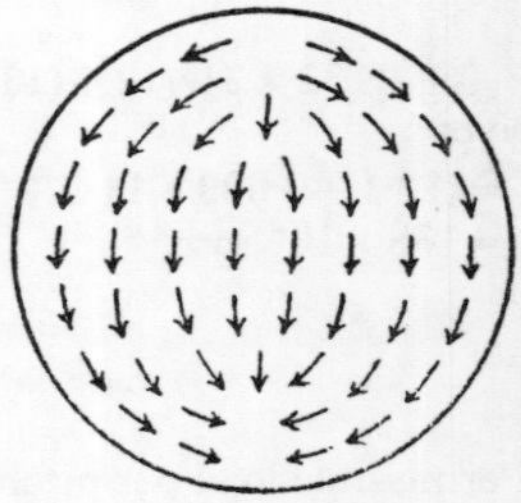

Fig. 7.10

This particular case is applicable to rivets in shear, but the ratio 4/3 may be assumed to be incorporated in the allowable stress value, which is then taken as uniform over the section.

7.7. Thin Circular Tube. It is necessary here to make use of the fact that the shear stress has to follow the direction of the boundary, that is tangential, if the thickness is small compared with the radius (Fig. 7.11).

If the bending is about XX let P and Q be two symmetrically placed positions defined by the angle θ, the shear stress being τ.

The complementary shear stress is again on longitudinal planes, and is balanced by the difference of normal stresses on the shaded area subtending the angle 2θ.

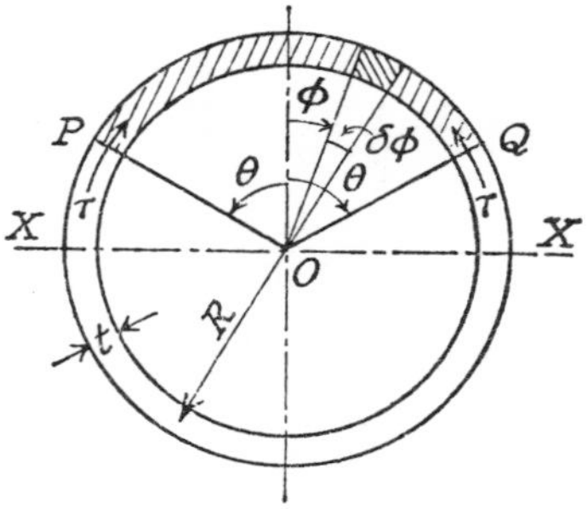

Fig. 7.11

For a length of beam δx

$$2\tau . t\delta x = \int_{-\theta}^{\theta} \delta\sigma . tR d\phi$$

$$\tau = \tfrac{1}{2}\int(\delta\sigma/\delta x) . R d\phi$$

But
$$\delta\sigma/\delta x = (\delta M/\delta x) . y/I_x$$
$$= \frac{F . R \cos\phi}{\frac{1}{2}(2\pi R t)R^2}$$

where $I_x = \frac{1}{2}$ Polar M.I. $= \frac{1}{2}$ (Area) × (Mean Radius)^2 (Para. 6.2)

$$\therefore \quad \tau = \frac{FR^2}{2\pi R^3 t}\int_{-\theta}^{\theta} \cos\phi . d\phi$$
$$= (F/2\pi R t) . 2 \sin\theta$$
$$= F \sin\theta/\pi R t$$
$$\hat{\tau} = F/\pi R t \text{ at the neutral axis}$$
$$= 2 \times \text{mean shear stress}$$

7.8. Miscellaneous Sections. The shear stress at any point in a cross-section can always be calculated from the basic formula $\tau = FA\bar{y}/zI$ of Para. 7.1, and the following example will illustrate the method of attack.

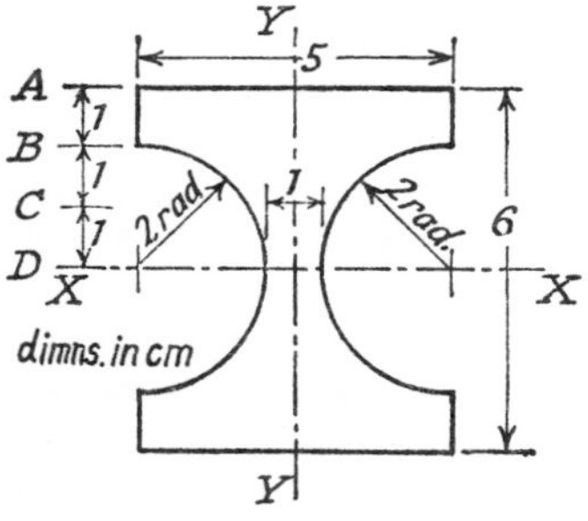

Fig. 7.12

EXAMPLE 5. *For the section shown in Fig. 7.12 determine the average shearing stress at A, B, C, and D for a shearing force of 20 kN, and find the ratio of maximum to mean stress. Draw to scale a diagram to show the variation of shearing stress across the section.* (*U.L.*)

$$I = 5 \times 6^3/12 - \pi \times 4^4/64$$
$$= 77{\cdot}4 \text{ cm}^4$$

At A: $A\bar{y} = 0$

$\therefore \quad \tau = 0$

At B: $A\bar{y} = (5 \times 1) \times 2{\cdot}5 = 12{\cdot}5 \text{ cm}^3$

$z = 5 \text{ cm}$

$$\therefore \quad \tau = \frac{20{,}000 \times 12{\cdot}5}{5 \times 77{\cdot}4 \times 100} = 6{\cdot}47 \text{ N/mm}^2$$

At C: $A\bar{y} = (5 \times 2)2 - \int_1^2 2x \,.\, dy \,.\, y$

$$= 20 - \int_1^2 \sqrt{(4 - y^2)} \,.\, 2y dy$$

$$= 20 + \tfrac{2}{3}[(4 - y^2)^{3/2}]_1^2$$

$$= 20 - 3{\cdot}47$$

$$= 16{\cdot}53 \text{ cm}^3$$

$$\therefore \quad \tau = \frac{20{,}000 \times 16{\cdot}53}{[5 - 2\sqrt{(4-1)}]77{\cdot}4 \times 100}$$

$$= 27{\cdot}7 \text{ N/mm}^2$$

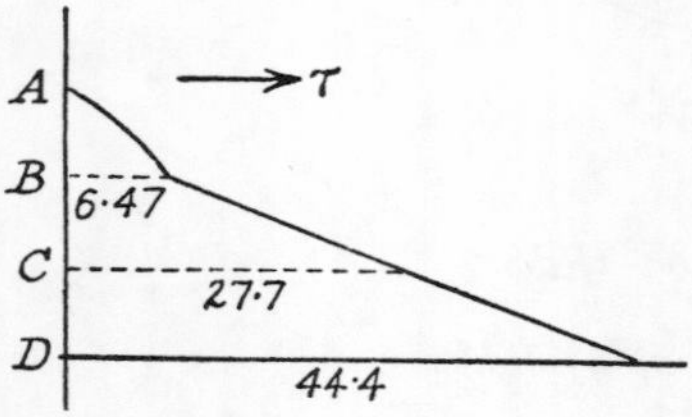

Fig. 7.13

At D: $A\bar{y} = (5 \times 3)1{\cdot}5 - \int_0^2 \sqrt{(4 - y^2)} \,.\, 2y dy$

$$= 22{\cdot}5 - \tfrac{2}{3} \times 4^{3/2}$$

$$= 17{\cdot}17 \text{ cm}^3$$

$$\therefore \quad \tau = \frac{20{,}000 \times 17{\cdot}17}{1 \times 77{\cdot}4 \times 100}$$

$$= 44{\cdot}4 \text{ N/mm}^2$$

The variation of shearing stress is shown in Fig. 7.13.

7·9. Shear Centre. For unsymmetrical sections, in particular angle and channel sections, summation of the shear stresses in each "leg" gives a set of forces which must be in equilibrium with the applied shearing force.

Consider the angle section, bending about a principal axis, with shearing force F at right angles to this axis. The sum of the shear stresses produces a force in the direction of each leg as shown in Fig. 7.14(a). It is clear that their resultant passes through the corner of the angle, and unless F is applied through this point there will be a twisting of the angle as well as bending. Consequently this point is known as the *shear centre* or *centre of twist*.

For a channel section with the loading parallel to the web (Fig. 7.14(b)), the total shearing force carried by the web must equal F, and that in the flanges produces two equal and opposite horizontal forces. It can be seen that for equilibrium the applied loads causing F must lie in a plane outside the channel, as indicated, its position being calculated as in the following example.

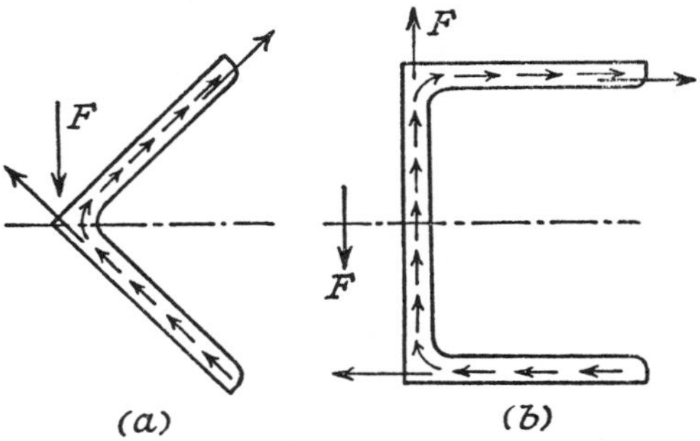

Fig. 7.14

EXAMPLE 6. *Explain why a single channel section with its web vertical subjected to vertical loading as a beam, will be in torsion unless the load is applied through a point outside the section known as the shear centre.*

Find its approximate position for a channel section 6 cm by 6 cm outside by 0·5 cm thick.

If F is the shearing force at the section, then the total vertical force in the web can be taken equal to F. It should be mentioned that, integrating for the height of the web only will give a value slightly less than F (compare Example 2, Para. 7.3), but the remaining vertical force is assumed to be carried by the "corners" of the section.

$$I_x = 0{\cdot}5 \times 6^3/12 + 2[5{\cdot}5(0{\cdot}5)^3/12 + 5{\cdot}5 \times 0{\cdot}5 \times 2{\cdot}75^2]$$
$$= 9 + 2(0{\cdot}055 + 20{\cdot}85)$$
$$= 50{\cdot}7 \text{ cm}^4$$

Proceeding as Para 7·3 (flanges), the shear stress in the flanges at a distance z from the tip is

$$\tau = F.A\bar{y}/tI \quad (t = 0{\cdot}5 \text{ cm})$$
$$= F(zt)2{\cdot}75/tI \quad \text{(Fig. 7.15)}$$
$$= 0{\cdot}0543Fz$$

Total force in each flange

$$R = \int \tau t dz$$
$$= \frac{0{\cdot}0543}{2} F \left[\frac{z^2}{2}\right]_0^{5{\cdot}75}$$
$$= 0{\cdot}448F$$

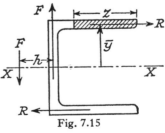

Fig. 7.15

If h is the distance of the shear centre (through which the applied shearing force must act for no twisting of the section) from the centre line of the web, then for equilibrium

$$Fh = R \times 5{\cdot}5$$

or

$$h = 2{\cdot}47 \text{ cm}$$

SUMMARY

Transverse Shear Stress $\tau = FA\bar{y}/zI$.

Rectangular Section $\hat{\tau} = 1{\cdot}5 \times \tau_{mean}$.

Circular Section $\hat{\tau} = 4/3 \times \tau_{mean}$.

Thin Tube $\hat{\tau} = 2 \times \tau_{mean}$.

I-Section: web carries 95% of shear. Maximum principal stress at top of web.

Loading plane through shear centre for no twist.

REFERENCE

TERRINGTON, J. S., *The Torsion Centre of Girders*. Engineering, Nov. 26, 1954.

PROBLEMS

1. A rectangular beam of depth d, width b, and length l, is simply supported at its ends and carries a central load W. Show that the principal stresses at a point in the central cross-section at a distance $d/4$ from the top are

$$\frac{3Wl}{8bd^2}\left[1 \pm \sqrt{\left(1 + \frac{9d^2}{4l^2}\right)}\right]$$

2. Show that the difference between the maximum and mean shearing stress in the web of an I-beam is $Fd^2/24I$, where d is the height of the web.

3. A water main of mean radius r and thickness t is subjected at a particular cross-section to a bending moment M and a shearing force F. Show that, at a point in the section where the radius is inclined at an angle θ to the neutral axis, the principal stresses are $(1/2\pi r^2 t)[M \sin\theta \pm \sqrt{(M^2 \sin^2\theta + 4F^2 r^2 \cos^2\theta)}]$.

4. A 30 cm by 12·5 cm R.S.J. of I-section, flanges 12·5 mm thick, web 8·25 mm thick, is subjected to a bending moment of 30 kNm and a shear force of 100 kN at a particular cross-section. Calculate the values of the maximum principal stress at (a) neutral axis, (b) top of web, (c) outer edge of flange.

(46·5 N/mm^2; 69 N/mm^2; 56 N/mm^2.)

5. A simply supported beam of span 3 m carries a point load of 10,000 kg at a distance of 1 m from one support. The beam is of hollow square section with outer dimensions of 150 mm and wall thickness 37·5 mm. Determine the greatest bending stress and transverse shear stress in the beam at 37·5 mm from the neutral axis, and from these values find the maximum principal stress and maximum shear stress at this point. (65; 7 N/mm^2; 66; 33 N/mm^2.)

6. A beam is of **T**-section, flange 12 cm by 1 cm, web 10 cm by 1 cm. What percentage of the shearing force at any section is carried by the web?

(93·5%.)

7. Two beams, particulars of which are given below, are simply supported at the ends over equal spans and carry central loads to give the same maximum bending stress. Determine the ratio of maximum shear stress in the webs.

Section	Web th.	Flange th.	Flange width	Total depth	Distance of N.A. from outer edge of flange
I	5	8·75	62·5	125	62·5 mm
T	12·5	12·5	125	100	26·2 mm

(3·38.)

8. Two steel flats of cross-section 10 cm by 3·75 cm are joined together by a single row of 20 mm diameter rivets so as to form a beam of breadth 10 cm and depth 7·5 cm. The beam is supported at the ends and has a load of 2000 kg at the centre. Find the pitch of the rivets if each is subjected to a shearing stress of 70 N/mm². (11 cm.)

9. A girder of effective span 8 m has to carry a uniformly distributed load, including its own weight, of 27,000 kg. A 45 cm by 15 cm R.S.J. with one 10 mm plate riveted to each flange is to be used. Find the width of the plates and the pitch of the rivets. Allowable bending stress 120 N/mm². Safe load per rivet 30 kN. Rivet diameter 22 mm; $I = 3{\cdot}5 \times 10^8$ mm⁴ for the R.S.J.; effective thickness of flanges 18 mm. (214 mm; 680 mm, double row.)

10. A hollow steel cylinder 20 cm external diameter, 10 cm internal diameter acting as a beam is subjected to a shearing force F perpendicular to the axis. Determine the mean stress, and the average shearing stress at the neutral axis and at 25 mm, 50 mm, and 75 mm from the neutral axis as fractions of the mean value. Draw a diagram to show the variation of average shearing stress across the section. ($F/75\pi$; 1·87; 1·65; 0·80; 0·465.)

11. A rectangular wooden beam 5 cm wide and 15 cm deep is reinforced by screwing a steel plate 6 mm thick and 5 cm wide on to the bottom. The screws are 6 mm diameter and are pitched 7·5 cm apart. They are a close fit in the plate. The beam is simply supported at the ends over a span of 3 m and is loaded at the centre by a load of 100 kg.

Calculate the maximum stresses in the steel plate and timber, and the maximum shearing stress in the screws. Neglect the weight of the beam itself and any weakening of the plate due to the screw holes. $E_s = 210{,}000$ N/mm². $E_t = 14{,}000$ N/mm².

(18·4 N/mm² tension, 2·5 N/mm² compression. 9·2 N/mm² shear. See Para. 6.9 for equivalent section.)

12. A beam of channel section carries a vertical load and is supported so that the two flanges are horizontal. The flanges and web have equal thicknesses which are small compared to the depth of the web (D) and the width of the flanges (B). Show that the shear centre is at a distance $3B^2/(6B + D)$ from the web. (U.L.)

13. A channel section has a web 192 mm deep and 6 mm thick and flanges 84 mm wide and 12 mm thick. Used as a horizontal cantilever with the web in a vertical plane, it carries an end load W. Determine the position of W relative to the web in order that the cantilever shall not be subjected to torsion.

(31 mm from back of web.)

CHAPTER VIII

Torsion

8.1. Circular Shafts. If a shaft is acted upon by a pure torque T about its polar axis, shear stresses will be set up in directions perpendicular to the radius on all transverse sections (Fig. 8.1).

The complementary shear stress on longitudinal planes will cause a distortion of filaments which were originally in the longitudinal direction. It will be assumed that points lying on a radius before twisting will remain on a radius, the angle of twist being θ over a length l of shaft. This assumption is justified by the symmetry of the cross-section.

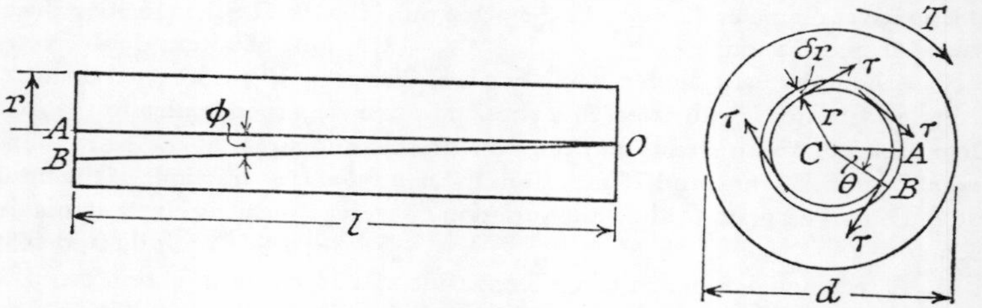

Fig. 8.1

The left-hand figure shows the shear strain ϕ of elements at a distance r from the axis (ϕ is constant for constant T), so that a line originally OA twists to OB, and $\angle ACB = \theta$, the relative angle of twist of cross-sections a distance l apart.

$$\text{Arc AB} = r\theta = l\phi \text{ approx.}$$

But $\phi = \tau/G$, where G is the modulus of rigidity (Para. 2.4).

By substitution and rearranging

$$\tau/r = G\theta/l \tag{1}$$

The torque can be equated to the sum of the moments of the tangential stresses on the elements $2\pi r\delta r$, i.e.

$$\begin{aligned} T &= \int \tau(2\pi r dr)r \\ &= (G\theta/l)\int(2\pi r dr)r^2 \quad \text{from (1)} \\ &= (G\theta/l)J \qquad (2) \end{aligned}$$

where J is called the polar moment of inertia.

Combining (1) and (2)

$$T/J = \tau/r = G\theta/l \tag{3}$$

Showing that, for a given torque, the **shear stress is proportional to the radius.**

For a solid shaft:

$$J = \pi D^4/32$$

and the maximum stress

$$\hat{\tau} = 16T/\pi D^3, \quad \text{at } r = D/2$$

For a hollow shaft:

$$J = (\pi/32)(D^4 - d^4)$$

and

$$\hat{\tau} = \frac{16D.T}{\pi(D^4 - d^4)}, \quad \text{at } r = D/2$$

Torsional stiffness k is defined as torque per radian twist, i.e.

$$k = T/\theta = GJ/l$$

EXAMPLE 1. *The working conditions to be satisfied by a shaft transmitting power are (a) that the shaft must not twist more than 1 degree on a length of 15 diameters, and (b) the shear stress must not exceed 55 N/mm².*

If $G = 80{,}000$ N/mm² what is the actual working stress, and the diameter of shaft to transmit 1 MW at 240 r.p.m.?

Calculate the torque which can be transmitted for a given diameter according to the two conditions.

(a)

$$T = (G\theta/l)J \text{ from (2)}$$
$$= \frac{80{,}000 \times \pi \times \pi D^4}{15D \times 180 \times 32}$$
$$= 9{\cdot}16D^3 \text{ N. mm}$$

(b)

$$T = (2\hat{\tau}/D) \times J \text{ from (3), putting } r = D/2$$
$$= \frac{2 \times 55 \times \pi D^4}{D \times 32}$$
$$= 10{\cdot}8D^3 \text{ N. mm}$$

Taking the smaller value, (a), it follows that the working stress is less than permitted by condition (b), in fact

$$\tau = (9{\cdot}16/10{\cdot}8) \times 55 = 46{\cdot}5 \text{ N/mm}^2$$

since stress is proportional to torque.

$$\text{Power} = 10^6 = \frac{T.2\pi n}{1000} \text{ (Nm)/s}$$
$$= \frac{9{\cdot}16D^3 \times 2\pi \times 240}{1000 \times 60}$$

giving

$$D = \sqrt[3]{(4{\cdot}35 \times 10^6)} = 163 \text{ mm}$$

EXAMPLE 2. *Compare the weights of equal lengths of hollow and solid shaft to transmit a given torque for the same maximum shear stress if the inside diameter is $\frac{2}{3}$ of the outside.*

$T/\hat{\tau} = 2J/D$ from (3)

$= \pi D^3/16$ for the solid shaft of diameter D,

and $= \pi(D_1^4 - d^4)/16D_1$ or $(\pi D_1^3/16)[1 - (\frac{2}{3})^4]$

i.e. $(65 \times \pi D_1^3)/(81 \times 16)$ for the hollow shaft of outside diameter D_1

Equating these two gives

$$D_1 = D.\sqrt[3]{(81/65)}$$
$$= 1{\cdot}075D$$

Ratio of weights of equal lengths

$$= (D_1^2 - d^2)/D^2$$
$$= (D_1/D)^2[1 - 4/9]$$
$$= (5/9) \times 1{\cdot}075^2$$
$$= 0{\cdot}642$$

8.2. Strain Energy in Torsion. Total strain energy of a shaft of length l under the action of a torque T is the work done in twisting, i.e.

$$U = \tfrac{1}{2}T\theta$$

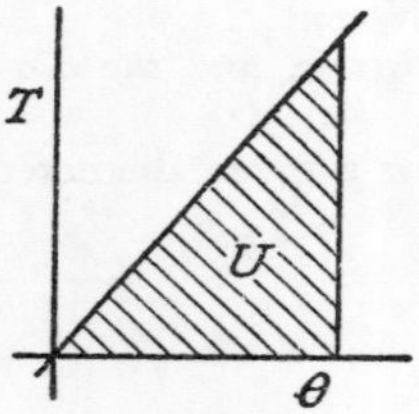

Fig. 8.2

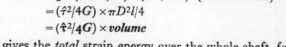

for a gradually applied torque (Fig. 8.2).

This form is most useful if T and θ have been previously found.

Expressed in terms of the maximum stress $\hat{\tau}$, for a solid shaft

$$U = \tfrac{1}{2} \times (\pi D^3\hat{\tau}/16) \times (2\hat{\tau}l/GD) \quad \text{(see Para. 8.1)}$$
$$= (\hat{\tau}^2/4G) \times \pi D^2 l/4$$
$$= (\hat{\tau}^2/4G) \times \textbf{volume}$$

Note that this gives the *total* strain energy over the whole shaft, for which the shear stress is varying from zero at the axis to $\hat{\tau}$ at the outside. The maximum strain energy per unit volume is $\hat{\tau}^2/2G$ (Para. 2.5).

For a hollow shaft:

$$U = \tfrac{1}{2}T\theta$$
$$= \tfrac{1}{2} \times [\pi(D^4 - d^4)\hat{\tau}/16D] \times (2\hat{\tau}l/GD)$$
$$= (\hat{\tau}^2/4G) \times [(D^2 + d^2)/D^2] \times \text{volume}$$

EXAMPLE 3. *A hollow shaft, subjected to a pure torque, attains a maximum shear stress of τ. Given that the strain energy per unit volume is $\tau^2/3G$, calculate the ratio of shaft diameters.*

Determine the actual diameters of such a shaft to transmit 4 MW at 110 r.p.m. when the energy stored is 20,000 Nm/m³ G = 80,000 N/mm².

Referring to the derivation just proved

$$\frac{U}{\text{volume}} = (\tau^2/4G) \times (D^2 + d^2)/D^2$$
$$= \tau^2/3G, \text{ given}$$
$$\therefore \quad (D^2 + d^2)/D^2 = 4/3$$

i.e. $$d/D=\sqrt{\tfrac{1}{3}}$$

or $$D/d=1{\cdot}732$$

If $$\tau^2/3G=20\times10^{-3}\ \text{Nmm/mm}^3$$

then $$\tau=\sqrt{(3\times80\times20)}=69{\cdot}3\ \text{N/mm}^2$$

$$T=\frac{4\times10^6\times60}{2\pi\times110}\ \text{from the power}$$

$$=348{,}000\ \text{Nm}$$

$$\tau=(T/J)\times D/2$$

$$=(16D.\ T)/\pi(D^4-d^4)\quad \text{(Para. 8.1)}$$

Substituting values:

$$69{\cdot}3=\frac{16D\times348{,}000\times10^3}{\pi\,D^4(1-\frac{1}{9})}$$

$$\therefore\quad D=\sqrt[3]{\frac{16\times348\times10^6\times9}{\pi\times69{\cdot}3\times8}}$$

$$=306\ \text{mm}$$

and $$d=\frac{306}{\sqrt{3}}=177\ \text{mm}$$

EXAMPLE 4. *A tube of mean diameter 5 cm and thickness 2 mm is made of mild steel with an elastic limit of 250 N/mm² under simple tension. Calculate the torque which may be transmitted by the tube with a factor of safety of 2·5 if the criterion of failure is (a) maximum shear stress, (b) maximum strain energy, (c) maximum shear strain energy. Poisson's ratio = 0·3.*

Treating the tube as "thin," it may be assumed that the cross-section is $50\pi\times2\ \text{mm}^2$ and is situated at 25 mm from the axis, giving a polar moment of inertia

$$J=100\pi\times25^2=196{,}000\ \text{mm}^4$$

Maximum shear stress

$$\hat{\tau}=(1000T/196{,}000)\times26\quad (T\ \text{in N.m.})$$

$$=0{\cdot}133T$$

Applying the factor of safety to the stress, the limiting simple tensile stress $=250/2{\cdot}5=100\ \text{N/mm}^2$

(a) Maximum shear stress in simple tension

$$=100/2=50\ \text{N/mm}^2\ \text{(Para. 3.2)}$$

$$=0{\cdot}133T,\ \text{from above}$$

$$\therefore\quad T=377\ \text{N.m}$$

(b) Maximum strain energy/unit volume

$$=\hat{\tau}^2/2G\ \text{in torsion (Para. 2.5)}$$

$$=\hat{\sigma}^2/2E\ \text{in tension (Para. 1.9)}$$

Substituting and equating

$$(0{\cdot}133T)^2/2G = 100^2/2E$$

$$T^2 = 100^2/2[0{\cdot}133^2 \times (1 + 0{\cdot}3)] \quad \text{(see Para. 4.2)}$$

$$\therefore\ T = 100/(0{\cdot}133 \times \sqrt{2{\cdot}6})$$

$$= 466 \text{ N.m}$$

(c) Shear strain energy $= (1/12G)[(\sigma_1 - \sigma_2)^2 + \sigma_2^2 + \sigma_1^2]$ for a two dimensional stress system (Para. 3.20).

In pure torsion $\sigma_1 = +\tau$, $\sigma_2 = -\tau$ (Para. 3.4), and in simple tension $\sigma_1 = \sigma$, $\sigma_2 = 0$.

Substituting and equating

$$(\tau + \tau)^2 + \tau^2 + \tau^2 = 2\sigma^2$$

i.e.

$$6(0{\cdot}133T)^2 = 2 \times 100^2$$

giving

$$T = 434 \text{ N.m}$$

8.3. Shafts of Varying Diameter.

EXAMPLE 5. *A shaft tapers uniformly from a radius $r + a$ at one end to $r - a$ at the other. If it is under the action of an axial torque T, and $a = 0{\cdot}1r$, find the percentage error in the angle of twist for a given length when calculated on the assumption of a constant radius r.* (*U.L.*)

If l is the length of shaft the radius at a distance x from the small end is $r - a + 2ax/l$, and the angle of twist of a length δx

$$= \frac{T.\delta x}{GJ} = \frac{T \times 2\delta x}{G.\pi(r - a + 2ax/l)^4}$$

Total

$$\theta = \frac{2T}{G\pi}\int_0^l \frac{dx}{(r - a + 2ax/l)^4}$$

$$= \frac{2T}{3G\pi}\cdot\frac{l}{2a}\left[\frac{1}{(r-a)^3} - \frac{1}{(r+a)^3}\right]$$

$$= \frac{Tl \times 10}{3G\pi r^4}\left(\frac{1000}{729} - \frac{1000}{1331}\right) \quad \text{when } a = r/10$$

$$= 2{\cdot}065\,Tl/G\pi r^4$$

For a shaft of uniform radius r

$$\theta = Tl/GJ$$

$$= 2Tl/G\pi r^4$$

$$\textbf{Percentage error} = [(2{\cdot}065 - 2)/2] \times 100$$

$$= 3{\cdot}25\%$$

EXAMPLE 6. *A steel shaft ABCD has a total length of 51 cm made up as follows: AB = 12 cm, BC = 15 cm, CD = 24 cm. AB is hollow, outside diameter 4 cm, inside d cm. BC and CD are solid, having diameters 4 cm and 3·5 cm respectively. If equal opposite torques are applied to the ends of the shaft, find to the nearest 0·05 cm the maximum permissible value of d for the maximum shearing stress in AB not to exceed that in CD.*

If the torque applied is 500 Nm what is the total angle of twist? G = 80,000 N/mm².

$$\tau = (T/J)D/2$$

For AB: $\tau = [32T/\pi(4^4 - d^4)] \times 4/2$

$$= 64T/\pi(256 - d^4)$$

For CD: $\tau(32T/\pi \times 3{\cdot}5^4) \times 3{\cdot}5/2$

$$= 16T/(\pi \times 42{\cdot}9)$$

Equating and multiplying out

$$256 - d^4 = 4 \times 42{\cdot}9 = 171{\cdot}6$$

giving $d = \sqrt[4]{84{\cdot}4} = 3{\cdot}05$ cm

$$\theta = \Sigma . Tl/GJ$$

$$= \frac{500}{80{,}000}\left[\frac{32 \times 12}{\pi(256 - 84{\cdot}4)} + \frac{32 \times 15}{\pi \times 256} + \frac{32 \times 24}{\pi \times 150}\right] \text{ radians}$$

$$= \frac{500 \times 32 \times 180}{80{,}000 \times \pi^2}(0{\cdot}07 + 0{\cdot}0586 + 0{\cdot}16) \text{ degrees}$$

$$= 1{\cdot}15°$$

8.4. Stress Concentrations in Torsion. Some results obtained by theoretical analysis, due to Willers and others, for the stress concentration factor at semi-circular fillets (Fig. 8.3 (a)) are tabulated below.

r/d	0·1	0·2	0·3	0·4
k	1·27	1·20	1·17	1·16

The effect of keyways in circular shafts depends on the radius *r* at the bottom of the keyway (Fig. 8.3 (b)). If *r*>0·4 *h* stress calculations

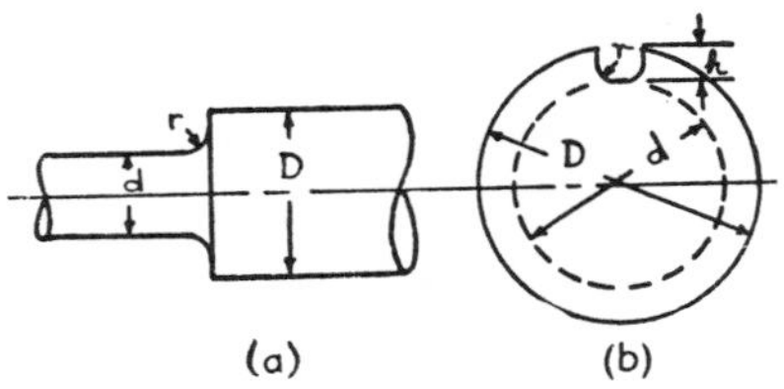

Fig. 8.3

based on the minimum metal (diameter *d*) will be on the "safe" side. For smaller values of *r* stress concentration should be allowed for, e.g.

at $r=0{\cdot}1\ h$ the strength is reduced to about 50% of that of a shaft of diameter d.

The same arguments as in Para. 1.15 apply to the redistribution of stress in ductile materials under steady loading.

8.5. Shafts under the Action of Varying Torque.

EXAMPLE 7. *A horizontal shaft, securely fixed at each end, has a free length of 9 m. Viewed from one end of the shaft axial couples of 30 kNm clockwise and 37·5kNm counter-clockwise act on the shaft, at distances of 3·6 m and 6 m from the viewed end. Determine the end fixing couples in magnitude and direction and find the diameter of solid shaft for a maximum shearing stress of 60 N/mm².*

Draw a diagram to show how a line, originally parallel to the axis and on the outer surface of the shaft, will appear, and find the position where the shaft suffers no angular twist.

If T is the fixing torque at the viewed end, the torque will be $T-30$ in the middle portion and $T-30+37{\cdot}5$ at the far end (Fig. 8.4)

$$\theta = Tl/GJ \propto Tl \quad \text{for a uniform shaft}$$

hence for no resultant twist

$$T\times 3{\cdot}6+(T-30)\times 2{\cdot}4+(T+7{\cdot}5)\times 3=0$$

giving $$T=5{\cdot}5 \text{ kNm}$$

The other fixing couple $=T+7{\cdot}5=13$ kNm

Maximum torque $=T-30=24{\cdot}5$ kNm numerically.

Maximum shearing stress, $60=16\times 24{\cdot}5\times 10^6/\pi D^3$

$$\therefore \quad D=145 \text{ mm}$$

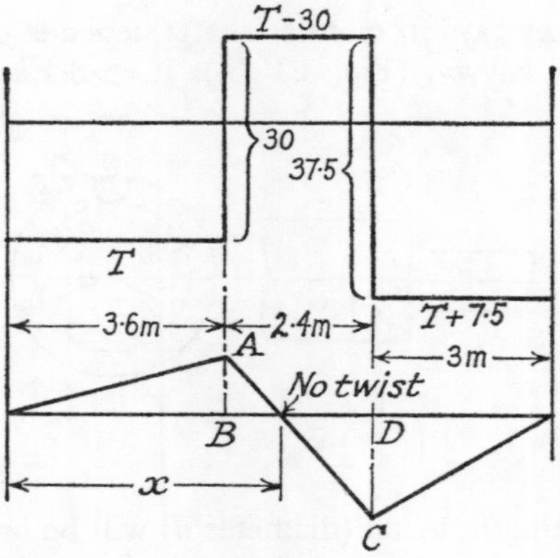

Fig. 8.4

In Fig. 8.4, $AB \propto 5\cdot5 \times 3\cdot6 = 19\cdot8$, $CD \propto 13 \times 3 = 39$

By proportion

$$x = 3\cdot6 + \left(\frac{19\cdot8}{19\cdot8 + 39}\right) \times 2\cdot4 = 4\cdot41 \text{ m}$$

8.6. Compound Shafts. For shafts made up of different materials two cases will be examined, one where the shafts are joined in "series," and the other where they are joined in "parallel."

EXAMPLE 8. *A solid alloy shaft 5 cm diameter is to be coupled in series with a hollow steel shaft of the same external diameter. Find the internal diameter of the steel shaft if the angle of twist per unit length is to be 75% of that of the alloy shaft. Determine the speed at which the shafts are to be driven to transmit 200 kW, if the limits of shearing stress are to be 55 N/mm² and 75 N/mm² in alloy and steel respectively.* $G_{steel} = 2\cdot2G_{alloy}$.

Angle of twist per unit length $= \theta/l$

$$= T/GJ$$

$$\therefore \quad (T/GJ)_{steel} = 0\cdot75(T/GJ)_{alloy}$$

i.e.

$$\frac{32T}{\pi(5^4 - d^4)} = \frac{0\cdot75 \times 2\cdot2 \times 32T}{\pi \times 5^4}$$

or

$$625 - d^4 = 625/(0\cdot75 \times 2\cdot2) = 379$$

giving

$$d = \sqrt[4]{246} = 3\cdot96 \text{ cm}$$

$$2\tau/D = G\theta/l$$

and since θ/l for the steel is 0·75 of that for the alloy

$$\tau_{steel}/\tau_{alloy} = (G_s/G_a)(D_s/D_a) \times 0\cdot75$$

$$= 2\cdot2 \times 0\cdot75$$

$$= 1\cdot65$$

The limits of shearing stresses are 75 N/mm² steel and 55 N/mm² alloy, but the actual maximum stresses must be 75 N/mm² steel and 75/1·65 = 45·4 N/mm² alloy.

Calculate the torque from the solid shaft, i.e.

$$T = \pi D^3\tau/16$$

$$= \frac{\pi \times 125 \times 45\cdot4}{16}$$

$$= 1100 \text{ N.m}$$

$$\text{Power} = 200{,}000 = \frac{1110 \times 2\pi N}{60}$$

$$\therefore \quad N = 1720 \text{ r.p.m.}$$

EXAMPLE 9. *A gun-metal sleeve is fixed securely to a steel shaft and the compound shaft is subjected to a torque. If the torque on the sleeve is twice that on the shaft find the ratio of external diameter of sleeve to diameter of shaft.*

If the limits of shearing stress in the gun-metal and steel are 45 and 80 N/mm² respectively, find the torque that may be transmitted by the compound shaft when the steel shaft diameter is 50 mm. $G_{steel} = 2{\cdot}5\ G_{gm}$ *(U.L.)*

Since the shafts are securely fixed together it can be assumed that strain is proportional to distance from the central axis (compare composite beams, Para. 6.9), being the same for each at the common surface. This implies that the twist per unit length is the same for shaft and sleeve, hence

$$(T_{st}/T_{gm})(J_{gm}/J_{st}) = (\tau_{st}/\tau_{gm})(r_{gm}/r_{st}) = G_{st}/G_{gm} = 2{\cdot}5$$

giving the ratio of torques T_{st}/T_{gm}, i.e.

$$\frac{1}{2} = \frac{\pi d^4 \times 32}{32 \times \pi(D^4 - d^4)} \times 2{\cdot}5$$

$$\therefore \quad D^4 - d^4 = 5d^4$$

$$D/d = \sqrt[4]{6} = 1{\cdot}565$$

The ratio of maximum stresses is found by putting

$$r_{gm}/r_{st} = 1{\cdot}565$$

$$\therefore \quad \tau_{st}/\tau_{gm} = 2{\cdot}5/1{\cdot}565 = 1{\cdot}6$$

so that the actual maximum stresses are 45 N/mm² gun-metal and $45 \times 1{\cdot}6 = 72$ N/mm² steel.

The torque carried by the steel shaft

$$= \pi \times 50^3 \times 72/16 \text{ N.mm}$$

$$= 1760 \text{ Nm}$$

Total torque of composite shaft

$$= 3 \times 1760$$

$$= 5300 \text{ Nm}$$

8.7. Torsion Beyond the Yield Point. It has been shown that the maximum shear stress when a circular shaft is twisted occurs at the outside surface. If the torque is increased until the yield stress is reached, plastic strain will take place in the outer metal. For an ideal elastic-plastic material (approximately true for mild steel), the strain obeys Hooke's law up to the yield point, and beyond this the stress remains constant for a considerable increase in strain (see Fig. 12.1, Para. 12.2). If it is further assumed that strain is proportional to the distance from the axis of the twisted shaft (even in the plastic region), then the angle of twist can be determined from the stress in the elastic core. The total torque is obtained from first principles by integration of the moment of the forces on elemental rings about the axis.

EXAMPLE 10. *A steel shaft 84 mm diameter is solid for a certain distance from one end but hollow for the remainder of its length with an inside diameter of 36 mm. If a pure torque is transmitted of such a magnitude that yielding just occurs at the surface of the solid part of the shaft, find the depth of yielding in the hollow part and the ratio of the angles of twist per unit length for the two parts of the shaft.* (*U.L.*)

Let τ be the shear stress at yield, and d mm the diameter of the hollow section at which yielding commences. It may be assumed that the shear strain in the outer layers of this shaft is insufficient to cause strain hardening (this will be true of any steel with a plastic strain at yield several times the value of the elastic strain) and that the stress is uniform and equal to τ.

$$\text{Torque in the yielded part} = \tau\int_{d/2}^{42} 2\pi r dr . r$$

$$= (84^3 - d^3)\pi\tau/12 \qquad \text{(i)}$$

$$\text{Torque in the unyielded part} = (d^4 - 36^4)\pi\tau/16d \qquad \text{(ii)}$$

$$\text{Torque in the solid shaft} = 84^3\pi\tau/16 \qquad \text{(iii)}$$

Equating (i) + (ii) = (iii)

$$4(84^3 - d^3) + 3(d^4 - 36^4)/d = 3 \times 84^3$$

or

$$d^4 - 59 \times 10^4 d + 5 \times 10^6 = 0$$

By trial and error, $d = 81$ mm

Ratio of angles of twist per unit length,

$$\frac{\text{Hollow}}{\text{Solid}} = \frac{\tau/d}{\tau/84} = 1{\cdot}04$$

(this is based on the "elastic" part of each shaft).

8.8. Combined Bending and Twisting. This condition occurs frequently in practice, shafts being subjected to bending moments due to gravity or inertia loads. Stresses are set up due to bending moment, torque, and shearing force, but the latter is usually unimportant, particularly as its maximum value occurs at the neutral axis (Para. 7.6), where the bending stress is zero. Sometimes, for instance propeller shafts, there is also an end thrust, which is assumed to be distributed uniformly over the cross-section.

For design purposes it is necessary to find the principal stresses, maximum shear stress, strain energy, etc., whichever is to be used as a criterion of failure (see Para. 3.21). The importance of these applications is sufficient to warrant the derivation of formulae for these quantities.

If σ_b is the greatest bending stress and τ the greatest shear stress due to torsion, then

$$\sigma_b = 32M/\pi D^3$$

(where M is the bending moment), and

$$\tau = 16T/\pi D^3, \text{ for a solid shaft.}$$

These stresses will occur together at the ends of a vertical diameter, for loading in a vertical plane, and since there is no normal stress on longitudinal planes of the shaft, the maximum principal stress

$$\begin{aligned}\sigma &= \tfrac{1}{2}\sigma_b + \tfrac{1}{2}\sqrt{(\sigma_b^2 + 4\tau^2)} \text{ (Para. 3.8)}\\ &= 16M/\pi D^3 + \tfrac{1}{2}\sqrt{[(32M/\pi D^3)^2 + 4(16T/\pi D^3)^2]}\\ &= (16/\pi D^3)[M + \sqrt{(M^2 + T^2)}] \qquad (1)\end{aligned}$$

Note that $\tfrac{1}{2}[M + \sqrt{(M^2 + T^2)}]$ is the equivalent bending moment which would give the same maximum stress.

Maximum shear stress

$$\begin{aligned}\hat{\tau} &= \tfrac{1}{2}\sqrt{(\sigma_b^2 + 4\tau^2)} \text{ (Para. 3.10)}\\ &= (16/\pi D^3)\sqrt{(M^2 + T^2)} \qquad (2)\end{aligned}$$

This is the same as the shear stress produced by a pure torque of magnitude $\sqrt{(M^2 + T^2)}$.

The resilience

$$U = (1/2E)(\sigma_1^2 + \sigma_2^2 - 2\nu\sigma_1\sigma_2) \text{ (Para. 3.19)}$$

where σ_1 and σ_2 are the principal stresses, i.e.

$$(16/\pi D^3)[M \pm \sqrt{(M^2 + T^2)}] \text{ from (1)}$$

giving

$$U = (256/\pi^2 D^6 E)[2M^2 + T^2(1 + \nu)] \qquad (3)$$

EXAMPLE 11. *A flywheel weighing 500 kg is mounted on a shaft 75 mm diameter and midway between bearings 0·6 m apart. If the shaft is transmitting 30 kW at 360 r.p.m. calculate the principal stresses and the maximum shear stress at the ends of a vertical and horizontal diameter in a plane close to the flywheel.*

$$\begin{aligned}M &= Wl/4 = (500 \times 9{\cdot}81 \times 0{\cdot}6)/4\\ &= 736 \text{ Nm}\end{aligned}$$

$$T = \frac{\text{power} \times 60}{2\pi N}$$

$$= \frac{30{,}000 \times 60}{2\pi \times 360} = 796 \text{ Nm}$$

At the ends of a vertical diameter

$$\begin{aligned}\text{Principal stresses} &= (16/\pi D^3)[M \pm \sqrt{(M^2 + T^2)}] \text{ from (1)}\\ &= [16/(\pi \times 75^3)][736 \pm \sqrt{(736^2 + 796^2)}]\ 10^3 \text{ N/mm}^2\\ &= 0{\cdot}0121(736 \pm 1083)\\ &= 22 \text{ N/mm}^2 \text{ and } -4{\cdot}2 \text{ N/mm}^2\end{aligned}$$

i.e. on the "tension" side of the shaft the principal stresses are 22 N/mm² tension and 4·2 N/mm² compression. On the "compression" side the principal stresses are 22 N/mm² compression and 4·2 N/mm² tension.

$$\text{Maximum shear stress} = (16/\pi D^3)\sqrt{(M^2 + T^2)} \text{ from (2)}$$
$$= 13{\cdot}1 \text{ N/mm}^2$$

At the ends of a horizontal diameter the bending stress is zero and the torsional shear stress has a value

$$16T/\pi D^3 = 0{\cdot}0121 \times 796$$
$$= 9{\cdot}6 \text{ N/mm}^2$$

This is a "pure shear stress" system, and the principal stresses are $\pm 9{\cdot}6$ N/mm², the maximum shear stress being $9{\cdot}6$ N/mm² (Para. 3.4).

EXAMPLE 12. *A hollow steel shaft 10 cm external diameter, 5 cm internal diameter, transmits 600 kW at 500 r.p.m. and is subjected to an end thrust of 50 kN. Find what bending moment may be safely applied to the shaft if the greater principal stress is not to exceed 100 N/mm². What will then be the value of the smaller principal stress?*

Let the greatest normal and shear stresses on transverse planes be σ and τ. Then

$$\tau = (T/J)\cdot D/2$$
$$= \frac{32 \times 600{,}000 \times 60 \times 10}{2\pi \times 500\pi(10^4 - 5^4) \times 2}$$
$$= 62{\cdot}4 \text{ N/mm}^2$$

Maximum principal stress

$$= \sigma/2 + \tfrac{1}{2}\sqrt{(\sigma^2 + 4\tau^2)}$$

i.e.
$$100 = \sigma/2 + \tfrac{1}{2}\sqrt{(\sigma^2 + 15{,}600)}$$

Rearranging and squaring

$$\sigma^2 + 15{,}600 = (200 - \sigma)^2$$
$$= 40{,}000 - 400\sigma + \sigma^2$$

giving
$$\sigma = 24{,}400/400 = 61{\cdot}0 \text{ N/mm}^2$$

The limiting case is obtained when both the end thrust and bending stress are compressive, the maximum principal stress being also compressive.

Normal stress accounted for by end thrust

$$= \frac{50{,}000 \times 4}{\pi(100^2 - 50^2)} = 8{\cdot}5 \text{ N/mm}^2$$

$$\therefore \quad \text{Stress due to bending} = 61{\cdot}0 - 8{\cdot}5$$
$$= 52{\cdot}5 \text{ N/mm}^2$$
$$= My/I$$
$$= (64M \times 5)/\pi(10^4 - 5^4)$$

(M in N.m)

$$\therefore \quad M = 52{\cdot}5 \times \pi \times 9375/320$$
$$= 4830 \text{ N.m}$$

8.9. Rectangular Shafts. For shafts of non-circular section warping of the cross-section takes place under the action of a torque, and the analysis of stresses and angle of twist is outside the scope of this book. Results are quoted here for rectangular and square sections.

The maximum shear stress is found to occur at the mid-point of the longer side. If the dimensions are b and d, with d greater than b, then

$$\hat{\tau} = \frac{(1\cdot8b+3d).T}{b^2d^2}$$

The angle of twist

$$\theta = \frac{7Tl(b^2+d^2)}{2Gb^3d^3}$$

8.10. Torsion of Thin Tubular Sections. (*Bredt-Batho Theory*). Consider a closed tube of small thickness acted upon by a torque T in a transverse plane (Fig. 8.5). If it is assumed that the shear stress τ

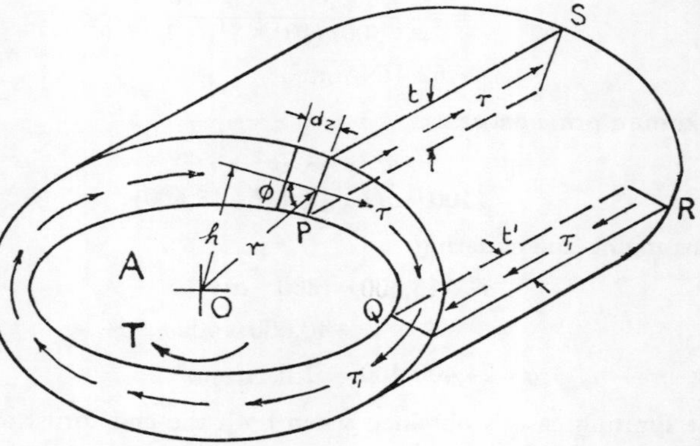

Fig. 8.5

at a point P where the thickness is t is constant across the tube wall, then if τ' is the shear stress at Q and t' the thickness, it follows from the equilibrium of the complementary shear stresses on PS and QR that

$$\tau t = \tau' t' = k \quad \text{say} \tag{1}$$

If dz is an element round the circumference, then the force on this element is $\tau t dz$. and taking moments about O,

$$T = \int \tau t dz . r \sin\phi$$
$$= k\int h . dz$$

where h is the perpendicular distance from O on to τ; hence

$$T=2kA \tag{2}$$

where A = area enclosed by the mean circumference.

The strain energy of a length l of tube is

$$U=\int(\tau^2/2G)ltdz$$
$$=(kl/2G)\int\tau dz \quad \text{from (1)}$$

But $U=\frac{1}{2}T\theta$, where θ is the angle of twist, hence

$$\theta=(kl/TG)\int\tau dz$$
$$=(l/2GA)\int\tau dz \quad \text{from (2)} \tag{3}$$

If t is constant

$$\theta=l\tau z/2GA \tag{4}$$
$$=lTz/4GA^2t \quad \text{from (2)} \tag{5}$$

Example 13. *Show that, for a uniform hollow tube of outside and inside diameters D and d, the Bredt-Batho theory underestimates the maximum shear stress due to a given torque by about 5% when $d/D=0{\cdot}9$. Show that the error in the angle of twist, however, is less than 1%.*

From (1) and (2)

$$\tau=T/2tA$$
$$=\frac{T\times2\times4}{2(D-d)\pi}\left(\frac{2}{D+d}\right)^2$$
$$=\frac{16T}{\pi D^3(1-0{\cdot}9)(1+0{\cdot}9)^2}$$
$$=\frac{16T}{0{\cdot}361\pi D^3} \tag{i}$$

Applying the normal theory for hollow shafts,

$$\hat{\tau}=\frac{16DT}{\pi(D^4-d^4)}$$
$$=\frac{16T}{0{\cdot}344\pi D^3} \qquad (d=0{\cdot}9D) \tag{ii}$$

From (i) and (ii)

$$\frac{\tau}{\hat{\tau}}=\frac{0{\cdot}344}{0{\cdot}361}=0{\cdot}95$$

i.e. τ is 5% less than $\hat{\tau}$.

From (5)

$$\frac{G\theta}{l} = \frac{Tz}{4A^2t}$$

$$= \frac{T\pi(D+d)\times 4^2}{4\times 2\times \pi^2}\left(\frac{2}{D+d}\right)^4 \frac{2}{D-d}$$

$$= \frac{64T}{0{\cdot}684\pi D^4} \qquad \text{(iii)}$$

By shaft theory

$$\frac{G\theta}{l} = \frac{32T}{\pi(D^4-d^4)}$$

$$= \frac{32T}{0{\cdot}344\pi D^4} \qquad \text{(iv)}$$

The ratio between (iii) and (iv) is 0·995, i.e. a difference of about 0·5%.

EXAMPLE 14. *Fig. 8.6*(a) *shows a circular tube for which the inside is eccentric to the outside. Calculate the maximum shear stress and twist per metre length for a torque of 100 Nm. G = 80,000 N mm².*

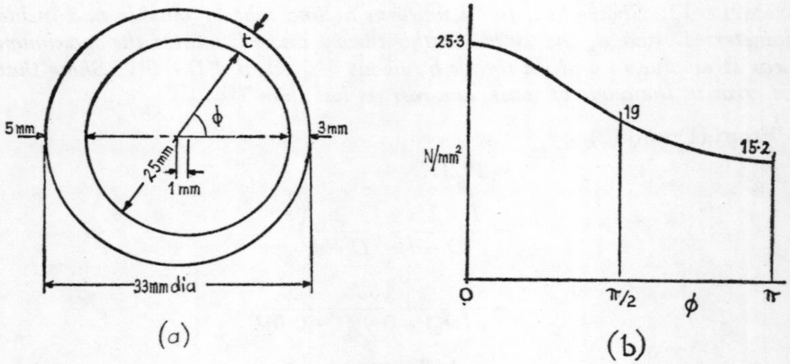

Fig. 8.6

From (1) and (2)

$$\tau = T/2tA$$

$$= \frac{100\times 10^3\times 4}{2\times 3\times \pi\times 29^2} \quad \text{taking the least thickness}$$

$$= 25{\cdot}3 \text{ N/mm}^2$$

Since τ is varying continuously, θ must be obtained from (3), where $dz = 14{\cdot}5d\phi$ and $\int \tau dz = 1800$ N/mm (graphically from Fig. 8.6(b)).

Then, for 1 m length

$$\theta = \frac{1000\times 4\times 1800}{2\times 80{,}000\times \pi\times 29^2}\times 57{\cdot}3$$

$$= 0{\cdot}98°$$

8.11. Torsion of Thin-Walled Cellular Sections. Consider the twin-celled section shown in Fig. 8.7, the mean area of the two cells being A_1 and A_2. If the length ABC is of uniform thickness t_1 and

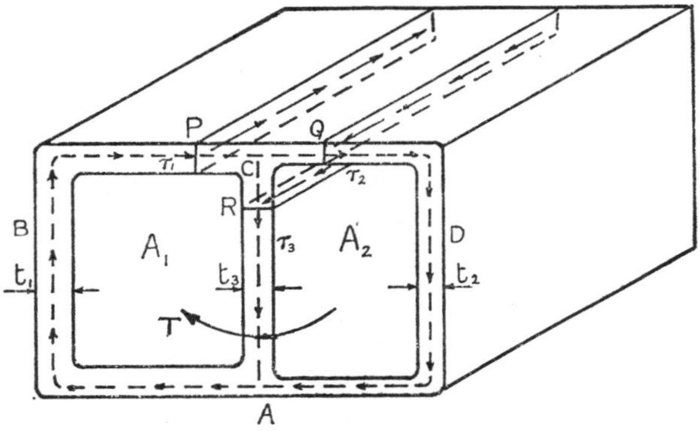

Fig. 8.7

stress τ_1, CDA of thickness t_2 and stress τ_2, and CA of thickness τ_3 and stress τ_3, it follows from the equilibrium of complementary shear stresses on a longitudinal section through PQR that

$$\tau_1 t_1 = \tau_2 t_2 + \tau_3 t_3 \qquad (1)$$

The total torque on the section by using eqn. (2) of Para. 8.10 and adding for the two cells, i.e.

$$T = 2(\tau_1 t_1 A_1 + \tau_2 t_2 A_2) \qquad (2)$$

Applying eqn. (4) of Para. 8.10 to each cell in turn gives

$$2G\theta/l = (\tau_1 z_1 + \tau_3 z_3)/A_1 \qquad (3)$$

$$= (\tau_2 z_2 - \tau_3 z_3)/A_2 \qquad (4)$$

where z_1, z_2 and z_3 are the mean perimeters ABC, CDA, and CA respectively, the negative sign indicating a traverse against the direction of stress.

EXAMPLE 15. *In Fig. 8.7 the mean dimensions of the two cells are 5 cm × 2·5 cm and 2·5 cm square, $t_1 = 2{\cdot}5$ mm, $t_2 = 5$ mm, and $t_3 = 3$mm. Calculate the shear stress in each section, and the angle of twist per metre length for a torque of 200 Nm. $G = 80{,}000$ N/mm².*

From the dimensions given,

$$A_1 = 1250 \text{ mm}^2 \quad \text{and} \quad A_2 = 625 \text{ mm}^2$$

$$z_1 = 125 \text{ mm}, \; z_2 = 75 \text{ mm}, \; z_3 = 25 \text{ mm}$$

Equation (1) gives

$$\tau_1 \times 2{\cdot}5 = \tau_2 \times 5 + \tau_3 \times 3$$

i.e.

$$2{\cdot}5\tau_1 = 5^{-}{}_2 + 3\tau_3 \qquad \text{(i)}$$

Equation (2) becomes

$$200{,}000 = 2(\tau_1 \times 2{\cdot}5 \times 1250 + \tau_2 \times 5 \times 625)$$

i.e.

$$\tau_1 + \tau_2 = 32 \qquad \text{(ii)}$$

Equating (3) and (4) gives

$$\tau_1 \times 125 + \tau_3 \times 25 = 2(\tau_2 \times 75 - \tau_3 \times 25)$$

i.e.

$$5\tau_1 = 6\tau_2 - 3\tau_3 \qquad \text{(iii)}$$

Eliminating τ_3 between (i) and (iii) gives

$$7{\cdot}5\tau_1 = 11\tau_2 \qquad \text{(iv)}$$

and from (ii) and (iv)

$$\tau_1 = (11/18{\cdot}5)32$$
$$= 19 \text{ N/mm}^2$$
$$\tau_2 = 32 - \tau_1$$
$$= 13 \text{ N/mm}^2$$

From (i)

$$\tau_3 = -5{\cdot}8 \text{ N/mm}^2$$

(i.e. in the opposite direction to that assumed).

From (3)

$$\theta = \frac{(\tau_1 z_1 + \tau_3 z_3)l}{2GA_1}$$
$$= \frac{(19 \times 125 - 5{\cdot}8 \times 25)1000}{2 \times 80{,}000 \times 1250} \times 57{\cdot}3$$
$$= 0{\cdot}638^\circ$$

8.12. Torsion of Thin Rectangular Members. In a rectangular cross-section the shear stress must flow as in Fig. 8.8, being a maximum τ along the long edge d, and a value τ' along the short edge t. It will be assumed that the variation of stress in both the OX and OY directions is linear, being zero in both directions at O by symmetry. It will be further assumed, and this has been confirmed by experiment, that the ratio

$$\tau'/\tau = t/d \qquad (1)$$

The total torque on the cross-section is found by adding together the sum of the moments about OY of the forces on elements parallel to d and the sum of the moments about OX of the forces on elements parallel to t, i.e.

$$T = 2\int_0^{t/2} (2\tau x/t)d\,.\,dx\,.\,x + 2\int_0^{d/2} (2\tau' y/d)t\,.\,dy\,.\,y$$

$$= \tfrac{1}{6}\tau dt^2 + \tfrac{1}{6}\tau' d^2 t$$

$$= \tfrac{1}{3}\tau dt^2 \quad \text{from (1)} \qquad (2)$$

where τ is the maximum stress in the section.

If θ is the angle of twist of a length l, equating the strain energy from the torque and from the stresses,

$$\tfrac{1}{2}T\theta = 2\int_0^{t/2} (2\tau x/t)^2 (dl/2G)dx + 2\int_0^{d/2} (2\tau' y/d)^2 (tl/2G)dy$$

$$= \tfrac{1}{6}(\tau^2/G)dtl + \tfrac{1}{6}(\tau'^2/G)dtl$$

$$= \tfrac{1}{6}\tau^2 dtl(1 + t^2/d^2)/G \quad \text{from (1)} \qquad (3)$$

For a long thin rectangle t^2/d^2 can be neglected, and by substitution from (2)

$$\theta = \tau l/tG \qquad (4)$$

$$= 3Tl/dt^3G \qquad (5)$$

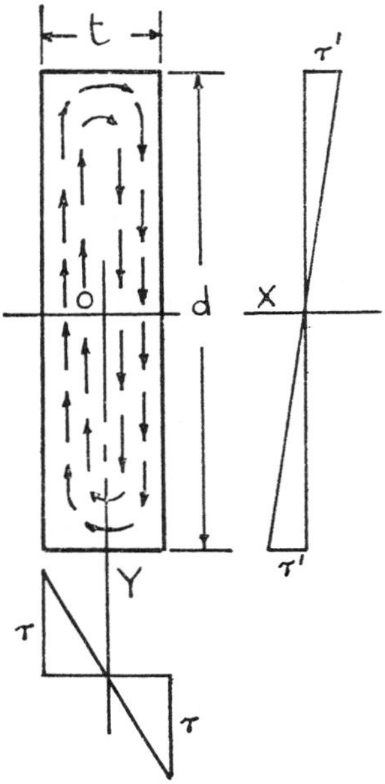

Fig. 8.8

These results should be compared with those of Para. 8.9, in which the dimension b can be neglected in comparison with d.

8.13. Torsion of Thin Open Sections. I, channel and angle sections, and curved sections which do not form closed tubes may be treated approximately by the methods of Para. 8.12, equations (2) and (5) becoming

$$T = \tfrac{1}{3}\tau\,.\,\Sigma dt^2$$

and

$$\theta = 3Tl/G\Sigma dt^3$$

(for curved sections d = mean perimeter).

EXAMPLE 16. *An I-section 120 mm × 80 mm has flanges 5 mm thick and web 4 mm thick and is subjected to a torque T. Find the maximum value of T if the shear stress is limited to 35 N/mm² and the twist per metre length to 6°. G = 82,000 N/mm²*

$$\Sigma dt^2 = 120 \times 4^2 + 2 \times 80 \times 5^2$$

$$= 5920 \text{ mm}^3$$

hence

$$T = \tfrac{1}{3} \times 35 \times 5920$$

$$= 69{,}000 \text{ Nmm}$$

$$\Sigma dt^3 = 120 \times 4^3 + 2 \times 80 \times 5^3$$
$$= 27{,}700 \text{ mm}^4$$

hence
$$\theta = 3T \times 1000/(27{,}700 \times 82{,}000)$$

or
$$T = 6 \times 27{,}700 \times 82/3 \times 57{\cdot}3$$
$$= 79{,}000 \text{ Nmm}$$

The permissible torque is therefore 69 Nm.

SUMMARY

Torsion of Circular Shafts $T/J = \tau/r = G\theta/l$.
Maximum shear stress $\hat{\tau} = 16T/\pi D^3$, for solid shafts.
Strain Energy $U = \frac{1}{2}T\theta$

$$= T^2 l/2GJ$$

$$= (\hat{\tau}^2/4G) \times \text{volume}, \quad \text{for solid shafts.}$$

Stiffness $k = T/\theta = GJ/l$.
Combined Bending and Twisting:

Maximum Principal Stress $\hat{\sigma} = (16/\pi D^3)[M + \sqrt{(M^2 + T^2)}]$.

Maximum Shear Stress $\hat{\tau} = (16/\pi D^3)\sqrt{(M^2 + T^2)}$, for solid shafts.

PROBLEMS

1. Two lengths of shaft, 15 cm diameter, are connected by a flange coupling, with 6 bolts on a 25 cm diameter pitch circle. If the limits of shearing stress are 48 N/mm² in the shaft and 40 N/mm² in the bolts (assumed uniform), calculate the power transmitted at 280 r.p.m., and the diameter of bolt required.
(933 kW; 37 mm.)

2. A solid steel shaft transmits 560 kW at 300 rev./min with a maximum shear stress of 60 N/mm². What is the shaft diameter?
What would be the diameters of a hollow shaft of the same material (diameter ratio 2), to transmit the same power at the same speed and stress?
Compare the stiffness of equal lengths of these shafts.
(115 mm; 117 mm; 58·5 mm; 0·98.)

3. A hollow steel shaft has to transmit 6000 kW at 110 r.p.m. If the allowable shear stress is 60 N/mm^2 and inside diameter $=\frac{3}{5}$ of outside, find the dimensions of the shaft, and the angle of twist on a 3 m length. G=80,000 N/mm^2.
(370 mm; 222 mm; 42′.)

4. A shaft 3 m long stores 300 Nm of energy when transmitting 1500 kW at 360 r.p.m. What is the shaft diameter and maximum shear stress? $G=80,000$ N/mm^2.
(178 mm; 35·9 N/mm^2.)

5. A solid phosphor-bronze shaft, 5 cm diameter, rotating at 400 r.p.m., is subjected to torsion only. An electrical resistance strain gauge is mounted on the shaft with the axis of the gauge at 45° to the axis of the shaft. Determine the power being transmitted if the strain gauge reading is $4{\cdot}17\times10^{-4}$. For phosphor-bronze $E=105,000$ N/mm^2.
(45 kW.)

6. A hollow marine propeller shaft turning at 110 r.p.m. is required to propel a vessel at 25 knots for the expenditure of 6300 kW, the efficiency of the propeller being 68%. The diameter ratio is $\frac{2}{3}$ and the direct stress due to the thrust is not to exceed 7·72 N/mm^2. Calculate (a) the shaft diameters, (b) maximum shear stress due to torque. 1 knot =0·515 m/s. (U.L.)
(315 mm, 210 mm; 112 N/mm^2)

7. A hollow steel shaft 200 mm external diameter and 125 mm internal diameter transmits 1600 kW at 180 rev./min. Calculate the shear stress at the inner and outer surfaces and the strain energy per metre length. $G=84,000$ N/mm^2.
(40·5; 64·5 N/mm^2; 325 Nm.)

8. A hollow shaft of diameter ratio 3/5 is required to transmit 600 kW at 110 r.p.m., the maximum torque being 12% greater than the mean. The shear stress is not to exceed 60 N/mm^2 and the twist in a length of 3 m not to exceed 1°. Calculate the minimum external diameter satisfying these conditions. $G=$ 80,000 N/mm^2.
(195 mm.)

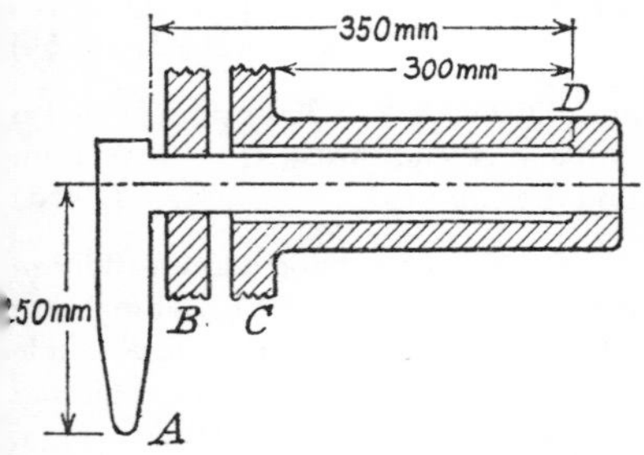

9. The figure shows a steel shaft 25 mm diameter which is rigidly joined at D to a tube 38 mm outside diameter which is anchored at C. The shaft is carried in a bearing at B and a load of 500 N is applied at A perpendicular to the plane of the figure. Calculate the bore of the tube so that the maximum stress in tube and shaft are equal, and calculate the movement of A assuming the lever rigid. $G=80,000$ N/mm^2.
(35 mm; 5·58 mm.)

10. A case-hardened shaft is 25 mm diameter with a case depth of 1·5 mm. Assuming the case remains perfectly elastic up to its failing stress in shear of 300 N/mm^2 and that the inner core becomes perfectly plastic at a shearing stress of 180 N/mm^2, calculate (a) the torque to cause elastic failure in torsion in the

case and (b) the angle of twist per metre length at failure. $G = 84{,}000$ N/mm² for all the material while elastic. (820 Nm, 16·4°.)

11. A hollow steel shaft having outside and inside diameters of 45 mm and 19 mm respectively is subjected to a gradually increasing axial torque. The yield stress is reached at the surface when the torque is 1 kNm, the angle of twist per metre length then being 2·43°. Find the magnitude of the yield stress.

If the torque is increased to 1·08 kNm calculate (a) the depth to which yielding will have penetrated, (b) the angle of twist per metre length. State any assumptions made and prove any special formula used. (58 Nmm², 2·3 mm, 2·7°.)

12. A steel shaft ABCD of circular section is 2 m long and is supported in bearings at the ends A and D. AB = 0·75 m, BC = 0·5 m, CD = 0·75 m. The shaft is horizontal, and two horizontal arms, rigidly connected to it at B and C, project at right angles on opposite sides. Arm B carries a vertical load of 2000 kg at 0·333 m from the shaft axis, and C carries a vertical balancing load at 0·417 m from the axis. If the shear stress is not to exceed 80 N/mm² find the minimum diameter of shaft. Assume the bearings give simple support. (99 mm.)

13. The 300 mm diameter steel tail shaft of a ship which runs at 200 r.p.m., has a 25 mm thick bronze bushing shrunk over its entire length of 8·5 m. If the shaft has been designed for a maximum shearing stress in the steel of 10 N/mm² find (a) the torsional stiffness of the tail shaft, (b) the power of the engine. $G_s = 84{,}000$ N/mm²; $G_b = 42{,}000$ N/mm². (13×10^6 Nm/rad.; 16,000 kW.)

14. A solid shaft transmits 1000 kW at 107 rev/min, the maximum torque being 1·8 times the mean. The bearings are 1·54 m apart with a 9000 kg flywheel midway between bearings. There is also a bending moment due to steam pressure which is numerically equal to 0·8 of the mean twisting moment. Find the shaft diameter if the maximum permissible tensile stress is 60 N/mm². (290 mm.)

15. In a shaft subjected to bending and twisting the greater principal stress is numerically 5 times the lesser one. Find the ratio of $M:T$ and the angle which the plane of greater principal stress makes with the plane of bending stress. (U.L.) ($2/\sqrt{5}$; 24° 5′.)

16. A solid shaft 127 mm diameter transmits 600 kW at 300 r.p.m. It is also subjected to a bending moment of 9·1 kNm and an end thrust. If the maximum principal stress is limited to 77 N/mm² find the end thrust. (39 kN.)

17. A horizontal shaft of 76 mm dia. projects from a bearing and, in addition to the torque transmitted, the shaft carries a vertical load of 7·5 kN at 300 mm from the bearing. If the safe stress for the material, as determined in a simple tension test, is 140 N/mm², find the torque to which the shaft may be subjected using as a criterion (*a*) the maximum shear stress, (*b*) the maximum strain energy. Poisson's ratio = 0·29. ((*a*) 5·6 kNm. (*b*) 6·9 kNm.)

18. A tube subjected to torsion is of rectangular form, the outside dimensions being 50 mm × 25 mm and the thickness 1·6 mm. Show that for calculating both shear stress and angle of twist such a section may be treated as practically equivalent to a thin circular tube in which the mean radius is $2A/S$ and with a thick-

ness $S^2t/4\pi A$, where A is the cross-sectional area, S the perimeter and t the thickness of the non-circular tube.

If the material is brass ($G = 34{,}500$ N/mm²) calculate the safe torque and maximum angle of twist per metre if the shear stress is not to exceed 27·5 N/mm².

(100 Nm, 2·9°.)

19. The figure shows the dimensions of a double-celled cross-section in the

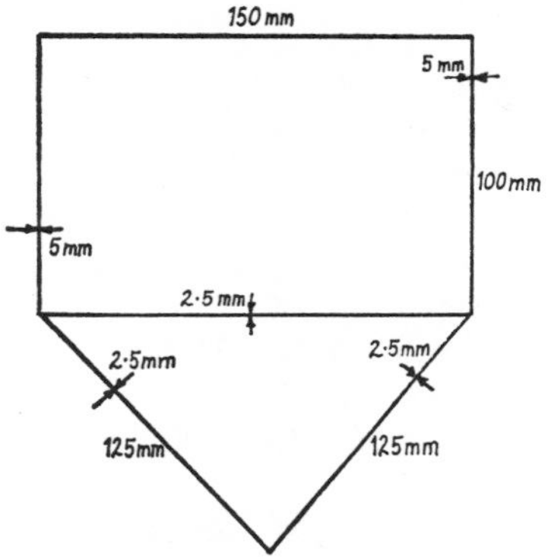

form of a triangle and rectangle of thin section. If a torque of 10,000 Nm is applied, calculate the shear stress in each part and the angle of twist per metre length. $G = 83{,}000$ N/mm².

What thickness of the internal web would make the stress in it zero?

(49·5 N/mm² "rectangle", 65 N/mm² "triangle"
34 N/mm² "internal", 0·965°, 7·15 mm.)

20. The dimensions of an angle section are 75 mm × 50 mm × 3·2 mm. Calculate the maximum shear stress and twist per metre length if a torque of 10 Nm is applied. $G = 83{,}000$ N/mm². (23·5 N/mm², 5·1°.)

21. An extruded section in light alloy is in the form of a semicircle 50 mm mean diameter and 2·5 thick. If a torque is applied to the section and the angle of twist is to be limited to 4° in a length of 1 m estimate the torque and maximum shear stress. $G = 26{,}000$ N/mm². (0·745 Nm, 4·56 N/mm².)

CHAPTER IX

Deflection of Beams

9.1. Strain Energy due to Bending. Consider a short length of beam δx, under the action of a bending moment M. If σ is the bending stress on an element of the cross-section of area δA at a distance y from the neutral axis, the strain energy of the length δx is given by

$$\delta U = \int(\sigma^2/2E) \times \text{volume} \quad \text{(Para. 1.9)}$$
$$= \delta x \int \sigma^2 . dA/2E$$
$$= (\delta x/2E)\int M^2 y^2 dA/I^2$$

But $\int y^2 . dA = I$

hence $\delta U = (M^2/2EI)\delta x$

For the whole beam:

$$U = \int M^2 . dx/2EI$$

The product EI is called the *Flexural Rigidity* of the beam.

EXAMPLE 1. *A simply supported beam of length l carries a concentrated load W at distances of a and b from the two ends. Find expressions for the total strain energy of the beam and the deflection under the load.*

The integration for strain energy can only be applied over a length of beam for which a continuous expression for M can be obtained. This usually implies a separate integration for each section between two concentrated loads or reactions.

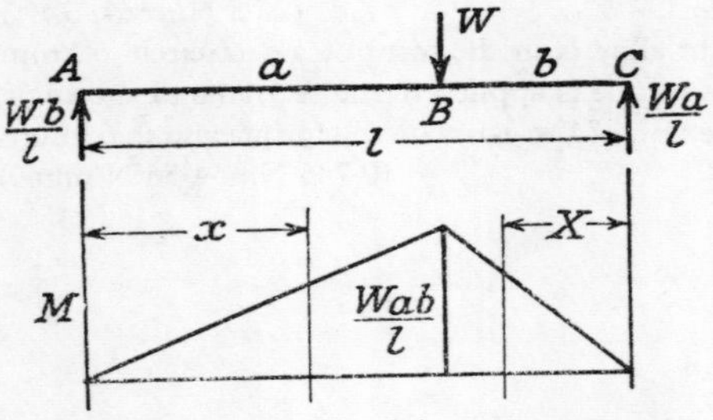

Fig. 9.1

Referring to Fig. 9.1, for the section AB,

$$M = (Wb/l)x$$

$$U_a = \int_0^a \frac{W^2 b^2 x^2}{2l^2 EI} . dx$$

$$= \frac{W^2 b^2}{2l^2 EI}\left[\frac{x^3}{3}\right]_0^a$$

$$= W^2 a^3 b^2/6EIl^2$$

Similarly, by taking a variable X measured from C

$$U_b = \int_0^b \frac{W^2 a^2 X^2}{2l^2 EI} . dX = W^2 a^2 b^3/6EIl^2$$

$$\text{Total } U = U_a + U_b = (W^2 a^2 b^2/6EIl^2)(a+b)$$
$$= W^2 a^2 b^2/6EIl$$

But, if δ is the deflection under the load, the strain energy must equal the work done by the load (gradually applied), i.e.

$$\tfrac{1}{2}W\delta = W^2a^2b^2/6EIl$$
$$\therefore\ \delta = Wa^2b^2/3EIl$$

For a central load, $a = b = l/2$, and

$$\delta = (W/3EIl)(l^2/4)(l^2/4)$$
$$= Wl^3/48EI$$

It should be noted that this method of finding deflection is limited to cases where only one concentrated load is applied (i.e. doing work), and then only gives the deflection under the load. A more general application of strain energy to deflection is found in Castigliano's theorem (Para. 11.4).

EXAMPLE 2. *Compare the strain energy of a beam, simply supported at its ends and loaded with a uniformly distributed load, with that of the same beam centrally loaded and having the same value of maximum bending stress.* (*U.L.*)

If l is the span and EI the flexural rigidity, then for a uniformly distributed load w, the end reactions are $wl/2$, and at a distance x from one end

$$M = (wl/2)x - wx^2/2$$
$$= (wx/2)(l - x)$$

$$U_1 = \int_0^l \frac{w^2x^2(l-x)^2dx}{4 \times 2EI}$$
$$= \frac{w^2}{8EI}\int_0^l (l^2x^2 - 2lx^3 + x^4)dx$$
$$= (w^2l^5/8EI)(\tfrac{1}{3} - \tfrac{2}{4} + \tfrac{1}{5})$$
$$= w^2l^5/240EI \qquad \text{(i)}$$

For a central load of W,

$$U_2 = \tfrac{1}{2}W\delta$$
$$= W^2l^3/96EI \qquad \text{(ii)}$$

see also Example 1.

Maximum bending stress $= \hat{M}/Z$, and for a given beam depends on the maximum bending moment.

Equating maximum bending moments,

$$wl^2/8 = Wl/4 \quad \text{(Chap. 5)} \qquad \text{(iii)}$$
$$\therefore\ wl = 2W$$

$$\text{Ratio } U_1/U_2 = (w^2l^5/240)(96/W^2l^3) \quad \text{from (i) and (ii)}$$
$$= (96/240)(w^2l^2/W^2)$$
$$= (96/240)4 \quad \text{from (iii)}$$
$$= 8/5$$

9.2. Application to Impact.

EXAMPLE 3. *A concentrated load W gradually applied to a horizontal beam simply supported at its ends produces a deflection y at the load point. If this load falls through a distance h on to the beam find an expression for the maximum deflection produced.*

In a given beam, for a load W, y=0·5 cm and the maximum stress is 60 N/mm². Find the greatest height from which a load of 0·1W can be dropped without exceeding the elastic limit of 270 N/mm². (U.L.)

$$\text{Loss of P.E. of load} = \text{Gain of S.E. of beam}$$

i.e.
$$W(h+\delta) = \tfrac{1}{2}P\delta$$

where δ is the maximum deflection produced by dropping the load W on to the beam and P is the equivalent gradually applied load which would cause the same deflection. But a gradually applied load of W produces a deflection y, hence $\delta = (P/W) \times y$ by proportion, or $P = W\delta/y$.

Substituting in above

$$W(h+\delta) = W\delta^2/2y$$

Rearranging
$$\delta^2/2 - y\delta - hy = 0$$

Solving
$$\delta = y + \sqrt{(y^2 + 2hy)}$$

Energy equation for dropping $0{\cdot}1W$ is

$$0{\cdot}1W(h' + \delta') = \tfrac{1}{2}P'\delta'$$

But the equivalent gradually applied load (and hence the deflection δ') is proportional to the maximum stress, i.e.

$$P' = W \times 270/60 = 9W/2$$

and
$$\delta' = y \times 270/60 = 2{\cdot}25 \text{ cm}$$

Substituting,
$$0{\cdot}1W(h' + 2{\cdot}25) = \tfrac{1}{2}(9W/2)2{\cdot}25$$

giving
$$0{\cdot}1h' = 5{\cdot}065 - 0{\cdot}225$$

i.e.
$$h' = 48{\cdot}4 \text{ cm}$$

9.3. Deflection by Calculus. It was proved in Para. 6.1 that, for bending about a *principal axis*

$$M/EI = 1/R \qquad (1)$$

and in terms of co-ordinates x and y

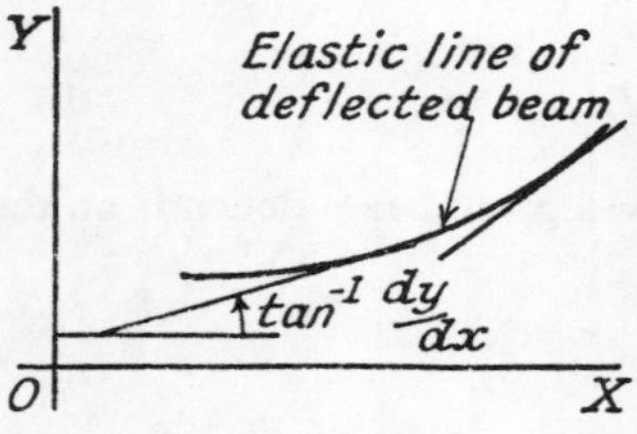

Fig. 9.2

$$\frac{1}{R} = \frac{\pm d^2y/dx^2}{[1 + (dy/dx)^2]^{3/2}} \qquad (2)$$

where the sign depends on the convention for axes. For beams met with in engineering practice the slope dy/dx is everywhere small, and may be neglected in comparison with 1 in the denominator.

Taking *y positive upwards*, under the action of a positive bending moment the curvature of the beam is as shown in Fig. 9.2. It can be seen that dy/dx is increasing as x increases, i.e. d^2y/dx^2 is positive, and $1/R = d^2y/dx^2$ from (2).

Hence $$M/EI = d^2y/dx^2 \quad \text{from (1)}$$

or $$EI.d^2y/dx^2 = M \tag{3}$$

Provided M can be expressed as a function of x equation (3) can be integrated to give the slope dy/dx, and the deflection y, of the beam for any value of x. Two constants of integration will be involved, and these can be obtained by substituting known values of slope or deflection at particular points. A mathematical expression is thus obtained for the form of the deflected beam, or "*elastic line.*"

Differentiating (3)

$$EI.d^3y/dx^3 = dM/dx = F \tag{4}$$

and $$EI.d^4y/dx^4 = dF/dx = -w \quad \text{(Para. 5.5)} \tag{5}$$

These forms are of use in some cases, though generally the bending moment relation is the most convenient.

Notes on application

(i) Take the X axis through the level of the supports.

(ii) Take the origin at one end, or at a point of zero slope.

(iii) For a built-in or fixed end, or where the deflection is a maximum, the slope $dy/dx = 0$.

(iv) For points on the X axis, usually supports, the deflection $y = 0$.

Units. It is convenient to measure:

E in N/mm^2
I in mm^4
y in mm
M in Nm
x in m

In numerical problems it will then be necessary to apply correction factors to the slope and deflection equations.

EXAMPLE 4. *Obtain expressions for the maximum slope and deflection of a cantilever of length l carrying (a) a concentrated load W at its free end, (b) a uniformly distributed load w along its whole length.*

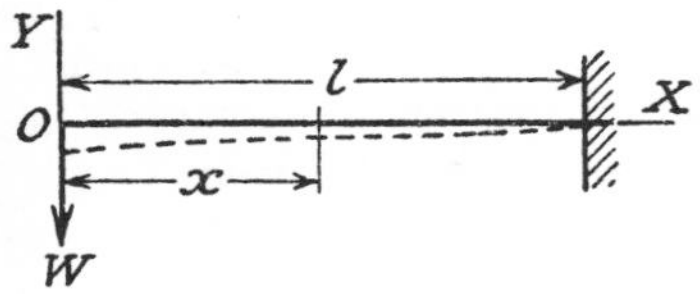

Fig. 9.3

(a) Taking the origin at the free end, the X axis through the fixed end, then at a distance x from the origin $M = -Wx$ (Fig. 9.3) and

$$EI.d^2y/dx^2 = M = -Wx \quad \text{from (3)}$$

Integrating $$EI.dy/dx = -Wx^2/2 + A$$

But $dy/dx = 0$ at $x = l$

$$\therefore \quad A = Wl^2/2$$

Integrate again

$$EIy = -Wx^3/6 + Wl^2x/2 + B$$

At $x = l$, $y = 0$

$$\therefore \quad B = Wl^3/6 - Wl^3/2$$
$$= -Wl^3/3$$

The slope and deflection at the free end (where they are a maximum) are given by the values of dy/dx and y when $x = 0$, i.e.

$$\text{slope} = Wl^2/2EI$$

$$\text{Deflection} = -Wl^3/3EI \quad \text{(indicating downward)}$$

The deflected shape is shown dotted.

(b) $$EI.d^2y/dx^2 = M = -wx^2/2 \quad \text{(Fig. 9.4)}$$

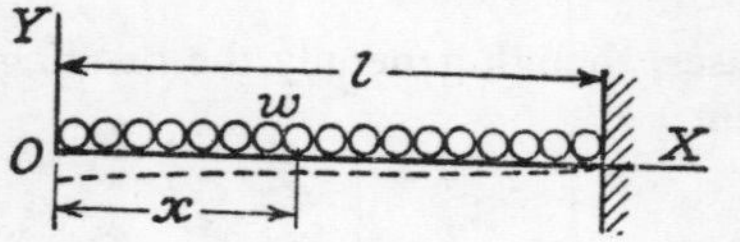

Fig. 9.4

Integrating $EI.dy/dx = -wx^3/6 + A$

when $x = l$, $dy/dx = 0$

$$\therefore \quad A = wl^3/6$$

Integrating

$$EIy = -wx^4/24 + (wl^3/6).x + B$$

when $x = l$, $y = 0$

$$\therefore \quad B = -wl^4/8$$

Putting $x = 0$, maximum slope $= wl^3/6EI$

and maximum deflection $= -wl^4/8EI$

It is left to the reader to perform the analysis for the two standard cases of simply supported beam, the results of which are quoted in the summary at the end of this chapter. They will be treated by a different method under Para. 9.5.

9.4. Macaulay's Method. In applying the method of Para. 9.3 normally a separate expression for bending moment must be obtained for each section of the beam between adjacent concentrated loads or reactions, each producing a different equation with its own constants of integration. It will be appreciated that in any but the simplest cases the work involved will be laborious, the separate equations being linked together by equating slopes and deflections given by the expressions on either side of each "junction" point. However, a method devised by Macaulay enables one continuous expression for bending moment to be obtained, and provided certain rules are followed the constants of integration will be the same for all sections of the beam.

For the purpose of illustration, it is advisable to deal with the different types of loading separately.

(1) *Concentrated loads*

Measuring x from one end, write down an expression for the *bending moment in the last section of the beam,* enclosing all distances less than x in square brackets, i.e.

$$EI.d^2y/dx^2 = M = -W_1x + R[x-a] - W_2[x-b] - W_3[x-c] \text{ (Fig. 9.5)}$$

Subject to the condition that *all terms for which the quantity inside the square brackets is negative are omitted* (i.e. given a value zero), this expression may be said to represent the bending moment for all values of x. If x is less than c the last term is omitted, if x is less than b then both the last two terms are omitted, and so on.

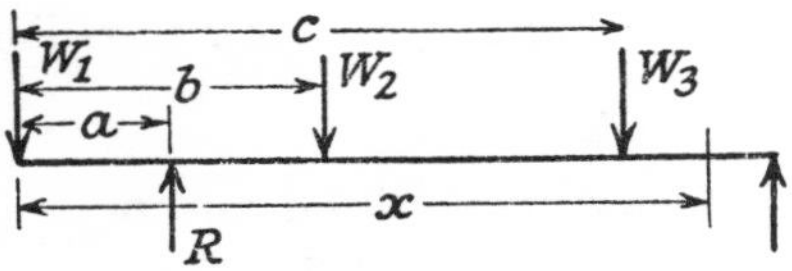

Fig. 9.5

The brackets are to be *integrated as a whole,* i.e.

$$EI.dy/dx = -W_1x^2/2 + (R/2)[x-a]^2 - (W_2/2)[x-b]^2 - (W_3/2)[x-c]^2 + A$$

and

$$EIy = -W_1x^3/6 + (R/6)[x-a]^3 - (W_2/6)[x-b]^3 - (W_3/6)[x-c]^3 + Ax + B$$

By so doing it can be shown that the constants of integration are common to all sections of the beam, e.g. if $x = b - \Delta$

$$EI.dy/dx = -(W_1/2)(b-\Delta)^2 + (R/2)(b-\Delta-a)^2 + A$$

and $$EIy = -(W_1/6)(b-\Delta)^3 + (R/6)(b-\Delta-a)^3 + A(b-\Delta) + B$$

and if $x = b + \Delta$

$$EI.dy/dx = -(W_1/2)(b+\Delta)^2 + (R/2)(b+\Delta-a)^2 - (W_2/2)\Delta^2 + A'$$

and

$$EIy = -(W_1/6)(b+\Delta)^3 + (R/6)(b+\Delta-a)^3 - (W_2/6)\Delta^3 + A'(b+\Delta) + B'$$

Now as $\Delta \to 0$ these slope and deflection values must correspond (i.e. at $x = b$), from which it is seen that $A = A'$ and $B = B'$.

The values of A and B are found as before.

(2) *Uniformly distributed loads*

Supposing a load w is stretched from a distance a to a distance b from one end (Fig. 9.6). Then in order to obtain an expression for the bending moment at a distance x from the end, which will apply for all values of x, it is necessary to continue the loading up to the section x, compensating with an equal negative load from b to x, i.e.

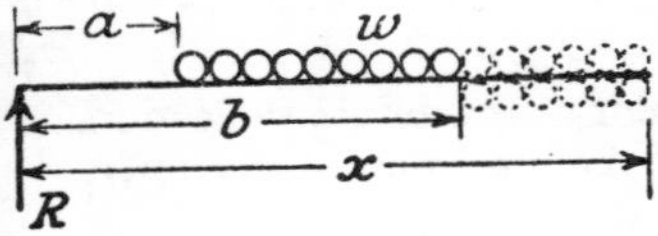

Fig. 9.6

$$M = Rx - (w/2)[x-a]^2 + (w/2)[x-b]^2$$

each length of loading acting at its centre of gravity, square brackets being interpreted as before.

For $x>a$ but $<b$, omit $[x-b]$, and $M=Rx-(w/2)(x-a)^2$, which is clearly correct.

The remaining steps of integration and constant enumeration are as before.

(3) *Concentrated bending moment*

As shown in Fig. 9.7, write

$$EI.d^2y/dx^2=M=-Rx+M_0[x-a]^\circ$$

then $$EI.dy/dx=-Rx^2/2+M_0[x-a]+A, \text{ etc.}$$

EXAMPLE 5. *A simply supported beam of length L carries a load W at a distance a from one end, b from the other (a>b). Find the position and magnitude of the maximum deflection and show that the position is always within L/13, approximately, of the centre.* (U.L.)

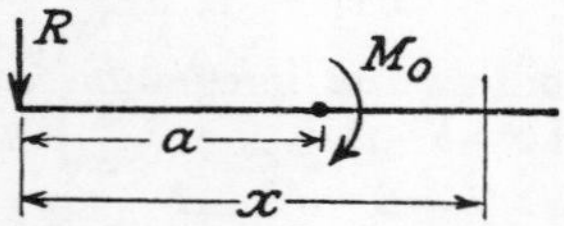

Fig. 9.7

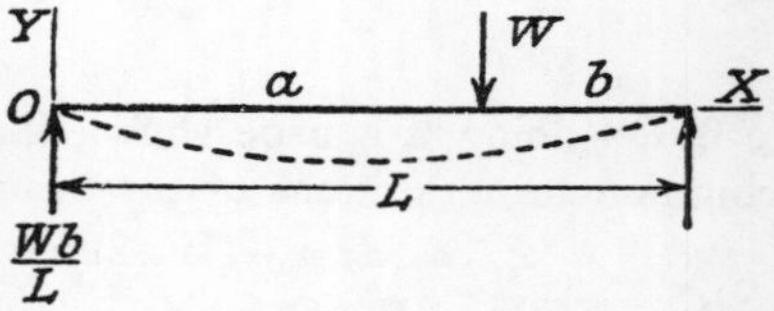

Fig. 9.8

The maximum deflection (i.e. zero slope) will occur on the length a since $a>b$.

Taking the axes as shown in Fig. 9.8,

$$EI.d^2y/dx^2=M=(Wb/L)x-W[x-a]$$

$$EI.dy/dx=(Wb/L)(x^2/2)-(W/2)[x-a]^2+A \quad \text{(i)}$$

$$EIy=(Wb/L)(x^3/6)-(W/6)[x-a]^3+Ax+B \quad \text{(ii)}$$

At $x=0$, $y=0$, $\therefore \quad B=0$

At $x=L$, $y=0$, $\therefore \quad AL=-(Wb/L)(L^3/6)+(W/6)b^3$

giving $$A=-(Wb/6L)(L^2-b^2)$$

$dy/dx=0$ at a value of x given by

$(Wb/L)(x^2/2)-(Wb/6L)(L^2-b^2)=0$, from (i), omitting $[x-a]$ since $x<a$ for zero slope when $a>b$.

This gives $x=\sqrt{[(L^2-b^2)/3]}$ at the point of maximum deflection.

Substituting in (ii) to find the value of the maximum deflection:

$$EIy=\frac{Wb}{L}\cdot\frac{(L^2-b^2)^{3/2}}{6\times 3\sqrt{3}}-\frac{Wb}{6L}\cdot\frac{(L^2-b)^{3/2}}{\sqrt{3}}$$

giving $$y=-\frac{Wb(L^2-b^2)^{3/2}}{9\sqrt{3}.EIL}$$

Distance of point of maximum deflection from centre

$$= \sqrt{[(L^2 - b^2)/3]} - L/2$$

which has a maximum value of $L/\sqrt{3} - L/2$, or approximately $L/13$.

EXAMPLE 6. *A simply supported beam of span 20 m carries two concentrated loads 4 kN at 8 m and 10 kN at 12 m from one end. Calculate (a) the deflection under each load, (b) the maximum deflection. E = 200,000 N/mm²; I = 10⁹mm⁴.*

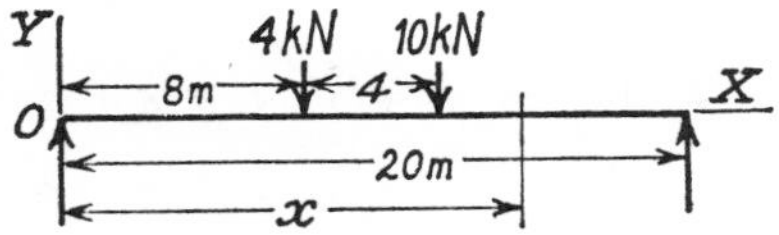

Fig. 9.9

$$\text{Reaction at O} = \frac{4 \times 12 + 10 \times 8}{20} = 6{\cdot}4 \text{ kN, Fig. 9.9}$$

$$EI.d^2y/dx^2 = M$$
$$= 6{\cdot}4x - 4[x - 8] - 10[x - 12]$$

Integrating $\quad EI.dy/dx = 3{\cdot}2x^2 - 2[x-8]^2 - 5[x-12]^2 + A$

Integrating again

$$EIy = (3{\cdot}2/3)x^3 - \tfrac{2}{3}[x-8]^3 - \tfrac{5}{3}[x-12]^3 + Ax + B$$

When $x = 0$, $y = 0$, $\qquad \therefore \quad B = 0$

When $x = 20$, $y = 0$

$$= (3{\cdot}2/3) \times 20^3 - \tfrac{2}{3} \times 12^3 - \tfrac{5}{3} \times 8^3 + 20A$$

giving $\quad A = -(3{\cdot}2/3) \times 400 + (2 \times 1728)/60 + (5 \times 512)/60$

$$= -326{\cdot}5 \text{ kNm}^2$$

(a) Under the 4 kN load, $x = 8$ m, and

$$Ely = (3{\cdot}2/3) \times 8^3 - 326{\cdot}5 \times 8 = -2066 \text{ kN-m}^3$$

$$\text{Deflection } y = -\frac{2066 \times 10^3 \times 10^9}{200{,}000 \times 10^9} = 10{\cdot}3 \text{ mm downwards}$$

Under the 10 kN load, $x = 12$ m, and

$$Ely = (3{\cdot}2/3) \times 12^3 - \tfrac{2}{3} \times 4^3 - 326{\cdot}5 \times 12 = -2118 \text{ kN-m}^3$$

$$\text{Deflection } y = -\frac{2118 \times 10^3 \times 10^9}{200{,}000 \times 10^9} = 10{\cdot}6 \text{ mm downwards}$$

(b) The maximum deflection can be judged to lie between the loads, and, omitting the term in $[x - 12]$, the following equation is obtained for zero slope:

$$3{\cdot}2x^2 - 2(x-8)^2 - 326{\cdot}5 = 0$$

i.e. $$1{\cdot}2x^2 + 32x - 454{\cdot}5 = 0$$

giving $$x = \frac{-32 + \sqrt{(32^2 + 4 \times 1{\cdot}2 \times 454{\cdot}5)}}{2 \times 1{\cdot}2}$$

$$= 10{\cdot}3 \text{ m}$$

(Note that this does lie within the section assumed.)

$$\text{Maximum deflection} = \frac{((3\cdot2/3) \times 10\cdot3^3 - \frac{2}{3} \times 2\cdot3^3 - 326\cdot5 \times 10\cdot3)10^{12}}{200{,}000 \times 10^9}$$

$$= -\frac{2203 \times 10^{12}}{200{,}000 \times 10^9}$$

$$= 11 \text{ mm}$$

EXAMPLE 7. *A cantilever 4 m long is supported at the free end by a prop, at the same level as the fixed end. A uniformly distributed load of 6000 kg/m is carried along the middle half of the beam, together with a central concentrated load of 5000 kg. Determine the load on the prop and the maximum bending moment.*

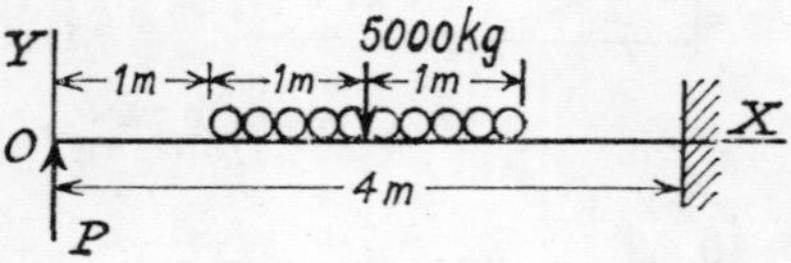

Fig. 9.10

Let P be the load on the prop.
Taking the origin at the prop

$$EI\cdot d^2y/dx^2 = Px - 6000[x-1]^2/2 + 6000[x-3]^2/2 - 5000[x-2]$$

$$EI\cdot dy/dx = Px^2/2 - 1000[x-1]^3 + 1000[x-3]^3 - 2500[x-2]^2 + A$$

$$EIy = Px^3/6 - 250[x-1]^4 + 250[x-3]^4 - 2500[x-2]^3/3 + Ax + B$$

When $x = 4$ m,

$$dy/dx = 0 = 8P - 27{,}000 + 1000 - 10{,}000 + A$$

i.e. $$A = 36{,}000 - 8P \qquad \text{(i)}$$

also $$y = 0 = 10\cdot67P - 26{,}670 + 4A + B$$

From (i) $$B = -10\cdot67P + 26{,}670 - 4 \times 36{,}000 + 4 \times 8P$$

$$= 21\cdot33P - 117{,}330 \qquad \text{(ii)}$$

When $x = 0$, $y = 0$, $\therefore B = 0$

giving $$P = 117{,}330/21\cdot33 \text{ from (ii)}$$

$$= 5500 \text{ kg}$$

A point of maximum bending moment occurs at a value of x giving zero shear force (Para. 5.5), which will be in the distributed load such that the downward load equals the load on the prop, i.e. at

$$x = 1 + 5500/6000$$

$$= 1\cdot917 \text{ m from the prop}$$

where $$M = 5500 \times 1\cdot917 - 6000\ (1\cdot917 - 1)^2/2$$

$$= 8020 \text{ kg m}$$

Check against the value at the built-in end

$$M = 5500 \times 4 - 3000(4-1)^2 + 3000(4-3)^2 - 5000(4-2)$$

$$= 12{,}000 \text{ kgm}$$

The greatest bending moment is therefore 12,000 kgm

EXAMPLE 8. *A horizontal beam, simply supported at its ends, carries a load which varies uniformly from 1000 kg/m at one end to 5000 kg/m at the other. Estimate the central deflection if the span is 10 m, the section 0·4 m deep, and the maximum bending stress 90 N/mm² E = 205,000 N/mm².*

Divide the loading diagram (Fig. 9.11) into a uniform rate of 1000 kg/m together with a varying load (from 0 to 4000 kg/m), which has a value $4000x/10 = 400x$ kg/m at x m from the end. Let R be the reaction on the support at that end.

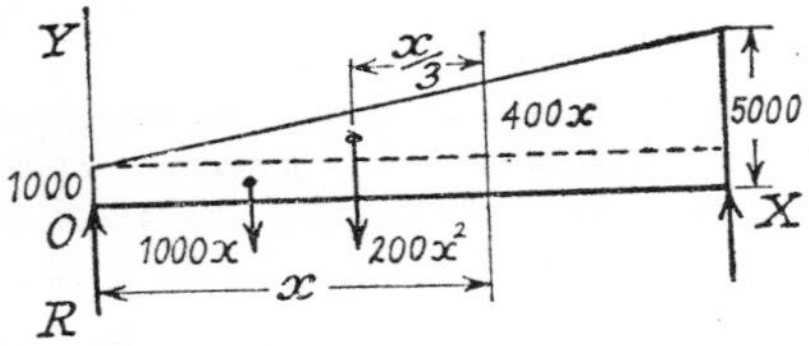

Fig. 9.11

Taking moments about the other end

$$10R = (1000 \times 10) \times 5 + (\tfrac{1}{2} \times 4000 \times 10) \times 10/3$$

where the varying load has a total value given by the mean intensity times the span, and acts at the centroid of the triangular figure

$$\therefore \quad R = 11{,}670 \text{ kg} = 114 \text{ kN}$$

Repeating the same method to obtain an expression for the bending moment at a distance x from the support

$$EI \cdot d^2y/dx^2 = 114x - 9{\cdot}81x^2/2 - [\tfrac{1}{2}(3{\cdot}92x)x]x/3$$
$$= 114x - 4{\cdot}9x^2 - 0{\cdot}655x^3 \text{ kNm}$$
$$EI \cdot dy/dx = 57x^2 - 1{\cdot}63x^3 - 0{\cdot}164x^4 + A$$
$$EIy = 19x^3 - 0{\cdot}408x^4 - 0{\cdot}0327x^5 + Ax + B$$

At $x = 0$, $y = 0$, $\quad \therefore \quad B = 0$

At $x = 10$ m, $y = 0$,

$$\therefore \quad A = -1900 + 408 + 327$$
$$= -1165 \text{ kNm}^2$$

The maximum bending moment occurs at zero shear force

$$d^3y/dx^3 = 0 = 114 - 9{\cdot}81x - 1{\cdot}96x^2 \text{ from above,}$$

or

$$1{\cdot}96x^2 + 9{\cdot}81x - 114 = 0$$

giving

$$x = \frac{-9{\cdot}81 + \sqrt{(96{\cdot}3 + 894)}}{3{\cdot}92} = 5{\cdot}54 \text{ m}$$

$$\hat{M} = 114 \times 5{\cdot}54 - 4{\cdot}9 \times 5{\cdot}54^2 - 0{\cdot}655 \times 5{\cdot}54^3 = 362 \text{ kNm}$$

$$\text{Maximum stress } 90 = \hat{M} \times (\tfrac{1}{2} \text{ depth})/I$$

giving

$$I = 362 \times 10^6 \times 200/90 = 8{\cdot}05 \times 10^8 \text{ mm}^4$$

At the centre

$$EIy = 19 \times 5^3 - 0{\cdot}408 \times 5^4 - 0{\cdot}0327 \times 5^5 - 1165 \times 5$$
$$= -3807 \text{ kNm}^3$$

giving

$$y = -\frac{3807 \times 10^{12}}{205{,}000 \times 8{\cdot}05 \times 10^8} = 23 \text{ mm}$$

Alternatively, the above problem may be commenced from the rate of loading equation

$$EI \cdot d^4y/dx^4 = -9{\cdot}81 - 3{\cdot}92x \text{ kN/m}$$

integrating twice to obtain the bending moment equation, the constants of integration being found from $M=0$ at $x=0$ and $x=10$ m.

Example 9. *If the rate of loading on a beam of length l, simply supported at its ends, is given by $w=p \sin \pi x/l$, where x is the distance from one end, find the reactions at the supports and the maximum bending moment.*

$$dF/dx = -w = -p \sin(\pi x/l) \quad \text{(Para. 5.5)}$$

$$\therefore \quad F = (pl/\pi)\cos(\pi x/l) + A \qquad \text{(i)}$$
$$= dM/dx$$

$$\therefore \quad M = (pl^2/\pi^2)\sin(\pi x/l) + Ax + B \qquad \text{(ii)}$$

But $M=0$ at $x=0$ and at $x=l$,

$$\therefore \quad B=0 \quad \text{and} \quad A=0$$

Maximum bending moment $= pl^2/\pi^2$ from (ii)

Reaction at support = value of F at $x=0$
$= pl/\pi$ from (i).

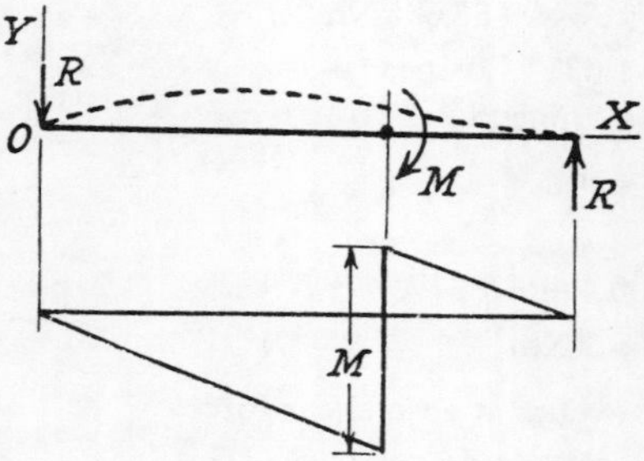

Fig. 9.12

Example 10. *A beam, which is supported through pin joints at its ends, is acted upon by a couple M in a plane containing the axis of the beam, applied at a point two-thirds of the span from one end. Find an expression for the slope and deflection at the point of application, and indicate the shape of the deflected beam.*

The reactions must be equal and opposite, i.e.

$$R = M/l$$

The bending moment diagram is shown in Fig. 9.12, giving

$$EI.d^2y/dx^2 = -Rx + M[x-2l/3]^\circ$$

$$EI.dy/dx = -Rx^2/2 + M[x-2l/3] + A$$

$$EIy = -Rx^3/6 + M/2[x-2l/3]^2 + Ax + B$$

When $x=0$, $y=0$ $\quad \therefore \quad B=0$

When $x=l$, $y=0$ $\quad \therefore \quad Al = Rl^3/6 - (M/2)(l/3)^2$

giving $\quad A = Ml/9$

At $x = 2l/3$

$$EI.dy/dx = -(R/2)(2l/3)^2 + Ml/9$$
$$= -Ml/9$$

i.e. slope $= -Ml/9EI$, indicating downwards to the right

$$EIy = -(R/6)(2l/3)^3 + (Ml/9)(2l/3)$$

i.e. Deflection $= 2Ml^2/81EI$, upwards

There must be a point of zero slope for $x < 2l/3$, given by

$$-Rx^2/2 + A = 0$$

i.e. $$x = (\sqrt{2/3})l$$

The maximum deflection $= [-(M/6l)(2\sqrt{2/27})l^3 + (Ml/9)(\sqrt{2/3})l]/EI$
$= 2\sqrt{2}Ml^2/81EI$

At $x = l$

$$\text{slope} = [-(M/l)(l^2/2) + Ml/3 + Ml/9]/EI$$
$$= -Ml/18EI$$

so that the beam lies entirely "above" the OX axis, its shape being similar to the dotted line in Fig. 9.12.

9.5. Moment-area Method. Fig. 9.13 shows the bending moment diagram and the shape of the deflected beam between two chosen points P and Q.

The area of the B.M. diagram is A, and its centroid is at a distance $\bar{x}$ from a chosen line OY. The tangents at P and Q to the elastic line cut off an intercept z on OY.

$$d^2y/dx^2 = M/EI$$

Integrating between P and Q

$$\left[\frac{dy}{dx}\right]_P^Q = \int \frac{Mdx}{EI}$$

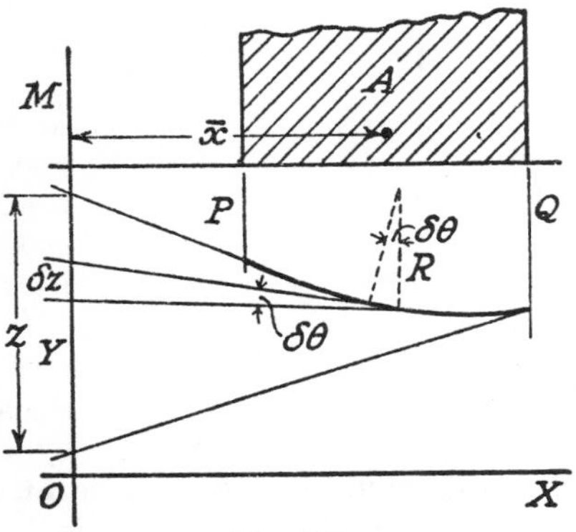

Fig. 9.13

If EI is constant

$$\left(\frac{dy}{dx}\right)_Q - \left(\frac{dy}{dx}\right)_P = \frac{A}{EI} \qquad (1)$$

i.e. *The increase of slope between any two points on a beam is equal to the net area of the bending moment diagram between those points divided by EI.*

If R is the radius of curvature of the beam at some point between P and Q, then the angle between the tangents at the ends of a short length δx is $\delta\theta$, where $\delta x = R.\delta\theta$. The intercept of these tangents on OY is δz, and since the slope is everywhere small,

$$\delta z \doteqdot x\delta\theta$$
$$= x\delta x/R = Mx\delta x/EI$$

Integrating $$z = \int Mx.dx/EI$$
$$= A\bar{x}/EI \quad \text{if } EI \text{ is constant} \qquad (2)$$

i.e. *The intercept on a given line between the tangents to the beam at any points* P *and* Q *is equal to the net moment about that line of the bending moment diagram between* P *and* Q *divided by EI.*

Account is to be taken of positive and negative areas, and frequently it is convenient to break down the bending moment diagram into a number of simple figures, so that the moment is obtained from $\Sigma A\bar{x}$.

The intercept z is positive when the tangent at Q strikes OY below the tangent at P.

This method will only be used for particular applications in which it produces a quicker solution than the mathematical treatment. These cases can generally be labelled as those for which a point of zero slope is known. If this point is chosen as "Q," and OY is taken through P (Fig. 9.14), then (1) reduces to

$$\text{Slope at P} = -A/EI$$

and (2)

$$\text{Deflection of P relative to Q} = A\bar{x}/EI$$

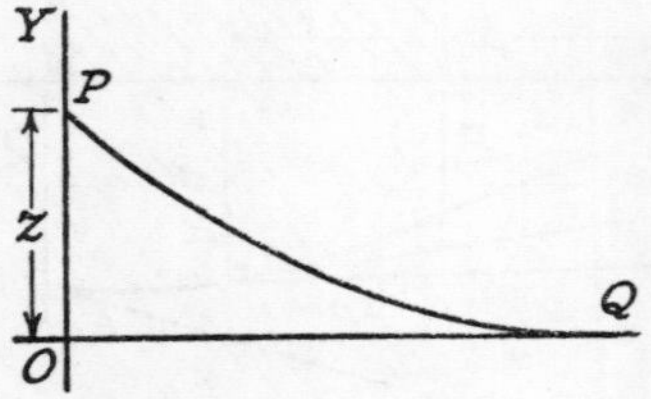

Fig. 9.14

i.e the deflection at any point can be found by working between there and a point of zero slope, and taking moments about the point where the deflection is required.

It is very helpful in applying these theorems to sketch the approximate shape of the deflected beam, and then by drawing the tangents at chosen points it should be clear which intercept gives the relative deflection (e.g. if OY is taken through Q in Fig. 9.14 the intercept does *not* give the deflection).

Summarising the cases in which this method proves advantageous:

(a) most cantilever problems (zero slope at fixed end);

(b) symmetrically loaded simply supported beams (zero slope at centre);

(c) Built-in beams (zero slope at each end) (Chapter X).

For uniformly distributed loads the B.M. diagram is a parabola, and the following properties of area and centroids should be known.

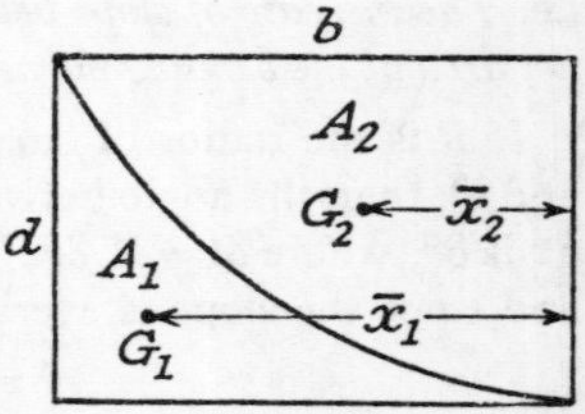

Fig. 9.15

In Fig. 9.15, *bd* is the surrounding rectangle, and the parabola is tangential to the base.

Then $A_1 = \frac{1}{3}bd$

and $\bar{x}_1 = \frac{3}{4}b$

$A_2 = \frac{2}{3}bd$

and $\bar{x}_2 = \frac{3}{8}b$

EXAMPLE 11. *Obtain expressions for the maximum slope and deflection of a simply supported beam of span l (a) with a concentrated load W at mid-span (b) with a uniformly distributed load w over the whole span.*

In both cases, by symmetry, the slope is zero at the centre, and the maximum slope and deflection can be found from the area of the bending moment diagram over half the beam, i.e. "P" at support, "Q" at centre (cf. Fig. 9.14).

(a) If A is the area of B.M. diagram for half the beam

$$A = \tfrac{1}{2}(Wl/4)(l/2) \quad \text{(Fig. 9.16)}$$
$$= Wl^2/16$$

Then from (1)

$$\text{Slope at support} = -A/EI$$
$$= -Wl^2/16EI$$

From (2)

$$\text{Deflection of support relative to centre} = A\bar{x}/EI$$
$$= \frac{Wl^2}{16} \cdot \frac{l/3}{EI}$$
$$= Wl^3/48EI$$

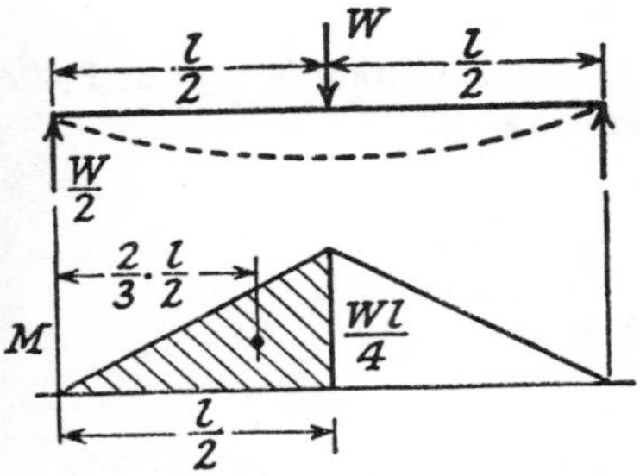

Fig. 9.16

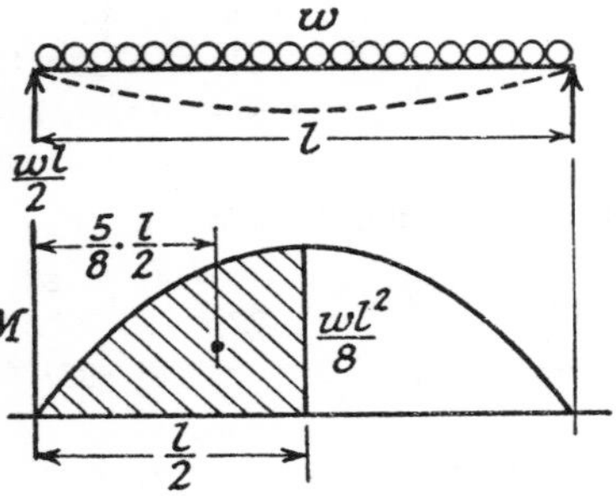

Fig. 9.17

(b) Shaded area $A = \frac{2}{3}(wl^2/8)(l/2)$ (Fig. 9.17)

$$= wl^3/24$$
$$\text{Slope at support} = -A/EI$$
$$= -wl^3/24EI$$

$$\text{Deflection of support relative to centre} = A\bar{x}/EI$$
$$= \frac{(wl^3/24)(\frac{5}{16}l)}{EI}$$
$$= 5wl^4/384EI$$

EXAMPLE 12. *A horizontal cantilever ABC, 15 m long, is built in at A and supported at B, 12 m from A, by a rigid prop so that AB is horizontal. If AB and BC carry uniformly distributed loads of 0·5 kN/m and 1·0 kN/m respectively, find the load taken by the prop.*

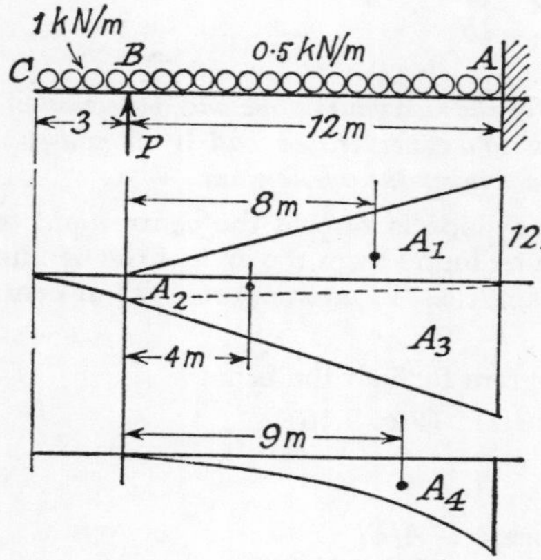

Fig. 9.18

If the bending moment diagram is broken down into the areas shown in Fig. 9.18, each area can be dealt with as a triangle or parabola of standard type.

If P is the load on the prop

$$A_1 = \tfrac{1}{2}\ 12P \times 12$$
$$= 72P \text{ kNm}^2$$

Due to the load on BC, the bending moment at B $= -3 \times 3/2 = -9/2$ kNm, and at A $= -3 \times 27/2 = -81/2$ kNm, the trapezium between A and B being split up into two triangles

$$A_2 = -\tfrac{1}{2} \times (9/2) \times 12 = -27 \text{ kNm}^2$$

and

$$A_3 = -\tfrac{1}{2} \times (81/2) \times 12 \times -243 \text{ kNm}^2$$

Due to the load on AB, the area A_4 is a parabola with a maximum value of $(0{\cdot}5 \times 12^2)/2$, or 36 kNm, i.e.

$$A_4 = \tfrac{1}{3} \times 36 \times 12 = 144 \text{ kNm}^2$$

Slope is zero at the built-in end A, and deflection is zero at B, i.e.

$$z = \Sigma A\bar{x}/EI = 0 \quad \text{(from (2))}$$

for the portion AB about B, or

$$A_1\bar{x}_1 = A_2\bar{x}_2 + A_3\bar{x}_3 + A_4\bar{x}_4$$

giving

$$72P \times 8 = 27 \times 4 + 243 \times 8 + 144 \times 9$$

from which

$$P = 93/16 = 5{\cdot}81 \text{ kN}$$

EXAMPLE 13. *A horizontal beam rests on two supports at the same level and carries a uniformly distributed load. If the supports are symmetrically placed find their positions when the greatest downward deflection has its least value.* (*U.L.*)

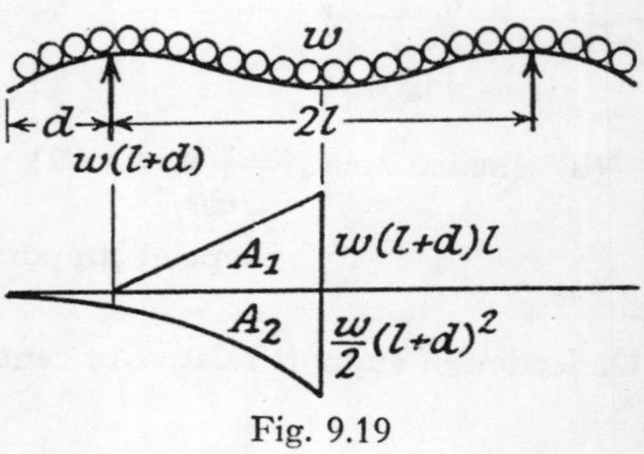

Fig. 9.19

Let the distance between the supports be $2l$, and the overhanging distance d (Fig. 9.19).

Then the reaction at each support $= w(l+d)$.

The condition for the greatest downward deflection to have its least value occurs when the deflections at the end and centre are the same, since any variation of the supports from this position will increase either one or other of these values. Since the slope is zero at the centre then $\Sigma A\bar{x} = 0$ for half the beam about one end.

Breaking down the bending moment diagram into A_1 due to the support, and A_2 due to the load, then

$$A_1\bar{x}_1 = A_2\bar{x}_2$$

i.e. $$[\tfrac{1}{2}.w(l+d)l.l](d+\tfrac{2}{3}l) = [\tfrac{1}{3}(w/2)(l+d)^2(l+d)]\tfrac{3}{4}(l+d)$$

×24: $$5l^3 + 3l^2d - 9ld^2 - 3d^3 = 0$$

By trial and error: $$l = 1{\cdot}24d$$

EXAMPLE 14. *A long steel strip of uniform width and 3 mm thick is laid on a level floor, but passes over a 5 cm diameter roller lying on the floor at one point. For what distance on either side of the roller will the strip be clear of the ground and what will be the maximum stress induced? Density of steel = 7950 kg/m³ E = 205,000 N/mm².*

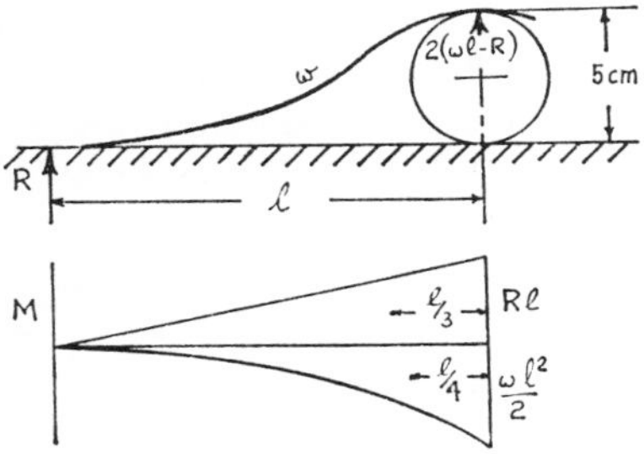

Fig. 9.20

For that part of the strip lying on the floor, the ground reaction just balances the weight, and, since there is no change of slope, there is no bending moment in this length. However, where the strip leaves the floor, there will be a point reaction R, and the conditions are as though the surplus length in contact with the floor were cut off.

The forces and bending moment diagram are shown in Fig. 9.20, w being the weight per unit length.

Since there is no change of slope between R and the top of the roller, equating areas gives

$$\tfrac{1}{2}Rl.l = \tfrac{1}{3}(wl^2/2)l$$

i.e. $$R = \tfrac{1}{3}wl \qquad \text{(i)}$$

By moment areas about the roller,

$$\frac{1}{EI}\left(\frac{Rl}{2}.l.\frac{l}{3} - \frac{wl^2}{3\times 2}.l.\frac{l}{4}\right) = 5$$

i.e. $$l^4 = 5EI \times 72/w \quad \text{from (i)} \qquad \text{(ii)}$$

$$= \frac{5 \times 205{,}000b \times 3^3 \times 72 \times 10^6}{12 \times 3b \times 7950 \times 9{\cdot}81} \quad (b\text{mm} = \text{width of strip})$$

$$= 7{\cdot}3 \times 10^8 \text{ cm}^4$$

$$\therefore\ l = 164 \text{ cm}$$

It should be noted that equation (ii) can be obtained by treating the roller as a 'fixed end' and taking the difference between the 'cantilever' deflections due to R and w.

The maximum bending moment is at the roller, where

$$M = Rl - wl^2/2$$
$$= wl^2/6 \text{ numerically, from (i)}$$

(there is a point of zero shearing force at $l/3$ from R, but here $M = Rl/3 - wl^2/18 = wl^2/18$)

$$\hat{\sigma} = 6M/bd^2$$
$$= \frac{6 \times 3b \times 7950 \times 9{\cdot}81 \times 164^2}{10^7 \times 6 \times b \times 3^2}$$
$$= 68{\cdot}5 \text{ N/mm}^2$$

EXAMPLE 15. *A cantilever of uniform strength is to be turned from a mild-steel bar 50 mm diameter. A load of 4000 N is to be supported from the free end, and the maximum stress is limited to 70 N/mm². Determine the maximum length of the cantilever and its end deflection. E = 205,000 N/mm².*

The maximum bending moment is $4000l$, at the fixed end, and the strongest section is 50 mm diameter. Applying the bending stress formula

$$70 = \frac{(4000l) \times 25}{(\pi/64) \times 50^4}$$

from which $l = 214$ mm

Let the diameter be d mm at x mm from the free end, then, applying the condition for uniform strength (i.e. constant maximum stress)

$$70 = \frac{4000x}{\pi d^4/64} \cdot \frac{d}{2}$$

or $d^3 = 583x$

The I value is varying along the bar, but the deflection can be found by the moment-area method, using the form $z = \int Mxdx/EI$, z giving the end deflection if moments are taken about the free end, i.e.

$$\text{Deflection} = \int_0^l \frac{64(4000x)x \, . \, dx}{205{,}000 \times \pi d^4}$$

$$= \frac{64}{51{\cdot}25\pi(583)^{4/3}} \int_0^{214} \frac{x^2 \, . \, dx}{x^{4/3}} \text{ from above,}$$

$$= \frac{64}{51{\cdot}25\pi \times (583)^{4/3}} \cdot \frac{3}{5} \cdot (214)^{5/3}$$

$$= 0{\cdot}375 \text{ mm}$$

9.6. Method of Deflection Coefficients. It should be realised that any beam of length l and flexural rigidity EI carrying a total load W, however distributed, will have a maximum deflection $= k \cdot Wl^3/EI$, the value of k depending on the type of loading and supports.

k has been found for standard cases of cantilever and simply supported beam (Examples 4 and 11), and deflection in other cases may frequently be built up by the **principle of superposition** (see Para. 1.5.)

Two types of problem will be solved by this method.

EXAMPLE 16. *A beam of uniform section and length 2l is simply supported at its ends and by an elastic prop at the centre. If the prop deflects an amount α times the load it carries and the beam carries a total uniformly distributed load W show that the load carried by the prop* $= \dfrac{5W}{8(1+6EI\alpha/l^3)}$.

If $l = 3$ *m,* $I = 6 \times 10^6$ *mm*^{4}, $W = 50$ *kN, and* $\alpha = 4 \times 10^{-3}$ *mm/N, find the position and value of the maximum bending moment.* $E = 200{,}000$ *N/mm*^{2}. *(U.L.)*

If P is the load on the prop, then its deflection is αP.

Downward deflection due to load only

$$= (5/384)[W(2l)^3/EI] \quad \text{(see Ex. 11, part (b))}$$

Upward deflection due to prop only

$$= P(2l)^3/48EI \quad \text{(Ex. 11, part (a))}$$

By superposition, the net downward deflection

$$\alpha P = (5/384)[W(2l)^3/EI] - P(2l)^3/48EI$$

from which $P(\alpha + l^3/6EI) = (5/48)(Wl^3/EI)$

and
$$P = \frac{5W}{8(6EI\alpha/l^3 + 1)}$$

Substituting the numerical values gives

$$P = \frac{5 \times 50{,}000}{8[(6 \times 200{,}000 \times 6 \times 10^6 \times 4 \times 10^{-3})/3000^3 + 1]}$$
$$= 15{,}000 \text{ N}$$

The reaction at the end supports

$$= \tfrac{1}{2}(50{,}000 - 15{,}000) = 17{,}500 \text{ N}$$

and for $x < 3$ m

$$M = 17{,}500x - (50{,}000/6)(x^2/2)$$

For a maximum $dM/dx = 0$, giving

$$x = 17{,}500 \times 6/50{,}000 = 2{\cdot}1 \text{ m}$$

and
$$\hat{M} = 18{,}400 \text{ Nm}$$

EXAMPLE 17. *A horizontal steel beam,* $I = 80 \times 10^6$ *mm*^{4}, *carries a uniformly distributed load of 50 kN over its length of 3 m. The beam is supported by three vertical steel tie rods, each 2 m long, one at each end and one in the middle, the end rods having diameters of 24 mm and the centre rod 30 mm.*

Calculate the deflection at the centre of the beam below the end points and the stress in each tie rod. $E = 208{,}000$ *N/mm*^{2}. *(U.L.)*

Let P kN be the load in the centre rod (Fig. 9.21).

Then by superposition the following compatibility equation is obtained: Stretch of centre rod − Stretch of end rod
= Deflection of beam due to load − Deflection due to centre rod

i.e.
$$\frac{P \times 2000}{\pi \times 15^2 E} - \frac{(50 - P) \times 2000}{2(\pi \times 12^2)E} = \frac{5 \times 50 \times 3000^3}{384E \times 80 \times 10^6} - \frac{P \times 3000^3}{48E \times 80 \times 10^6}$$

or
$$2{\cdot}83P - 111 + 2{\cdot}22P = 219 - 7{\cdot}05P$$

giving
$$P = 330/12{\cdot}1 = 27{\cdot}5 \text{ kN}$$

$$\text{Stress in centre rod} = \frac{27{,}500}{\pi \times 15^2} = 39 \text{ N/mm}^2$$

$$\text{Stress in end rods} = \frac{(50{,}000 - 27{,}500)}{2 \times \pi \times 12^2} = 25 \text{ N/mm}^2$$

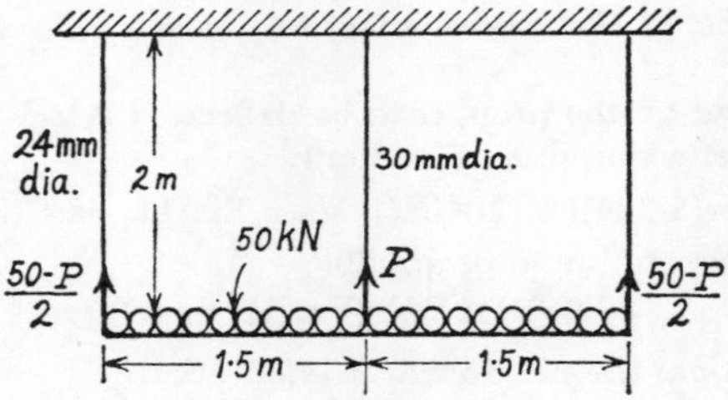

Fig. 9.21

Deflection of centre relative to ends

$$= \text{Difference of stretches of tie rods}$$

$$= \frac{39 \times 2000 - 25 \times 2000}{208{,}000}$$

$$= 0{\cdot}135 \text{ mm}$$

9.7. Deflection due to Shear. It was shown in Chapter VII how a shear stress was set up on transverse sections of a beam, and the accompanying shear strain will cause a distortion of the cross-section, and, since the shear stress varies from zero at the extreme fibres to a maximum at the neutral axis, cross-sections can no longer remain plane after bending.

In fact the "warping" will be of the form shown in Fig. 9.22, the left-hand view being for positive shear and the right-hand for negative shear. These strains are incompatible with the theory of pure bending, but nevertheless a good approximation to the deflection due to shear can be obtained by strain energy methods. It

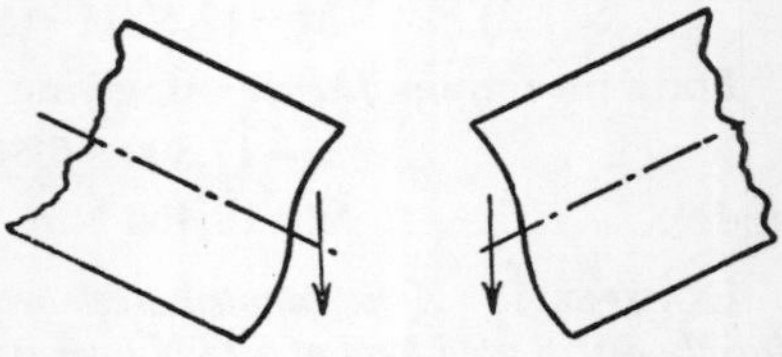

Fig. 9.22

should also be noted that the shear distribution near to the application of a concentrated load must differ considerably from that given by the theory in Para. 7.1, since there can be no sudden change of shear strain from one type to the other, as would be implied for a simply supported beam with a central load.

Strain energy due to shear $=(\tau^2/2G)\times$ volume (Para. 2.5)

For the whole beam

$$U_s=(1/2G)\iint\tau^2 dA\,.\,dx \qquad (1)$$

where dA is an element of cross-section and dx an element of length.

The integration can only be performed for particular cross-sections over which the variation of τ is known, and rectangular and I-sections will be dealt with below.

Rectangular Section

It was shown in Para. 7.2 that $\tau=(6F/bd^3)(d^2/4-y^2)$ where y is the distance from the neutral axis. $dA=bdy$, then

$$U_s=\frac{1}{2G}\int\left[\int_{-d/2}^{d/2}\frac{36F^2}{b^2d^6}\left(\frac{d^4}{16}-\frac{d^2y^2}{2}+y^4\right)bdy\right].dx \quad \text{from (1)}$$

$$=\frac{1}{2G}\int\frac{36F^2}{bd^6}\left[\frac{d^4y}{16}-\frac{d^2y^3}{6}+\frac{y^5}{5}\right]_{-d/2}^{d/2}.dx$$

$$=\frac{18}{Gbd}\int F^2.2\left(\frac{1}{32}-\frac{1}{48}+\frac{1}{160}\right).dx$$

$$=\frac{3}{5Gbd}\int_0^l F^2.dx \qquad (2)$$

Cantilever with load W at free end.

$$F=W$$

$$\therefore \quad U_s=\frac{3W^2l}{5Gbd} \quad \text{from (2)}$$

But $U_s=\frac{1}{2}W\delta_s$, where δ_s is the deflection due to shear

$$\therefore \quad \delta_s=6Wl/5Gbd$$

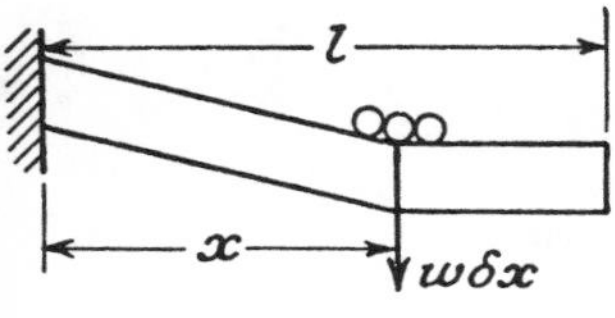

Fig. 9.23

Cantilever with uniformly distributed load. The load $w\delta x$, on a length δx at a distance x from the fixed end, treated as a concentrated load, will produce a deflection due to shear $=(6w\delta x\,.\,x)/5Gbd$ at this point. For this load alone the distortion produced is indicated in Fig. 9·23, being uniform shear force over the length x and zero over $l-x$, hence the total deflection due to shear for all the distributed load

$$= \int_0^l \frac{6wx\,dx}{5Gbd}$$

$$= 3wl^2/5Gbd$$

Simply supported beam with central load W.

$$F = \pm W/2$$

$$U_s = \int_0^l \frac{3(W^2/4)}{5Gbd}\,.dx \quad \text{from (2)}$$

$$= 3W^2l/20Gbd$$

$$= \tfrac{1}{2}W\delta_s$$

$$\therefore \quad \delta_s = 3Wl/10Gbd$$

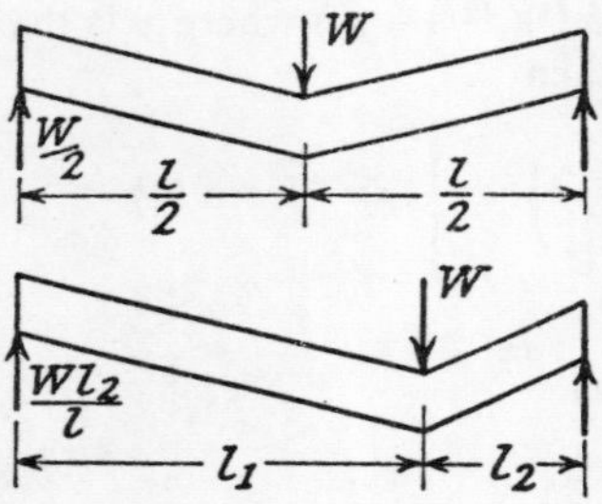

Fig. 9.24

The "simplified" deflection is as shown in the upper diagram of Fig. 9.24, and since the shearing force is constant over each half this case is equivalent to a cantilever of length $l/2$ carrying an end load of $W/2$.

If the load is not centrally applied, but divides the length into l_1 and l_2 then treating either section as a cantilever with an end load equal to the reaction on that side

$$\delta_s = \frac{6(Wl_2/l)l_1}{5Gbd}$$

$$= 6Wl_1l_2/5Gbdl \quad \text{under the load (Fig. 9.24).}$$

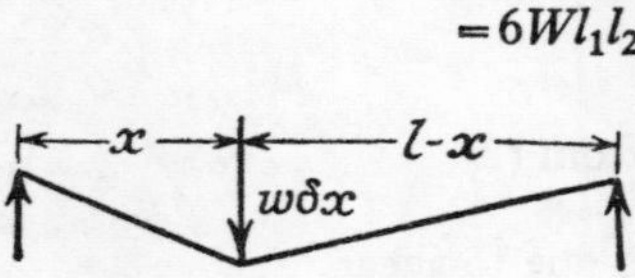

Fig. 9.25

Simply supported beam with uniformly distributed load. Due to a load $w\delta x$ only, at a distance x from one end ($x < l/2$), the deflection at the load

$$= 6w\delta x(l-x)x/5Gbdl \quad \text{just proved.}$$

By proportion, the deflection at the centre of the beam

$$= \frac{6w\delta x(l-x)}{5Gbdl}x.\left(\frac{l/2}{l-x}\right) \quad \text{(Fig. 9.25)}$$

Then the total central deflection due to shear

$$= 2\int_0^{l/2} \frac{3wx\,dx}{5Gbd}$$

$$= 3wl^2/20Gbd$$

I-section

Treating the shearing force as uniformly distributed over the web area bd (see Para. 7.3), then $\tau = F/bd$ and $\int dA = bd$.

$$\therefore \quad U_s = (1/2G)\int(F^2/b^2d^2)bd.dx \quad \text{from (1)}$$

$$= (\int F^2.dx)/2Gbd \qquad (3)$$

By similar methods to those employed for a rectangular section the deflections due to shear may be obtained as follows:

Cantilever with end load, $\delta_s = Wl/Gbd$

Cantilever with distributed load, $\delta_s = Wl/2Gbd$

Simply supported beam with central load, $\delta_s = Wl/4Gbd$

Simply supported beam with distributed load, $\delta_s = Wl/8Gbd$.

The strain energy method known as "Castigliano's Theorem" (Para. 11.4) may be used where a number of loads exist concurrently, or to find the deflection due to a distributed load by imposing a concentrated load at the deflection point and later giving it a value zero (i.e. $\delta_s = (\partial U_s/\partial P)_{P=0}$).

EXAMPLE 18. *For a given cantilever of rectangular cross-section, length l, and depth d, show that, if δ_s and δ_b are the deflections due to shear and bending due to a concentrated load at the free end, $\delta_s/\delta_b = k\cdot(d/l)^2$, and find the value of k for steel. $E = 205{,}000$ N/mm²; $G = 80{,}000$ N/mm².*

Hence find the least value of l/d if the deflection due to shear is not to exceed 1% of the total.

It has been shown that

$$\delta_s = 6Wl/5Gbd$$

and

$$\delta_b = Wl^3/3EI = 4Wl^3/Ebd^3$$

for a rectangular section.

$$\therefore \quad \delta_s/\delta_b = [6/(5\times4)](E/G)(d/l)^2 = k(d/l)^2$$

where

$$k = (3/10)(E/G) = (3/10)(205/80)$$

$$= 0{\cdot}77$$

If $\delta_s/(\delta_b + \delta_s) = 0{\cdot}01$

$$\therefore \quad \delta_s/\delta_b = 0{\cdot}01/0{\cdot}99$$

$$= 0{\cdot}77(d/l)^2 \quad \text{from above,}$$

i.e.

$$\text{Least value of } l/d = \sqrt{(0{\cdot}77\times 99)}$$

$$= 8{\cdot}7$$

EXAMPLE 19. *A 250 mm by 150 mm R.S.J. with web 10 mm, flanges 17·5 mm thick, acts as a horizontal cantilever 4 m long and carries a load of 2000 kg at 2 m from the end. Assuming the shear force is carried by the web and is uniformly distributed, calculate the deflection at the end. $E = 200{,}000$ N/mm²; $G = 78{,}000$ N/mm². (U.L.)*

$$I = (150\times 250^3 - 140\times 215^3)/12 = 78{\cdot}5\times 10^6 \text{ mm}^4$$

By the moment-area method (Para. 9.5), end deflection due to bending

$$\left(\tfrac{1}{2} \times 2000 \times 9{\cdot}81 \times 2000^2\right)\frac{10{,}000}{3 \times 200{,}000 \times 78{\cdot}5 \times 10^6} = 8{\cdot}34 \text{ mm} \quad \text{(Fig. 9.26)}$$

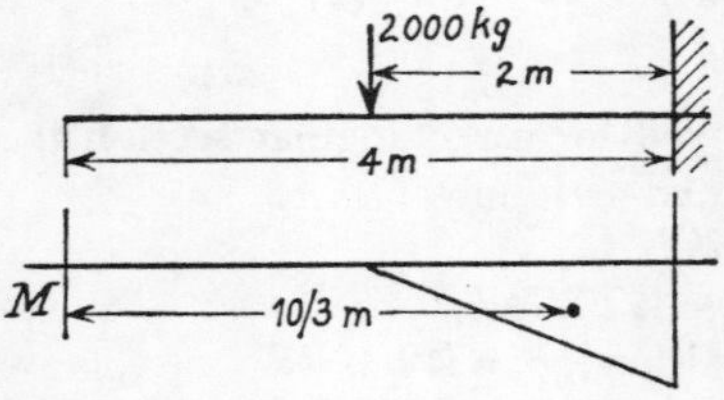

Fig. 9.26

Deflection due to shear at the load is given by

$$\frac{Wl}{Gbd} = \frac{2000 \times 9{\cdot}81 \times 2000}{78{,}000 \times 10 \times 215} = 0{\cdot}234 \text{ mm}$$

But since the shearing force is zero beyond the load this is also the deflection due to shear at the free end (see also Fig. 9.23).

Combined deflection at free end $= 8{\cdot}34 + 0{\cdot}234 = 8{\cdot}57$ mm

9.8. Deflection by Graphical Method. It was shown in Para. 5.10 how a "funicular polygon" could be used to perform a double integration of the load curve and produce the bending moment diagram. Since $d^2y/dx^2 = M/EI$ it follows that a double integration of the bending moment curve will produce the deflection curve.

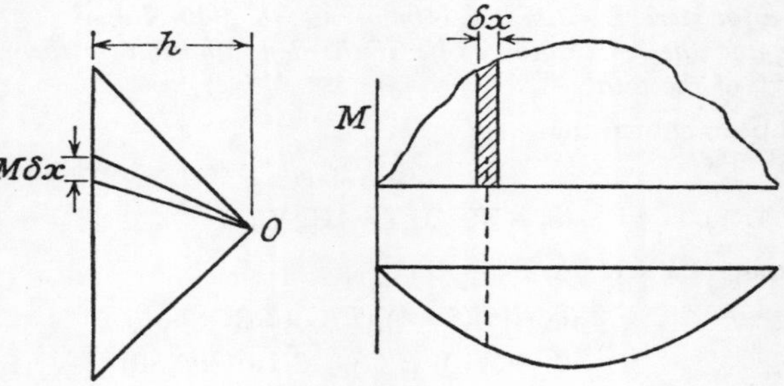

Fig. 9.27

If EI is constant, draw the B.M. diagram and divide into a number of strips δx (Fig. 9.27). Draw a vertical line to represent the areas $M\delta x$ and join to a pole O, on the right of this line. Proceed in the normal way to draw the funicular polygon, being a series of straight lines to be smoothed out into a curve. The vertical ordinates on this diagram represent deflection, and it will usually be necessary to "shear" the diagram through an angle in order to produce a horizontal base (e.g. for a simply supported beam).

If the scales are 1 mm $= s_1$ Nm² "$M\delta x$" units, 1 mm $= s_2$ m length, and 1 mm $= s_3$ Nm³ "EIy" units, then the distance h is given by s_3/s_1s_2 mm. If then the deflection scale required is 1 mm $= s_4$ mm $= s_3/EI$, $h = EIs_4/s_1s_2$.

SUMMARY

Strain Energy $U = \int M^2 . dx/2EI$. Applications to deflection and impact.

Deflection by Calculus $EId^2y/dx^2 = M$. Macaulay's method.

Moment-Area Method. Increase of slope $= \Sigma A/EI$
Intercept $z = \Sigma A\bar{x}/EI$

Deflection Coefficients. Maximum slope $= k_1 . Wl^2/EI$
Maximum deflection $= k_2 . Wl^3/EI$

Beam and Loading	k_1	k_2
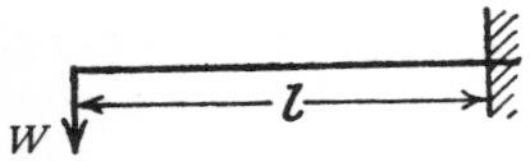	1/2	1/3
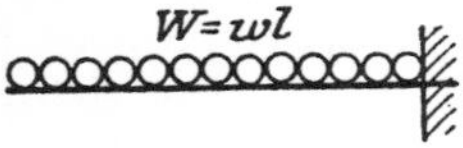	1/6	1/8
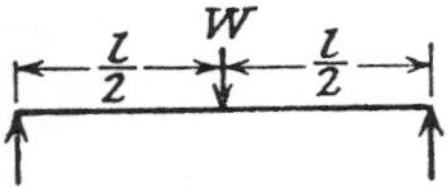	1/16	1/48
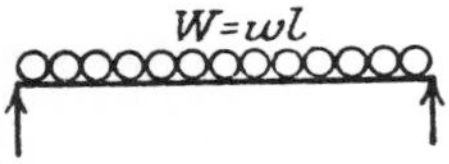	1/24	5/384

Deflection due to Shear. Strain energy method.
Graphical Method.

PROBLEMS

1. Prove that the strain energy of a beam is given by $\int_0^l \frac{M^2}{2EI} dx$.

Strain energy may also be expressed in the form $C.(\sigma^2/E) \times$ volume, where σ is the maximum stress. Find the value of C for a beam of square section simply supported at the ends and carrying a uniformly distributed load. (U.L.) (4/45.)

2. A timber beam of rectangular section 8 cm deep and 5 cm wide was simply supported at its ends over a span of 1 m. The following readings were taken from a test in which the beam was loaded at the centre.

Load (kg)	0	250	500	750	1000	1250	1500	1750	1880
Deflection (mm)	0	1·9	3·8	5·6	7·5	9·6	12·0	15·0	Broke

Find the load which, falling from a height of 15 cm on to the middle of a similar beam, (1) would just not overstrain the beam, (2) would just cause fracture. (U.L.) (30 kg; 110 kg.)

3. Prove, by the method of resilience, that the deflection of a cantilever of length l due to a load W at its free end is $Wl^3/3EI$.

What load falling through 25 mm on to the end of a cantilever 3 m long will cause a maximum deflection of 12 mm? $I=80\times10^6$ mm^4; $E=200{,}000$ N/mm^2. (353 kg.)

4. A horizontal steel beam of I-section rests on a rigid support at one end, the other end being supported by a vertical steel rod 18 mm diameter whose upper end is rigidly held in a support 2·5 m above the end of the beam. The beam is 200 mm by 100 mm for which $I=22\times10^6$mm^4 and the distance between the points of support is 3 m. A load of 200 kg falls on to the beam at mid-span from a height of 18 mm. Determine the maximum stresses set up in the beam and rod and find also the deflection at mid-span measured from the unloaded position. $E=207{,}000$ N/mm^2. (U.L.)

(125 N/mm^2; 67·5 N/mm^2 2·53 mm.)

5. A beam simply supported at its ends over an 8 m span is loaded with 40, 80, and 120 kN at 2, 4, and 6 m respectively from one end. The maximum stress is 90 N/mm^2 and the beam is 300 mm deep. If $E=203{,}000$ N/mm^2 find the maximum deflection and state where it occurs. (18.5 mm; 4·1 m.)

6. A girder 6 m long is supported at one end and at 1·5 m from the other end. It carries a uniformly distributed load of 100 kN/m along its whole length and a concentrated load of 60 kN at the overhanging end. Calculate the maximum downward deflection and state where it occurs. $EI=16{\cdot}7\times10^{12}$ N mm^2.

(16·8 mm; 2·0 m)

7. A beam of uniform section and 12 m span is freely supported at its ends and carries a load varying from 30 kN/m at the left-hand end to 20 kN/m at the right. Find the position and magnitude of the maximum deflection. $I=20\times10^8$ mm^4; $E=208{,}000$ N/mm^2 (6·03 m from right; 16 mm.)

8. A beam of uniform cross-section and flexural rigidity EI, length $3l$, is hinged at one end and rests on a support distant $2l$ from the hinge. There is a load W at the free end and a uniformly distributed load of total W spread over a l ength between l and $2l$ from the hinge. Show that the deflection of the concentrated load is $(13/16)(Wl^3/EI)$.

9. A horizontal propped cantilever of length L is securely fixed at one end and freely supported at the other, and is subjected to a bending couple M in the vertical plane applied about an axis $0{\cdot}75L$ from the fixed end. Determine the end fixing moment and the reaction at the prop.

Sketch the B.M. diagram. (U.L.) $(13/32)M$; $(45/32)(M/L)$.)

10. An initially straight and horizontal cantilever of uniform section and length L is rigidly built-in at one end and carries a uniformly distributed load of intensity w for a distance $L/2$ measured from the built-in end. The second moment of area is I and the modulus of elasticity E. Determine, in terms of w L E and I, (a) an expression for the slope of the cantilever at the end of the load, (b) the deflexion at the free end, (c) the force in a vertical prop which is to be applied at the free end in order to restore this end to the same horizontal level as the built-in end. (U.L.)

((a) $wL^3/48\,EI$, (b) $7wL^4/384\,EI$, (c)$7wL/128$)

11. A beam of constant cross-section 10 m long is freely supported at its ends and loaded with 10 kN at points 3 m from each end. Find the ratio of central deflection to that under each load. (33/27.)

12. A beam 9 m long is symmetrically placed on two supports 6 m apart. The loading is 16·5 kN/m between the supports and 20 kN at each end. What is the central deflection and the slope at the supports? $E=200{,}000$ N/mm² in.; $I=175\times10^6$ mm⁴. (4·3 mm; 0·1°.)

13. A cantilever of length l carries a total distributed load W and is propped at a distance of nl from the fixed end so that the load on the prop is W. Find the ratio between the deflection at the free end of the propped cantilever and that at the free end of an unpropped cantilever. Plot a curve of this ratio against n and hence find the position of the prop when the end deflection is zero.
($1-4n^2+4n^3/3$; 0·555.)

14. A horizontal cantilever 2 m long has its free end attached to a vertical tie rod 3 m long and 300 mm² area, initially unstrained. Determine the load taken by the tie rod and the deflection of the cantilever when a distributed load of 30 kN/m is applied to the outer 1 m of the beam $I=6\times10^6$mm⁴; $E=205{,}000$ N/mm² for both. (18·8 kN; 0·915 mm.)

15. A beam is simply supported on two supports a distance L apart, and overhangs each support by $L/3$. It carries a distributed load of W spread between the supports, and a load of $W/4$ at each end. If the deflection at the centre is equal to that at the free ends, find the value of the second moment of area for the overhanging portions when that between the supports is I. (U.L.) ((32/27)I.)

16. A long flat strip of steel 50 mm wide and 3·2 mm thick is lying on a flat horizontal plane. One end of the strip is now lifted 25 mm from the plane by a vertical force applied at the end. The strip is so long that the other end remains undisturbed. Calculate (a) the force required to lift the end, (b) the maximum stress in the steel. Take the weight of steel as 7800 kg/m³. $E=205{,}000$ N/mm². (U.L.) ((a) 6·7 N; (b) 21 N/mm².)

17. A circular steel pipe 450 mm bore and 6·4 mm thick is supported freely at each end and at the centre over a span of 15 m. When the pipe is full of water the central support sinks 12·5 mm below the ends. Find the load on each support and draw the B.M. diagram. Determine also the maximum bending stress in the pipe. Steel $=7800$ kg/m³; $E=208{,}000$ N/mm²; water $=1000$ kg/m³. (U.L.)
(13 kN centre; 11 kN; 24 N/mm².)

18. An aluminium cantilever of length 250 mm and rectangular cross-section 40 mm wide by 25 mm deep carries a concentrated load at its end. Show that deflection will be underestimated by less than 1% if shear strains are neglected. $E=70{,}000$ N/mm²; $G=27{,}000$ N/mm². (U.L.)

19. A cast-iron cantilever 0·6 m long consists of an I-section 150 mm deep by 100 mm wide, having flanges 50 mm deep and web 25 mm thick. If a load of 2000 kg is carried at the free end find the deflection due to shear. $G=38{,}000$ N/mm². (U.L.) (0·25 mm.)

20. Determine the end deflection, in magnitude and direction, for the unsymmetrical angle used as a cantilever in Ex. 14, Para. 6.12. $E=208{,}000$ N/mm².
($\delta_u=1{\cdot}8$ mm. $\delta_y=4{\cdot}2$ mm. Total deflection 4·6 mm at 47° to the vertical.)

CHAPTER X

Built-In and Continuous Beams

10.1. Moment-Area Method for Built-in Beams. A beam is said to be built-in or encastre when both its ends are rigidly fixed so that the slope remains horizontal. Usually also the *ends are at the same level*.

It follows from the moment-area method (Para. 9.5) that, for a beam of *uniform section*, since the change of slope from end to end and the intercept z are both zero

$$\Sigma A = 0 \qquad (1)$$

and

$$\Sigma A\bar{x} = 0 \qquad (2)$$

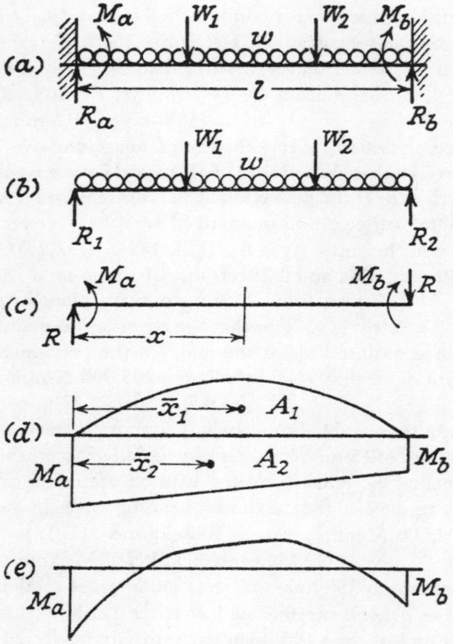

Fig. 10.1

It will be found convenient to show the bending moment diagram due to any loading such as Fig. 10.1(a) as the algebraic sum of two parts, one due to the loads, treating the beam as simply supported (Fig. 10.1(b)), and the other due to the end moments introduced to bring the slopes back to zero (Fig. 10.1(c)).

The area and end reactions obtained if freely supported will be referred to as the *free moment diagram* and the *free reactions*, A_1, R_1 and R_2 respectively.

The fixing moments at the ends are M_a and M_b, and in order to maintain equilibrium when M_a and M_b are unequal, the reactions $R = (M_a - M_b)/l$ are introduced, being upwards at the left-hand end and downwards at the right-hand end. Due to M_a, M_b, and R, the bending moment at a distance x from the left-hand end

$$= -M_a + Rx = -M_a + [(M_a - M_b)/l]x.$$

'his gives a straight line going from a value $-M_a$ at $x=0$ to $-M_b$ at $=l$, and hence the *fixing moment diagram*, A_2 (Fig. 10.1(d)).

For downward loads, A_1 is a positive area (sagging B.M.), and A_2 a egative area (hogging B.M.) consequently the equations (1) and (2) educe to

$$A_1 = A_2 \quad (1)$$

nd

$$A_1\bar{x}_1 = A_2\bar{x}_2 \quad \text{(numerically)} \quad (2)$$

.e. **Area of free moment diagram = Area of fixing moment diagram**

nd **Moments of areas of free and fixing diagrams are equal.**

It may be necessary to break down the areas still further to obtain onvenient triangles and parabolas.

These two equations enable M_a and M_b to be found, and the total eactions at the ends are

$$R_a = R_1 + R = R_1 + (M_a - M_b)/l$$

and

$$R_b = R_2 - R = R_2 - (M_a - M_b)/l$$

Finally, the combined bending moment diagram is shown in Fig. 10.1(e) as the algebraic sum of the two components.

EXAMPLE 1. *Obtain expressions for the maximum bending moment and deflection of a beam of length l and flexural rigidity EI, fixed horizontally at both ends, carrying a load W (a) concentrated at mid-span, (b) uniformly distributed over the whole beam.*

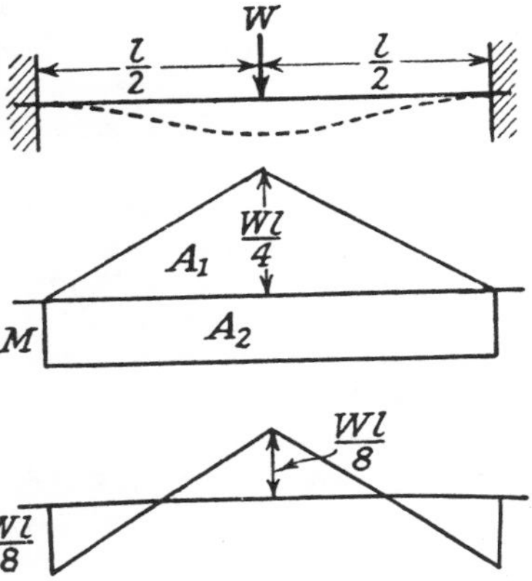

Fig. 10.2

(a) By symmetry $M_a = M_b = M$, say (Fig. 10.2).

The free moment diagram is a triangle with maximum ordinate $Wl/4$ (Chap. V).

$$\therefore \quad \text{Area } A_1 = \tfrac{1}{2}(Wl/4)l = Wl^2/8$$

$$\text{Area } A_2 = Ml$$

Equating $A_1 = A_2$ from (1), gives

$$M = Wl/8$$

The combined bending moment diagram is therefore as shown in the lower diagram, Fig. 10.2, and the maximum bending moment is $Wl/8$, occurring at the end (hogging), and the centre (sagging).

By taking moment-areas about one end for half the beam, the intercept gives the deflection, i.e.

$$\delta = \frac{[\frac{1}{2}(Wl/4)(l/2)]\frac{2}{3}.l/2 - M(l/2)l/4}{EI}$$
$$= Wl^3/192EI$$

(b) Free moment area

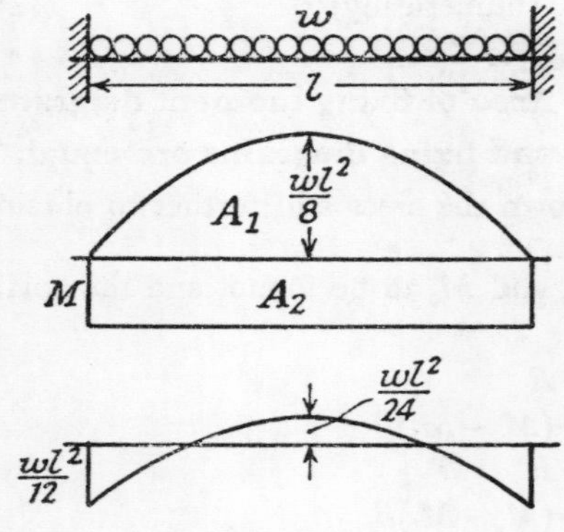

Fig. 10.3

$A_1 = \frac{2}{3}(wl^2/8)l = wl^3/12$ (Fig. 10.3) (properties of parabola, Para. 9.5)

Fixing moment area

$$A_2 = Ml.$$

Equating gives $M = wl^2/12$ and this is the maximum bending moment.

Again, for half the beam, the intercept about one end gives the deflection, i.e.

$$\delta = \frac{[\frac{2}{3}(wl^2/8)(l/2)]\frac{5}{8}.l/2 - M(l/2)l/4}{EI}$$
$$= wl^4/384EI$$

EXAMPLE 2. *A beam of span l has its ends fixed horizontally at the same level and carries a load W at a distance a from one end and b from the other. Deduce expressions for the fixing moments at the ends. Hence show that, for a distributed load on the same beam, the fixing moment at one end is given by* $\int_0^l \frac{px(l-x)^2}{l^2}.dx$ *where p = rate of loading at a distance of x from the end considered.*

Apply the above result to find the fixing moments when l = 20 m and p varies uniformly from zero at one end to 20 kN/m at the other.

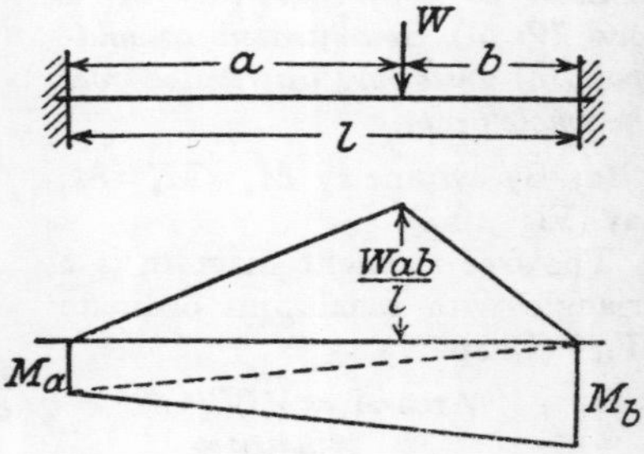

Fig. 10.4

The free moment diagram is a triangle of height Wab/l, and the fixing moments are M_a and M_b (Fig. 10.4).

Equating areas

$$\tfrac{1}{2}(M_a + M_b)l = \tfrac{1}{2}(Wab/l)l$$

i.e. $$M_a + M_b = Wab/l \qquad (1)$$

By moment-areas about the left-hand end, splitting each figure into two triangles

$$(\tfrac{1}{2}M_a.l)l/3 + (\tfrac{1}{2}M_b.l)2l/3 = [\tfrac{1}{2}(Wab/l)a]2a/3 + [\tfrac{1}{2}(Wab/l)b](a + b/3)$$

i.e. $$(M_a + 2M_b)l^2/3 = 2Wa^3b/3l + (Wab^2/l)(a + b/3)$$

or $$M_a + 2M_b = (Wab/l^3)(2a^2 + 3ab + b^2) \qquad (2)$$

Subtract (1), giving

$$\begin{aligned} M_b &= (Wab/l^3)(2a^2 + 3ab + b^2 - l^2) \\ &= (Wab/l^3)(a^2 + ab), \quad l = a + b \\ &= (Wab/l^3)a(a + b) \\ &= Wa^2b/l^2 \end{aligned}$$

From (1)

$$M_a = Wab/l - Wa^2b/l^2 = Wab^2/l^2$$

For a distributed load the fixing moment δM_a due to the load $p\delta x$ on a short length at a distance x from that end $= p\delta x . x(l - x)^2/l^2$ from above.

Integrating for all the load

$$M_a = \int_0^l \frac{px(l-x)^2 dx}{l^2}$$

$p = x$ kN/m

$$\therefore \quad M_a = \int_0^{20} \frac{x^2(20-x)^2}{20^2} . dx$$

$$= \frac{1}{400} \int_0^{20} (400x^2 - 40x^3 + x^4) dx$$

$$= 267 \text{ kNm}$$

Similarly

$$M_b = \int_0^{20} \frac{x^3(20-x)}{20^2} . dx$$

$$= \frac{1}{400} \int_0^{20} (20x^3 - x^4) dx$$

$$= 400 \text{ kNm}$$

It will be seen from Examples 1 and 2 that for standard cases the maximum bending moment occurs at one of the fixed ends. More complicated loadings may be built up by superposition (see Example 3, below), and it may be accepted in general that, ***for any combination of downward loads the maximum bending moment is given by the greater fixing moment.***

EXAMPLE 3. *A built-in beam of span 12 m carries a uniformly distributed load of 10 kN/m over its whole length together with concentrated loads of 20 kN at 3 m and 30 kN at 8 m from one end. If the bending stress is limited to 100 N/mm² calculate the section modulus required, and sketch the bending moment diagram.*

For each concentrated load $M_a = Wab^2l^2$, $M_b = Wa^2b/l^2$ (Example 2), and for the distributed load $M = wl^2/12$ (Example 1).

By combination

$$\text{total } M_a = (20 \times 3 \times 9^2)/12^2 + (30 \times 8 \times 4^2)/12^2 + 10 \times 12^2/12$$
$$= 180 \text{ kNm}$$

and $$M_b = (20 \times 3^2 \times 9)/12^2 + (30 \times 8^2 \times 4)/12^2 + 10 \times 12^2/12$$
$$= 185 \text{ kNm}$$

$$\text{Maximum bending moment} = 185 \text{ kNm}$$
$$= \sigma Z$$

$$\therefore \quad \text{Section modulus } Z = 185 \times 10^6/100$$
$$= 1{\cdot}85 \times 10^6 \text{ mm}^3$$

In Fig. 10.5 the combined bending moment diagram has been built up from its component parts, and the main values are shown.

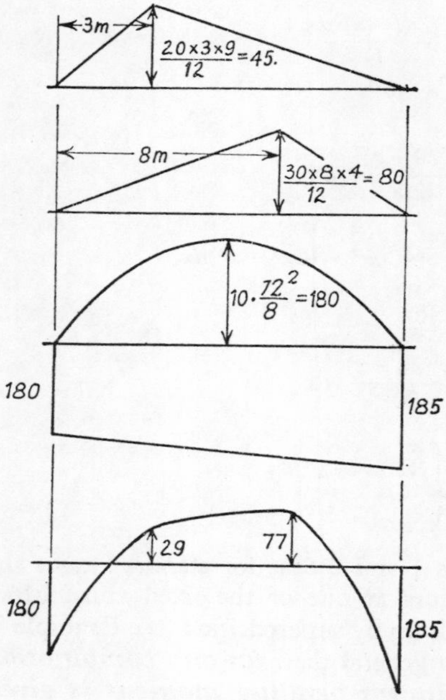

Fig. 10.5

The effects of complete and perfect end fixing are to reduce the maximum bending moment (and hence the stress) and to reduce the deflection, as may be appreciated from the previous examples. In practice, however, it is almost impossible to ensure no change of slope at the ends, so that usually the degree of fixing is imperfect and indeterminate. A rotation of the ends proportional to the fixing couples may be allowed for, as occurs in Example 4, the "stiffness" of the built-in end being estimated empirically.

A further disadvantage is the danger of "settlement" of one end relative to the other, which will cause an appreciable change in the values of the fixing moments. This will be illustrated in Example 5.

EXAMPLE 4. *A rung of a vertical ladder is in a horizontal plane and has the form of three sides of a rectangle, the short sides of length b and the long side 4b. The rung is made of steel of circular section and the short sides are securely built in to the vertical sides of the ladder. If a vertical load W is carried in the middle of the long side, find the twisting moment on each of the short sides in terms of W and b.* $E = 208{,}000$ *N/mm²;* $G = 80{,}000$ *N/mm².* (U.L.)

Let T be the twisting moment on each of the short sides; then this acts as a bending moment on each end of the long sides, and if θ is the angle of twist of the short sides it is also the angle of slope of the long side (see Fig. 10.6).

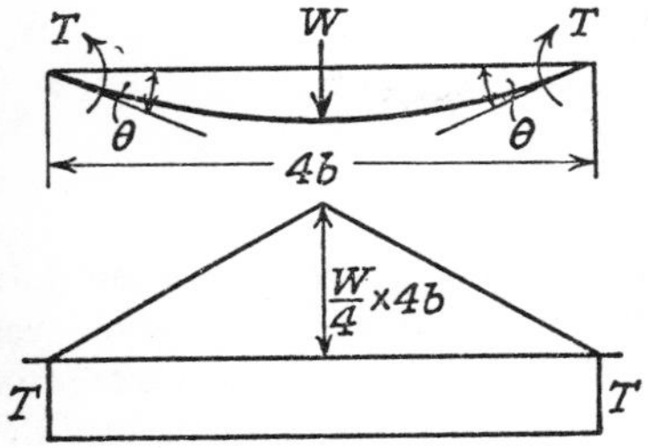

Fig. 10.6

For twisting a short side

$$T/J = G\theta/b$$

or $$\theta = Tb/GJ \qquad \text{(i)}$$

Treating the long side as a centrally loaded beam with "incomplete" fixing moments T,

increase of slope from end to end $= \Sigma A/EI$

i.e. $$2\theta = \frac{\frac{1}{2}(W/4)4b \times 4b - T.4b}{EI}$$

or $$\theta = (Wb^2 - 2Tb)/EI \qquad \text{(ii)}$$

Equating (i) and (ii) and noting that $J = 2I$

$$Tb/2GI = (Wb^2 - 2Tb)/EI$$

from which $$T = 2GWb/E - 4GT/E$$

and rearranging $$= \frac{2(G/E)Wb}{1 + 4G/E}$$

$$= \frac{(160/208)Wb}{1 + 320/408}$$

$$= 0{\cdot}303Wb$$

EXAMPLE 5. *Find an expression for the change in fixing moments and end reactions when one end of a built-in beam of span l sinks an amount u below the other, the ends remaining horizontal.*

If M is the change of fixing moment, it must be hogging at one end and sagging at the other. The change in end reactions R must then be given by $R = 2M/l$ for equilibrium.

The bending moment is shown in Fig. 10.7, and

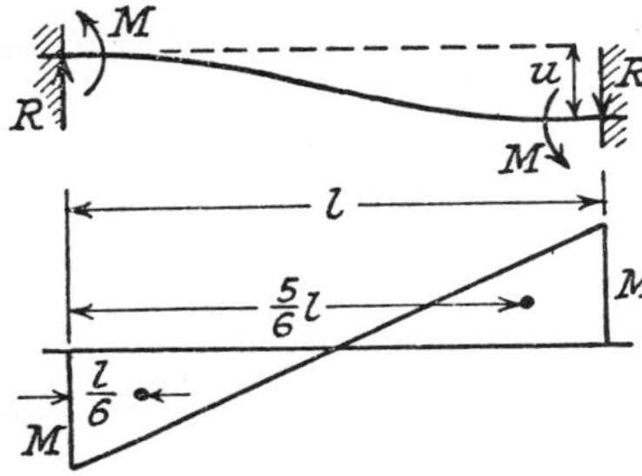

Fig. 10.7

$$u = \Sigma A\bar{x}/EI \quad \text{about the left-hand end}$$

$$= \frac{(\frac{1}{2}M.l/2)\frac{5}{6}l - (\frac{1}{2}M.l/2)l/6}{EI}$$

$$= Ml^2/6EI$$

$$= Rl^3/12EI \quad \text{since } R = 2M/l$$

or $$M = 6EIu/l^2$$

and $$R = 12EIu/l^3$$

Alternatively, treating as two cantilevers of length $l/2$ carrying end loads R,

$$u = \frac{2 . R(l/2)^3}{3EI}$$
$$= Rl^3/12EI$$

and $$M = R . l/2 \quad \text{as before.}$$

10.2. Macaulay Method. When the bending moment diagram does not lend itself to simplification into convenient areas it may be quicker to use the calculus method (Para. 9.4); it also has the advantage of giving directly the fixing moments and end reactions, and enables the maximum deflection to be found.

EXAMPLE 6. *A beam of uniform section is built in at each end and has a span of 20 m. It carries a uniformly distributed load of 8 kN/m on the left-hand half together with a 120 kN load at 15 m from the left-hand end. Find the end reactions and fixing moments and the magnitude and position of the maximum deflection. E = 200,000 N/mm²; I = 5 × 10⁸ mm⁴*

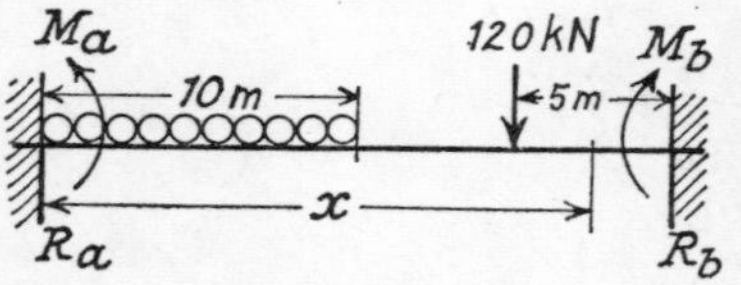

Fig. 10.8

Take the origin at the left-hand end, and let the fixing moments be M and M_b, the reactions R_a and R_b (Fig. 10.8).

Then $EId^2y/dx^2 = -M_a + R_a x - 8x^2/2 + 8[x - 10]^2/2 - 120[x - 15]$

Integrating

$$EI . dy/dx = -M_a x + R_a x^2/2 - 4x^3/3 + 4[x - 10]^3/3 - 60[x - 15]^2 + A$$

when $x = 0$, $dy/dx = 0$ $\quad \therefore \quad A = 0$

Integrating

$$EIy = -M_a x^2/2 + R_a x^3/6 - x^4/3 + [x - 10]^4/3 - 20[x - 15]^3 + B$$

when $x = 0$, $y = 0$ $\quad \therefore \quad B = 0$

When $x = 20$, $dy/dx = 0$ and $y = 0$, i.e.

$$-M_a . 20 + R_a . 20^2/2 - 4 \times 20^3/3 + 4 \times 10^3/3 - 60 \times 5^2 = 0$$

or $$10R_a - M_a = 542 \qquad \text{(i)}$$

and $$-M_a . 20^2/2 + R_a . 20^3/6 - 20^4/3 + 10^4/3 - 20 \times 5^3 = 0$$

or $$(20/3)R_a - M_a = 262 \qquad \text{(ii)}$$

Subtract (ii) from (i): $(10/3)R_a = 280$

giving $$R_a = 84 \text{ kN}$$

From (i): $$M_a = 298 \text{ kNm}$$

But $$R_a + R_b = \text{Total downward load}$$
$$= 200 \text{ kN}$$
$$\therefore \quad R_b = 116 \text{ kN}$$

nd $\quad -M_b =$ value of B.M. at $x = 20$

$$= -298 + 84 \times 20 - (8 \times 20^2)/2 + (8 \times 10^2)/2 - 120 \times 5$$
$$= -420 \text{ kNm}$$

Since the concentrated load is greater than the total distributed load nd acts at an equal distance from the nearest end, it may be deduced that ero slope occurs at a value of x between 10 and 15 m., i.e.

$$EIdy/dx = -298x + 84x^2/2 - 4x^3/3 + 4(x-10)^3/3 = 0$$

or

$$2x^2 + 102x - 1333 = 0$$

Solving

$$x = \frac{-102 + \sqrt{(10{,}400 + 10{,}650)}}{4}$$
$$= 10 \text{ m}$$

Substituting this value in the deflection equation gives

$$EIy = -(298 \times 10^2)/2 + (84 \times 10^3)/6 - 10^4/3$$
$$= -4230 \text{ kNm}^3$$

$$\therefore \text{ Maximum deflection} = (4230 \times 10^{12})/(200{,}000 \times 5 \times 10^8)$$
$$= 42{\cdot}3 \text{ mm}$$

10.3. Continuous Beams. When a beam is carried on more than two supports it is said to be continuous. It is possible to employ an extension of the moment-area method given in Para. 9.5 to obtain a relation between the bending moments at three points (usually supports).

In Fig. 10.9 the areas A_1 and A_2 are "free" bending moment areas, treating the beam as simply supported over two separate spans l_1 and l_2. If the actual bending moments at these points are M_1, M_2, and M_3, a "fixing" moment diagram consisting of two trapezia will be introduced, the actual B.M. being the algebraic sum of the two diagrams.

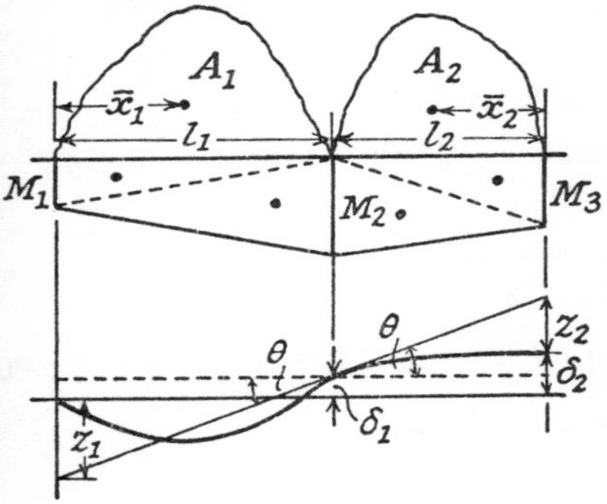

Fig. 10.9

In the lower figure the elastic line of the deflected beam is shown, the deflections δ_1 and δ_2 being relative to the left-hand support and positive upwards. θ is the slope of the beam over the centre support, and z_1 and z_2 the intercepts for l_1 and l_2.

Then $\quad \theta = (z_1 + \delta_1)/l_1 = (z_2 + \delta_2 - \delta_1)/l_2$

(slopes being everywhere small)

i.e. $$\frac{A_1\bar{x}_1-(M_1l_1/2)(l_1/3)-(M_2l_1/2)(2l_1/3)}{EI_1l_1}+\frac{\delta_1}{l_1}$$

$$=-\frac{A_2\bar{x}_2-(M_3l_2/2)(l_2/3)-(M_2l_2/2)(2l_2/3)}{EI_2l_2}+\frac{\delta_2-\delta}{l_2}$$

(note that x_2 is a negative intercept

or $$M_1l_1/I_1+2M_2(l_1/I_1+l_2/I_2)+M_3l_2/I_2$$
$$=6(A_1\bar{x}_1/I_1l_1+A_2\bar{x}_2/I_2l_2)+6E[\delta_1/l_1+(\delta_1-\delta_2)/l_2] \quad (1)$$

If $I_1=I_2$

$$M_1l_1+2M_2(l_1+l_2)+M_3l_2$$
$$=6(A_1\bar{x}_1/l_1+A_2\bar{x}_2/l_2)+6EI[\delta_1/l_1+(\delta_1-\delta_2)/l_2] \quad (2)$$

If the supports are at the same level

$$M_1l_1+2M_2(l_1+l_2)+M_3l_2=6(A_1\bar{x}_1/l_1+A_2\bar{x}_2/l_2) \quad (3)$$

and if the ends are simply supported ($M_1=M_3=0$)

$$M_2(l_1+l_2)=3(A_1\bar{x}_1/l_1+A_2\bar{x}_2/l_2) \quad (4)$$

Equation (1) is the most general form of the *equation of three moments*, also called *Clapeyron's equation.* The others are simplifications to meet particular cases, (3) being the form in which it is most frequently required.

EXAMPLE 7. *A beam AD, 20 m long, rests on supports at A, B, and C at the same level. AB = 8m; BC = 10 m. The loading is 3000 kg/m throughout and in addition a concentrated load of 5000 kg acts at the mid-point of AB and a load of 2000 kg acts at D. Draw the S.F. and B.M. diagrams.*

$M_a=0.$

$M_c=2000\times2+6000\times1=10{,}000$ kg.m

Applying equation (3) to the spans ABC (Fig. 10.10).

$$2M_b\times18+10{,}000\times10$$
$$=6\left[\left(\frac{1}{2}.\frac{5000\times8}{4}.8\right)\times\frac{4}{8}+\left(\frac{2}{3}.\frac{3000\times8^2}{8}\times8\right)\times\frac{4}{8}+\left(\frac{2}{3}.\frac{3000}{8}\times10^2\times10\right)\times\frac{5}{10}\right]=6\times209{,}000$$

$$\therefore\quad M_b=32{,}000 \text{ kg.m}$$

B.M. at mid-point of AB

$$=5000\times8/4+3000\times8^2/8-M_b/2$$
$$=18{,}000 \text{ kg.m}$$

B.M. at mid-point of BC

$$=3000\times10^2/8-\tfrac{1}{2}(M_b+10{,}000)$$
$$=16{,}500 \text{ kg.m}$$

To find the reactions at the supports, note that

$$M_b = -R_a \times 8 + 24{,}000 \times 4 + 5000 \times 4 \quad \text{for AB}$$
$$= -R_c \times 10 + 36{,}000 \times 6 + 2000 \times 12 \quad \text{for BCD}$$
$$\therefore \quad R_a = 10{,}500 \text{ kg}$$

nd

$$R_c = 20{,}800 \text{ kg}$$

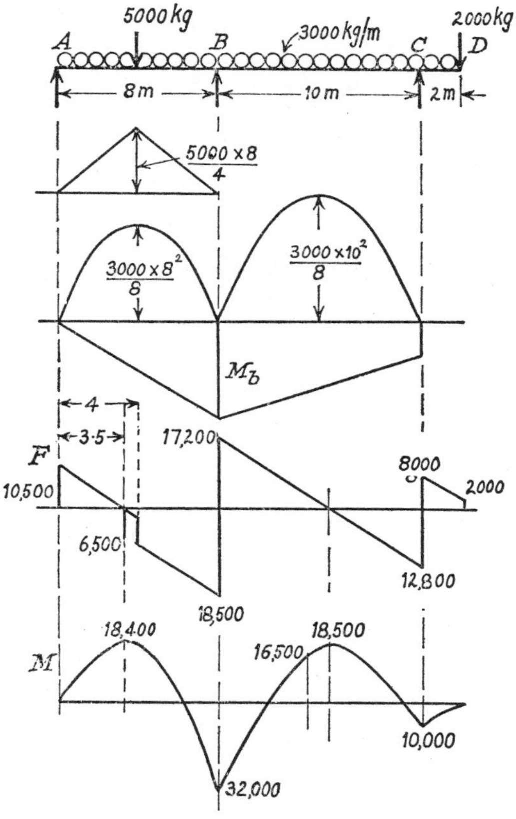

Fig. 10.10

By difference

$$R_b = 60{,}000 + 5000 + 2000 - 10{,}500 - 20{,}800$$
$$= 35{,}700 \text{ kg}$$

From the shear force diagram it can be seen that the maximum bending moment occurs either at a distance of 4·27 m from C, where

$$M = 20{,}800 \times 4{\cdot}27 - 3000 \times 6{\cdot}27^2/2 - 2000 \times 6{\cdot}27 = 18{,}500 \text{ kg.m},$$

or at a distance of 3·5m from A, where

$$M = 10{,}500 \times 3{\cdot}5 - 3000 \times 3{\cdot}5^2/2 = 18{,}400 \text{ kg.m}$$

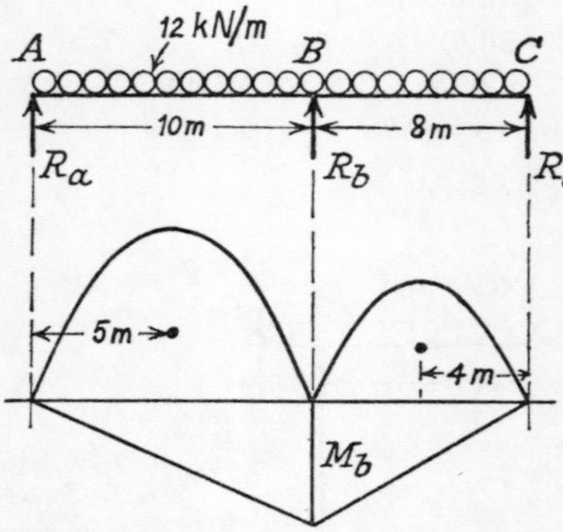

Fig. 10.11

The combined B.M. diagram is shown in Fig. 10.10.

EXAMPLE 8. *A beam ABC of uniform cross-section rests on elastic supports at A, B, and C, each support sinking by 1/100 mm per kN of load carried. If AB = 10 m and BC = 8 m, and the loading is 12 kN/m, find the reactions at the supports and the maximum bending moment. E = 200,000 N/mm², I = 5 × 10⁸ mm⁴.*

Applying the theorem of three moments (equation (2)), and noting that $M_a = M_c = 0$ (Fig 10.11)

$$2M_b \times 18 = 6\left[\left(\frac{2}{3}.\frac{12\times10^2}{8}\times10\right)\times\frac{5}{10}+\left(\frac{2}{3}.\frac{12\times8^2}{8}\times8\right)\times\frac{4}{8}\right]$$
$$+6EI\left[\frac{R_a-R_b}{100\times10}+\frac{R_c-R_b}{100\times8}\right]\frac{1}{1000}\ \text{kNm}^2$$

where $\delta_1 = (R_a - R_b)/100$ mm

and $\delta_1 - \delta_2 = (R_c - R_b)/100$ mm upwards

i.e. $M_b = 126 + 0{\cdot}00417(4R_a - 9R_b + 5R_c)$ (i)

But $M_b =$ hogging B.M. at B

$= -10R_a + 12.10^2/2$

$\therefore\ R_a = 60 - M_b/10$ (ii)

also $M_b = -8R_c + 12\ 8^2/2$

$\therefore\ R_c = 48 - M_b/8$ (iii)

Hence $R_b = 12 \times 18 - R_a - R_c = 108 + 9M_b/40$ (iv)

Substituting in (i)

$M_b = 126 + 0{\cdot}00417[240 - 2M_b/5 - 972 - (81/40)M_b + 240 - (5/8)M_b]$

$= 126 + 0{\cdot}00417[-492 - (122/40)M_b]$

giving $M_b = 124/1{\cdot}013 = 122$ kNm

From (ii) $R_a = 47{\cdot}8$ kN

From (iii) $R_c = 32{\cdot}8$ kN

From (iv) $R_b = 135{\cdot}4$ kN

Zero shear force occurs at 47·8/12 = 4 m from A and at 32·8/12 = 2·73 m from C.

Maximum bending moment between A and B

$= 47{\cdot}8 \times 4 - 12.4^2/2 = 95$ kNm

Maximum bending moment between B and C

$= 32{\cdot}8 \times 2{\cdot}73 - 12.2{\cdot}73^2/2 = 45$ kNm

$\therefore$ 122 kNm is the maximum bending moment.

Where the beam extends over more than three supports the equation of three moments is to be applied to each group of three in turn. In general, if there are n supports there will be $n-2$ unknown bending moments (excluding the ends), and $n-2$ equations to solve simultaneously.

10.4. Beams on Elastic Foundations. There are many problems in which a beam is supported on a compressible foundation which exerts a distributed reaction on the beam, of intensity proportional to the compressibility. In some cases the foundation can exert upward forces only, and the beam may, if sufficiently long, lose contact with the foundation; in others pressure may be exerted either way. Again, the support may not be truly continuous (such as holding down a railway line) but can be replaced by an equivalent distributed support.

If y is the upward deflection of the foundation at any point, the rate of upward reaction is $-ky$, and by Para. 9.3

$$EId^4y/dx^4 = -ky$$

or

$$d^4y/dx^4 = -4\alpha^4 y \qquad (1)$$

where $\alpha^4 = k/4EI$

A number of standard cases will now be considered.

(a) *Long Beam Carrying Central Load W* (Fig. 10.12 (a)).

Assuming that the foundation can exert upward forces only, let $2l$

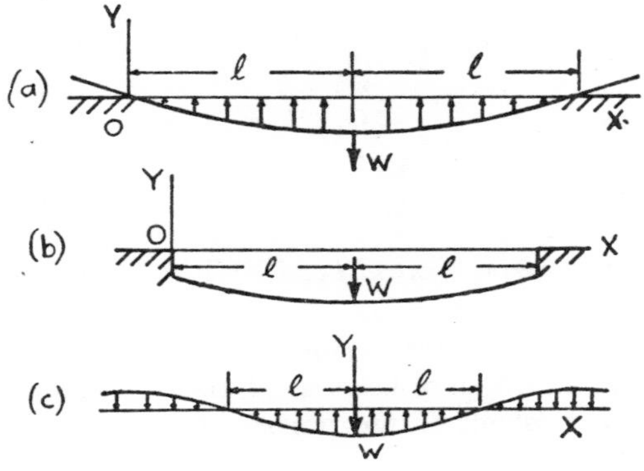

Fig. 10.12

be the length of beam in contact with the foundation, and take the origin O at the left-hand end.

The solution to (1) can be written

$$y = A \sin \alpha x . \sinh \alpha x + B \cos \alpha x . \sinh \alpha x + C \sin \alpha x . \cosh \alpha x + D \cos \alpha x . \cosh \alpha x$$

At $x=0, y=0$ $\quad \therefore\ D=0$

and $M=EId^2y/dx^2=0$ $\quad \therefore\ A=0$

also $F=EId^3y/dx^3=0$

giving

$$EI.2\alpha^3[B(-\cos 0.\cosh 0 - \sin 0.\sinh 0) + C(-\sin 0.\sinh 0 + \cos 0.\cosh 0)] = 0$$

i.e. $\quad C=B$

The equation is now reduced to

$$y = B(\cos \alpha x . \sinh \alpha x + \sin \alpha x . \cosh \alpha x)$$

At $x=l$, $dy/dx=0$

$$\therefore\ B\alpha \cos \alpha l . \cosh \alpha l = 0$$

The least solution of this is $\alpha l = \pi/2$ which determines the length in contact with the ground. The value of the constant B is obtained from the condition that the shear force at the centre is $W/2$, since by symmetry it must be numerically the same on either side of the load and it must change by an amount W on passing through the load. Hence

$$W/2 = EId^3y/dx^3$$
$$= -EI.4\alpha^3 B \sin \alpha l . \sinh \alpha l$$

or

$$B = -W\alpha/2k \sinh \tfrac{1}{2}\pi$$

The maximum deflection and bending moment are at the centre, $\alpha x = \pi/2$,

$$\hat{y} = -(W\alpha/2k) \coth \tfrac{1}{2}\pi$$
$$\hat{M} = EI(W\alpha^3/k) \coth \tfrac{1}{2}\pi$$
$$= (W/4\alpha) \coth \tfrac{1}{2}\pi$$

(b) *Short Beam Carrying Central Load W* (Fig. 10.12 (b)).

If $\alpha l < \pi/2$ in case (a), the beam will sink below the unstressed level of the foundation at all points. Again taking the origin at the left-hand end and the overall length of beam as $2l$, the following conditions are obtained for the constants of integration of the general solution of the previous paragraph.

At $x=0$, $d^2y/dx^2=0$ $\quad \therefore\ A=0$

and $d^3y/dx^3=0$ $\quad \therefore\ B=C$

and

$$y = B(\cos \alpha x . \sinh \alpha x + \sin \alpha x . \cosh \alpha x) + D \cos \alpha x . \cosh \alpha x$$

At $x=l$, $dy/dx=0$ giving

$$B.2\cos\alpha l.\cosh\alpha l+D(-\sin\alpha l.\cosh\alpha l+\cos\alpha l.\sinh\alpha l)=0$$

and
$$EId^3y/dx^3=W/2$$

giving

$$-B.2\sin\alpha l.\sinh\alpha l-D(\sin\alpha l.\cosh\alpha l+\cos\alpha l.\sinh\alpha l)=W/4EI\alpha^3$$
$$=W\alpha/k$$

Solving for B and D gives

$$B=-\frac{W\alpha}{k}\frac{\sin\alpha l.\cosh\alpha l-\cos\alpha l.\sinh\alpha l}{\sin 2\alpha l+\sinh 2\alpha l}$$

and
$$D=-\frac{2W\alpha}{k}\frac{\cos\alpha l.\cosh\alpha l}{\sin 2\alpha l+\sinh 2\alpha l}$$

The complete solution for y is now known, the maximum deflection and bending moment being under the load.

(c) *Infinite Beam Carrying Load W* (Fig. 10.12 (c)).

Assuming that the support can exert pressure either upwards or downwards, and taking the Y axis through the load and the X axis at the undeformed level, a solution of equation (1) can be written in the form

$$y=e^{\alpha x}(A\sin\alpha x+B\cos\alpha x)+e^{-\alpha x}(C\sin\alpha x+D\cos\alpha x)$$

For the length to the right of W, since $y\to 0$ as $x\to\infty$, $A=B=0$.

At $x=0$, $dy/dx=0$ $\quad\therefore\quad C=D$

and
$$EId^3y/dx^3=-W/2$$

giving
$$C=-W/8\alpha^3EI=-W\alpha/2k$$

and
$$y=-(W\alpha/2k)e^{-\alpha x}(\sin\alpha x+\cos\alpha x)$$

The distance from the load at which $y=0$ is given by

$$\sin\alpha l+\cos\alpha l=0$$

the least solution being
$$\alpha l=3\pi/4$$

The maximum deflection and bending moment are at $x=0$,

$$\hat{y}=-W\alpha/2k$$

and
$$\hat{M}=EIW\alpha^3/k=W/4\alpha$$

EXAMPLE 9. *A steel railway track is supported on timber sleepers which exert an equivalent load of 2800 N/m length of rail per mm deflection from its unloaded position. For each rail* $I=12\times10^6$ *mm*^{4}, $Z=16\times10^4$ *mm*^{3}

and E = 205,000 N/mm². If a point load of 100 kN acts on each rail, find the length of rail over which the sleepers are depressed and the maximum bending stress in the rail.

$$\alpha^4 = k/4EI$$

$$= \frac{2800}{4 \times 10^3 \times 205{,}000 \times 12 \times 10^6}$$

giving $\alpha = 0{\cdot}731 \times 10^{-3}\ \text{mm}^{-1}$

Each rail can be treated as an infinitely long beam, for which the length over which downward deflection occurs is given by paragraph (c),

$$2l = 3\pi/2\alpha$$
$$= 3\pi \times 10^3/2 \times 0{\cdot}731$$
$$= 6440\ \text{mm} = 6{\cdot}44\ \text{m}$$

and $\hat{M} = W/4\alpha$

$$= 100 \times 10^3/4 \times 0{\cdot}731$$
$$= 34{,}200\ \text{Nm}$$
$$\sigma = \hat{M}/Z$$
$$= 214\ \text{N/mm}^2$$

10.5. Portal Frames. Fig. 10.13 shows a portal frame ABCD, in which the ends A and D are fixed vertically, and a distributed load w is carried on BC.

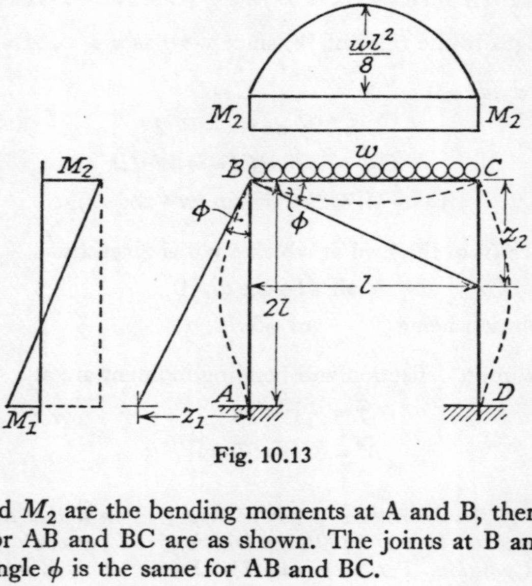

Fig. 10.13

If M_1 and M_2 are the bending moments at A and B, then the B.M. diagrams for AB and BC are as shown. The joints at B and C being rigid, the angle ϕ is the same for AB and BC.

For AB: Intercept at B = 0, i.e. by moment-areas about B (Para. 9.5)

$$\tfrac{1}{2}(M_1+M_2)2l.4l/3-M_2 2l.l=0$$

giving
$$M_1=\tfrac{1}{2}M_2 \qquad \text{(i)}$$

$$\phi=\frac{z_1}{2l}=\frac{M_2 2l.l-\tfrac{1}{2}(M_1+M_2)2l.2l/3}{2EIl}$$

$$=M_2 l/2EI \qquad \text{(ii)}$$

For BC:
$$\phi=\frac{z_2}{l}=\frac{[\tfrac{2}{3}(wl^2/8)l]l/2-M_2 l.l/2}{EIl}$$

$$=\frac{wl^3/24-M_2 l/2}{EI} \qquad \text{(iii)}$$

Equating (ii) and (iii) $M_2=wl^2/24$

and from (i) $M_1=wl^2/48$

The maximum bending moment occurs at the middle of BC, and

$$\hat{M}=wl^2/8-wl^2/24$$
$$=wl^2/12$$

SUMMARY

Built-in Beams:

Area of fixing moments = Area of free moments (1).

Moment area of fixing diagram = Moment area of free diagram (2).

For single concentrated load: $M_a=Wab^2/l^2$, $M_b=Wa^2b/l^2$.

If $a=b=l/2$, $M=Wl/8$, $\delta=Wl^3/192EI$.

For distributed load: $M=wl^2/12$

$\delta=wl^4/384EI$

Reactions: R_a = Free reaction + $(M_a-M_b)/l$

R_b = Free reaction − $(M_a-M_b)/l$.

Continuous Beams:

$$M_1l_1+2M_2(l_1+l_2)+M_3l_2=6(A_1\bar{x}_1/l_1+A_2\bar{x}_2/l_2)+6EI[\delta_1/l_1+(\delta_1-\delta_2)/l_2]$$

Beams on Elastic Foundations—solution for point loads.

Stiff-jointed Frameworks—application of moment-area.

REFERENCES

BUTTERWORTH, S., *Structural Analysis by Moment Distribution*. Longmans, 1949.

FISHER CASSIE, W., *Structural Analysis*. Longmans, 1948.

PROBLEMS

1. A beam of 8 m span is built in horizontally at the ends and carries a distributed load of 16 kN/m in addition to a concentrated load of 60 kN at 3 m from) one end. Find the reactions and fixing moments and the position of the points of contraflexure. (105, 83 kN; 155·6, 127·5 kNm; 1·72, 6·13 m.

2. A beam, fixed at its ends, span 3 m, carries a load of 60 kN at 1 m from one end. Find the fixing moments at the ends and the deflection of the load. $E = 205{,}000\ N/mm^2$; $I = 8000\ cm^4$. (26·7, 13·3 kNm; 0·362 mm.)

3. A beam of 6 m span, fixed horizontally at the ends, supports concentrated loads of 80 kN and 40 kN at 2·25 m and 4·5 m respectively from the left-hand end. Calculate the central deflection if $I = 5500\ cm^4$ and $E = 204{,}000\ N/mm^2$. (8·7 mm.)

4. A steel beam of 9 m span is built-in at both ends and carries two point loads each of 90 kN at points 2·4 m from the ends of the beam. The middle 3 m has a section of second moment of area $2{\cdot}4 \times 10^8\ mm^4$ and the 3 m lengths at either end have second moment of area $3{\cdot}2 \times 10^8\ mm^4$. Find the fixing moments at the ends and calculate the central deflection. $E = 205{,}000\ N/mm^2$.
(Equate areas of M/EI diagrams for "fixing" and "free" moments. $M = 164$ kNm. Deflection $= \Sigma M\bar{x}/EI$ for half beam about one end $= 6{\cdot}3$ mm.)

5. A horizontal steel bar 63·5 mm diameter is rigidly fixed at each end, the fixings being 1·22 m apart. A rigid bracket is fixed to the middle of the bar at right angles to the axis and in the same horizontal plane. Determine the maximum radius arm of the bracket at which a vertical load of 1330 N can be suspended if the deflection of the load is not to exceed 0·51 mm. $E = 206{,}000\ N/mm^2$; $G = 79{,}000\ N/mm^2$. (0·37 m.)

6. A beam of uniform section 9 m long is carried on three supports at the same level, one at each end and one at 6 m from the left-hand end. A uniformly distributed load of 16 kN/m is carried across the whole span, and a point load of 20 kN at 4·5 m from the end. Calculate the magnitude and position of the maximum bending moment. (68 kNm at support.)

7. A beam of length $2l$ is continuous over two equal spans and carried on three supports at the same level. If one span has moment of inertia I and supports a uniformly distributed load of w, the other span has moment of inertia $2I$ and carries a central load of wl, show that the maximum bending moment is $wl^2/6$.

8. A beam ABCD rests on four supports at the same level. AB = 3·6 m, BC = 7·2 m, CD = 4·8 m. There is a load of 40 kN at the centre of AB, a distributed load of 16 kN/m along BC, and a load of 30 kN at the centre of CD. Determine the reactions at the supports and the maximum bending moment. (10, 88, 80, 8 kN; 72·5 kNm.)

9. A beam rests on three supports A, B, and C. A and C are rigid, but B compresses 0·0005 mm per kg of load carried. If AB = BC = 4·5 m, what is the deflection at B when the beam is loaded with 16 kN/m run? What is the maximum bending moment and where does it occur? $E = 204{,}000\ N/mm^2$; $I = 9350\ cm^4$. (4·2 mm; 28·5 kNm, 1·85 m.)

10. A timber beam 15 cm wide by 10 cm deep, rests on compressible ground which exerts an upward pressure of 7000 N/m^2 per mm compression. It supports a load of 1000 kg at its mid-point. Compare the maximum bending stresses when the beam is (a) 1·8 m long, (b) 3 m long. $E = 10{,}000\ N/mm^2$.
($\alpha = 0{\cdot}0012\ mm^{-1}$, (a) 12·6 N/mm^2; (b) 9·3 N/mm^2.)

11. A rigid frame ABCD forms three sides of a rectangle and is hinged to the ground at A and D. If AB = CD = $l/2$ and BC = l and two loads each W are carried at $l/3$ and $2l/3$ from B, show that the bending moment at B is $Wl/6$.

CHAPTER XI

Bending of Curved Bars and Rigid Frames

11.1. Stress in Bars of Small Initial Curvature. Where the radius of curvature is large compared with the dimensions of the cross-section the analysis of stress is similar to that for pure bending (Para. 6.1).

Assume plane sections remain plane after bending.

Let R_0 be the initial (unstrained) radius of curvature of the neutral surface, and R the radius of curvature under the action of a pure bending moment M (Fig. 11.1).

The strain in an element at a distance y from the neutral axis

$$=\frac{PQ'-PQ}{PQ}=\frac{(R+y)(\theta+\delta\theta)-(R_0+y)\theta}{(R_0+y)\theta}$$

$$=\frac{R(\theta+\delta\theta)-R_0\theta+y\delta\theta}{(R_0+y)\theta}$$

$$=\frac{y\delta\theta}{(R_0+y)\theta}$$

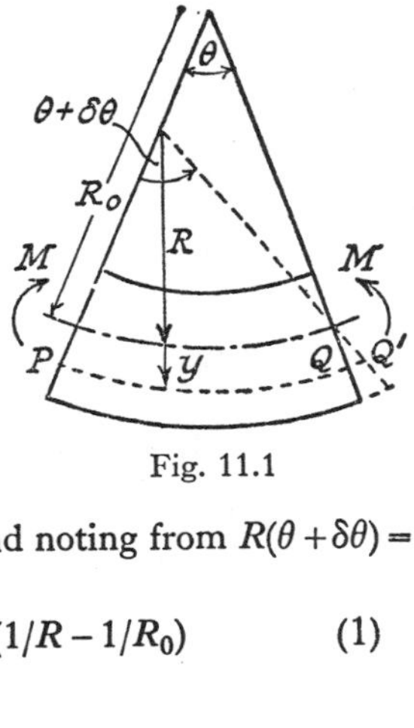

Fig. 11.1

since $R(\theta+\delta\theta)=R_0\theta=$ length along neutral surface.

If y is neglected in comparison with R_0, and noting from $R(\theta+\delta\theta)=R_0\theta$ that $\delta\theta=[(R_0-R)/R]\theta$,

then $$\text{strain}=(y/R_0)[(R_0-R)/R]=y(1/R-1/R_0) \quad (1)$$

Neglecting lateral stress, normal stress

$$\sigma=E\times\text{strain}$$
$$=Ey(1/R-1/R_0) \quad \text{from (1)} \quad (2)$$

Total normal stress $=0$

i.e. $$\int\sigma.dA=E(1/R-1/R_0)\int ydA=0 \quad \text{from (2)},$$

which shows that the neutral axis passes through the centroid of the section.

$$\text{Moment of resistance } M=\int\sigma ydA$$
$$=E(1/R-1/R_0)\int y^2.dA \quad \text{from (2)}$$
$$=EI(1/R-1/R_0) \quad (3)$$

Combining equations (2) and (3)

$$\boldsymbol{\sigma/y = M/I = E(1/R - 1/R_0)}$$

Strain energy of a short length δs (measured along the neutral surface), under the action of bending moment M, is

$$\begin{aligned}\delta U &= \tfrac{1}{2}M\delta\theta \\ &= \tfrac{1}{2}M[(R_0 - R)/R]\theta \\ &= \tfrac{1}{2}MR_0\theta(1/R - 1/R_0) \\ &= \tfrac{1}{2}M\delta s\,.\,M/EI \quad \text{from (3)} \\ &= (M^2/2EI)\delta s \qquad (4)\end{aligned}$$

(See also Para. 9.1.)

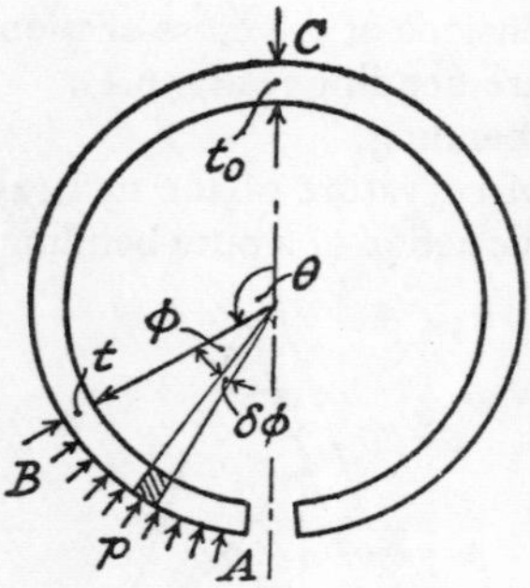

Fig. 11.2

Application to piston ring. Suppose it is required to design a split ring so that its outside surface will be circular in the stressed and unstressed condition, and that the radial pressure exerted is uniform.

If p is the uniform pressure on the outside, then the bending moment at B (Fig. 11.2) is

$$M = \int_0^{\pi-\theta} (p\,.\,dRd\phi)R\sin\phi \quad \text{approx.,}$$

where d is the depth of the ring in the axial direction.

Integrating

$$M = pR^2d(1 + \cos\theta) \qquad (5)$$

But $\quad M/I = E(1/R - 1/R_0) = \text{constant for given conditions.}$

i.e.
$$\frac{pR^2d(1+\cos\theta)}{dt^3/12} = \text{constant}$$
$$= 24pR^2/t_0^3 \quad \text{when } \theta = 0,\ t = t_0$$

giving
$$t/t_0 = \sqrt[3]{[(1+\cos\theta)/2]} \qquad (6)$$

the required variation of thickness.

Maximum bending stress at any section

$$\begin{aligned}&= (M/I)(t/2) = (6pR^2/t^2)(1+\cos\theta) \quad \text{from (5)} \\ &= 12pR^2t/t_0^3 \quad \text{from (6),}\end{aligned}$$

and has its greatest value at $\theta = 0$, i.e.

$$\sigma = 12pR^2/t_0^2 \qquad (7)$$

$$\begin{aligned}1/R - 1/R_0 &= \sigma/Ey = 24pR^2/Et_0^3 \quad \text{from (7)} \\ \therefore\quad 1/R_0 &= (1/R)[1 - 24pR^3/Et_0^3] \\ &= (1/R)[1 - 2\sigma R/Et_0]\end{aligned}$$

which determines the initial radius when values for t_0 and σ are assumed.

11.2. Stresses in Bars of Large Initial Curvature. When the radius of curvature is of the same order as the dimensions of the cross-section it is no longer possible to neglect y in comparison with R, and it will be found that the neutral axis does *not* pass through the centroid, and stress is *not* proportional to distance from the neutral axis.

Referring to Fig. 11.1, and writing

$$\sigma = E \times \text{strain} = E.QQ'/PQ$$

$$= \frac{Ey.\delta\theta}{(R_0+y)\theta} \qquad (1)$$

where y is the distance from the neutral axis as before, and R_0 the initial radius of the neutral surface.

Total normal force on cross-section $=0$ for pure bending, i.e.

$$\int \sigma.dA = \frac{E\delta\theta}{\theta}\int \frac{ydA}{R_0+y} = 0 \qquad (2)$$

Moment of resistance $M = \int \sigma y dA$

$$= \frac{E\delta\theta}{\theta}\int \frac{y^2 dA}{R_0+y} \quad \text{from (1)} \qquad (3)$$

But

$$\int \frac{y^2 dA}{R_0+y} = \int \frac{[y(y+R_0) - R_0 y]}{R_0+y}.dA$$

$$= \int ydA - R_0 \int y.dA/(R_0+y)$$

$$= Ae - 0 \quad \text{from (2)},$$

where e is the distance between the neutral axis and the principal axis through the centroid (e being positive for the neutral axis to be on the same side of the centroid as the centre of curvature).

Substituting in equation (3) gives

$$M = (E\delta\theta/\theta)Ae$$

$$= [\sigma(R_0+y)/y]Ae \quad \text{from (1).}$$

Rearranging

$$\boldsymbol{\sigma = My/Ae(R_0+y)} \qquad (4)$$

In this equation *y is positive measured outwards, a positive bending moment being one which tends to increase the curvature.*

The above derivation neglects lateral stresses and strains, but it can be shown that allowance for these does not materially affect the results.

Rectangular Cross-section. Working from equation (2)

$$\int \frac{ydA}{R_0+y} = 0$$

Let $z = y - e =$ distance from centroid axis (Fig. 11.3),

also mean radius of curvature $R_m = R_0 + e$

and $dA = bdz$

Then $\int \frac{z+e}{R_m+z}.bdz=0$ from above,

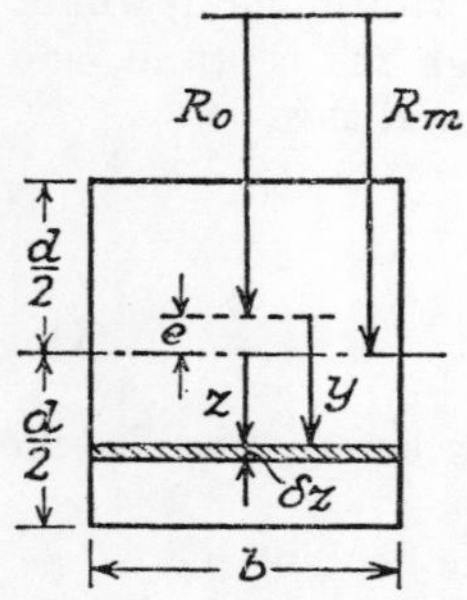

Fig. 11.3

i.e. $$\int_{-d/2}^{d/2} \frac{R_m+z-(R_m-e)}{R_m+z}.dz=0$$

$$\int_{-d/2}^{d/2} dz-(R_m-e)\int_{-d/2}^{d/2} \frac{dz}{R_m+z}=0$$

or $$d-(R_m-e)\log\frac{R_m+d/2}{R_m-d/2}=0$$

giving $$e=R_m-d/\log\frac{R_m+d/2}{R_m-d/2} \tag{5}$$

As e is small compared with R_m and d, it is difficult to calculate with sufficient accuracy from this expression, and an expansion of the log term into a convergent series is of advantage.

Then

$$e=R_m-\frac{d}{2[d/2R_m+\frac{1}{3}(d/2R_m)^3+\frac{1}{5}(d/2R_m)^5+\ldots]}$$
$$=R_m-\frac{R_m}{1+\frac{1}{12}(d^2/R_m^2)+\frac{1}{80}(d^4/R_m^4)+\ldots}$$
$$=R_m-R_m[1-\frac{1}{12}(d^2/R_m^2)+\frac{1}{144}(d^4/R_m^4)-\frac{1}{80}(d^4/R_m^4)\ldots]$$
$$\doteqdot(d^2/R_m)[\tfrac{1}{12}+\tfrac{1}{180}(d^2/R_m^2)] \tag{6}$$

EXAMPLE 1. *A curved bar of square section, 3-cm sides and mean radius of curvature $4\frac{1}{2}$ cm is initially unstressed. If a bending moment of 300 Nm is applied to the bar tending to straighten it, find the stresses at the inner and outer faces.* (*U.L.*)

$R_m=45$ mm $\quad d=30$ mm

$$e=R_m-d/\log\frac{R_m+d/2}{R_m-d/2} \quad \text{(Eq. (5))}$$
$$=45-30/\log_e 2=1{\cdot}72 \text{ mm}$$
$$R_0=R_m-e=43{\cdot}28 \text{ mm}$$
$$M=-300\times10^3 \text{ Nmm}$$
$$\sigma=My/Ae(R_0+y) \quad \text{(Eq. (4))}$$

At the inside face

$$y=-(d/2-e)$$
$$=-13{\cdot}28 \text{ mm}$$

$$\therefore \quad \sigma=[-300\times10^3\times(-13{\cdot}28)]/[900\times1{\cdot}72(43{\cdot}28-13{\cdot}28)]$$
$$=86 \text{ N/mm}^2 \text{ tension.}$$

At the outside face

$$y = d/2 + e$$
$$= 16{\cdot}72 \text{ mm}$$

$$\therefore \quad \sigma = (-300 \times 10^3 \times 16{\cdot}72)/[900 \times 1{\cdot}72(43{\cdot}28 + 16{\cdot}72)]$$
$$= 54{\cdot}5 \text{ N/mm}^2 \quad \text{compression.}$$

The actual stress distribution is shown in Fig. 11.4.

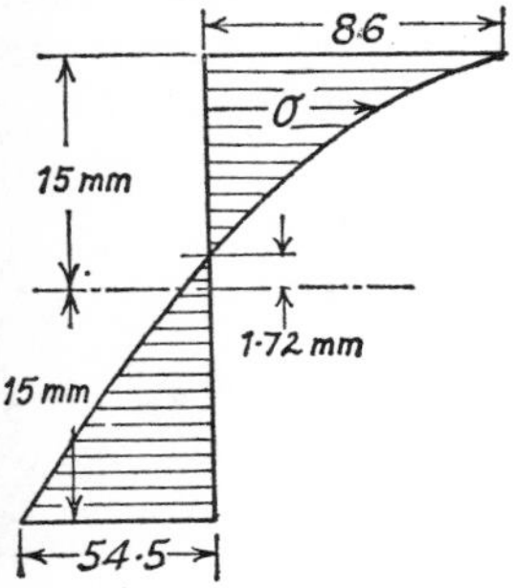

Fig. 11.4

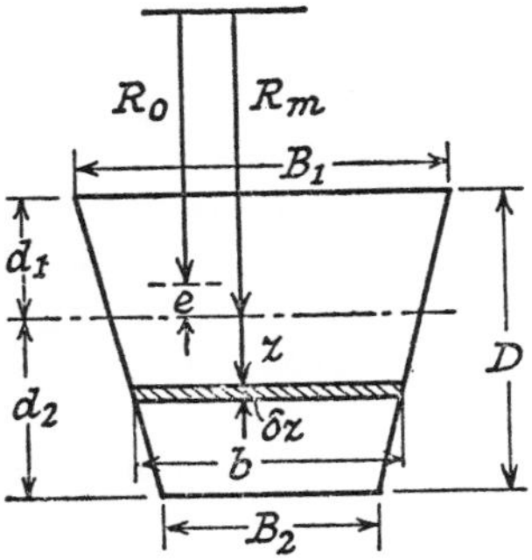

Fig. 11.5

Trapezium Cross-section. By moments

$$d_1 = [(B_1 + 2B_2)/(B_1 + B_2)](D/3)$$

and

$$d_2 = [(2B_1 + B_2)/(B_1 + B_2)](D/3) \quad \text{(Fig. 11.5)}$$

Putting $z = y - e$ and $R_m = R_0 + e$, equation (2) becomes

$$\int \frac{z + e}{R_m + z} . dA = 0$$

i.e.

$$A - (R_m - e)\int dA/(R_m + z) = 0$$

or

$$e = R_m - \frac{A}{\int dA/(R_m + z)} \tag{7}$$

$$dA = b . dz = \{B_2 + [(B_1 - B_2)/D](d_2 - z)\}dz$$

$$\therefore \int \frac{dA}{R_m + z} = \int \frac{B_2 + [(B_1 - B_2)/D]d_2 - [(B_1 - B_2)/D]z}{R_m + z} . dz$$

$$= \int_{-d_1}^{d_2} \frac{B_2 + \dfrac{B_1 - B_2}{D} . d_2 + \dfrac{B_1 - B_2}{D} . R_m - \dfrac{B_1 - B_2}{D}(R_m + z)}{R_m + z} . dz$$

$$= \{B_2 + [(B_1 - B_2)/D] . d_2 + [(B_1 - B_2)/D] . R_m\} \log \frac{R_m + d_2}{R_m - d_1} - [(B_1 - B_2)/D](d_2 + d_1)$$

$$= \{B_2 + [(B_1 - B_2)/D](R_m + d_2)\} \log \frac{R_m + d_2}{R_m - d_1} - (B_1 - B_2) \tag{8}$$

and since $A = [(B_1 + B_2)/2].D$, e can be evaluated from (7) and (8)

$$e = R_m - \frac{A}{\int dA/(R_m + z)}$$

EXAMPLE 2. *A crane hook whose horizontal cross-section is trapezoidal, 50 mm wide at the inside and 25 mm wide at the outside, thickness 50 mm, carries a vertical load of 1000 kg whose line of action is 38 mm from the inside edge of this section. The centre of curvature is 50 mm from the inside edge. Calculate the maximum tensile and compressive stresses set up.*

Referring to Fig. 11.5

$$d_1 = [(50 + 2 \times 25)/(50 + 25)](50/3) = 22{\cdot}2 \text{ mm}$$

$$d_2 = [(2 \times 50 + 25)/(50 + 25)](50/3) = 27{\cdot}8 \text{ mm}$$

$$R_m = 50 + d_1 = 72{\cdot}2 \text{ mm}$$

$$\int dA/(R_m + z) = \{25 + [(50 - 25)/50](72{\cdot}2 + 27{\cdot}8)\} \log_e [(72{\cdot}2 + 27{\cdot}8)/(72{\cdot}2 - 22{\cdot}2)] - (50 - 25) \text{ from (8)}$$

$$= 75 \log_e 2 - 25 = 27 \text{ mm}$$

$$A = [(50 + 25)/2]50 = 1875 \text{ mm}^2$$

$$\therefore \quad e = 72{\cdot}2 - 1875/27 = 2{\cdot}75 \text{ mm from (7)}$$

$$\text{Direct stress} = \text{Load/Area} = 1000 \times 9{\cdot}81/1875 = 5{\cdot}23 \text{ N/mm}^2$$

$$\text{Bending stress} = My/Ae(R_0 + y), \quad \text{Eq. (4)}$$

$$= M(z + e)/Ae(R_m + z)$$

At the inside edge

$$z = -d_1 = -22{\cdot}2 \text{ mm}$$

$$M = -1000 \times 9{\cdot}81(38 + d_1)$$

$$= -59 \times 10^4 \text{ Nmm (tending to decrease the curvature)}$$

$$\text{Bending stress} = \frac{-59 \times 10^4(-22{\cdot}2 + 2{\cdot}75)}{1875 \times 2{\cdot}75(72{\cdot}2 - 22{\cdot}2)}$$

$$= 44{\cdot}5 \text{ N/mm}^2 \text{ tensile}$$

$$\text{Combined stress} = 44{\cdot}5 + 5{\cdot}23 = 49{\cdot}7 \text{ N/mm}^2 \text{ tensile.}$$

At the outside edge

$$z = d_2 = 27{\cdot}8 \text{ mm}$$

$$\text{Bending stress} = \frac{-59 \times 10^4(27{\cdot}8 + 2{\cdot}75)}{1875 \times 2{\cdot}75(72{\cdot}2 + 27{\cdot}8)}$$

$$= -34{\cdot}9 \text{ N/mm}^2$$

$$\text{Combined stress} = -34{\cdot}9 + 5{\cdot}23$$

$$= 29{\cdot}7 \text{ N/mm}^2 \text{ compressive.}$$

Circular Cross-section. Following the method already established (see "Trapezium Cross-section")

$$e = R_m - \frac{A}{\int dA/(R_m + z)}$$

where
$$\int \frac{dA}{R_m+z} = 2\int_{-r}^{r} \frac{\sqrt{(r^2-z^2)}dz}{R_m+z} \quad \text{(Fig. 11.6)}$$
$$= 2\pi[R_m - \sqrt{(R_m^2 - r^2)}] \text{ by calculus methods}$$

Hence
$$e = R_m - r^2/\{2[R_m - \sqrt{(R_m^2-r^2)}]\}$$
$$= R_m - \frac{r^2}{2}\cdot\frac{R_m+\sqrt{(R_m^2-r^2)}}{R_m^2-(R_m^2-r^2)}$$
$$= \tfrac{1}{2}[R_m - \sqrt{(R_m^2-r^2)}]$$
$$= \tfrac{1}{2}[R_m - R_m + \tfrac{1}{2}R_m(r^2/R_m^2) + \tfrac{1}{8}R_m(r^4/R_m^4) + \ldots]$$
$$= \tfrac{1}{4}R_m(r^2/R_m^2)[1 + \tfrac{1}{4}(r^2/R_m^2) + \tfrac{1}{8}(r^4/R_m^4) + \ldots]$$

and
$$\sigma = My/Ae(R_0+y) \quad \text{as before.}$$

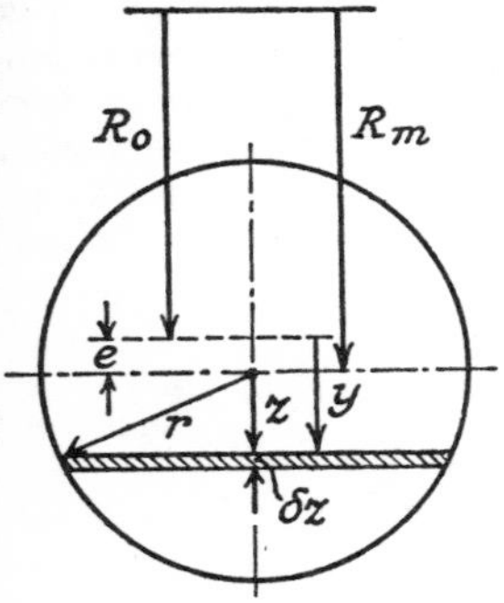

Fig. 11.6

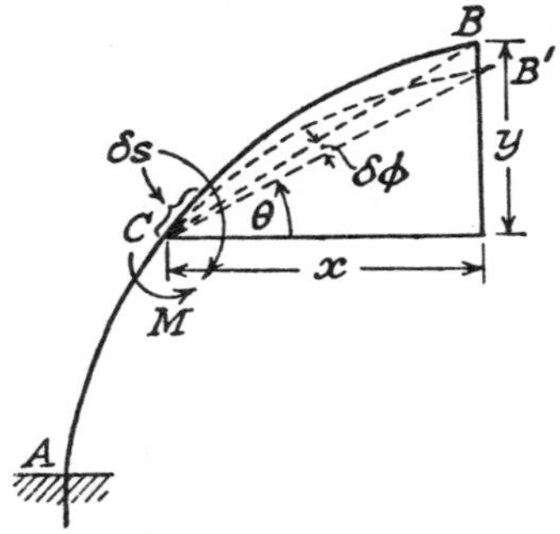

Fig. 11.7

11.3. Deflection of Curved Bars (Direct Method). If a length δs of an initially curved beam is acted upon by a bending moment M, it follows from (3), Para. 11.1, that $M\delta s/EI = \delta s(1/R - 1/R_0)$.

But $\delta s/R - \delta s/R_0$ is the change of angle subtended by δs at the centre of curvature, and consequently is the angle through which the tangent at one end of the element rotates relative to the tangent at the other end, i.e.

$$\delta\phi = M\delta s/EI \quad \text{(Fig. 11.7)} \tag{1}$$

Fig. 11.7 shows a loaded bar AB which is fixed in direction at A, and it is required to find the deflection at the other end B.

Due to the action of M on δs at C only, the length CB is rotated through an angle $\delta\phi = M\delta s/EI$. B moves to B′, where BB′ = CB.$\delta\phi$.

The vertical deflection of B = BB′.$\cos\theta$
$$= \text{CB}.\cos\theta.\delta\phi$$
$$= x.\delta\phi.$$

The horizontal deflection of $B = BB'.\sin\theta$

$$= y.\delta\phi.$$

Due to the bending of all the elements along AB

$$\text{Vertical deflection at } B = \int x.d\phi$$

$$= \int Mxds/EI \quad \text{from (1)} \qquad (2)$$

$$\text{Horizontal deflection at } B = \int y.d\phi$$

$$= \int Myds/EI \qquad (3)$$

It is interesting to compare this with the moment-area method for deflection of initially straight beams, given in Para. 9.5.

The advantage of this method, as against that of the following paragraph, is that the deflection can readily be found at any point and in any direction, even when there is no load at that point.

EXAMPLE 3. *A steel tube having outside diameter 5 cm, bore 3 cm, is bent into a quadrant of 2 m radius. One end is rigidly attached to a horizontal base plate to which a tangent to that end is perpendicular, and the free end supports a load of 100 kg. Determine the vertical and horizontal deflections of the free end under this load.* $E = 208{,}000$ *N/mm²*. *(U.L.)*

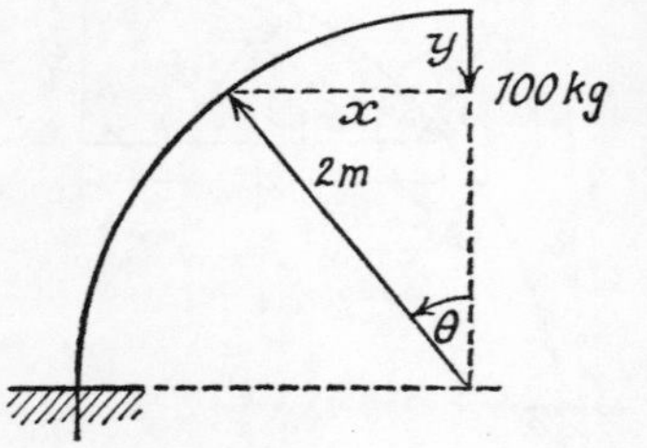

Fig. 11.8

$$I = (\pi/64)(5^4 - 3^4)$$
$$= (\pi/64)(25 - 9)(25 + 9)$$
$$= 26{\cdot}7 \text{ cm}^4$$
$$x = 2000 \sin\theta \text{ mm} \quad \text{(Fig. 11.8)}$$
$$y = 2000(1 - \cos\theta) \text{ mm}$$
$$M = 100 \times 9{\cdot}81x \text{ Nmm}$$
$$\delta s = 2000\delta\theta \text{ mm}$$

$$\text{Vertical deflection} = \int Mxds/EI \quad \text{(Eq. (2))}$$

$$= \int_0^{\pi/2} \frac{981 \times 2000^3 \sin^2\theta.d\theta}{208{,}000 \times 26{\cdot}7 \times 10^4}$$

$$= 141 \int_0^{\pi/2} \frac{1 - \cos 2\theta}{2}.d\theta$$

$$= 141 \times \pi/4$$
$$= 110 \text{ mm}$$

$$\text{Horizontal deflection} = \int Myds/EI \quad \text{(Eq. (3))}$$

$$= \frac{981 \times 2000^3}{208{,}000 \times 26{\cdot}7 \times 10^4} \int_0^{\pi/2} \sin\theta(1 - \cos\theta)d\theta$$

$$= 141\left[-\cos\theta + \tfrac{1}{4}\cos 2\theta\right]_0^{\pi/2}$$
$$= 141 \times \tfrac{1}{2}$$
$$= 70{\cdot}5 \text{ mm}$$

11.4. Deflection from Strain Energy (Castigliano's Theorem).

Theorem: *If U is the total strain energy of any structure due to the application of external loads W_1, W_2 . . . at O_1,O_2 . . . in the directions O_1X_1, O_2X_2 . . ., and to couples M_1, M_2 . . ., then the deflections* at O_1, O_2 . . . *in the directions* O_1X_1, O_2X_2 . . . are $\partial U/\partial W_1$, $\partial U/\partial W_2$ . . ., *and the angular rotations of the couples are* $\partial U/\partial M_1$, $\partial U/\partial M_2$ . . . *at their applied points.*

Proof for concentrated loads. If the displacements (in the direction of the loads) produced by gradually applied loads W_1, W_2, W_3 . . . are x_1, x_2, x_3 . . ., then

$$U = \tfrac{1}{2}W_1x_1 + \tfrac{1}{2}W_2x_2 + \tfrac{1}{2}W_3x_3 + \dots \qquad (1)$$

Let W_1 alone be increased by δW_1, then

$$\delta U = \text{increase in external work done}$$
$$= (W_1 + \delta W_1/2)\delta x_1 + W_2\delta x_2 + W_3\delta x_3 + \dots$$

where δx_1, δx_2, δx_3 are the increases in x_1, x_2 and x_3.

$$= W_1\delta x_1 + W_2\delta x_2 + W_3\delta x_3 + \dots \qquad (2)$$

neglecting the product $\tfrac{1}{2}\delta W_1\delta x_1$.

But if the loads $W_1 + \delta W_1$, W_2, W_3 . . . were applied gradually from zero, the total strain energy

$$U + \delta U = \tfrac{1}{2}(W_1 + \delta W_1)(x_1 + \delta x_1) + \tfrac{1}{2}W_2(x_2 + \delta x_2) + \tfrac{1}{2}W_3(x_3 + \delta x_3) + \dots$$

Subtracting (1), and neglecting products of small quantities

$$\delta U = \tfrac{1}{2}W_1\delta x_1 + \tfrac{1}{2}\delta W_1x_1 + \tfrac{1}{2}W_2\delta x_2 + \tfrac{1}{2}W_3\delta x_3 + \dots \qquad (3)$$

or
$$2\delta U = W_1\delta x_1 + \delta W_1x_1 + W_2\delta x_2 + W_3\delta x_3 + \dots$$

Subtract (2), then $\delta U = \delta W_1 x_1$

and in the limit $\partial U/\partial W_1 = x_1$

Similarly for x_2 and x_3, and the proof can be extended to incorporate couples.

It is important to stress that U is the *total* strain energy, expressed in terms of the loads and not including statically determinate reactions, and that the partial derivative with respect to each load in turn (treating the others as constant) gives the deflection at the load point in the direction of the load.

The following principles should be observed in applying this theorem:

(1) In finding the deflection of curved beams and similar problems, only strain energy due to bending need normally be taken into account (i.e. $\int M^2.ds/2EI$ (4), Para. 11.1).

(2) Treat all the loads as "variables" initially, carry out the partial differentiation and integration, putting in numerical values at the final stage.

(3) If the deflection is to be found at a point where, or in a direction in which, there is no load, a load may be put in where required and given a value zero in the final reckoning (i.e. $x = (\partial U/\partial W)_{W=0}$).

Generally it will be found that the strain energy method requires less thought in application than the direct method of Para. 11.3, it being only necessary to obtain an expression for the bending moment; also there is no difficulty over the question of sign, as the strain energy is bound to be positive, and deflection is positive in the direction of the load. The only disadvantage occurs when a case such as note (3) above has to be dealt with, when the direct method of Para. 11.3 will probably be shorter.

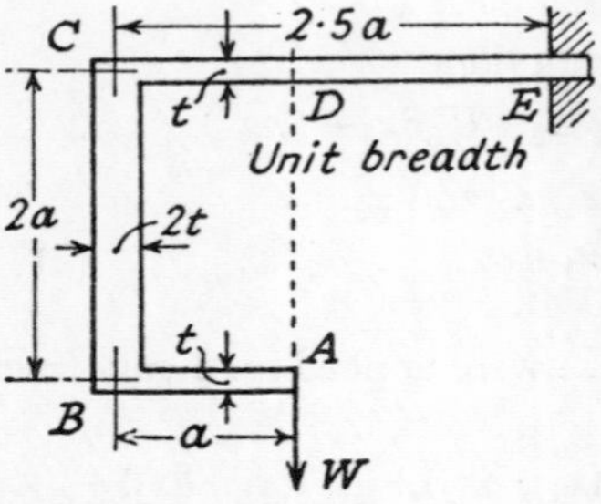

Fig. 11.9

EXAMPLE 4. *Obtain an expression for the vertical displacement at A of the beam shown in Fig. 11.9.*

The bending moments in the various sections can be written as follows:

AB, $M = Wx$, (at x from A)

BC, $M = Wa$, constant

CD, $M = Wx'$, (at x' from D)

DE, $M = Wx''$, (at x'' from D)

$U = \int M^2 . ds/2EI$

$$= \int_0^a \frac{W^2x^2 . dx}{2E \times t^3/12} + \int_0^{2a} \frac{W^2a^2 . ds}{2E \times (2t)^3/12} + \int_0^a \frac{W^2x'^2 . dx'}{2E \times t^3/12} + \int_0^{1\cdot 5a} \frac{W^2x''^2 . dx''}{2E \times t^3/12}$$

$$= (6W^2/Et^3)[a^3/3 + 2a^3/8 + a^3/3 + 1\cdot 5^3a^3/3]$$

$$= 24\cdot 5W^2a^3/2Et^3$$

Displacement of load at A $= \partial U/\partial W$ vertically

$$= 24\cdot 5Wa^3/Et^3$$

An allowance could be made for the linear extension of the portion BC

$$= (W . 2a)/(2t . E)$$

which is clearly negligible compared with the deflection due to bending.

EXAMPLE 5. *Fig. 11.10 shows a steel rod of 12 mm diameter with one end fixed into a horizontal table. The remainder of the rod is bent into the form of three-quarters of a circle and the free end is constrained to move vertically. Determine the vertical deflection for a load of 10 kg. E = 208,000 N/mm². (U.L.)*

Let the vertical load be W, and the normal reaction due to the constraint be R.

Then $M = R\times 150(1-\cos\theta) - W\times 150\sin\theta$

$\delta s = 150\delta\theta$

$U = \int M^2.ds/2EI$

$$= (150^3/2EI)\int_0^{3\pi/2}[R(1-\cos\theta) - W\sin\theta]^2.d\theta$$

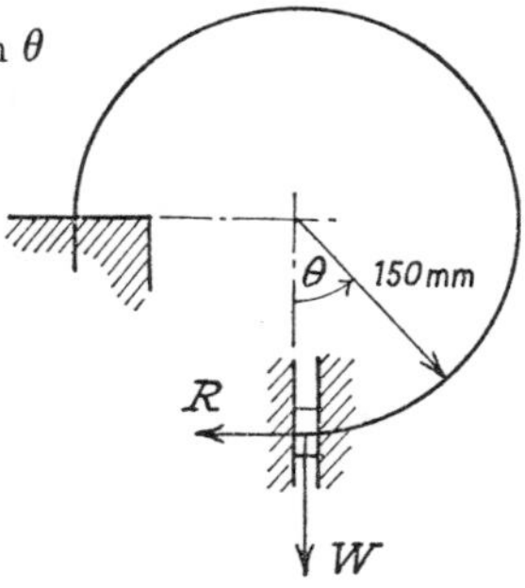

Fig. 11.10

Since there is no horizontal displacement, $\partial U/\partial R = 0$, i.e.

$$\int_0^{3\pi/2} 2[R(1-\cos\theta) - W\sin\theta](1-\cos\theta)\,d\theta = 0$$

or
$$\int_0^{3\pi/2}[2R - 4R\cos\theta + R(1+\cos 2\theta) - 2W\sin\theta + W\sin 2\theta]d\theta = 0$$

i.e.

$$3R\times(3\pi/2) - 4R\times(-1) + (R/2)\times(0) + 2W(0-1) - (W/2)(-1-1) = 0$$

giving
$$R = \frac{W}{9\pi/2+4} = 0{\cdot}55 \text{ kg} = 5{\cdot}4\text{N}$$

Vertical displacement

$$= \partial U/\partial W$$

$$= (150^3/2EI)\int_0^{3\pi/2} 2[R(1-\cos\theta) - W\sin\theta](-\sin\theta)d\theta$$

$$= (150^3/2EI)\int_0^{3\pi/2}[-2R\sin\theta + R\sin 2\theta + W(1-\cos 2\theta)]d\theta$$

$$= (150^3/2EI)[2R\times(-1) - (R/2)(-1-1) + W(3\pi/2) - (W/2)\times(0)]$$

$$= \frac{3{\cdot}375\times 10^6\times 64}{2\times 208{,}000\times\pi\times 12^4}\left[-5{\cdot}4 + \frac{98{\cdot}1\times 3\pi}{2}\right]$$

$$= 3{\cdot}65 \text{ mm}$$

Example 6. *If a ring of mean radius R is acted upon by equal and opposite pulls P along a diameter, find expressions for the maximum bending moment and the deflection along the line of P.*

The bending moment cannot immediately be obtained in terms of P and R, but, making use of the symmetry, let M_0 be the bending moment on cross-sections perpendicular to P (Fig. 11.11). There will also be a normal pull of $P/2$ on these cross-sections.

At an angle θ

$$M = (PR/2)(1-\cos\theta) - M_0$$

and
$$U = 4\int_0^{\pi/2}\frac{[PR(1-\cos\theta) - 2M_0]^2}{4\times 2EI}R\,d\theta$$

$$\partial U/\partial M_0 = (R/2EI)\int_0^{\pi/2} 2[PR(1-\cos\theta) - 2M_0](-2)d\theta$$

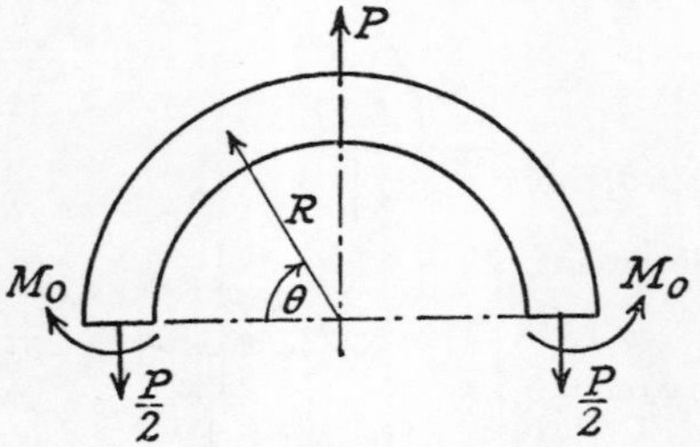

Fig. 11.11

$=$ rotation of M_0

$=0$ by symmetry.

$$\therefore \int_0^{\pi/2} (PR - PR\cos\theta - 2M_0)d\theta = 0$$

i.e. $PR.\pi/2 - PR - 2M_0.\pi/2 = 0$

giving $M_0 = PR(\frac{1}{2} - 1/\pi)$

The maximum bending moment occurs when $\theta = \pi/2$, and

$$\hat{M} = PR/2 - M_0$$
$$= PR/\pi$$

The deflection of P

$= \partial U/\partial P$

$= (R/2EI)\int_0^{\pi/2} 2[PR(1-\cos\theta) - 2M_0](1-\cos\theta)Rd\theta$

$= (R^2/2EI)\int_0^{\pi/2} [2PR - 4PR\cos\theta + PR(1+\cos 2\theta) - 4M_0 + 4M_0\cos\theta]d\theta$

$= (R^2/2EI)[PR\pi - 4PR + PR(\pi/2) + (PR/2)(0) - 2M_0\pi + 4M_0]$

$= (PR^3/2EI)[\pi - 4 + \pi/2 - \pi + 2 + 2 - 4/\pi]$

$= \dfrac{PR^3}{4EI}\cdot\dfrac{\pi^2 - 8}{\pi}$

11.5. Portal Frame by Strain Energy. In Para. 10.5 it was shown how a framework with stiff joints could be analysed by a "direct" method based on the moment-area equations. It is frequently simpler to make use of Castigliano's theorem to solve this type of problem, as the following example will illustrate.

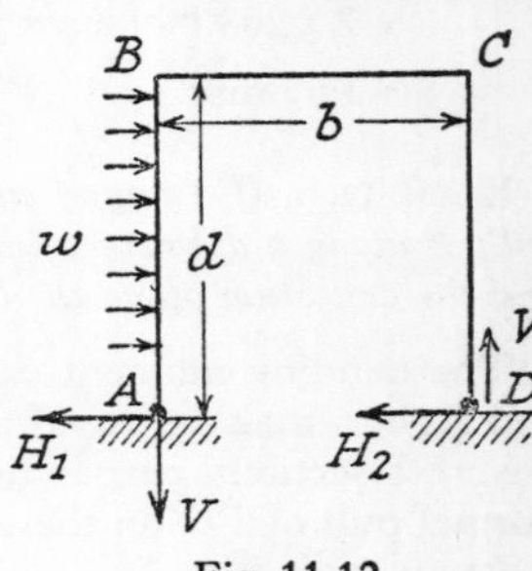

Fig. 11.12

EXAMPLE 7. *The framework shown in Fig. 11.12 is pin-jointed to the ground at A and D and is loaded along AB with a distributed load w. If the flexural rigidity EI is constant throughout, obtain expressions for the reactions at A and D.*

Resolving vertically, the vertical components of reaction, V, must be equal and opposite at A and D, and by moments about A

$$V = wd^2/2b \qquad \text{(i)}$$

Resolving horizontally

$$H_1 + H_2 = wd \qquad \text{(ii)}$$

Bending moment along AB, at a distance x from A, is

$$M_1 = H_1 x - wx^2/2$$

Bending moment along BC, at a distance x' from B, is

$$M_2 = H_1 d - Vx' - wd^2/2$$
$$= H_1 d - wd^2 x'/2b - wd^2/2 \quad \text{from (i)}$$

Bending moment along CD, at a distance x'' from D, is

$$M_3 = H_2 . x''$$
$$= (wd - H_1)x'' \quad \text{from (ii)}$$

Total strain energy due to bending

$$U = \int_0^d \frac{M_1^2 . dx}{2EI} + \int_0^b \frac{M_2^2 . dx'}{2EI} + \int_0^d \frac{M_3^2 . dx''}{2EI}$$

But, since the supports are fixed in position

$$\partial U/\partial H_1 = 0$$

$$\therefore \int_0^d M_1(\partial M_1/\partial H_1)dx + \int_0^b M_2(\partial M_2/\partial H_1)dx' + \int_0^d M_3(\partial M_3/\partial H_1)dx'' = 0$$

i.e. $$\int_0^d (H_1 x - wx^2/2)x . dx + \int_0^b [H_1 d - (wd^2/2b)x' - wd^2/2]d . dx' +$$
$$\int_0^d (wd - H_1)x''(-x'')dx\,' = 0$$

$$H_1 d^3/3 - wd^4/8 + H_1 d^2 b - wd^3 b/4 - wd^3 b/2 - wd^4/3 + H_1 d^3/3 = 0$$

giving $$H_1 = (wd/8)[(11d + 18b)/(2d + 3b)]$$

From (ii) $$H_2 = (wd/8)[(5d + 6b)/(2d + 3b)]$$

SUMMARY

Curvature Small: $\sigma/y = M/I = E(1/R - 1/R_0)$.
Curvature Large: $\sigma = My/Ae(R_0 + y)$.
e found from $\int y dA/(R_0 + y) = 0$.
Vertical Deflection $= \int Mx ds/EI$.
Horizontal Deflection $= \int My ds/EI$.
Castigliano: Displacement $= \partial U/\partial W$
Rotation $= \partial U/\partial M$.

PROBLEMS

1. A curved bar of rectangular section 38 mm wide by 50 mm deep and of mean radius of curvature 100 mm is subjected to a bending moment of 1·5 kNm tending to straighten the bar. Find the position of the neutral axis and the magnitudes of the greatest bending stresses. Draw a diagram to show the variation of stress across the section. $E = 206{,}000$ N/mm^2.

($e = 2{\cdot}1$ mm; 115, 81 N/mm^2.)

2. A bar 5 cm diameter, curved to a mean radius of 5 cm, is subjected to a bending moment of 760 Nm tending to open out the bend. Plot the stress distribution across the section. ($e = 3{\cdot}32$ mm; limiting stresses 101 N/mm^2 tension at inside, 44 N/mm^2 compression at outside.)

3. A bar of diameter d is bent as shown. Prove that the stiffness

$$s = \frac{P}{\delta} = \frac{3\pi E d^4/32}{4l^3 + 6\pi R l^2 + 24R^2 l + 3\pi R^3}$$

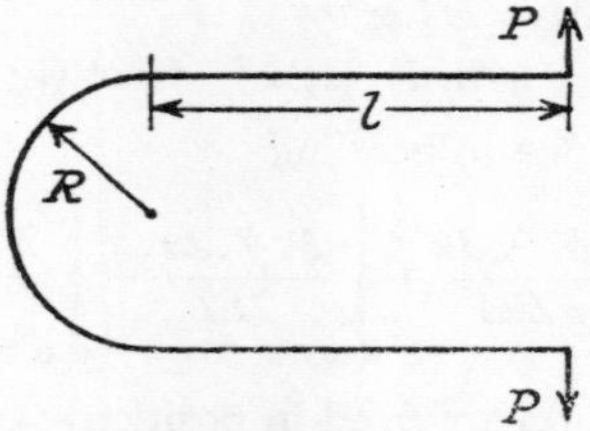

If $s = 1650$ N/m, $d = 6$ mm, $R = 36$ mm, find l. $E = 206{,}000$ N/mm^2. (U.L.)
(175 mm.)

4. A steel ring of rectangular cross-section 7·5 mm wide by 5 mm thick has a mean diameter of 300 mm. A narrow radial saw cut is made, and tangential separating forces of 1 N each are applied at the cut in the plane of the ring. Find the additional separation due to these forces. $E = 206{,}000$ N/mm^2. (2 mm.)

5. A proving ring is 250 mm mean diameter, 38 mm wide and 6·35 mm thick. The maximum stress permitted is 550 N/mm^2. Find the load to cause this stress, and the load to give a 1 mm deflection in the direction of loading. $E = 206{,}000$ N/mm^2. (3500 N; 585 N.)

6. A chain link made of circular section has the dimensions shown. Prove that if d, the diameter of the section, is assumed small compared with R, then the

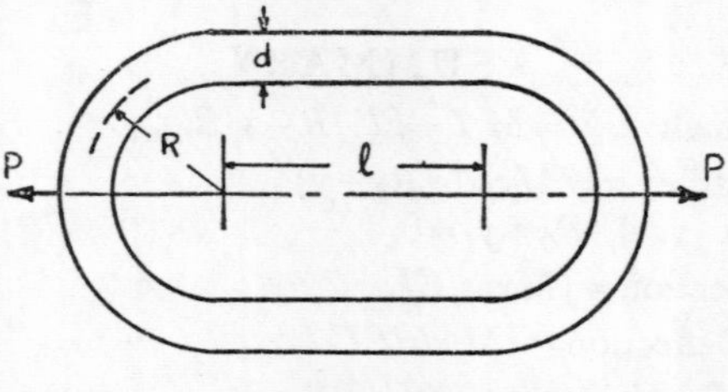

maximum bending moment occurs at the point of application of the load and is equal to

$$\frac{PR}{2}\left(\frac{l + 2R}{l + \pi R}\right)$$

If $R = 24$ mm, $d = 6$ mm, and $l = 42$ mm calculate the ratio of the maximum tensile stress at the section where the load is applied to that at a section half way along the straight portion. (U.L.) (2·89)

7. A portal frame is of height $2l$ and width l, and is loaded with W at the centre of the top member. Show that the maximum bending moment is $11Wl/56$ if the base is pin-jointed, and $3Wl/16$ if fixed into the ground.

CHAPTER XII

Plastic Theory of Bending

12.1. Bending beyond the Yield Stress. In the elastic theory of bending, as discussed in previous chapters, the method of design has been to calculate the maximum stresses occurring, and to keep them within the limits of working stresses in tension and compression, the working stresses being obtained by dividing the yield (or ultimate) stress by a factor of safety. However, mild-steel structures do not fail as soon as the edge stress at any cross-section reaches the yield point, and will continue to withstand the load as long as a central core of the section remains in the elastic state.

In any particular loaded beam, if the load system were increased gradually, yielding would first occur at the extreme fibres of the "weakest" section (if the material exhibits a drop in stress at yield, the lower yield stress is taken to apply—Para. 1.7). These fibres are then said to be in the *plastic* state, and further increase in loading will bring about a considerable increase in strain (and hence deflection) at that section of the beam, with a redistribution of stress. With mild steel this increase in strain can take place without the stress rising above the yield point (i.e. strain hardening effects can be neglected, the plastic strain at yield being of the order 10/20 times the elastic strain), so that the stress in the plastic region may be assumed constant. When the whole cross-section at any point in a structure becomes plastic, no further increase in the moment of resistance is possible without excessive strain (equivalent to an increase in curvature at that section) and a *plastic hinge* has been developed. Depending on the type of structure (e.g. simply supported beam, built-in beam, rigid frame, etc.) one or more plastic hinges are required to cause complete collapse. The value of the load to produce this state is called the *collapse load*, and the ratio collapse load : working load is called the *load factor*. In plastic design this factor is used to replace the normal factor of safety.

12.2. Assumptions in the Plastic Theory. The main aim is to calculate the bending moment required to form a plastic hinge for any particular cross-section, and to determine the distribution of bending moment along the beam at the collapse load. To that end the following assumptions are made:

(1) The material exhibits a marked yield, and can undergo consider-

able strain at yield without further increase in stress. This limits application of the theory generally to *mild steels*, and as there is a drop in stress at yield the lower yield stress is used in calculations (see Para. 1.7). Fig. 12.1 shows the idealised stress-strain diagram for such a material.

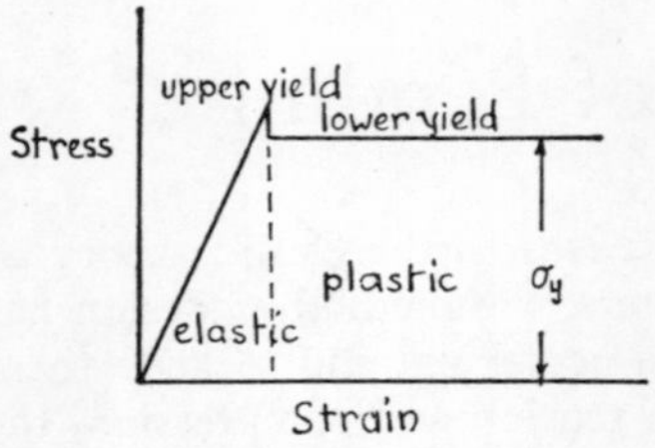

Fig. 12.1

(2) The yield stress is the same in tension and compression.

(3) Transverse cross-sections remain plane, so that strain is proportional to the distance from the neutral axis, though in the plastic region stress will be constant, and *not* proportional to strain.

(4) When a plastic hinge has developed at any cross-section the moment of resistance at that point remains constant until collapse of the whole structure takes place due to the formation of the required number of further plastic hinges at other points.

12.3. Moment of Resistance at a Plastic Hinge. Fig. 12.2(a) shows the variation of stress and strain in a symmetrical cross-section under the working load, by the simple theory of bending, Para. 6.1 (σ_w is the maximum working stress). If the load is increased until yielding occurs

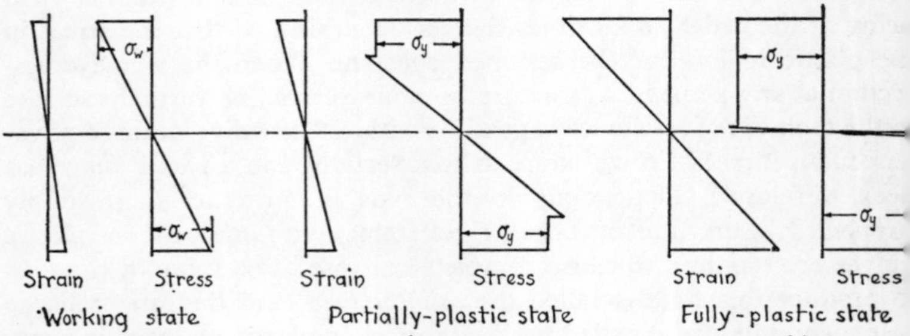

Fig. 12.2

in the extreme fibres the partially plastic state of Fig. 12.2(b) would be obtained, where σ_y is the lower yield stress (note how the assumptions of Para. 12.2 are applied). Further increase in load produces the fully plastic state of Fig. 12.2(c), in which the stress is assumed uniform and equal to σ_y. There will still be a very small elastic region around the eutral axis, as indicated in the diagram, but the effect of this on the alue of the moment of resistance is very small and will be neglected.

(a) *Rectangular Section.* If b is the width and d the depth, the total ads above and below the neutral axis are $(bd/2)\sigma_y$ each, acting at $d/4$ rom the neutral axis; hence the fully plastic moment

$$M_p = (bd/2)\sigma_y \times d/2$$
$$= (bd^2/4)\sigma_y \quad (1)$$

This compares with a working moment

$$M_w = Z\sigma_w = (bd^2/6)\sigma_w \quad (2)$$

rom elastic theory (Z is the normal section modulus), and a moment t first yield of

$$M_y = (bd^2/6)\sigma_y \quad (3)$$

The ratio M_p/M_y is called the *shape factor* S, since it depends only on he shape of the cross-section, i.e. for a rectangular section, from (1) nd (3)

$$S = 1{\cdot}5 \quad (4)$$

rom (2) and (3),

$$M_y/M_w = \sigma_y/\sigma_w$$
$$= \text{normal factor of safety based on initial yield} \quad (5)$$

rom (1) and (2),

$$M_p = S \times (\sigma_y/\sigma_w) \times M_w = SZ\sigma_y \quad (6)$$

Note that equations (5) and (6) will apply to *any section.*

EXAMPLE 1. *A steel bar of rectangular section 72 mm by 30 mm is used as a imply supported beam on a span of 1·2 m and loaded at mid-span. If the ield stress is 280 N/mm² and the long edges of the section are vertical, find he load when yielding first occurs.*

Assuming that a further increase in load causes yielding to spread inwards owards the neutral axis, with the stress in the yielded part remaining at 280 N/mm², find the load required to cause yielding for a depth of 12 mm at he top and bottom of the section at mid-span, and find the length of beam over which yielding has occurred. (U.L.)

If W_y is the load at first yield, then

$$M_y = (bd^2/6)\sigma_y \quad \text{from (3)}$$

i.e. $$W_y \times 300 = (30 \times 72^2/6)280$$

giving $$W_y = 24{\cdot}2 \text{ kN} \quad \text{(i)}$$

Under a higher load W, the central section of the beam is in a partially plastic state, the stress distribution being similar to Fig. 12.2(b), the outer

12 mm on each side of the neutral axis being under constant stress of 28 N/mm^2 with no drop of stress at yield. The moment of resistance calculated from the stress diagram is

$$M = (280 \times 12 \times 30)60 + (\tfrac{1}{2} \times 280 \times 24 \times 30)32$$
$$= 928 \times 10^4 \text{ Nmm}$$
$$= W \times 300 \text{ since the end reactions are } W/2$$

giving

$$W = 31 \text{ kN} \qquad \text{(i}$$

At first yield the moment of resistance is $W_y \times 0{\cdot}3$, i.e. 7·26 kNm from (i), and if this occurs at a distance x from either end under a central load W then

$$\tfrac{1}{2}Wx = 7{\cdot}26$$

i.e. $$x = 0{\cdot}468 \text{ m} \quad \text{from (ii)}$$

The length of beam over which yielding occurs

$$= 1{\cdot}2 - 2x$$
$$= 0{\cdot}264 \text{ m}$$

(b) **I**-*section*. The shape factor will vary slightly with the proportions of flange to web, an average value being about 1·15, as illustrated by the example below.

EXAMPLE 2. *A 300 mm by 125 mm* **I**-*beam has flanges 13 mm thick and web 8·5 mm thick. Calculate the shape factor and the moment of resistance in the fully plastic state. Take* $\sigma_y = 250$ N/mm^2 *and* $I_x = 85 \times 10^6$ mm^4.

At first yield,

$$M_y = (I/y)\sigma_y$$
$$= (85 \times 10^6/150)250 = 141 \times 10^6 \text{ Nmm} \qquad \text{(i}$$

In the fully plastic state the stress is equal to 250 N/mm^2 everywhere being tensile on one side and compressive on the other side of the neutral axis. By moment of the stress × area products, dividing the web into two parts,

$$M_p = (250 \times 125 \times 13)287 \text{ for the flanges}$$
$$+ (250 \times 8{\cdot}5 \times 137)137 \text{ for the web}$$
$$= 156 \times 10^6 \text{ Nmm} = 156 \text{ kNm} \qquad \text{(i}$$

The shape factor

$$S = M_p/M_y$$
$$= 1{\cdot}11 \quad \text{from (i) and (ii)}$$

(c) *Unsymmetrical Section.* If A is the total area of cross-section, hen it is clear that for pure bending in the fully plastic state the 'neutral axis" must divide the area into equal halves. If the centroids

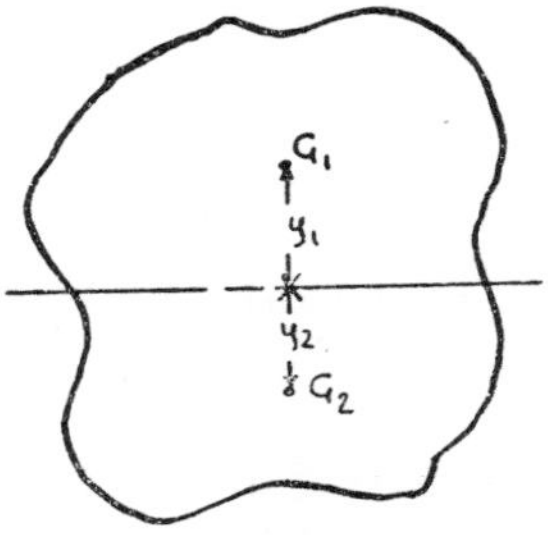

Fig. 12.3

of these halves are G_1 and G_2 (Fig. 12.3) at a distance $y_1 + y_2$ apart, then

$$M_p = (\tfrac{1}{2}\sigma_y A)(y_1 + y_2) \tag{7}$$

But at first yield

$$M_y = Z\sigma_y \text{ where } Z \text{ is the section modulus}$$

Hence

$$M_p/M_y = A(y_1 + y_2)/2Z \tag{8}$$

$$= S \text{ by definition.}$$

EXAMPLE 3. *Find the shape factor for a 150 mm by 75 mm channel in pure bending with the plane of bending perpendicular to the web of the channel. The dimensions are shown in Fig. 12.4, and $A = 2300$ mm² and $Z = 21{,}000$ mm³.*

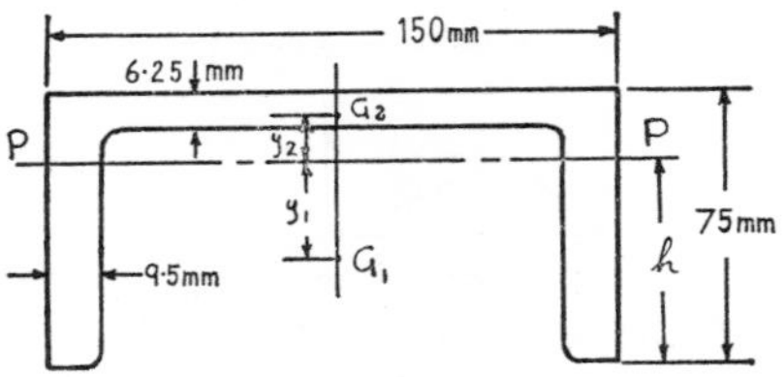

Fig. 12.4

Let PP be the neutral axis under fully plastic conditions, then this divides the total area equally. Assuming all corners are "square", then

$$2 \times 9{\cdot}5 \times h = 150 \times 6{\cdot}25 + 2 \times 9{\cdot}5(75 - h - 6{\cdot}25)$$

giving

$$h = 59 \text{ mm}$$

The centroids of the two areas on either side of PP are G_1 and G_2 a distances y_1 and y_2, where

$$y_1 = h/2 = 29{\cdot}5 \text{ mm}$$

and
$$y_2 = \frac{(150 \times 6{\cdot}25)(16 - 3{\cdot}125) + (2 \times 9{\cdot}5 \times 9{\cdot}75)4{\cdot}875}{150 \times 6{\cdot}25 + 2 \times 9{\cdot}5 \times 9{\cdot}75}$$

$$= 11{\cdot}8 \text{ mm}$$

from (8),
$$S = A(y_1 + y_2)/2Z$$
$$= 2300 \times 41{\cdot}3/2 \times 21{,}000$$
$$= 2{\cdot}26$$

12.4. Collapse Loads. Having determined the moments of resistance at a plastic hinge for the section of beam being used, the next step is to decide from the conditions at the supports how many such hinges are required to cause collapse, and to find the corresponding load in this condition. If there are a number of points of "local" maximum bending moment along the beam (under working load conditions) it is clear that the first plastic hinge will occur at the numerical maximum point. If further plastic hinges are necessary for collapse, these will occur at the next lower values chosen from the remaining local maxima. When sufficient plastic hinges have been formed to convert the structure into a "mechanism" (hinges to be considered as pin-joints), the state of collapse has been reached. The principal cases for a single beam will now be examined.

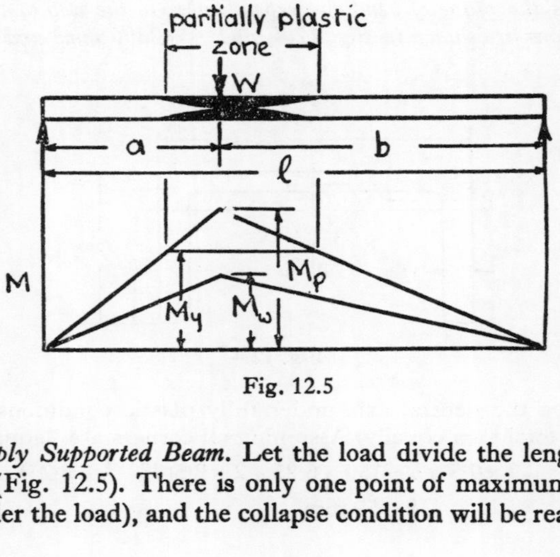

Fig. 12.5

(a) *Simply Supported Beam.* Let the load divide the length l in the ratio $a:b$ (Fig. 12.5). There is only one point of maximum B.M. (i.e. Wab/l under the load), and the collapse condition will be reached when a plastic hinge is formed at this point. The B.M. is then M_p, and hence the collapse load is given by

$$W_c = M_p l/ab$$
$$= S \times (\sigma_y/\sigma_w) \times M_w l/ab \qquad (1)$$

from Para. 12.3 (a), eqn. (6).

But $M_w = Wab/l$ where W is the working load. Rearranging (1) gives

$$W_c = S(\sigma_y/\sigma_w)W$$

or

$$\text{Load factor} = W_c/W$$
$$= S(\sigma_y/\sigma_w) \qquad (2)$$

This is the simple result which will always be obtained when only one plastic hinge is required for collapse. For a given material and working stress it is seen that the load factor is greater than the normal factor of safety on elastic design (which considers failure to occur at first yield) by the shape factor, and that a different load factor will be obtained for, say, rectangular and I-sections, even under the same system of loading. Alternatively, basing the design on a constant load factor, the working stress may be varied to suit the particular section, e.g. from (2),

$$\sigma_w = S\sigma_y/\text{load factor} \qquad (3)$$
$$= 1{\cdot}5\sigma_y/\text{load factor for rectangular section}$$
$$= 1{\cdot}15\ \sigma_y/\text{load factor for I-section.}$$

The results for distributed load and for a simple cantilever are also as (2) and (3) above.

(b) *Propped Cantilever*. Consider the case of a cantilever carrying a central load W and propped (to the same height as the fixed end) at the free end (Fig. 12.6). It can be shown by the methods of Chap. IX

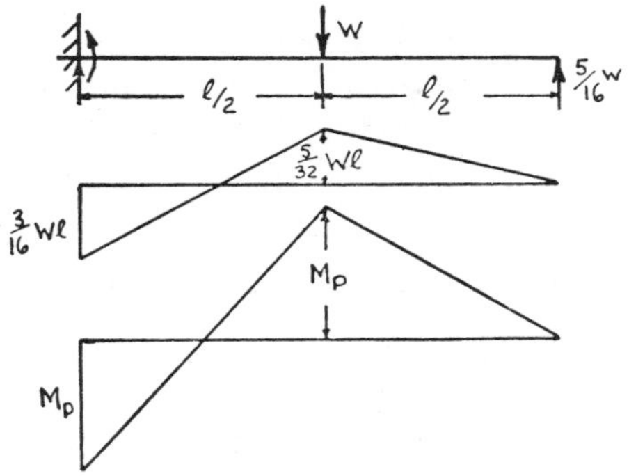

Fig. 12.6

that the load on the prop under elastic conditions is $(5/16)W$ and the B.M. diagram is shown immediately underneath. There are local maxima at the fixed end and under the load, and a gradual increase in load will cause a plastic hinge to form first at the fixed end, the central B.M. being somewhat less. However, due to the support at the free end a collapse condition will not be reached until a second plastic hinge has formed under the load, i.e. the B.M.'s at the end and centre are numerically M_p and the distribution is as shown in the lower diagram. Note that the shape of the B.M. diagram at collapse is *not* similar to that under working conditions, due to a redistribution of stress and strain when a plastic hinge is formed, the value of M_p being assumed the same at each hinge by Para. 12.2 (4). If P is the load on the prop at collapse, then equating the numerical value of B.M.'s at the end and centre:

$$M_p = W_c \times l/2 - Pl = Pl/2$$

i.e.
$$P = W_c/3$$

and
$$M_p = W_c l/6 \qquad (4)$$

The maximum bending moment under working conditions is

$$M_w = (3/16)Wl \qquad (5)$$

Hence
$$\begin{aligned} W_c &= 6M_p/l \quad \text{from (4)} \\ &= 6S(\sigma_y/\sigma_w)M_w/l \quad \text{(para. 12.3 (6))} \\ &= (9/8)S(\sigma_y/\sigma_w)W \quad \text{from (5)} \end{aligned} \qquad (6)$$

Load factor

$$L = W_c/W = (9/8)S(\sigma_y/\sigma_w)$$

i.e. an increase of 9:8 over the simply supported beam for the same working stress conditions.

(c) *Built-In Beam, Uniformly Distributed Load* (Fig. 12.7). For collapse, three plastic hinges must be formed, i.e. at each end and the centre, for this loading. The B.M. diagram at collapse is then formed by making the values equal to M_p at these points. By symmetry the reactions at the ends are then $W_c/2$, hence at the centre

$$M_p = (W_c/2)(l/2) - (W_c/2)(l/4) - M_p$$

giving
$$M_p = W_c l/16 \qquad (7)$$

$$M_w = Wl/12 \text{ from elastic theory} \qquad (8)$$

Hence
$$\begin{aligned} W_c &= 16M_p/l \quad \text{from (7)} \\ &= 16S(\sigma_y/\sigma_w)M_w/l \\ &= (4/3)S(\sigma_y/\sigma_w)W \quad \text{from (8)} \end{aligned}$$

giving
$$\text{Load factor} = (4/3)S(\sigma_y/\sigma_w)$$

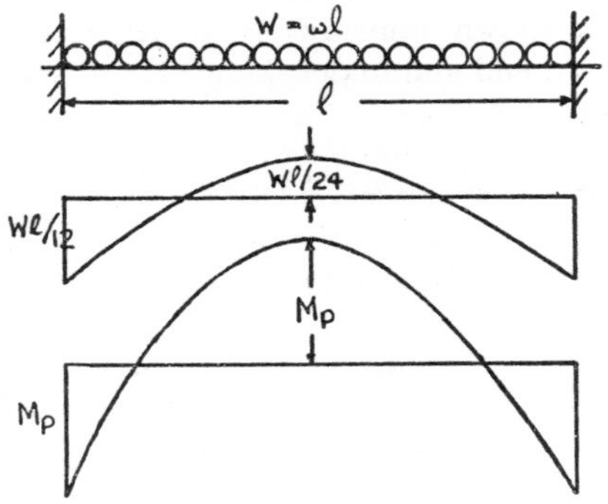

Fig. 12.7

For all cases of built-in beams *the collapse load is not affected by sinking of the supports* or lack of rigidity of the fixed ends, provided that the rigidity is sufficient to allow the fully plastic moment to develop.

EXAMPLE 4. *A 300 mm by 125 mm* **I**-*beam is carried over a span of 20 m the ends being rigidly built-in. Find the maximum point load which can be carried at 8 m from one end, and the maximum working stress set up. Take a load factor of 1·8 and $\sigma_y = 250$ N/mm². $Z = 56{\cdot}6 \times 10^4$ mm³ and $S = 1{\cdot}11$ (see Ex. 2).*

Under elastic conditions the maximum B.M. is at the end nearer the load, and by Ex. 2, Chap. 10,

$$M_w = W \times 12^2 \times 8/20^2$$
$$= (72/25)W \qquad \text{(i)}$$

At collapse, hinges must be formed at each end and under the load (Fig. 12.8) and it is clear that the collapse load W_c is given by equating the numerical B.M.'s, i.e.

$$W_c \times 12 \times 8/20 - M_p = M_p$$

or

$$W_c = (5/12)M_p \qquad \text{(ii)}$$

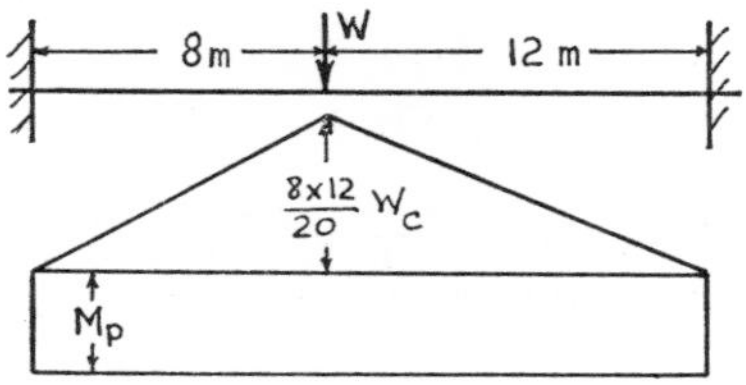

Fig. 12.8

Since load factor = 1·8, working load

$$W = W_c/1{\cdot}8$$
$$= (25/108)M_p \quad \text{from (ii)}$$
$$= (25/108)SZ\sigma_y$$
$$= (25/108)1{\cdot}11 \times 56{\cdot}6 \times 10^4 \times 250/10^3$$
$$= 36{,}000 \text{ N} = 36 \text{ kN}$$

from (i) $M_w = (72/25)36$ kNm

giving a working stress

$$\sigma_w = M_w/Z$$
$$= \frac{72 \times 36{,}000 \times 10^3}{25 \times 56{\cdot}6 \times 10^4}$$
$$= 183 \text{ N/mm}^2$$

12.5. Combined Bending and Direct Stress. For a beam or column subjected to an axial stress as well as a bending moment, the neutral axis will be displaced to one side of the centroid axis, the variations in working stress being shown in Fig. 12.9(a). An increase in load will cause the stress to reach the yield point on one side first, and spread

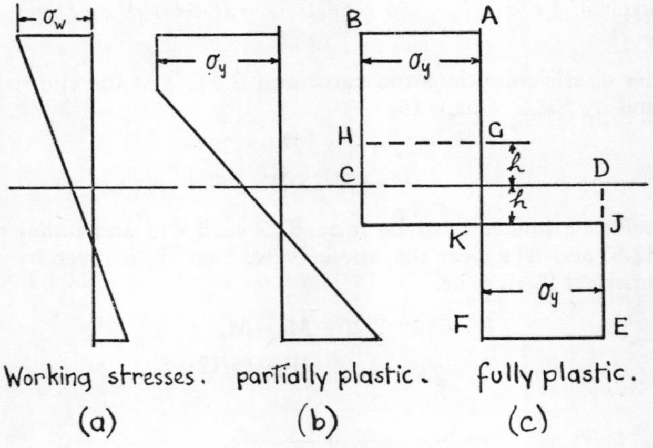

Fig. 12.9

over the section to give the fully plastic state of Fig. 12.9(c). It is clear that the displacement of the neutral axis in the plastic state is given by h such that

$$2h \times b \times \sigma_y = \text{axial load} \times \text{load factor} = PL \qquad (1)$$

(where b is the width of the section near the centroid axis) and the plastic moment of resistance

$$\begin{aligned} M_p &= \text{that given by ABCDEF} - \text{that given by GHCDJK} \\ &= SZ\sigma_y - (bh\sigma_y)h \\ &= SZ\sigma_y - P^2L^2/4b\sigma_y \quad \text{from (1)} \qquad (2) \end{aligned}$$

Comparing this with equation (6) of Para. 12.3, it is seen that the plastic moment is reduced by a term depending on the axial load, the load factor, and the shape of the section. The permissible working moment for a single plastic hinge is then obtained from M_p by dividing by the load factor L,

i.e. $$M_w = M_p/L = SZ\sigma_y/L - P^2L/4b\sigma_y \qquad (3)$$

EXAMPLE 5. *A 300 mm by 125 mm* **I**-*beam has to withstand an axial load of* 100 *kN. If a load factor of 1·8 is to be applied, determine the maximum permissible bending moment. Web thickness* $=8{\cdot}5$ *mm,* $Z=56{\cdot}6\times10^4$ *mm*^{3}, $S=1{\cdot}11$ (*see Ex. 2*). *Take* $\sigma_y=250$ *N/mm*^{2}.

At collapse, axial load $=1{\cdot}8\times100=180$ kN, which requires a depth of web $=180\times10^3/(8{\cdot}5\times\sigma_y)=84{\cdot}8$ mm. This will be spaced equally about the centroid, i.e. 42·4 mm either side (h of eqn. (1)).

The reduction in M_p is given by the product of half the axial load and the distance between the centres of areas of each half load (i.e. GHCDJK of Fig. 12.9). Giving

$$M_p = SZ\sigma_y - 90\times10^3\times42{\cdot}4$$

(check from eqn. (2)).

$$\begin{aligned} &= 1{\cdot}11\times56{\cdot}6\times10^4\times250 - 90\times10^3\times42{\cdot}4 \\ &= 151\times10^6 \text{ Nmm} = 151 \text{ kNm} \end{aligned}$$

Then $M_w = M_p/1{\cdot}8 = 84$ kNm.

Note that the reduction in M_w in this case is only about $2\frac{1}{2}\%$, whereas on the elastic theory, with a working stress of 150 N/mm^2, the permissible bending stress

$$\begin{aligned} \sigma_b &= 150 - \text{axial load/area of beam} \\ &= 131{\cdot}2 \text{ N/mm}^2 \quad (A = 5500 \text{ mm}^2) \end{aligned}$$

and the reduction in M_w due to the existence of the axial load is

$$\frac{(150-131{\cdot}2)100}{150} = 12{\cdot}5\%$$

EXAMPLE 6. *A rectangular bar of mild steel, 72 mm by 48 mm in cross-section, is subjected to an axial load applied eccentrically and cutting all sections at a point mid-way between the 72 mm sides and 24 mm from a 48 mm side. Calculate the maximum load which can be carried using a load factor of 2 and a yield stress of 270 N/mm*^{2}.

Applying equation (3), $S=1{\cdot}5$, $Z=bd^2/6$, $\sigma_y=270$, $L=2$, $b=48$, $d=72$ giving

$$M_w=\frac{1{\cdot}5\times 48\times 72^2\times 270}{6\times 2}-\frac{P^2\times 2}{4\times 48\times 270}$$
$$=84\times 10^5-P^2/25{,}900$$

But $M_w=P\times 12$ from the eccentricity,

Hence $\quad P^2/25{,}900+12P-84\times 10^5=0$

from which $\quad P=[-12+\sqrt{(144+1300)}]12{,}950$
$$=337{,}000\text{ N}=337\text{ kN.}$$

The working stress is then

$$P/A+Pe/Z=337{,}000/48\times 72+337{,}000\times 12\times 6/48\times 72^2$$
$$=195\text{ N/mm}^2$$

Note that the neutral axis (zero stress) is at the 48 mm edge opposite the load under elastic conditions with this eccentricity, but is at a distance of $\frac{1}{2}(337{,}000\times 2)/48\times 270=26$ mm from the centre of the section under fully plastic conditions (eqn. (1)).

12.6. Portal Frames—Collapse Loads. In a framework with rigid joints, points of local maximum bending moment will occur at the joints and under any applied load. At the collapse load some or all of these points will become plastic hinges.

Consider a portal of height h and span l as shown in Fig. 12.10. Under a central vertical load V and a horizontal load H, plastic hinges may form at any combination of the points ABCDE (if A and E are pin-

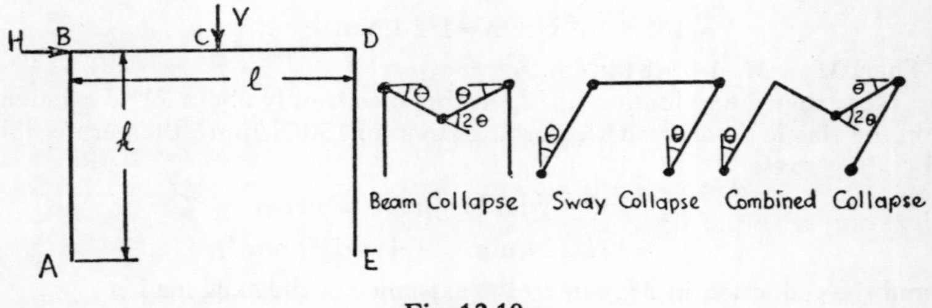

Fig. 12.10

joints they will rotate under zero bending moment). A collapse condition is reached when sufficient hinges are formed to create a "mechanism". The only three distinct forms of collapse mechanism are shown as beam collapse (hinges at B, C and D), sway collapse (hinges at A, B, D, and E) and combined collapse (hinges at A, C, D, and E). If one link of the mechanism is given a rotation θ (under the action of the plastic moment M_p), then the value of the collapse load can be calculated by the principle of virtual work, choosing the least load for all the possible mechanisms. Some standard cases will be considered below, and to allow for different section beams, the plastic moments will be indicated by M_{ps} for the stanchions AB and DE, and M_{pb} for the beam BD. At the corners B and D, the smaller plastic moment will be written M_p'.

(a) *Hinged Base Portal.*

(1) *Vertical Load Only.* The symmetrical beam collapse will apply, the joint rotations being θ at B and D, and 2θ at C. Neglecting the elastic strain and assuming that the whole strain takes place under a constant collapse load, the work done by the load is $V.\frac{1}{2}l\theta$ and the energy dissipated in the plastic hinges is $M_{pb}2\theta+2M_p'\theta$.

Equating, and dividing by 2θ

$$\tfrac{1}{4}Vl=M_{pb}+M_p' \qquad (1)$$

(2) *Horizontal Load Only.* Sway collapse will apply here, with rotations θ at B and D. Equating the work done by the load and at the plastic hinges,

$$H.h\theta=2M_p'\theta$$

or

$$\tfrac{1}{2}Hh=M_p' \qquad (2)$$

(3) *Combined Loading.* Generally, collapse will be by forming plastic hinges at C and D, there being no rotation of the joint at B.

The work equation becomes

$$V.\tfrac{1}{2}l\theta+H.h\theta=M_{pb}.2\theta+M_p'.2\theta$$

or

$$\tfrac{1}{4}Vl+\tfrac{1}{2}Hh=M_{pb}+M_p' \qquad (3)$$

It can be shown that, if the section is uniform throughout, collapse will occur by sway when $Hh>\frac{1}{2}Vl$, the collapse load being given by (2). In no event can the beam collapse occur under combined loading, by comparison of the corresponding sides of equations (1) and (3).

EXAMPLE 7. *If, in Fig. 12.10, $H=\frac{1}{2}V$ and $h=\frac{1}{2}l$, obtain an expression for the horizontal and vertical collapse loads when the plastic moment M_p is the same for beam and stanchions.*

From equation (3)

$$\tfrac{1}{4}Vl+\tfrac{1}{2}.\tfrac{1}{2}V.\tfrac{1}{2}l=2M_p$$

i.e.

$$V=16M_p/3l$$

Then

$$H=\tfrac{1}{2}V$$

$$=8M_p/3l$$

If the other two modes of collapse are checked, it will be found that higher collapse loads are required, and consequently the combined collapse mechanism gives the least values.

The most economical sections for a given loading are calculated by satisfying equations (2) and (3) simultaneously.

EXAMPLE 8. *A portal frame with hinged feet is 3 m high and 5 m wide and carries a central vertical load of 50 kN together with a horizontal load at beam height of 20 kN. Using a load factor of 2, determine the plastic moments required.*

Find the section moduli required, assuming a shape factor of 1·15 and a yield stress 280 N/mm².

From (2),

$$M_p' = \tfrac{1}{2}Hh \text{ at collapse}$$
$$= \tfrac{1}{2} \times 2 \times 20 \times 3$$
$$= 60 \text{ kNm}$$

From (2) and (3)

$$M_{pb} = \tfrac{1}{4}Vl$$
$$= \tfrac{1}{4} \times 2 \times 50 \times 5$$
$$= 125 \text{ kNm}$$

The section moduli required are, for the stanchions

$$Z = M_p'/S\sigma_y$$
$$= 60 \times 10^6/1{\cdot}15 \times 280$$
$$= 18{\cdot}7 \times 10^4 \text{ mm}^3$$

and for the beam

$$Z = M_{pb}/S\sigma_y$$
$$= 39 \times 10^4 \text{ mm}^3$$

(b) *Fixed Base Portal.*

(1) *Vertical Load Only.* The beam collapses in the same manner as a hinge-based portal giving

$$\tfrac{1}{4}Vl = M_{pb} + M_p' \tag{4}$$

(2) *Horizontal Load Only.* Sway collapse now requires the formation of 4 hinges, and the work equation is

$$Hh\theta = 2M_{ps}\theta + 2M_p'\theta$$

i.e.

$$\tfrac{1}{2}Hh = M_{ps} + M_p' \tag{5}$$

(3) *Combined Loading.* The combined collapse mechanism gives

$$V.\tfrac{1}{2}l\theta + H.h\theta = 2M_{ps}.\theta + M_p'.2\theta + M_{pb}.2\theta$$

or

$$\tfrac{1}{4}Vl + \tfrac{1}{2}Hh = M_{ps} + M_p' + M_{pb} \tag{6}$$

For economical design equation (6) and either (4) or (5) should be satisfied simultaneously.

EXAMPLE 9. *For the same dimensions and loading as Example 8, determine a suitable section if the base of the portal is fixed.*

Again, if H and V are the collapse loads,

$$\tfrac{1}{2}Hh = 60 \quad \text{and} \quad \tfrac{1}{4}Vl = 125 \text{ kNm}$$

If (4) and (6) are to be satisfied

$$M_{ps} = 60 \text{ kNm}$$

and

$$M_{pb} = 65 \text{ kNm}$$

Alternatively, if (5) and (6) are satisfied

$$M_{pb} = 125 \text{ kNm}$$

and

$$M_{ps} = 30 \text{ kNm} \quad (M_p' = M_{ps})$$

Choosing the first solution,

$$Z = M_p/S\sigma_y$$

$= 18{\cdot}7 \times 10^4$ mm^3 for the stanchions, and

$20{\cdot}2 \times 10^4$ mm^3 for the beam.

SUMMARY

$$\text{Load Factor} = \frac{\text{Collapse Load}}{\text{Working Load}}$$

$$\text{Shape Factor} = \frac{\text{Plastic Moment } M_p}{\text{Moment at First Yield } M}$$

$$M_y = Z\sigma_y$$

REFERENCES

BAKER, J. F., J. Inst. Civil Eng., Vol. 31, page 188, 1949.

BAKER, J. F., *The Steel Skeleton*, Vol. 2, C.U.P. 1956.

BRITISH CONSTRUCTIONAL STEELWORK ASSOCIATION. Publication No. 5. *The Collapse Method of Design.*

HEYMAN, J., *Plastic Design of Portal Frames*, C.U.P. 1957.

JOHNSON W., and MELLOR, P. B., *Plasticity for Mechanical Engineers*, Van Nostrand, 1962.

NEAL, B. G., *The Plastic Method of Structural Analysis*. Chapman & Hall. 1956.

PROBLEMS

1. The figure shows the section of a beam which is subjected to a bending moment of such magnitude that yielding occurs at the lower part of the web over a depth of 2 cm. The yield stress of 280 N/mm^2 may be assumed constant over

the yielded area, while over the remainder of the section the stress is proportional to the distance from the neutral axis. Determine:

(a) the position of the neutral axis,
(b) the stress at the top of the section,
(c) the moment of resistance of the section. (U.L.)

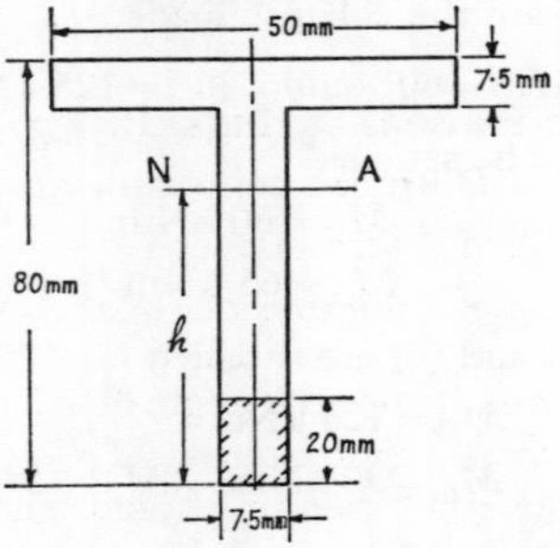

(Note: for (a), equate the tensile and compressive forces on either side of NA.)

((*a*) $h=5{\cdot}42$ cm; (b) 210 N/mm²; (c) 4350 Nm.)

2. Show that the shape factor for a circular cross-section bending about a diameter is approximately 1·7.

3. A 15 cm by 7·5 cm **I**-beam is built-in at one end and propped at the same level at the other. It carries a uniformly distributed load over the whole length. Determine the load factor using values of $\sigma_y = 240$ N/mm² and $\sigma_w = 150$ N/mm² The web thickness is 5·75 mm flange thickness 9·4 mm, and $I = 820$ cm⁴. (2·63).

4. Show that the plastic moment for a rectangular section beam carrying an axial stress p is given by

$$\left(\frac{\sigma_y^2 - L^2p^2}{\sigma_y}\right)\frac{bd^2}{4}$$

where σ_y is the yield stress, L the load factor, and b and d the dimensions.

5. A portal frame of height h and span l carries a central vertical load V together with a horizontal load H at beam level. If M_p is the plastic moment of the section (uniform throughout) and $Vl=6Hh$, find expressions for the collapse loads when the base is hinged or fixed in direction. (Hinged, $V=6M_p/l$, $H=M_p/h$. Fixed, $V=8M_p/l$, $H=4M_p/3h$.)

6. In Problem 5, if $h=3$ m and $l=6$ m, calculate the minimum plastic moments required in the stanchions and beam for collapse loads of 150 kN vertical and 50 kN horizontal.

(Hinged, $M_{ps}=75$, $M_{pb}=225$ kNm; Fixed, $M_{ps}=75$, $M_{pb}=150$ kNm.)

CHAPTER XIII

Springs

13.1. Close-coiled Helical Springs. In Fig. 13.1

D = mean coil diameter

d = wire diameter

n = number of coils

(a) *Under axial load W.* Since the angle of the helix is small the action on any cross-section is approximately a pure torque $= W.D/2$, and the bending and shear effects may be neglected.

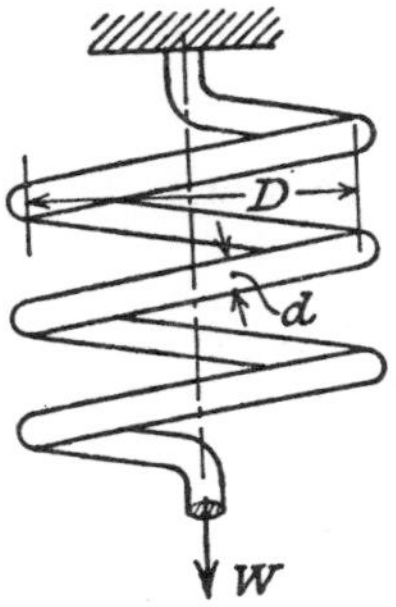

Fig. 13.1

The wire is therefore being twisted like a shaft, and if θ is the total angle of twist along the wire, and x the deflection of W along the axis of the coils, $x = (D/2)\theta$ approximately.

Applying the formula for torsion of shafts (Para. 8.1), making the above substitutions and also noting that $l = \pi Dn$ approx.,

$$\frac{W.D/2}{\pi d^4/32} = 2\hat{\tau}/d = \frac{G.2x/D}{\pi Dn}$$

or
$$8WD/\pi d^4 = \hat{\tau}/d = Gx/\pi D^2 n \qquad (1)$$

The spring stiffness $k = W/x = Gd^4/8D^3n$

The strain energy $U = \frac{1}{2}Wx$

which, by substitution in terms of $\hat{\tau}$ from (1), can be reduced to

$$U = (\hat{\tau}^2/4G) \times \text{volume} \qquad \text{(see also Para. 8.2).}$$

(b) *Under axial torque T.* This will produce approximately a pure bending moment of magnitude T at all cross-sections. The total strain energy is therefore

$$U = \frac{T^2 l}{2EI} = \frac{T^2.\pi Dn}{2E \times \pi d^4/64} \qquad \text{(Para. 11.1)}$$

$$= 32T^2Dn/Ed^4 \qquad (2)$$

But if T causes a rotation of one end of the spring through an angle ϕ about the axis, relative to the other end,

$$U = \tfrac{1}{2}T\phi$$

Equating to (2) gives

$$\phi = Tl/EI$$
$$= 64TDn/Ed^4 \quad (3)$$

$$\text{Maximum bending stress} = \frac{T \times d/2}{\pi d^4/64} = \frac{32T}{\pi d^3}$$

EXAMPLE 1. *A close-coiled helical spring has to absorb 50 Nm of energy when compressed 5 cm. The coil diameter is eight times the wire diameter. If there are ten coils, estimate the diameters of coil and wire and the maximum shear stress.* $G = 85{,}000$ N/mm^2.

$$U = \tfrac{1}{2}Wx$$

i.e. $$50 \times 100 = \tfrac{1}{2} \times W \times 5$$

$$\therefore \quad W = 2000 \text{ N}$$

$D = 8d$; $n = 10$.

Substitute in

$$8WD/\pi d^4 = Gx/\pi D^2 n$$
$$(8 \times 2000 \times 8d)/d^4 = (85{,}000 \times 50)/[(8d)^2 \times 10]$$

from which $$d = (8 \times 2000 \times 8 \times 64)/(85{,}000 \times 5)$$
$$= 19{\cdot}3 \text{ mm}$$
$$D = 8d = 154 \text{ mm}$$
$$8WD/\pi d^4 = \hat{\tau}/d \quad \text{from (1)}$$
$$\therefore \quad \hat{\tau} = (8 \times 2000 \times 154 \times 19{\cdot}3)/(\pi \times 19{\cdot}3^4)$$
$$= 108 \text{ N/mm}^2$$

EXAMPLE 2. *A close-coiled helical spring is to have a stiffness of 900 N/m in compression, with a maximum load of 45 N and a maximum shearing stress of 120 N/mm^2. The "solid" length of the spring (i.e. coils touching) is 45 mm. Find the wire diameter, mean coil radius, and number of coils. $G = 40{,}000$ N/mm^2. (U.L.)*

Stiffness $$k = Gd^4/8D^3n$$

i.e. $$900 \times 10^{-3} = \frac{40{,}000 \times d^4}{8D^3 n}$$

or $$d^4 = \frac{9}{5 \times 10^4} D^3 n \quad \text{(i)}$$

$$\text{Maximum stress} = 8WD/\pi d^3 \quad \text{from (1)}$$

i.e. $$120 = (8 \times 45 \times D)/\pi d^3$$

or $$D = 1{\cdot}05 d^3 \quad \text{(ii)}$$

i.e. $$\text{Solid length} = nd$$

i.e. $$45 = nd \quad \text{(iii)}$$

Substitute from (ii) and (iii) in (i)

$$d^4 = \frac{9}{5 \times 10^4} . (1{\cdot}05)^3 d^9 . \frac{45}{d}$$

giving $$d = 3{\cdot}22 \text{ mm}$$

From (ii) $D = 35{\cdot}2$ mm

i.e. Mean coil radius $= 17{\cdot}6$ mm

From (iii) $n = 14$

EXAMPLE 3. *In a compound helical spring the inner spring is arranged within and concentric with the outer one, but is 9 mm shorter. The outer spring has ten coils of mean diameter 24 mm, and the wire diameter is 3 mm. Find the stiffness of the inner spring if an axial load of 150N causes the outer one to compress 18 mm.*

If the radial clearance between the springs is 1·5 mm find the wire diameter of the inner-spring when it has eight coils. $G = 77{,}000$ N/mm². (U.L.)

The load carried by the outer spring for a compression of 18 mm

$$= \frac{77{,}000 \times 18}{8 \times 24^3 \times 10} \times 3^4 \quad \text{from (1)}$$

$$= 102 \text{ N}$$

Hence the load carried by the inner spring $= 150 - 102 = 48$ N, for a compression of $18 - 9 = 9$ mm.

$$\text{Stiffness of inner spring} = 48/9 = 5{\cdot}33 \text{ N/mm}$$

$D = 24 - 3 - 2 \times 1{\cdot}5 - d = 18 - d$

$n = 8.$

$$\text{Stiffness } 5{\cdot}33 = \frac{77{,}000 \times d^4}{8(18 - d)^3 \times 8}$$

or
$$226d^4 = (18 - d)^3$$

Since d is small compared with 18, for a first approximation

$$d = [5830/226]^{\frac{1}{4}} = 2{\cdot}26 \text{ mm}$$

Second approximation

$$d = (15{\cdot}74^3/226)^{\frac{1}{4}} = 2{\cdot}05 \text{ mm}$$

Final trial

$$d = (15{\cdot}95^3/226)^{\frac{1}{4}} = 2{\cdot}06 \text{ mm}$$

EXAMPLE 4. *A composite spring has two close-coiled helical springs connected in series; each spring has twelve coils at a mean diameter of 25 mm. Find the wire diameter in one if the other is 2·5 mm and the stiffness of the composite spring is 700 N/m.*

Estimate the greatest load that can be carried by the composite spring, and the corresponding extension, for a maximum shearing stress of 180 N/mm². $G = 80{,}000$ N/mm². (U.L.)

For springs in series the load is common to both, and the total extension is the sum of that for each, i.e.

$$x = x_1 + x_2$$

or
$$W/k = W/k_1 + W/k_2$$

where k is the equivalent stiffness of the composite spring,

or
$$1/k = 1/k_1 + 1/k_2$$

Here
$$\frac{10^3}{700}=\frac{8\times 25^3\times 12}{80{,}000\times 2{\cdot}5^4}+\frac{8\times 25^3\times 12}{80{,}000\times d^4}$$
$$\frac{18{\cdot}7}{d^4}=\frac{1}{0{\cdot}7}-\frac{18{\cdot}7}{2{\cdot}5^4}$$
$$=0{\cdot}95$$
$$\therefore\quad d=2{\cdot}1\text{ mm}$$

Since $W=\pi d^3\hat{\tau}/8D$, the limiting load will be found in the spring with the smaller wire diameter, i.e.
$$W=\frac{\pi\times 2{\cdot}1^3\times 180}{8\times 25}$$
$$=26{\cdot}3\text{ N}$$

Total extension
$$=W/k$$
$$=26{\cdot}3/0{\cdot}7$$
$$=37{\cdot}5\text{ mm}$$

EXAMPLE 5. *A close-coiled helical spring of circular section extends 1 cm when subjected to an axial load W, and there is an angular rotation of 1 radian when a torque T is independently applied about the axis. If D is the mean coil diameter, show that* $T/W=D^2(1+\nu)/4$, *where* ν *is Poisson's ratio.*

Determine Poisson's ratio if D = 3 cm, a load of 55 N extends the spring 5·4 cm, and a torque of 300 Nmm produces an angular rotation of 60°. (U.L.)

It has been shown that
$$W=Gd^4x/8D^3n \tag{1}$$
and
$$\phi=Tl/EI=64TDn/Ed^4$$
Since here $x=\phi=1$, then
$$T/W=D^2E/8G$$
$$=D^2(1+\nu)/4\quad\text{(Para. 4.3)}$$

$D=3$ cm; $T=300\times 3/\pi$ Nmm/radn.; $W=55/5{\cdot}4$ N/cm
$$\therefore\quad (90\times 5{\cdot}4)/(\pi\times 55)=(3^2/4)(1+\nu)$$
or
$$\nu=216/55\pi-1$$
$$=0{\cdot}255$$

13.2. Open-coiled Helical Springs. Let α be the angle of the helix, then the length of wire $l=\pi Dn/\cos\alpha$.

In Fig. 13.2, OX is the polar axis (axis of twisting) at any normal cross-section, and is inclined at α to the horizontal OH. OY is the bending axis, and is inclined at α to the vertical OV. All the axes OX, OY, OH, and OV are in the vertical plane which is tangential to the helix at O.

If now an axial load W and an axial torque T are applied to the spring, the latter tending to increase the curvature, the actions at O are couples $WD/2$ about OH and T about OV (effect of shearing force W may be neglected).

Resolving these couples about the axes OX and OY, the combined twisting couple

$$=(WD/2)\cos\alpha + T\sin\alpha$$

and the combined bending couple

$$=T\cos\alpha - (WD/2)\sin\alpha$$

tending to increase the curvature.

The total strain energy due to bending and twisting

$$U=\frac{[(WD/2)\cos\alpha + T\sin\alpha]^2 l}{2GJ}+\frac{[T\cos\alpha-(WD/2)\sin\alpha]^2 l}{2EI}$$

(Summary, Chapters VIII and IX)

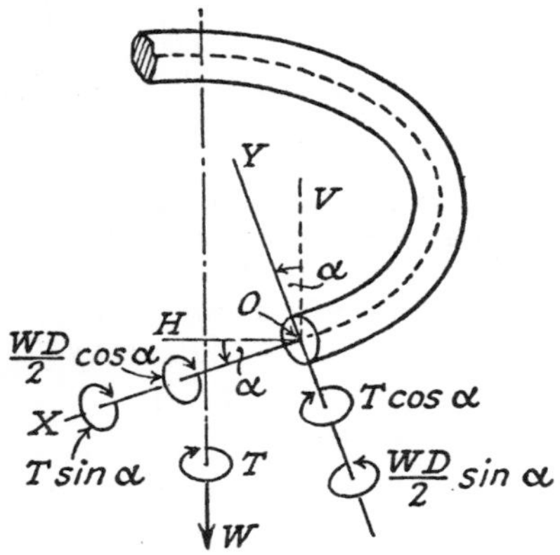

Fig. 13.2

By Castigliano's theorem (Para. 11.4), the axial deflection $x=\partial U/\partial W$, and the axial rotation $\phi=\partial U/\partial T$. The general case may be derived from the above expression, but usually the loading is either W only or T only, and the solution of these cases is given below.

(a) *Axial load only.*

$$x=(\partial U/\partial W)_{T=0}$$

$$=\frac{2[(WD/2)\cos\alpha](D/2)\cos\alpha\,.\,l}{2GJ}+\frac{2[-(WD/2)\sin\alpha][-(D/2)\sin\alpha]l}{2EI}$$

$$=(WD^2l/4)(\cos^2\alpha/GJ+\sin^2\alpha/EI)$$

$$=(8WD^3n/d^4\cos\alpha)(\cos^2\alpha/G+2\sin^2\alpha/E)$$

$(J=\pi d^4/32;\ I=\pi d^4/64)$

$$\phi=(\partial U/\partial T)_{T=0}$$

$$=\frac{2[(WD/2)\cos\alpha]\sin\alpha\,.\,l}{2GJ}+\frac{2[-(WD/2)\sin\alpha]\cos\alpha\,.\,l}{2EI}$$

$$=(WDl/2)\sin\alpha\,.\cos\alpha(1/GJ-1/EI)$$

$$=(16WD^2n\sin\alpha/d^4)(1/G-2/E)$$

(b) *Axial torque only.*

$$\phi=(\partial U/\partial T)_{W=0}$$

$$=\frac{2(T\sin\alpha)\sin\alpha\,.\,l}{2GJ}+\frac{2(T\cos\alpha)\cos\alpha\,.\,l}{2EI}$$

$$=Tl(\sin^2\alpha/GJ+\cos^2\alpha/EI)$$

$$=(32TDn/d^4\cos\alpha)(\sin^2\alpha/G+2\cos^2\alpha/E)$$

$$x=(\partial U/\partial W)_{W=0}$$
$$=\frac{2(T\sin\alpha)(D/2)\cos\alpha\,.\,l}{2GJ}+\frac{2(T\cos\alpha)[-(D/2)\sin\alpha]l}{2EI}$$
$$=[(TDl/2)\sin\alpha\,.\cos\alpha](1/GJ-1/EI)$$
$$=(16TD^2n\sin\alpha/d^4)(1/G-2/E)$$

EXAMPLE 6. *An open-coiled helical spring is made having ten turns wound to a mean diameter of 120 mm. The wire diameter is 10 mm and the coils make an angle of 30° with a plane perpendicular to the axis of the coil. Find (a) the axial extension with a load of 100 N, and (b) the angle the free end will turn through with this load if free to rotate. $E=208{,}000$ N/mm²; $G=83{,}000$ N/mm².*

(a) Axial extension

$$x=\frac{8WD^3n}{d^4\cos\alpha}\left(\frac{\cos^2\alpha}{G}+\frac{2\sin^2\alpha}{E}\right)$$
$$=\frac{8\times100\times120^3\times10}{10^4\cos 30^\circ}\left(\frac{\cos^2 30^\circ}{83{,}000}+\frac{2\sin^2 30^\circ}{208{,}000}\right)$$
$$=\frac{800\times1728\times2}{\sqrt{3}\times10^4}(0{\cdot}0905+0{\cdot}024)$$
$$=18{\cdot}3\text{ mm}$$

(b) Angle of rotation of free end

$$\phi=\frac{16WD^2n\sin\alpha}{d^4}\left(\frac{1}{G}-\frac{2}{E}\right)$$
$$=\frac{16\times100\times120^2\times10\sin 30^\circ}{10^4}\left(\frac{1}{83{,}000}-\frac{2}{208{,}000}\right)$$
$$=\frac{16\times144\times5}{10^4}(0{\cdot}1205-0{\cdot}098)$$
$$=0{\cdot}026\text{ radian}$$
$$=1{\cdot}48^\circ$$

13.3. Leaf Springs. This type of spring is commonly used in carriages such as cars, lorries, and railway wagons. It is made up of a number of leaves of equal width and thickness, but varying length, placed in laminations and loaded as a beam.

There are two main types, the "semi-elliptic," simply supported at its ends and centrally loaded, and the "quarter-elliptic" or cantilever type.

(1) *Semi-elliptic type.* In Fig. 13.3, let

l = the span (assumed constant)

b = width of leaves

t = thickness of leaves
W = central load
y = rise of crown above level of ends

It is assumed for the development of a simplified theory that the ends of each leaf—where it extends beyond its neighbour—are tapered uniformly to a point; also, in order to complete the set, the shortest leaf should be a diamond shape. Neither of these assumptions will be realised in practice, in particular the main leaf requiring to be maintained at the full width where it is supported, but slight departures from this design will not seriously affect the theory.

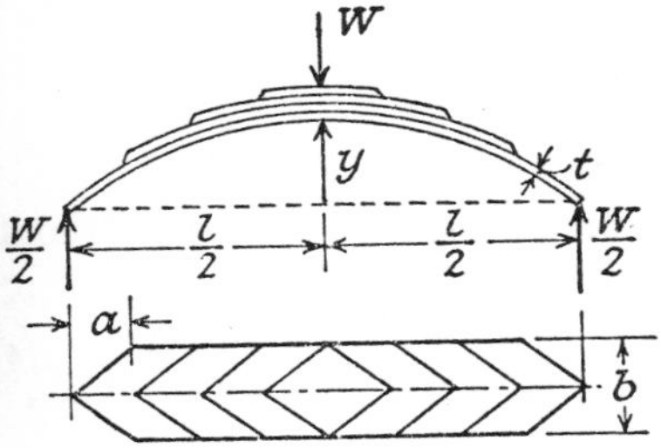

Fig. 13.3

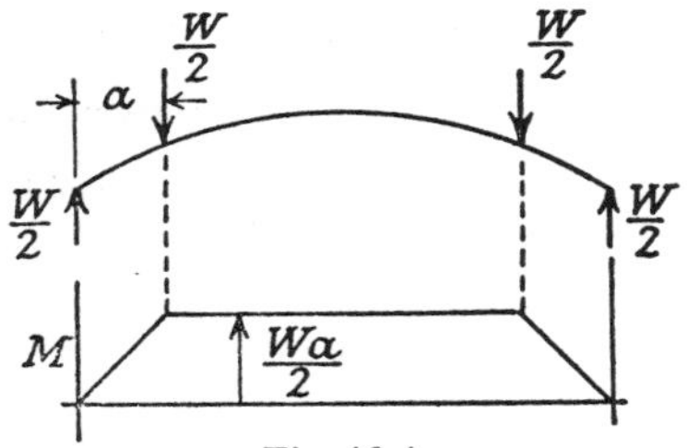

Fig. 13.4

If the leaves are initially curved to circular arcs of the same radius R_0, contact between the leaves will only take place at their ends, and consequently any one leaf will be loaded as shown in Fig. 13.4. Over the central portion both M and I are constant. Over the end portions both M and I are proportional to the distance from the end. Consequently for the whole leaf M/I is constant.

But $$M/EI = 1/R - 1/R_0 \quad \text{(Para.11.1)}$$

and since R_0 is assumed constant, the radius of curvature R in the strained state must be the same for all leaves, and contact continues through the ends only.

Friction between the plates being neglected, each leaf is free to slide over its neighbour, and since they all maintain the same radius of curvature they can be imagined to be arranged side by side to form a beam of constant depth and varying width, as shown in plan, Fig. 13.5.

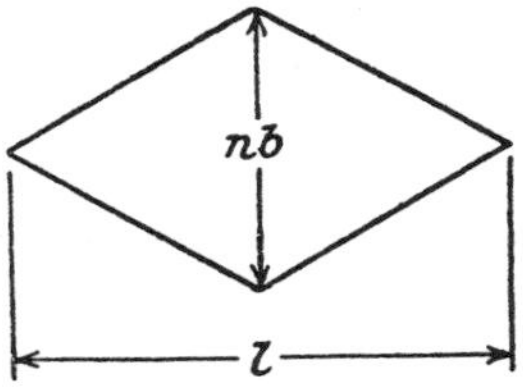

Fig. 13.5

As the bending moment for the equivalent section is directly proportional to the distance from either end, and I also varies uniformly, it can be seen that the spring is equivalent to a beam of uniform strength (i.e. same maximum stress at all sections).

The results can now be obtained by consideration of any convenient section, and in the following analysis the *central section* will be used.

$M = -Wl/4$, tending to decrease the curvature

$I = nbt^3/12$, n = number of leaves

By the geometry of a circle

$$y(2R - y) = (l/2)(l/2)$$

and treating y as small compared with R, this gives

$$1/R = 8y/l^2$$

Substituting in

$$M/EI = 1/R - 1/R_0$$

$$\frac{-Wl/4}{E.nbt^3/12} = \frac{8}{l^2}(y - y_0)$$

Deflection $\boldsymbol{\delta = y_0 - y = 3Wl^3/8nbt^3E}$

The load required to straighten the spring is called the "Proof Load," and is given by $8nbt^3Ey_0/3l^3$.

The maximum bending stress

$$\sigma = (M/I)(t/2)$$

$$= \frac{(Wl/4)(t/2)}{nbt^3/12}$$

$$= \boldsymbol{3Wl/2nbt^2}$$

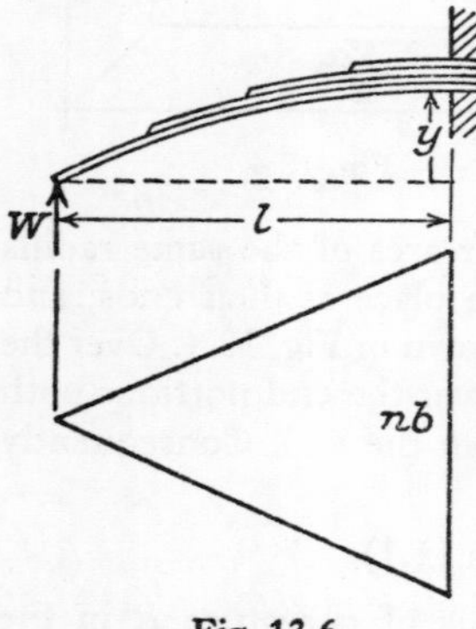

Fig. 13.6

(2) *Quarter-elliptic type.* By a similar argument, the equivalent plan section varies in width from zero to nb at the fixed end (Fig. 13.6), and the other values at this end are

$$M = -Wl$$

$$I = nbt^3/12$$

$$1/R = 2y/l^2$$

By substitution in

$$M/EI = 1/R - 1/R_0$$

$$\frac{-Wl}{E.nbt^3/12} = \frac{2}{l^2}(y - y_0)$$

$$\boldsymbol{\delta = y_0 - y = 6Wl^3/nbt^3E} \quad \text{from above}$$

and

$$\sigma = (M/I)(t/2) = \boldsymbol{6Wl/nbt^2}$$

EXAMPLE 7. *A laminated steel spring, simply supported at the ends and centrally loaded, with a span of 0·75 m, is required to carry a proof load of 750 kg, and the central deflection is not to exceed 50 mm; the bending stress must not exceed 380 N/mm². Plates are available in muliples of 1 mm for thickness and 4 mm for width. Determine suitable values for width, thickness, nd number of plates, and calculate the radius to which the plates should be ormed. Assume width = 12 × thickness. E = 208,000 N/mm².*

Deflection $\delta = 3Wl^3/8nbt^3E$ ("semi-elliptic")

.e.
$$50 = \frac{3 \times 750 \times 9{\cdot}81 \times 750^3}{8n(12t)t^3 \times 208{,}000}$$

giving $nt^4 = 9340$ (1)

Maximum stress $\sigma = 3Wl/2nbt^2$

.e.
$$380 = \frac{3 \times 750 \times 9{\cdot}81 \times 750}{2 \times n(12t)t^2}$$

giving $nt^3 = 1810$ (2)

Dividing (1) by (2)

$$t = 9340/1810$$
$$= 5{\cdot}16, \quad \text{say 6 mm}$$
$$b = 12t = 72 \text{ mm}$$

From (2)

$$n = 1810/6^3$$
$$= 8{\cdot}4, \quad \text{say 9 leaves}$$

The actual deflection under the proof load of 750 kg

$$= \frac{3 \times 750 \times 9{\cdot}81 \times 750^3}{8 \times 9 \times 72 \times 6^3 \times 208{,}000}$$
$$= 40 \text{ mm}$$

Since the spring is now straight, the initial radius of curvature is given by

$$R_0 = l^2/8\delta$$
$$= 750^2/(8 \times 40)$$
$$= 1750 \text{ mm} = 1{\cdot}75 \text{ m}$$

EXAMPLE 8. *A laminated spring of the quarter-elliptic type, 0·6 m long, is to provide a static deflection of 75 mm under an end load of 200 kg. If the leaf material is 60 mm wide and 6 mm thick, find the number of leaves required and the maximum stress.*

From what height can the load be dropped on to the undeflected spring to cause a maximum stress of 750 N/mm²? E = 208,000 N/mm². (U.L.)

$$\delta = 6Wl^3/nbt^3E \quad (\text{"quarter-elliptic"})$$

i.e.
$$75 = \frac{6 \times 200 \times 9{\cdot}81 \times 600^3}{n \times 60 \times 6^3 \times 208{,}000}$$

$$n = 12{\cdot}6, \quad \text{say 13 leaves.}$$

$$\sigma = 6Wl/nbt^2$$
$$= \frac{6 \times 200 \times 9{\cdot}81 \times 600}{13 \times 60 \times 6^2}$$
$$= 252 \text{ N/mm}^2$$

The equivalent gradually applied load to cause a maximum stress of 750 N/mm^2

$$=\frac{200\times 9{\cdot}81\times 750}{252}=5850 \text{ N}$$

and the corresponding deflection

$$=\frac{6\times 5850\times 600^3}{13\times 60\times 6^3\times 208{,}000}=217 \text{ mm}$$

$$\text{Loss of P.E.}=\text{Gain of S.E.}$$

i.e. $$200\times 9{\cdot}81(h+217)=\tfrac{1}{2}\times 5850\times 217$$

giving $$h=323-217$$
$$=106 \text{ mm}$$

13.4. Flat Spiral Springs. This is the type of spring used in clockwork mechanisms, and consists of a uniform thin strip wound into a spiral in one plane, and pinned at its outer end. The spring is "wound up" by applying a torque to a spindle attached to the centre of the spiral.

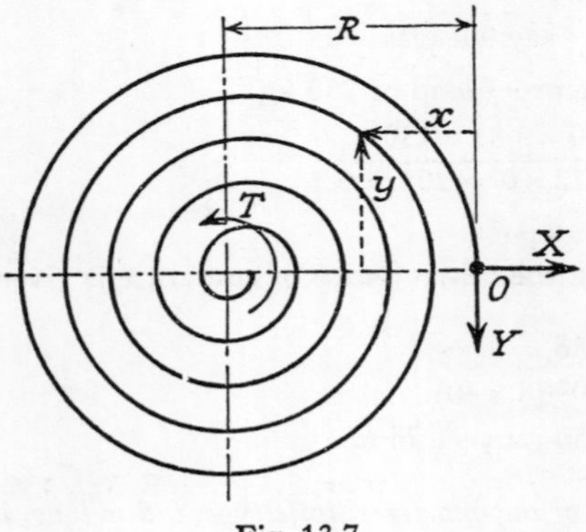

Fig. 13.7

Let T be the torque tending to wind up the spring, and X and Y the components of reaction at the outer end of the spring O (Fig. 13.7).

By moments about the spindle axis

$$T=YR \qquad (1)$$

where R is the maximum radius of the spiral.

At any point in the spring, defined by co-ordinates x and y, the bending moment $=Yx-Xy$ tending to increase the curvature.

The strain energy

$$U=\int(Yx-Xy)^2ds/2EI$$
$$=\int[(T/R)x-Xy]^2ds/2EI \quad \text{from (1)}$$

Since O is a fixed point $\partial U/\partial X=0$ (Para. 11.4) giving

$X=(T/R)\int xyds/\int y^2ds=0$ by symmetry.

Then $$\theta=\partial U/\partial T=(2T/R^2)\int x^2ds/2EI$$

But $\int x^2ds=(R^2/4+R^2)l$ approximately, treating the spiral as a uniform "disc".

$$\therefore \quad \theta = \mathbf{1{\cdot}25}\ \boldsymbol{Tl/EI} \qquad (2)$$

$$\text{Strain energy} = \tfrac{1}{2}T\theta$$
$$= 1{\cdot}25\ T^2l/2EI \quad \text{from (2)} \qquad (3)$$

$$\text{Maximum bending moment} = Y.2R \text{ at the left-hand edge}$$
$$= 2T \quad \text{from (1)}$$

$$\text{Maximum stress } \hat{\sigma} = 2T/Z$$
$$= \mathbf{12}\boldsymbol{T/bt^2} \qquad (4)$$

where b = width and t = thickness of spring material.

EXAMPLE 9. *A flat spiral spring is 6 mm wide, 0·25 mm thick, and 2·5 m long. Assuming the maximum stress of 800 N/mm² to occur at the point of greatest bending moment, calculate the torque, the work stored, and the number of turns to wind up the spring. E = 208,000 N/mm². (U.L.)*

$$\text{Maximum stress } \hat{\sigma} = 12T/bt^2 \quad \text{from (4)}$$

i.e. $800 = 12T/(6 \times 0{\cdot}25^2)$

giving $T = 25$ Nmm

$$\text{Angle of rotation } \theta = 1{\cdot}25\ Tl/EI \quad \text{from (2)}$$
$$= \frac{1{\cdot}25 \times 25 \times 2500 \times 12}{208{,}000 \times 6 \times 0{\cdot}25^3}$$
$$= 48 \text{ radians}$$
$$= 7{\cdot}6 \text{ turns of the spindle.}$$

$$\text{Work stored in spring} = \tfrac{1}{2}T\theta$$
$$= \tfrac{1}{2} \times 25 \times 48 = 600 \text{ Nmm}$$

REFERENCES

BERRY, W. R., *Spring Design* Emmott 1961.

WAHL, A. M., *Mechanical Springs*. Penton Publishing Co. 1963.

ASHWORTH, G., *The Disk Spring or Belleville Washer*. J.I.Mech.E. Vol. 155, 1946, p. 93.

SUMMARY

Close-coiled Springs:

$8WD/\pi d^4 = \hat{\tau}/d = Gx/\pi D^2 n$ under axial load.

$\phi = Tl/EI$ under axial torque.

Open-coiled Springs: $x = (8WD^3n/d^4 \cos\alpha)(\cos^2\alpha/G + 2\sin^2\alpha/E)$ under axial load.

Leaf Springs. Semi-elliptic:

$\delta = 3Wl^3/8nbt^3E$

$\hat{\sigma} = 3Wl/2nbt^2$

Quarter-elliptic:

$\delta = 6Wl^3/nbt^3E$

$\hat{\sigma} = 6Wl/nbt^2$

Spiral Springs:

$\theta = 1{\cdot}25\ Tl/EI$

$\hat{\sigma} = 12T/bt^2$

PROBLEMS

1. Determine the weight of a close-coiled helical spring to carry a load o 5000 N with a deflection of 5 cm and a maximum shearing stress of 400 N/mm If the number of active coils is eight, determine the wire diameter and mean co diameter. $G = 83{,}000$ N/mm²; $\rho = 7700$ kg/m³. (2 kg; 13·6 mm; 75 mm.

2. Close-coiled helical springs having n turns are made of round wire suc that the mean diameter of the coils D mm is ten times the wire diameter. Sho that the stiffness in N/mm for any such spring is $(D/n) \times$ constant, and deter mine the constant when $G = 83{,}000$ N/mm².

Such a spring is required to support a load of 1000 N with an extension o 10 cm and a maximum shear stress of 350 N/mm². Calculate (1) its weigh (2) mean coil diameter, (3) number of turns. The material weighs 7700 kg/m³ (1·04; 1·05 kg, 85·3 mm, 9.

3. A close-coiled helical spring of circular section has a mean coil diameter o 76 mm. When subjected to an axial torque of 6·1 Nm there is an angular rotatio of 90°, and when an axial load of 265 N is applied the spring extends 125 mm Find Poisson's ratio. (U.L.) (0·26.

4. The spring load against which a valve is opened is provided by an inne helical spring arranged within and concentric with an outer spring. The fre length of the inner spring is 6 mm longer than the outer. The outer spring ha twelve coils of mean diameter 25 mm, wire diameter 3 mm, and initial compres sion 5 mm when the valve is closed. Find the stiffness of the inner spring if th greatest force required to open the valve 10 mm is 150 N.

If the radial clearance between the springs is 1·5 mm, find the wire diamete of the inner spring if it has ten coils. $G = 80{,}000$ N/mm². (4 N/mm; 2·1 mm.

5. A composite spring has two close-coiled springs in series. Each spring ha a mean coil diameter eight times its wire diameter. One spring has twenty coil of wire diameter 2·54 mm. Find the diameter of wire in the other spring if it ha fifteen coils and the stiffness of the composite spring is 1·26 N/mm. Find th greatest axial load that can be applied, and the corresponding extension, for maximum shearing stress of 310 N/mm². $G = 80{,}000$ N/mm². (U.L.) (2 mm; 60·5N; 48 mm

6. Determine the maximum angle of helix for which the error in calculatin the extension of a helical spring under axial load by the "close-coiled" formul is less than 1%. (10° 20′.

7. In an open-coiled spring of ten coils the stresses due to bending and twist ing are 140 N/mm² and 150 N/mm² respectively when the spring is loade axially. Assuming the mean diameter of the coils to be eight times the wir diameter, find the maximum permissible axial load and the wire diameter for maximum extension of 18 mm. $E = 206{,}000$ N/mm²; $G = 76{,}000$ N/mm². (125 N; 3·9 mm.

8. An open-coiled spring carries an axial load W. Derive expressions for dis placement and angular twist of the free end.

Find the mean radius of an open-coiled spring of helix angle 30°, to give vertical displacement of 23 mm and an angular rotation of the load end o

·02 radians under an axial load of 35 N. The material available is steel rod 6 mm iameter. $E=200,000$ N/mm²; $G=80,000$ N/mm². (U.L.) (105 mm.)

9. Prove than in an open-coiled helical spring, subjected to an axial load, the alue of the maximum shear stress is the same as in a close-coiled spring of the ame dimensions.

An open-coiled helical spring made of steel rod 12·7 mm diameter has 10 coils f mean diameter 76 mm and pitch 50 mm. If the axial load is 890 N, find the eflection and maximum shear stress. $E=206,000$ N/mm²; $\nu=0{\cdot}3$. (U.L.)

(Combined bending and twisting, Para. 8.8.15·5 mm 84 N/mm².)

10. A carriage spring, centrally loaded and simply supported at its ends, has en steel plates each 50 mm wide by 6 mm thick. If the longest plate is 0·7 m, nd the initial radius of curvature if the maximum stress is 150 N/mm² and the lates are finally straight.

Neglecting loss of energy at impact, determine the height from which 20 kg an be dropped centrally on to the spring without exceeding the stress of 50 N/mm². $E=206,000$ N/mm². (4·15 m; 82 mm.)

11. A cantilever leaf spring of length 0·43 m has four leaves of thickness 9 mm. f an end load of 2·5 kN causes a deflection of 36 mm find the width of the leaves. $E=200,000$ N/mm². (57 mm.)

12. A leaf spring spans 1 m and is supported at each end. It carries two concentrated loads of 180 kg each at points 0·3 m from each end. It is made from eaves 5 cm wide and 6·3 mm thick.

Design the number and length of the leaves in order that the maximum stress n the material shall not exceed 280 N/mm².

(6 leaves, lengths 50, 60, 70, 80, 90, and 100 cm.)

13. Obtain from first principles the expression for energy stored in a flat piral spring per unit volume in terms of maximum stress and E.

Hence find the length of a spring 25 mm wide by 0·5 mm thick to store 8 Nm f energy for a limiting stress of 800 N/mm². Find also the torque required, and he number of turns of the winding spindle to wind up the spring. $E=$ 205,000 N/mm². (U.L.) ($5\sigma^2/96E$; 4 m; 0·417 Nm 6·2.)

14. A flat spiral spring is made of steel 12·5 mm broad and 0·5 mm thick, the ength of spiral being 6 m. Determine (a) the maximum turning moment which an be applied to the spindle if the stress is not to exceed 550 N/mm², and (b) the umber of turns then given to the spindle, and (c) the energy stored. $E=205,000$ N/mm². (0·143 Nm; 6·4; 2·88 Nm.)

CHAPTER XIV

Struts

14.1. Definition. Any member of a structure which is in compressio may be called a strut, but the term is usually reserved for "long slender members which are liable to fail by buckling, as distinct from "sho columns" (Para. 6.6), which fail by compressive stress.

The resistance of any member to bending is determined by its flexura rigidity EI, and I may be written as Ak^2 (A = cross-sectional area k = radius of gyration). For a given material, the load per unit are which the member can withstand is therefore related to k. There wi be two principal moments of inertia, and if the least of these is taken the ratio

$$\frac{\text{length of member}}{\text{least radius of gyration}} \quad \left(\text{i.e. } \frac{l}{k}\right)$$

is called the *slenderness ratio.* Its numerical value indicates whether th member falls into the class of columns or struts.

Struts which fail by buckling, before the limiting compressive stres is reached, can be analysed mathematically by the Euler theory, an several standard cases will now be treated.

14.2. Pin-ended (hinged) Strut Axially loaded. The strut i assumed to be initially straight, the end load being applied axiall through the centroid. The usual assumptions about the elasticity of th material are made.

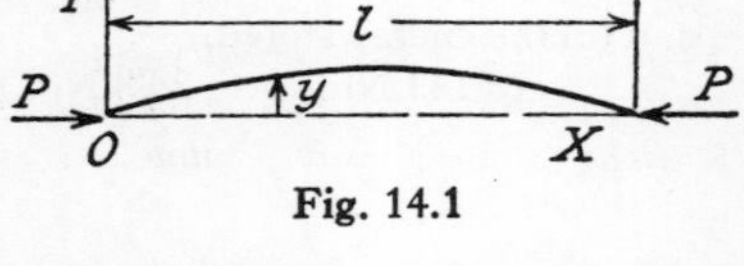

Fig. 14.1

In Fig. 14.1 the strut is show deflected under an end load P the origin O being taken at on end and the OX axis through th centroids of the end sections.

Applying the equation of bending of beams

$$EI.d^2y/dx^2 = M \quad \text{(Para. 9.3)}$$
$$= -Py$$

which can be written

$$d^2y/dx^2 + \alpha^2 y = 0 \quad \text{where} \quad \alpha^2 = P/EI$$

The solution is

$$y = A \sin \alpha x + B \cos \alpha x$$

At $x=0$, $y=0$

$$\therefore \quad B=0$$

At $x=l$, $y=0$

$$A \sin \alpha l=0$$

Either $A=0$, in which case $y=0$ for all values of x and the strut will ot buckle, or $\sin \alpha l=0$, which leaves A indeterminate. The least value) satisfy $\sin \alpha l=0$ is $\alpha l=\pi$, corresponding to

$$\alpha^2=\pi^2/l^2=P/EI$$

'rom this is obtained the least value of P which will cause the strut) buckle, and it is called the "Euler crippling load" P_e. From bove

$$\boldsymbol{P_e=\pi^2EI/l^2}$$

'he value of I here is the ***least moment of inertia.***

The interpretation of this analysis is that for all values of the load P, ther than those which make $\sin \alpha l=0$, the strut will remain perfectly traight ($y=A \sin \alpha x=0$). For the particular value $P_e=\pi^2EI/l^2$, $\sin \alpha l=0$ nd $y=A \sin \pi x/l$. The strut is in a state of neutral equilibrium, and heoretically any deflection which it is given will be maintained. This is subject to the limitation that l remains sensibly constant, nd in practice any slight increase in load at the critical value will ause the deflection to increase appreciably until the material fails by 'ielding.

It should be noted that deflection is ***not*** proportional to load, and this pplies to all strut problems; likewise it will be found that maximum tress is ***not*** proportional to load.

The higher solutions of $\sin \alpha l=0$ correspond to higher harmonics of he deflected strut, and are of no practical importance.

EXAMPLE 1. *A straight bar of alloy, 1 m long and 12·5 mm by 4·8 mm in 'ection, is mounted in a strut-testing machine and loaded axially until it uckles. Assuming the Euler formula to apply, estimate the maximum central leflection before the material attains its yield point of 280 N/mm². E= '2,000 N/mm². (U.L.)*

There will be no deflection at all until the Euler load is reached, i.e.

$$\text{load}=\pi^2EI/l^2$$

$$=\frac{\pi^2 \times 72{,}000 \times 12{\cdot}5 \times 4{\cdot}8^3}{1000^2 \times 12}$$

(using the smaller moment of inertia)

$$=82 \text{ N}$$

Maximum bending moment occurs at centre, $=P\delta=82\delta$, where δ is the central deflection.

Maximum stress is the sum of direct and bending stresses at the centr (Para. 6.6), i.e.

$$280 = \frac{82}{12{\cdot}5 \times 4{\cdot}8} + \frac{82\delta \times 6}{12{\cdot}5 \times 4{\cdot}8^2}$$

$$= 1{\cdot}37 + 1{\cdot}71\delta$$

$$\therefore \quad \delta = 278{\cdot}6/1{\cdot}71$$

$$= 163 \text{ mm}$$

EXAMPLE 2. *A uniform bar of cross-sectional area A and flexural stiffne EI is heated so that its temperature varies linearly from ½t at one end to at the other end. One end is pin-jointed to a rigid foundation; the other en is pin-jointed so that it can slide in the direction of the length of the bar, th thermal expansion of which is resisted by a compression spring of stiffness k If there is no load in the spring when t = 0, obtain an expression for the stre in the bar when it is heated and show that it buckles in flexure when*

$$t = \frac{4\pi^2 I}{3\alpha l^2 A}\left(1 + \frac{EA}{kl}\right)$$

where α = *coefficient of linear thermal expansion.*

The average temperature along the bar is $\frac{3}{4}t$, and hence the therm expansion of the bar is $\frac{3}{4}\alpha lt$.

If P is the force exerted by the spring on the bar, the compression pro duced is Pl/AE, and the compression of the spring is P/k.

Net expansion of bar = compression of spring,

i.e. $$\tfrac{3}{4}\alpha lt - Pl/AE = P/k$$

from which $$P = \frac{\frac{3}{4}\alpha lt}{l/AE + 1/k}$$

$$\text{Stress in bar} = P/A$$

$$= \frac{\frac{3}{4}\alpha lt}{l/E + A/k}$$

The bar will buckle when $P = \pi^2 EI/l^2$, and substitution in above give

$$\frac{\pi^2 EI}{l^2} = \frac{\frac{3}{4}\alpha lt}{l/AE + 1/k}$$

rearranging, $$t = \frac{4\pi^2 I}{3\alpha l^2 A}\left(1 + \frac{AE}{kl}\right)$$

14.3. Direction-fixed at Both Ends. Suppose the strut to have de flected, and let M be the end fixing moment (Fig. 14.2).

Then $$EI\,.\,d^2y/dx^2 = -Py + M$$

or $$d^2y/dx^2 + \alpha^2 y = M/EI, \quad \alpha^2 = P/EI$$

Complete solution is

$$y = A \sin \alpha x + B \cos \alpha x + M/EI\alpha^2$$

When $x=0$, $y=0$

$$\therefore \quad B = -M/EI\alpha^2 = -M/P$$

nd $dy/dx = 0$

$$\therefore \quad A = 0$$

$$\therefore \quad y = (M/P)(1 - \cos \alpha x)$$

When $x = l$, $y = 0$

$$\therefore \quad \cos \alpha l = 1$$

The least solution is

$$\alpha l = 2\pi,$$

iving buckling load $P_e = 4\pi^2 EI/l^2$

Note that this case is equivalent to a pin-ended strut of length $l/2$. To llow for imperfect fixing an equivalent length of $0{\cdot}6l$ to $0{\cdot}8l$ is freuently employed (see also Para. 14.4. below).

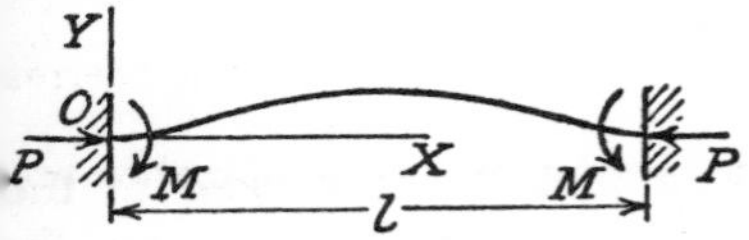

Fig. 14.2

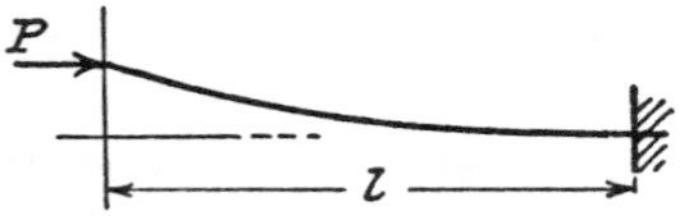

Fig. 14.3

14.4. Partial Fixing of the Ends.

EXAMPLE 3. *A strut of length 2a has each end fixed in an elastic material which exerts a restraining moment μ per unit angular displacement. Prove that the critical load P is given by the equation $\mu n \tan na + P = 0$, where $n^2 = P/EI$. Such a strut, 2·5 m in length, has a theoretical critical load of 15 kN on the assumption of pinned ends. Determine the percentage increase in the critical load if the constraint offered at the ends is 170 Nm per degree of rotation.* (U.L.)

Let M be the restraining moment at each end, then the general solution is obtained as in Para. 14.3,

$$y = A \sin nx + B \cos nx + M/P$$

using the notation given in the question.

At $x=0$, $y=0$

$$\therefore \quad B = -M/P$$

also $$M = \mu(dy/dx)_0$$

$$= \mu . An$$

i.e. $$A = M/\mu n$$

giving $$y = (M/\mu n) \sin nx + (M/P)(1 - \cos nx)$$

At the centre, $x=a$, $dy/dx=0$,

i.e. $$(M/\mu)\cos na+(Mn/P)\sin na=0$$

or $$\mu n\tan na+P=0 \qquad (i)$$

For pinned ends

$$\pi^2EI/(2a)^2=15{,}000$$

giving $$EI=9500\ \text{Nm}^2$$

$$n=\sqrt{(P)}/97{\cdot}5$$

$$\mu=170\times 57{\cdot}3\ \text{Nm/radn.}$$

Condition (i) can now be written

$$\tan(0{\cdot}0128\sqrt{P})=-0{\cdot}01\sqrt{P}$$

The least solution of this equation is for $\sqrt{P}=166$, i.e. $P=27{,}500$N an increase of 83% over the value for pinned ends.

14.5. Direction-fixed at One End and Free at the Other. This is clearly equivalent to a pin-ended strut of length $2l$ (see Fig. 14.3).

Hence $$P_e=\pi^2EI/4l^2$$

14.6. Direction-fixed at One End and Position-fixed at the Other. Let V be the lateral force required to maintain the position of the pinned-end.

Then $$EI\,.\,d^2y/dx^2=-Py-Vx \quad \text{(Fig. 14.4)}$$

or $$d^2y/dx^2+\alpha^2y=-Vx/EI,\quad \alpha^2=P/EI$$

Complete solution is

$$y=A\sin\alpha x+B\cos\alpha x-Vx/P$$

When $x=0$, $y=0$.

$$\therefore\ B=0$$

When $x=l$, $y=0$

$$\therefore\ A\sin\alpha l=Vl/P \qquad (1)$$

and $dy/dx=0$

$$\therefore\ A\alpha\,.\cos\alpha l=V/P \qquad (2)$$

By dividing corresponding sides of (1) and (2)

$$\tan\alpha l=\alpha l$$

the least solution of which is

$$\alpha l=4{\cdot}49$$

or $$P_e=20{\cdot}2EI/l^2$$

$$=2{\cdot}05\pi^2EI/l^2$$

As a departure from the "perfect" strut of Para. 14.2, the effects of ccentricity of load and initial curvature of strut will now be examined.

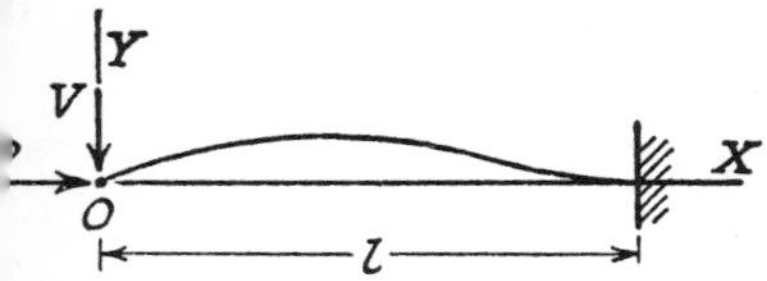

Fig. 14.4

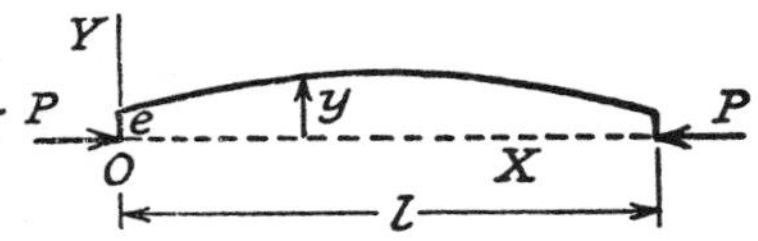

Fig. 14.5

14.7. Strut with Eccentric Load. Let e be the eccentricity of the pplied end load, and measure y from the line of action of the load Fig. 14.5).

Then $$EI.d^2y/dx^2 = -Py$$
r $$d^2y/dx^2 + \alpha^2 y = 0$$
iving $$y = A\sin\alpha x + B\cos\alpha x$$

When $x = 0$, $y = e$
$$\therefore \quad B = e$$
When $x = l/2$, $dy/dx = 0$
$$\therefore \quad A\cos\alpha l/2 - B\sin\alpha l/2 = 0$$
.e. $$A = e\tan\alpha l/2$$
iving $$y = e[(\tan\alpha l/2)\sin\alpha x + \cos\alpha x]$$

Note that with an eccentric load the strut deflects for all values of P, nd not only for the critical value as was the case with an axially applied oad. The deflection becomes infinite for $\tan\alpha l/2 = \infty$, i.e. $\alpha l = \pi$, giving he same crippling load $P_e = \pi^2 EI/l^2$. However, due to the additional ending moment set up by deflection, the strut will always fail by compressive stress before the Euler load is reached.

$$\hat{y} = e[(\tan\alpha l/2)\sin\alpha l/2 + \cos\alpha l/2], \quad \text{at the centre}$$
$$= e\left(\frac{\sin^2\alpha l/2 + \cos^2\alpha l/2}{\cos\alpha l/2}\right)$$
$$= e\sec\alpha l/2$$

The maximum bending moment is
$$\hat{M} = P\hat{y}$$
$$= Pe.\sec\alpha l/2, \quad \text{from above}$$
and the maximum stress is then obtained by combined bending and direct stress
$$\sigma = P/A + M/Z$$

Using Webb's approximation for sec $\alpha l/2$

$$M = Pe.\frac{1+0{\cdot}26(4/\pi^2)(\alpha l/2)^2}{1-(4/\pi^2)(\alpha l/2)^2}$$

$$= Pe.\frac{1+0{\cdot}26.P/P_e}{1-P/P_e}$$

$$= Pe.(P_e+0{\cdot}26P)/(P_e-P)$$

which is a more convenient expression to use for calculating the valu of P corresponding to a given maximum stress.

14.8. Strut with Initial Curvature. Treating as a beam with initi radius of curvature

$$R_0 = \frac{1}{d^2y_0/dx^2} \quad \text{approximately}$$

and using the form

$$EI(1/R - 1/R_0) = M \quad \text{(Para.11.1)}$$

then $$EI.d^2y/dx^2 = M + EI.d^2y_0/dx^2$$

or $$d^2y/dx^2 + \alpha^2 y = d^2y_0/dx^2$$

under an end load P.

The initial shape of the strut y_0 may be assumed circular, parabolic or sinusoidal without making much difference to the final result, bu the most convenient form is

$$y_0 = c.\sin \pi x/l$$

which satisfies the end conditions and corresponds to a maximun deviation of c. Any other shape could be analysed into a Fourier serie of sine terms.

Then $$d^2y/dx^2 + \alpha^2 y = -(c.\pi^2/l^2)(\sin \pi x/l)$$

The complete solution is

$$y = A\sin\alpha x + B\cos\alpha x - \frac{c.\pi^2/l^2}{-\pi^2/l^2+\alpha^2}.\sin\frac{\pi x}{l}$$

When $x=0$, $y=0$

$$\therefore \quad B=0$$

When $x=l/2$, $dy/dx=0$

$$\therefore \quad A=0$$

and hence $$y = \frac{c.\pi^2/l^2}{\pi^2/l^2-\alpha^2}.\sin\frac{\pi x}{l}$$

$$= [cP_e/(P_e-P)](\sin \pi x/l)$$

The crippling load is again $P = P_e = \pi^2 EI/l^2$,

and

$$\hat{M} = P\hat{y}$$
$$= c . PP_e/(P_e - P)$$

By comparison with Para. 14.7, it may be said that an initial curvature of maximum deviation c is equivalent to an eccentricity of load

$$= cP_e/(P_e + 0{\cdot}26P)$$

which lies between 1 and 1/1·26 (approx. 0·8). The total eccentricity due to both causes can then be taken as $e + 0{\cdot}8c$ for purposes of calculation of bending moment and stress.

To allow for imperfections due to loading and initial curvature Case (*Strength of Materials*) gives an equivalent eccentricity $= l/500 + B/50$ where B is the width of the section in the plane of bending.

Fig. 14.6

EXAMPLE 4. *A strut of length l is encastered at its lower end; its upper end is elastically supported against lateral deflection so that the resisting force is k times the end deflection. Show that the crippling load P is given by*

$$\frac{\tan \alpha l}{\alpha l} = 1 - \frac{P}{kl} \quad \text{where } \alpha^2 = P/EI$$

(U.L.)

Taking axes as shown in Fig. 14.6

$$EI . d^2y/dx^2 = P(Y_0 - y) - kY_0x$$

where Y_0 is the end deflection, i.e.

$$d^2y/dx^2 + \alpha^2 y = \alpha^2 Y_0 - kY_0x/EI$$

The complete solution is

$$y = A \sin \alpha x + B \cos \alpha x + Y_0 - kY_0x/P$$

When $x = 0$, $y = Y_0$

$$\therefore \quad B = 0$$

When $x = l$, $y = 0$

$$\therefore \quad A \sin \alpha l + Y_0 - kY_0 l/P = 0 \qquad \text{(i)}$$

and $dy/dx = 0$

$$\therefore \quad A\alpha \cos \alpha l - kY_0/P = 0 \qquad \text{(ii)}$$

Substituting for $A = kY_0/P\alpha \cos \alpha l$ from (ii) in (i) gives $kY_0 \tan \alpha l/P\alpha + Y_0 - kY_0 l/P = 0$

Multiply by $P/kY_0 l$ and rearrange

$$\frac{\tan \alpha l}{\alpha l} = 1 - \frac{P}{kl}$$

EXAMPLE 5. *A tubular steel strut is 60 mm external diameter and 48 mm internal diameter. It is 2·2 m long and has hinged ends. The load is parallel to the axis but eccentric. Find the maximum eccentricity for a crippling load of 0·75 of the Euler value, the yield stress being 310 N/mm². E = 207,000 N/mm².* (U.L.)

The Euler load $P_e = \pi^2 EI/l^2$

$$I = (\pi/64)(60^2 - 48^2)(60^2 + 48^2)$$
$$= 37{\cdot}6 \times 10^4 \text{ mm}^4$$
$$\therefore \quad P_e = (\pi^2 \times 207{,}000 \times 37{\cdot}6 \times 10^4)/2200^2$$
$$= 158{,}000 \text{ N}$$

Actual load to cause failure = 0·75 × 158,000 N

For an eccentricity e

$$M = Pe \sec \alpha l/2 \quad \text{(Para. 14.7)}$$
$$= 0{\cdot}75 \times 158{,}000 e \sec \left(\sqrt{\frac{0{\cdot}75 \times 158{,}000}{207{,}000 \times 37{\cdot}6 \times 10^4}}\right)\frac{2200}{2}$$
$$= 119{,}000 e \sec 1{\cdot}36$$

Maximum stress $310 = P/A + M/Z$

$$= \frac{119{,}000}{(\pi/4) \times 1300} + \frac{119{,}000 e \sec 1{\cdot}36}{37{\cdot}6 \times 10^4} \times \frac{60}{2}$$
$$= 117 + 45{\cdot}4e$$
$$\therefore \quad e = 193/45{\cdot}4$$
$$= 4{\cdot}25 \text{ mm}$$

14·9. Limitations of Euler Theory. In practice the ideal case of Para. 14.2 is never realised, and there is always some eccentricity and initial curvature present. These factors can be dealt with according to Paras. 14.7 and 14.8 provided the magnitude of these deviations is known. There is, however, usually considerable uncertainty as to their values, and it is necessary to apply an empirical formula.

It will be realised that, due to the above-mentioned imperfections the strut will suffer a deflection which increases with the load, and consequently a bending moment is introduced which causes failure before the Euler load is reached. In fact failure is by stress rather than buckling and the deviation from the Euler value is more marked as the slenderness ratio l/k is reduced. For values of $l/k < 120$ approx. the error in applying the Euler theory is too great to allow of its use.

In Fig. 14.7 the stress to cause buckling, from the Euler formula for pin-ended struts, is

$$\sigma_e = \frac{P_e}{A} = \frac{\pi^2 EI}{Al^2} = \frac{\pi^2 E}{(l/k)^2}$$

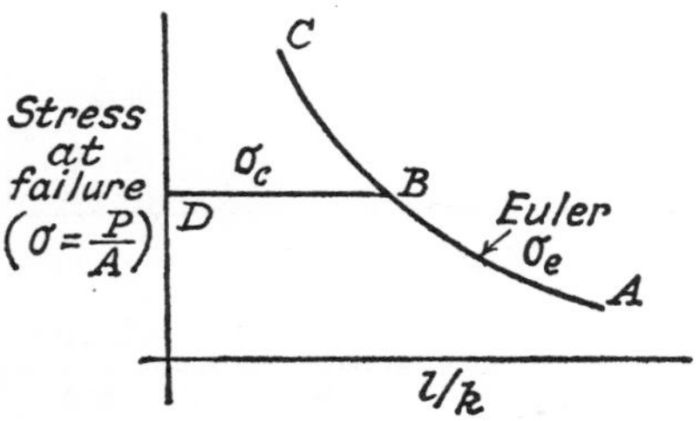

Fig. 14.7

iving the curve ABC. If, however, σ_e exceeds σ_c, the elastic imit or yield stress in compression, the strut must fail by rushing along the line BD (this s the region of short columns). Allowing for imperfections of oading and strut, actual values t failure must lie within and elow the line ABD. Practical trut formulae, of which the nain types are given below, have been devised to cover the intermediate one between "columns" and "struts," and to allow for imperfections.

Note that for structural steel, taking $\sigma_c = 320$ N/mm^2 and $E =$ 205,000 N/mm^2, the point B corresponds to

$$l/k = \pi\sqrt{(205{,}000/320)} \doteqdot 80$$

14.10. Rankine-Gordon Formula. If σ is the actual stress to cause failure, and σ_c and σ_e have meanings as in Para. 14.9, the equation

$$1/\sigma = 1/\sigma_c + 1/\sigma_e$$

will produce a curve which is tangential to σ_c as $l/k \to 0$, and tangential to σ_e as $l/k \to \infty$ (since σ_e is very large in one case and very small in the other). This satisfies both limiting conditions, and for intermediate values σ will be less than both σ and σ_e.

Proceeding

$$\sigma = \frac{\sigma_c \sigma_e}{\sigma_c + \sigma_r}$$

$$= \frac{\sigma_c}{1 + \sigma_c/\sigma_e}$$

For a pin-ended strut

$$\sigma_e = \pi^2 E k^2 / l^2$$

hence $$\sigma = \frac{\sigma_c}{1 + (\sigma_c/\pi^2 E)(l/k)^2}$$ from above

$\sigma_c/\pi^2 E$ is now replaced by a constant a, to make allowance for unknown imperfections, the value of a depending on the material and on the end conditions.

The permissible load is then given by

$$P = \sigma A = \frac{\sigma_c A}{1 + a(l/k)^2}$$

Material	σ_c	a	
	N/mm²	Pinned ends	Fixed ends
Mild steel . . .	320	1/7500	1/30,000
Wrought iron . .	250	1/9000	1/36,000
Cast iron . . .	550	1/1600	1/6400
Timber . . .	35	1/3000	1/12,000

Note that the ratio for a between the two end conditions is maintained at 4, as in the Euler analysis; other end conditions may be treated by a similar argument.

If the quantity $\sigma_c/\pi^2 E$ is calculated for steel, a value of about 1/6400 is obtained, to compare with $a = 1/7500$.

A factor of safety may be included in the Rankine formula by reducing the value of σ_c, which then becomes the "working stress."

EXAMPLE 6. *A compound stanchion is made up of two 20 cm by 7·5 cm channel sections placed back to back 10 cm apart, and two 25 cm by 1·25 cm plates riveted one to each flange. Calculate the safe load to be carried on a length of 6 m with a factor of safety of 3·5. Assume fixed ends, $\sigma_c = 320$ N/mm², and $a = 1/30,000$. For each channel $A = 30$ cm², $I_X = 1900$ cm⁴, $I_Y = 150$ cm⁴, and distance of centroid from back of web = 2·1 cm.*

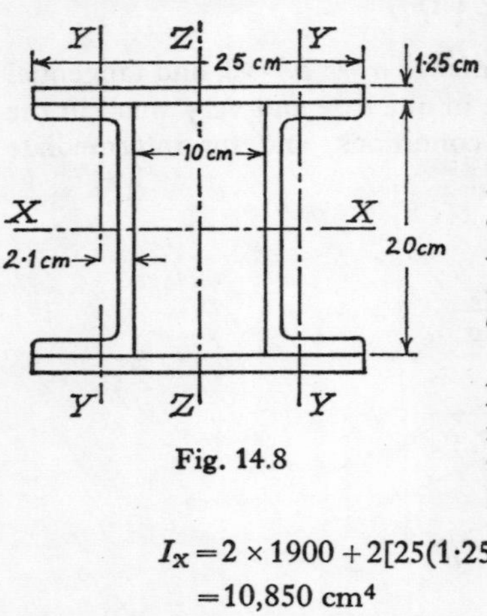

Fig. 14.8

The principal axes of inertia are XX and ZZ (Fig. 14.8), and it is necessary to determine which gives the smaller I value (and hence the least k^2).

$$I_X = 2 \times 1900 + 2[25(1{\cdot}25)^3/12 + (25 \times 1{\cdot}25)10{\cdot}63^2]$$
$$= 10{,}850 \text{ cm}^4$$

$$I_Z = 2(150 + 30 \times 7{\cdot}1^2) + 2 \times 1{\cdot}25 \times 25^3/12$$
$$= 6570 \text{ cm}^4$$

$$\text{Total Area} = 2(30 + 25 \times 1{\cdot}25)$$
$$= 122{\cdot}5 \text{ cm}^2$$

$$\text{Least } k^2 = 6570/122{\cdot}5 = 53{\cdot}7 \text{ cm}^2$$

$$\text{Safe load} = \frac{1}{3{\cdot}5} \cdot \frac{\sigma_c A}{1 + a(l/k)^2}$$

$$= \frac{320 \times 122{\cdot}5 \times 10^2}{3{\cdot}5(1 + 600^2/53{\cdot}7 \times 30{,}000)} \text{ N}$$

$$= 915 \text{ kN}$$

EXAMPLE 7. *A hollow cast-iron column, with fixed ends, supports an axial ɔad of 1 MN. If the column is 5 m long and has an external diameter of ·25 m, find the thickness of metal required.*

Use the Rankine formula, taking a constant of 1/6400 and a working stress f 80 MN/m². (*U.L.*)

$$A = (\pi/4)(0{\cdot}0625 - d^2), \quad d = \text{internal diameter}$$

$$k^2 = (\pi/64)(0{\cdot}25^4 - d^4)/A = (0{\cdot}0625 + d^2)/16$$

$$\text{Load } 1 = \frac{80 \times \pi(0{\cdot}0625 - d^2)}{4\{1 + (1/6400)[5^2 \times 16/(0{\cdot}0625 + d^2)]\}}$$

$$\therefore \quad 1 + 1/16(0{\cdot}0625 + d^2) = 20\pi(0{\cdot}0625 - d^2)$$

nd $$1 + 16d^2 + 1 = 3{\cdot}93 - 1000d^4$$

r $$1000d^4 + 16d^2 - 1{\cdot}93 = 0$$

ɔolving $$d^2 = [-16 + \sqrt{(256 + 7700)}]/2000 = 0{\cdot}0366$$

$$\therefore \quad d = 0{\cdot}191 \text{ m}$$

$$\text{Thickness of metal} = (250 - 191)/2 = 29{\cdot}5 \text{ mm}$$

14.11. Johnson's Parabolic Formula.

$$P = \sigma_c A[1 - b(l/k)^2]$$

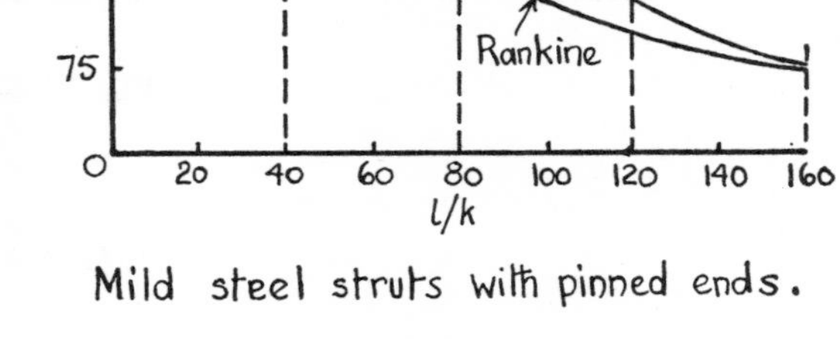

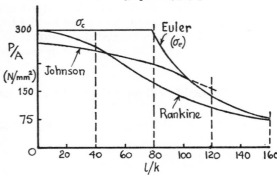

Mild steel struts with pinned ends.

Fig. 14.9

The following values are given for mild steel: $\sigma_c = 290$ N/mm^2, $b = 0{\cdot}00003$ for pinned ends and 0·00002 for fixed ends.

A graphical comparison of the Euler, Rankine, and Johnson formulae is given in Fig. 14.9.

14.12. Perry-Robertson Formula. It was shown in Para. 14.8 that initial curvature of the strut and eccentricity of the load can be combined to give an equivalent initial curvature of amplitude c, and the maximum compressive stress due to bending and direct load is then

$$\sigma_c = \frac{cPP_e}{P_e - P} \cdot \frac{r}{I} + \frac{P}{A}$$

where r is the maximum distance from the neutral axis

$$= \frac{\eta(P/A)\,\sigma_e}{\sigma_e - P/A} + \frac{P}{A}$$

where $\eta = cr/k^2$ and is taken as $0{\cdot}003\ l/k$ in B.S. Code of Practice 113. Rearranging as a quadratic in P/A

$$(P/A)^2 - [\sigma_c + (\eta + 1)\sigma_e](P/A) + \sigma_c\sigma_e = 0$$

and solving,

$$P/A = \tfrac{1}{2}[\sigma_c + (\eta+1)\sigma_e] - \tfrac{1}{2}\sqrt{\{[\sigma_c + (\eta+1)\sigma_e]^2 - 4\sigma_c\sigma_e\}}$$

14.13. Straight-line Formulae.

$$P = \sigma_c A[1 - n(l/k)]$$

Formulae of this type are commonly used in America, and can be made sufficiently accurate over a given range. Typical values are $\sigma_c =$ 110 N/mm^2, $n = 1/200$ for pinned ends and 1/250 for fixed ends, for mild-steel struts. A similar form is suggested for structural steel in B.S. 153, with $\sigma_c = 140$ N/mm^2, $n = 0{\cdot}0054$ for pinned ends and 0·0038 for riveted ends.

14.14. Strut with Lateral Loading. If the lateral load is uniformly distributed, of intensity w, then

$$EI \,.\, d^2y/dx^2 = M = P(-y) + (wl/2)x - wx^2/2 \quad \text{(Fig. 14.10)} \quad (1)$$

Differentiating twice

$$\begin{aligned} d^2M/dx^2 &= -P \,.\, d^2y/dx^2 - w \\ &= -P \,.\, M/EI - w \quad \text{from (1)} \end{aligned}$$

Rearranging

$$d^2M/dx^2 + \alpha^2 M = -w \quad (\alpha^2 = P/EI) \qquad (2)$$

which is a differential equation in M with a simpler particular integral than (1), and is frequently more useful because it leads directly to the value of the maximum bending moment.

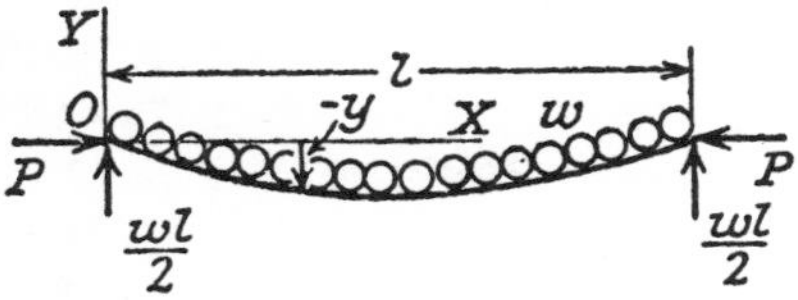

Fig. 14.10

Solving

$$M = A \sin \alpha x + B \cos \alpha x - w/\alpha^2$$

When $x = 0$, $M = 0$

$$\therefore \quad B = w/\alpha^2$$

When $x = l/2$, $dM/dx = 0$ (zero shear)

$$\therefore \quad A = B \tan \alpha l/2 = (w/\alpha^2) \tan \alpha l/2$$

Hence $\qquad M = (w/\alpha^2)[(\tan \alpha l/2) \sin \alpha x + \cos \alpha x - 1]$

At $x = l/2$

$$\hat{M} = \frac{wEI}{P}\left(\frac{\sin^2 \alpha l/2}{\cos \alpha l/2} + \cos \alpha l/2 - 1\right)$$
$$= (wEI/P)(\sec \alpha l/2 - 1)$$

The corresponding maximum deflection may be obtained from (1), i.e.

$$\hat{y} = -(wEI/P^2)(\sec \alpha l/2 - 1) + wl^2/8P$$

The maximum stress is then obtained in the usual way

$$\hat{\sigma} = P/A + \hat{M}/Z$$

EXAMPLE 8. *A horizontal strut 3 m long, having pin joints at its ends, is of rectangular cross-section 40 mm wide by 100 mm deep, and carries an axial thrust of 90 kN together with a vertical load of 9 kN uniformly distributed. Estimate the maximum stress induced and find the percentage error if the additional bending moment caused by the eccentricity of the thrust were neglected.* $E = 202{,}000$ N/mm². (*U.L.*)

$$\frac{\alpha l}{2} = \frac{3000}{2}\sqrt{\frac{90{,}000 \times 12}{202{,}000 \times 40 \times 100^3}}$$
$$= 0{\cdot}547 \text{ radians.}$$

$$\hat{M} = (wEI/P)(\sec \alpha l/2 - 1)$$
$$= \frac{9000 \times 202{,}000 \times 40 \times 100^3(1{\cdot}17 - 1)}{3000 \times 90{,}000 \times 12}$$
$$= 3{\cdot}8 \times 10^6 \text{ Nmm}$$

$$\hat{\sigma} = P/A + \hat{M}/Z$$
$$= 90{,}000/(40 \times 100) + (3{\cdot}8 \times 10^6 \times 6)/(40 \times 100^2)$$
$$= 22{\cdot}5 + 57$$
$$= 79{\cdot}5 \text{ N/mm}^2 \text{ compression.}$$

If the eccentricity of the thrust (i.e. central deflection) is neglected

$$\hat{M} = wl^2/8$$
$$= (9000 \times 3000^2)/(3000 \times 8)$$
$$= 3{\cdot}375 \times 10^6 \text{ Nmm}$$

giving

$$\hat{\sigma} = 22{\cdot}5 + 50{\cdot}7$$
$$= 73{\cdot}2 \text{ N/mm}^2$$

$$\text{Percentage error} = [(79{\cdot}5 - 73{\cdot}2)/79{\cdot}5] \times 100$$
$$= 8\%$$

EXAMPLE 9. *A horizontal bar of uniform section and length L is simply supported at its ends. In addition to the uniform load w per unit length due to its own weight, the bar is subjected to longitudinal thrusts F acting at points on the vertical centre-lines of the end sections at a distance e below the centres. Show that the resultant maximum bending moment in the beam will have its least possible value if*

$$e = \frac{w(\sec mL/2 - 1)}{Fm^2(\sec mL/2 + 1)}, \quad \text{where } m^2 = \frac{F}{EI}$$

If the bar is of steel, 2·5 m long, of rectangular cross-section 80 mm wide and 25 mm deep and weighs 150 N/m, and if the end thrust is 13·3 kN, find the eccentricity e as already defined and also the corresponding maximum deflection. E = 200,000 N/mm². (U.L.)

Equation (1) becomes

$$EI \,.\, d^2y/dx^2 = M = -F(y+e) + wLx/2 - wx^2/2 \qquad \text{(i)}$$

Differentiating twice

$$d^2M/dx^2 = -F \,.\, d^2y/dx^2 - w$$
$$= -F \,.\, M/EI - w \quad \text{from (i) above}$$

Rearranging

$$d^2M/dx^2 + m^2M = -w$$

Solving

$$M = A \sin mx + B \cos mx - w/m^2 \qquad \text{(ii)}$$

When

$$x = 0, \quad M = -Fe \qquad \text{(iii)}$$
$$\therefore \quad B = w/m^2 - Fe$$

When

$$x = L/2, \quad dM/dx = 0$$
$$\therefore \quad A = B \tan mL/2 = (w/m^2 - Fe) \tan mL/2$$

Hence (ii) becomes

$$M = (w/m^2 - Fe)(\tan mL/2 \,.\, \sin mx + \cos mx) - w/m^2$$

At $x = L/2$,

$$M = (w/m^2 - Fe) \sec mL/2 - w/m^2 \qquad \text{(iv)}$$

nd this will be a local maximum value. When it is equal and opposite o the bending moment at the ends, the condition stated will be satisfied. rom (iii) and (iv),

$$Fe = (w/m^2 - Fe)\sec mL/2 - w/m^2$$

giving
$$e = \frac{w(\sec mL/2 - 1)}{Fm^2(\sec mL/2 + 1)}$$

$$m^2 = F/EI = 13{,}300/(200{,}000 \times \tfrac{1}{12} \times 80 \times 25^3) = 0{\cdot}64 \times 10^{-6}\ \text{mm}^{-2}$$

$$mL/2 = 0{\cdot}8 \times 10^{-3} \times 2500/2 = 1 \text{ radian}$$

$$e = \frac{150(1{\cdot}85 - 1)}{10^3 \times 13{,}300 \times 0{\cdot}64 \times 10^{-6}(1{\cdot}85 + 1)} = 5{\cdot}27 \text{ mm}$$

Maximum deflection will be at the centre, where

$$M = Fe = 13{,}300 \times 5{\cdot}27 \text{ Nmm}$$
$$= -13{,}300(y + 5{\cdot}27) + (150/10^3)2500^2/8 \quad \text{from (i)}$$

giving
$$y = -2 \times 5{\cdot}27 + 8{\cdot}8$$
$$= -1{\cdot}74 \text{ mm}$$

The deflected shape will be as shown in Fig. 14.11.

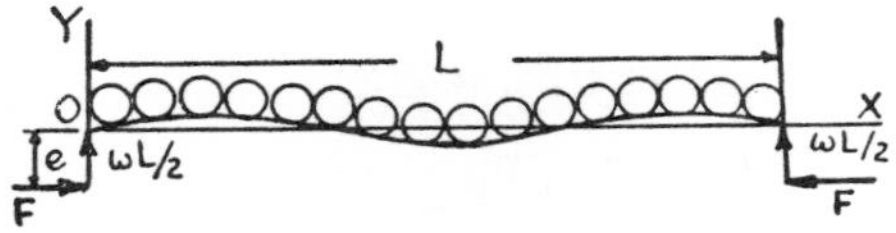

Fig.14.11

14.15. Tie with Lateral Loading. Although this is not a strut, the end load being tensile, a very similar differential equation is obtained.

$$EI.d^2y/dx^2 = M = -P(-y) + (wl/2)x - wx^2/2 \qquad (1)$$

Differentiating twice

$$d^2M/dx^2 = P.d^2y/dx^2 - w$$
$$= (P/EI)M - w \quad \text{from (1)}$$

or
$$d^2M/dx^2 - \alpha^2 M = -w \qquad (2)$$

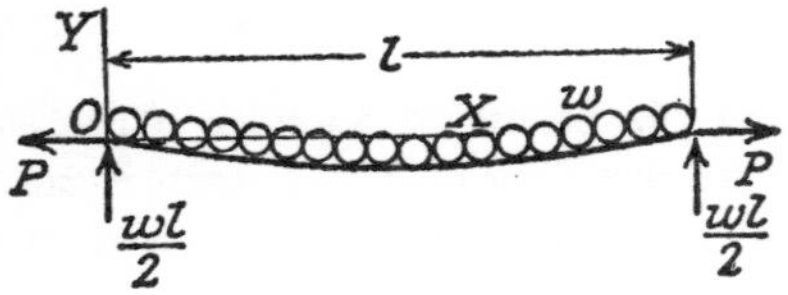

Fig. 14.12

The solution is

$$M = A\sinh \alpha x + B\cosh \alpha x + w/\alpha^2$$

When $x = 0$, $M = 0$

$$\therefore \quad B = -w/\alpha^2$$

When $x = l/2$, $dM/dx = 0$

$$\therefore \quad A = -B \tanh \alpha l/2$$
$$= (w/\alpha^2) \tanh \alpha l/2$$

giving $$M = (w/\alpha^2)[(\tanh \alpha l/2) \sinh \alpha x - \cosh \alpha x + 1]$$

When $x = l/2$

$$\hat{M} = (w/\alpha^2)\left(\frac{\sinh^2 \alpha l/2}{\cosh \alpha l/2} - \cosh \alpha l/2 + 1\right)$$
$$= (wEI/P)(1 - \text{sech}\, \alpha l/2)$$

EXAMPLE 10. *A steel tie bar, 38 mm diameter and 5 m long, is supported horizontally through pin joints at the ends, and sustains an axial pull of 18 kN. Find the greatest tensile stress in the bar, indicating how any formula used may be deduced. $E = 203{,}000$ N/mm². Density of steel $= 7800$ kg/m³.*

$$\frac{\alpha l}{2} = \frac{5000}{2}\sqrt{\frac{18{,}000 \times 64}{203{,}000 \times \pi \times 38^4}}$$
$$= 2{\cdot}33 \text{ radians}$$

$$w = \frac{7800 \times 9{\cdot}81 \times \pi \times 38^2}{10^9 \times 4}$$
$$= 0{\cdot}087 \text{ N/mm}$$

$$\hat{M} = (wEI/P)(1 - \text{sech}\, \alpha l/2)$$
$$= \frac{0{\cdot}087 \times 203{,}000 \times \pi \times 38^4}{18{,}000 \times 64}(1 - 0{\cdot}1775)$$
$$= 82{,}700 \text{ Nmm}$$

$$\hat{\sigma} = P/A + M/Z$$
$$= \frac{18{,}000}{(\pi/4) \times 38^2} + \frac{82{,}700 \times 32}{\pi \times 38^3}$$
$$= 15{\cdot}9 + 15{\cdot}4$$
$$= 31{\cdot}3 \text{ N/mm}^2 \text{ tension.}$$

14.16. Struts of Varying Cross-section—Energy Method. If a is the crippling load of a strut, it can be considered to remain constant for any small axial movements Δ of the ends, and the work done by the load during this movement will be $P\Delta$. Since the strut remains stable for values of the load less than the critical, $P\Delta$ will represent approximately the total strain energy of the strut. In the deflected form this strain energy will be mainly due to the bending moment.

If s is the distance measured along the axis of the deflected strut, and x the distance measured along its undeflected line, the approach of the ends is

$$\Delta = \int_0^l (ds - dx)$$

$$= \int_0^l \sqrt{[1+(dy/dx)^2]}dx - \int_0^l dx$$

$$= \tfrac{1}{2}\int_0^l (dy/dx)^2 dx \quad \text{approx.} \qquad (1)$$

Then, equating energy,

$$P\Delta = \tfrac{1}{2}\int_0^l (M^2/EI)dx \qquad (2)$$

giving

$$P = \frac{\int_0^l (M^2/EI)dx}{\int_0^l (dy/dx)^2 dx} \quad \text{from (1) and (2)} \qquad (3)$$

This expression can be evaluated if the form of the deflected strut is known or assumed, and for a pin-ended strut of length l, $y = A \sin \pi x/l$ will usually be found satisfactory. For a strut fixed at one end the suggested form is $y = A\ (1 - \cos \pi x/2l)$. M can then be expressed in terms of P and y and the integration performed taking into account variations in I.

EXAMPLE 11. *A steel strut 20 cm long is made up of two lengths of 10 cm, one at 5 mm diameter and the other at 7·5 mm diameter. It is built-in at the larger end and carries an axial load at the smaller end. Estimate the magnitude of the crippling load.* $E = 206{,}000\ N/mm^2$.

Take the X axis through the built-in end, and assume the deflected form under the action of the crippling load is

$$y = A(1 - \cos \pi x/40) \text{ cm}$$

$$dy/dx = A(\pi/40) \sin \pi x/40$$

$$\int_0^l \left(\frac{dy}{dx}\right)^2 dx = \frac{A^2\pi^2}{40^2}\int_0^{20} \frac{1 - \cos \pi x/20}{2} .dx$$

$$= (A^2\pi^2/1600)(20/2) = 0{\cdot}0617A^2 \text{ cm} \qquad \text{(i)}$$

$$M = P(A - y) \quad \text{since } A \text{ is the deflection at the free end}$$

$$= PA \cos \pi x/40$$

$$\int_0^l \frac{M^2 dx}{EI} = \frac{P^2A^2}{E}\left\{\int_0^{10} \frac{1 + \cos \pi x/20}{2I_1} .dx + \int_{10}^{20} \frac{1 + \cos \pi x/20}{2I_2} .dx\right\}$$

where $I_1 = (\pi/64)0{\cdot}75^4 = 0{\cdot}0155 \text{ cm}^4$

and $I_2 = (\pi/64)0{\cdot}5^4 = 0{\cdot}00307 \text{ cm}^4$

then
$$\int \frac{M^2 dx}{EI} = \frac{P^2A^2}{2E}\left(\frac{10+20/\pi}{0{\cdot}0155} + \frac{10-20/\pi}{0{\cdot}00307}\right)$$
$$= 1120P^2A^2/E \qquad \text{(ii)}$$

But
$$P = \frac{\int(M^2/EI)dx}{\int(dy/dx)^2 dx} \quad \text{from (3)}$$
$$= \frac{1120P^2A^2}{206{,}000 \times 10^2 \times 0{\cdot}0617A^2} \quad \text{from (i) and (ii)}$$

giving
$$P = 206{,}000 \times 10^2 \times 0{\cdot}0617/1120$$
$$= 1130 \text{ N}$$

SUMMARY

Euler Crippling Load $P_e = k.\pi^2 EI/l^2$.

	Pinned	Fixed	Fixed one end, free other	Fixed one end, pinned other
k	1	4	$\frac{1}{4}$	2·05

Eccentric Load: $\hat{M} = Pe.\sec \alpha l/2$.
Initial Curvature: $\hat{M} = c.PP_e/(P_e - P)$.
Rankine Formula: $P = \dfrac{\sigma_c A}{1 + a(l/k)^2}$
Johnson's Parabolic Formula: $P = \sigma_c A[1 - b(l/k)^2]$.
Straight-line Formula: $P = \sigma_c A[1 - n(l/k)]$
Strut with Lateral Loading: $\hat{M} = (wEI/P)(\sec \alpha l/2 - 1)$
Tie with Lateral Loading: $\hat{M} = (wEI/P)(1 - \text{sech } \alpha l/2)$.
Energy Method: $P = \int(M^2/EI)dx / \int(dy/dx)^2 dx$

REFERENCES

SALMON, E. H., *Columns*. Oxford Technical Publications. 1921.
TIMOSHENKO, S., *Theory of Elastic Stability*. McGraw-Hill. 1936.

PROBLEMS

1. A strut of length l has its ends built into a material which exerts a constraining couple equal to k times the angular rotation in radians. Show that the buckling load P is given by the equation $\tan \alpha l/2 = -P/\alpha k$, $\alpha^2 = P/EI$.

In the case of a strut 3·05 m long for which the buckling load for freely hinged ends is 10 kN, show that the buckling load will be approximately doubled if the ends are under a constraint of 180 Nm per degree of rotation.

2. A vertical strut, initially straight, is subject to a thrust P acting with eccentricity e. If buckling at the centre is prevented by a horizontal force F, show that $F = \dfrac{2Pe(1 - \sec al/2)}{l/2 - (1/a)\tan al/2}$ (U.L.)

3. A long strut of constant section is initially straight. A thrust is applied eccentrically at both ends and on the same side of the centre-line, with the eccentricity at one end twice that at the other. If the length is L and the thrust P, show that the maximum bending moment occurs at a distance X from the end with the smaller eccentricity, where $\tan mX = (2 - \cos mL)/\sin mL$ and $m = \sqrt{(P/EI)}$.

If in the above problem $L = 0{\cdot}76$ m and the strut is 25 mm diameter, calculate the value of the eccentricities which will produce a maximum stress of 310 N/mm² with $P = 35$ kN. $E = 200{,}000$ N/mm². (U.L.) (Note the equal and opposite lateral forces at the ends for equilibrium. Answer, 3 mm, 6 mm.)

4. A long strut, originally straight, securely fixed at one end and free at the other, is loaded at the free end with an eccentric load whose line of action is parallel to the original axis. Deduce an expression for the deviation of the free end from its original position.

Determine the deviation and the greatest compressive stress for a steel strut under these conditions. Length 3 m, circular cross-section 50 mm external diameter, 25 mm internal diameter. Load 3500 N and eccentricity 75 mm. $E = 206{,}000$ N/mm². (U.L.) ($e(\sec al - 1)$; 25 mm, 31 N/mm².)

5. A hollow circular steel strut, with its ends position fixed, has a length of 2·44 m, external diameter 101 mm, and internal diameter 89 mm. Before loading, the strut is bent with a maximum deviation of 4·5 mm. Assuming the centre line is sinusoidal, determine the maximum stress due to a central compressive end load of 10 kN. $E = 205{,}000$ N/mm². (U.L.) (6·3 N/mm².)

6. Show that, if a strut has an initial curvature in the form of a parabolic arc and is hinged at both ends (i.e. position fixed only), the maximum compressive stress produced by a load P is

$$\frac{P}{A}\left[1 + \frac{es}{k^2}\cdot\frac{8P_e}{\pi^2 P}\left(\sec\frac{\pi}{2}\sqrt{\frac{P}{P_e}} - 1\right)\right]$$

where A is the cross-sectional area, e the initial central deflection, P_e the Eulerian crippling load, k the least radius of gyration and s the distance of the extreme fibres from the neutral axis. (U.L.) (Para. 14.8. $y_0 = 4ex(1 - x)/l^2$)

7. Compare the crippling loads given by Euler's and Rankine's formulae for a tubular steel strut 2·3 m long having outer and inner diameters of 38 mm and 33 mm, loaded through pin joints at both ends. Take the yield stress as 320 N/mm² and the Rankine constant as 1/7500. $E = 200{,}000$ N/mm².

For what length of strut does the Euler formula cease to apply? (U.L.)

(17 kN, 17·1 kN; 1 m.)

8. Working from first principles, derive a formula for the Euler collapsing load for a strut having its bottom end fixed and the loaded top end free to move laterally. Sketch a curve showing how the collapsing load per unit area of cross-section varies with L/k, the slenderness ratio. Assuming the yield stress for steel is 320 N/mm² show that the Euler formula cannot be applied to a strut of circular cross-section of diameter d if $L < 10d$. (I.Mech.E.)

9. A steel pipe 38 mm inside diameter, 6·3 mm thick, and 1·22 m long, has its ends rigidly attached to flanges which are themselves so fixed as to prevent any expansion in the length of the pipe. The pipe is fixed in position under normal temperature conditions, and is then unstressed, but may be subjected to a temperature rise of 50° C. Calculate the temperature stress in the pipe and the factor of safety against failure as a strut. Use the Rankine formula, $\sigma_c = 320$ N/mm^2, $a = 1/7500$ for a strut with hinged ends. $\alpha = 11{\cdot}1 \times 10^6/°$ C.; $E = 206{,}000$ N/mm^2. (115 N/mm^2; 2·4.)

10. A 2200 kN load is to be carried by a column 3 m long built up by a 20 cm by 15 cm I-beam with flange plates 30 cm wide. Find the thickness of the flange plates if the allowable concentric load per unit area is $p = 103 - 0{\cdot}00172(l/k)^2$ N/mm^2. For the beam, $A = 65$ cm^2, $I_x = 4500$ cm^4, $I_y = 750$ cm^4. (U.L.) (25 mm.)

11. A rod of rectangular section 76 mm deep and 38 mm wide, is supported horizontally through pin joints at its ends, and carries a vertical load of 350 kg/m length and an axial thrust of 80 kN. If its length is 2·75 m estimate the maximum stress induced. $E = 206{,}000$ N/mm^2. (U.L.) (145 N/mm^2.)

12. A straight strut of length L and of uniform section is hinged at both ends and is loaded along its axis with a thrust P. It also carries a transverse distributed load which varies uniformly in intensity from w per unit length at one end A to zero at the other end B.

Show that the distance x from the end B to the section at which the maximum bending moment occurs is given by $\cos mx = (\sin mL)/mL$, where $m^2 = P/EI$.

If the thrust P is 81% of the Eulerian crippling load, find the position and value of the maximum bending moment. (U.L.) ($0{\cdot}52L$, $0{\cdot}338wL^2$.)

13. Obtain expressions for the bending moments at the ends and centre of a uniform strut, built in at both ends, and subjected to a uniform lateral load of intensity w. The strut length is L, the end thrust P, and the elastic properties EI. Take $\mu^2 = P/EI$. Show without elaborate analysis, from the expressions derived, that for practical struts the end moments are greater numerically than the central moment and of opposite sign. (U.L.)

14. An initially straight slender strut of uniform section and length l has hinged ends through which it is loaded by an axial force P. In addition, one half of the strut from the middle to one end carries a uniform transverse load w per unit length. If $Pl^2/EI = \pi^2/4$, find an expression for the central deflection.

If $l = 1$ m and $w = 1750$ N/m, find the bending moment at the centre. (U.L.)

(Apply Macaulay's method, Para. 9.4. $0{\cdot}043\ w\ l^4/EI$. 300 Nm.)

15. A steel tie rod, of length 3 m and diameter 25 mm, carries a tensile load of 4500 N. Due to wind pressure and dead weight a transverse load of 88 N/m occurs. Calculate the maximum bending moment. $E = 206{,}000$ N/mm^2. (47 Nm.)

16. A horizontal pin-ended strut 4·5 m long is formed from a standard T-section 15 cm by 10 cm by 1·25 cm at 24 kg/m. The axial compressive load is 180 kN. Find the maximum stress if the XX axis is horizontal and the table of the tee forms the compression face. The centroid is 2·4 cm below the top. $I_x = 250$ cm^4; $A = 31$ cm^2; $E = 206{,}000$ N/mm^2. (U.L.) (81 N/mm^2.)

17. A 25 mm-diameter steel rod 0·75 m long has a 12·5 mm-diameter hole bored centrally from each end for a distance of 0·25 m, leaving the central 0·25 m solid. Estimate the buckling load if used as a strut with pinned ends. $E = 206{,}000$ N/mm^2. (67·5 kN.)

CHAPTER XV

Cylinders and Spheres

15.1. Thin Cylinder under Internal Pressure. By symmetry the three principal stresses in the shell will be the *circumferential or hoop stress*, the *longitudinal stress*, and the radial stress.

If the ratio of thickness to internal diameter is less than about 1/20 (see Para. 15.9), it may be assumed with reasonable accuracy that the hoop and longitudinal stresses are constant over the thickness, and that the *radial stress* is small and *can be neglected* (in fact it must have a value equal to the internal pressure at the inside surface, and zero at the outside surface).

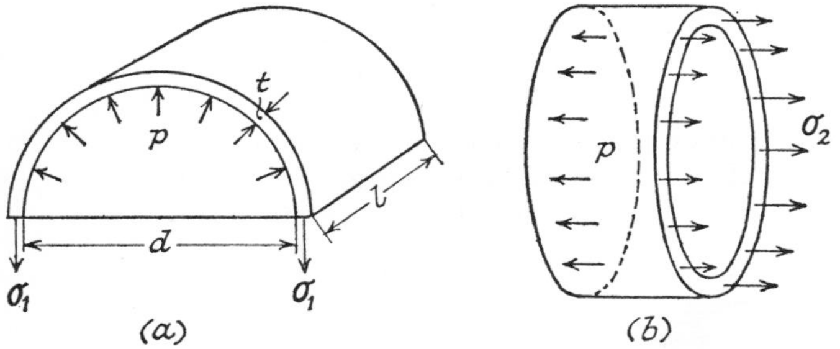

Fig. 15.1

Let the internal diameter be d, and the thickness t; p is the applied internal pressure, σ_1 the hoop stress, and σ_2 the longitudinal stress (Fig. 15.1).

Consider the equilibrium of a half cylinder of length l, sectioned through a diametral plane (Fig. 15.1(a)). σ_1 acts on an area $2tl$, and the resultant vertical pressure force is found from the projected horizontal area dl.

Equating forces

$$\sigma_1 . 2tl = pdl$$

i.e.

$$\boldsymbol{\sigma_1 = pd/2t} \qquad (1)$$

Consider the equilibrium of a section cut by a transverse plane (Fig. 15.1(b)). σ_2 acts on an area approximately $= \pi dt$ (this should be the mean diameter), and p acts on a projected area of $\pi d^2/4$ whatever the actual shape of the end.

Equating forces

$$\sigma_2 . \pi dt = p . \pi d^2/4$$

i.e.
$$\boldsymbol{\sigma_2 = pd/4t} \tag{2}$$

In the case of long cylinders, or tubes which are braced by stays or carried on brackets, the longitudinal stress may be much less than that given by (2), and is sometimes neglected.

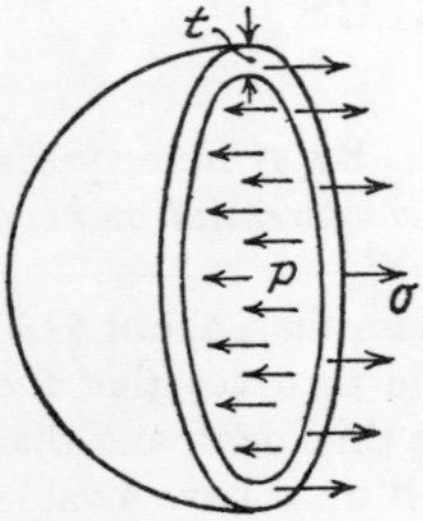

Fig. 15.2

15.2. Thin Spherical Shell under Internal Pressure. Again the radial stress will be neglected and the circumferential or hoop stress will be assumed constant.

By symmetry the two principal stresses are equal, in fact the stress in any tangential direction is equal to σ.

From Fig. 15.2 it is seen that

$$\sigma . \pi dt = p . \pi d^2/4$$

(where d is the internal diameter)

i.e.
$$\boldsymbol{\sigma = pd/4t}$$

15.3. Cylindrical Shell with Hemispherical Ends. Let t_1 be the thickness of the cylinder and t_2 the thickness of the hemisphere, the internal diameter being assumed the same for both (Fig. 15.3).

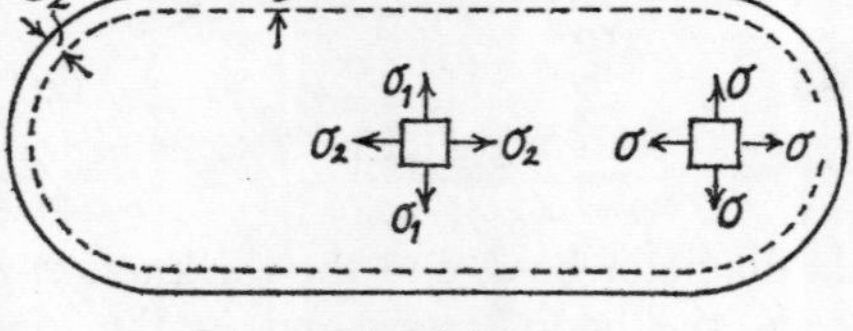

Fig. 15.3

If the shell is subjected to an internal pressure p, the stresses in the cylinder will be:

$$\text{Hoop stress } \sigma_1 = pd/2t_1$$

and
$$\text{Longitudinal stress } \sigma_2 = pd/4t_1 \quad \text{(Para. 15.1)}$$

Then
$$\text{Hoop strain } \epsilon_1 = (1/E)(\sigma_1 - \nu\sigma_2) \quad \text{(Para. 3.13)}$$
$$= (pd/4t_1E)(2-\nu)$$

For the hemispherical ends:

$$\text{Hoop stress } \sigma = pd/4t_2 \quad \text{(Para. 15.2)}$$
$$\text{Hoop strain } \epsilon = (1/E)(\sigma - \nu\sigma)$$
$$= (pd/4t_2E)(1-\nu)$$

For no distortion of the junction under pressure,

$$\epsilon_1 = \epsilon$$

i.e.

$$\frac{2-\nu}{t_1} = \frac{1-\nu}{t_2}$$

or

$$\frac{t_2}{t_1} = \frac{1-\nu}{2-\nu} = 7/17$$

taking a value of 0·3 for Poisson's ratio.

Note that the maximum stress will then occur in the ends, i.e.

$$\sigma = pd/4t_2 = (17/7)(pd/4t_1)$$

which is greater than the hoop stress σ_1 in the cylinder. For equal maximum stress t_2/t_1 should equal 0·5.

15.4. Volumetric Strain on Capacity. The capacity of a *cylinder* $=\pi d^2 l/4$, and if the dimensions are increased by δd and δl, the Volumetric strain

$$= [(d+\delta d)^2(l+\delta l) - d^2 l]/d^2 l$$
$$= [d^2 l + d^2.\delta l + 2\delta d.dl + 2\delta d.d.\delta l + (\delta d)^2 l + (\delta d)^2 \delta l - d^2 l]/d^2 l$$
$$= (d^2.\delta l + 2\delta d.dl)/d^2 l \quad \text{neglecting products of small quantities}$$
$$= 2.\delta d/d + \delta l/l$$
$$= 2 \times \text{diametral strain} + \text{longitudinal strain}$$
$$= 2 \times \text{hoop strain} + \text{longitudinal strain}$$

(since circumference = constant × diameter)

Notice that this is the sum of the linear strains in the three principal directions (compare Para. 3.18).

By a similar argument, for a *spherical shell* it can be shown that the

$$\text{Volumetric strain} = 3 \times \text{hoop strain}$$

To find the increase in capacity it is only necessary to multiply the volumetric strain by the original volume.

EXAMPLE 1. *A boiler drum consists of a cylindrical portion 2 m long, 1 m diameter, and 25 mm thick, closed by hemispherical ends. In a hydraulic test to 10 N/mm² how much additional water will be pumped in, after initial filling at atmospheric pressure? Assume the circumferential strain at the junction of cylinder and hemisphere is the same for both. For the drum material, $E = 207{,}000$ N/mm²; $\nu = 0{\cdot}3$. For water $K = 2100$ N/mm².*

For the cylinder:

$$\text{Hoop stress } \sigma_1 = pd/2t = (10 \times 1000)/(2 \times 25) = 200 \text{ N/mm}^2$$

$$\text{Longitudinal stress } \sigma_2 = pd/4t$$
$$= 100 \text{ N/mm}^2$$
$$\text{Hoop strain } \epsilon_1 = (1/E)(\sigma_1 - \nu\sigma_2)$$
$$= 100 \times 1{\cdot}7/E$$
$$\text{Longitudinal strain } \epsilon_2 = (1/E)(\sigma_2 - \nu\sigma_1)$$
$$= 100 \times 0{\cdot}4/E$$
$$\text{Increase in capacity} = (2\epsilon_1 + \epsilon_2) \times \text{volume}$$
$$= \frac{100 \times 3{\cdot}8}{207{,}000} \times \frac{\pi \times 1000^2}{4} \times 2000$$
$$= 2{\cdot}9 \times 10^6 \text{ mm}^3 \qquad \text{(i)}$$

For the two hemispherical ends:

$$\text{Hoop strain } \epsilon = \epsilon_1 \quad \text{(same as cylinder)}$$
$$\text{Increase in capacity} = 3\epsilon \times \text{volume}$$
$$= \frac{100 \times 5{\cdot}1}{207{,}000} \times \frac{\pi \times 1000^3}{6}$$
$$= 1{\cdot}3 \times 10^6 \text{ mm}^3 \qquad \text{(ii)}$$

Decrease in volume of water originally in

$$= (p/K) \times \text{volume} \quad \text{(Para. 4.2)}$$
$$= \frac{10}{2100}\left[\frac{\pi \times 1000^2}{4} \times 2000 + \frac{\pi \times 1000^3}{6}\right]$$
$$= 10 \times 10^6 \text{ mm}^3 \qquad \text{(iii)}$$

Additional volume of water required

$$= \text{(i)} + \text{(ii)} + \text{(iii)}$$
$$= 14{\cdot}2 \times 10^6 \text{ mm}^3 \text{ at } 10\text{N/mm}^2$$

or $= 14{\cdot}25 \times 10^6 \text{ mm}^3$ at atmospheric pressure

EXAMPLE 2. *A cylindrical tank is 2 m diameter, 2·5 m long, and 12 mm thick. Its ends are flat and are joined by nine tie bars, each 38 mm diameter, equally spaced. If the tie bars are initially stressed to 50 N/mm² and the tank filled with water, find the increase in capacity when the pressure is raised to 1·2 N/mm², and the final stress in the tie bars. E = 207,000 N/mm²; ν = 0·28.*

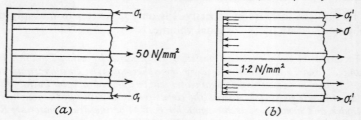

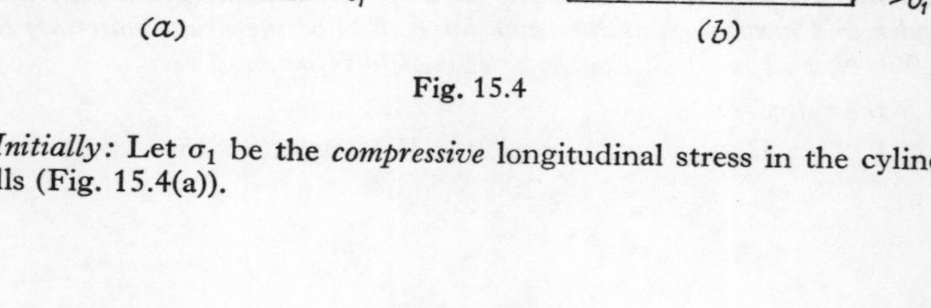

Fig. 15.4

Initially: Let σ_1 be the *compressive* longitudinal stress in the cylinder walls (Fig. 15.4(a)).

Equilibrium equation

$$\sigma_1 . \pi \times 2000 \times 12 = 50 \times 9\pi \times 38^2/4$$

giving $$\sigma_1 = 6{\cdot}77 \text{ N/mm}^2$$

There is no hoop stress initially.

Finally: Let σ be the final tensile stress in the tie bars and σ_1' the final *tensile* longitudinal stress in the cylinder (Fig. 15.4(b)).

Equilibrium equation

$$\sigma'_1 . \pi \times 2000 \times 12 + \sigma(9\pi \times 38^2/4) = 1{\cdot}2(\pi \times 2000^2/4 - 9\pi \times 38^2/4)$$

or $$\sigma_1' + 0{\cdot}135\sigma = 49{\cdot}8 \qquad \text{(i)}$$

$$\begin{aligned}\text{Hoop stress in cylinder} &= pd/2t \quad \text{(not affected by tie bars)}\\ &= (1{\cdot}2 \times 2000)/(2 \times 12)\\ &= 100 \text{ N/mm}^2\end{aligned}$$

Compatibility equation. The increase in longitudinal strain must be the same for both tie bars and cylinder, i.e.

$$\begin{aligned}(\sigma - 50)/E &= \text{Final} - \text{Initial longitudinal strain in cylinder}\\ &= (1/E)(\sigma_1' - 0{\cdot}28 \times 100) - (1/E)(-6{\cdot}77)\end{aligned}$$

or $$\sigma = \sigma_1' + 28{\cdot}8 \qquad \text{(ii)}$$

Substituting for σ_1' from (i) in (ii)

$$\sigma = 49{\cdot}8 - 0{\cdot}135\sigma + 28{\cdot}8$$

giving $$\begin{aligned}\sigma &= 78{\cdot}6/1{\cdot}135\\ &= 69{\cdot}3 \text{ N/mm}^2\end{aligned}$$

From (i), $\sigma_1' = 40{\cdot}5$ N/mm^2.

Increase in capacity

$$= (2 \times \text{increase of hoop strain} + \text{increase of longitudinal strain}) \times \text{volume}$$

$$= \frac{1}{207{,}000}[2(100 - 0{\cdot}28 \times 40{\cdot}5 - 0{\cdot}28 \times 6{\cdot}77) + 69{\cdot}3 - 50]\frac{\pi \times 2000^2 \times 2500}{4}$$

$$= 7{\cdot}32 \times 10^6 \text{ mm}^3.$$

EXAMPLE 3. *A thin cylinder 150 mm internal diameter, 2·5 mm thick, has its ends closed by rigid plates and is then filled with water. When an external axial pull of 37 kN is applied to the ends the water pressure is observed to fall by 0·1 N/mm². Determine the value of Poisson's ratio.* $E = 140{,}000$ *N/mm²;* $K = 2200$ *N/mm.²* (*U.L.*)

Assuming the cylinder remains full of water, then

Increase in volume of water = Increase in capacity of cylinder.

Since the volumetric strain is determined by *change* of stresses, only stresses due to the drop in pressure need be considered.

$$\begin{aligned}\text{Reduction in hoop stress } \sigma_1 &= pd/2t\\ &= (0{\cdot}1 \times 150)/(2 \times 2{\cdot}5)\\ &= 3 \text{ N/mm}^2 \text{ ("compressive")}\end{aligned}$$

Increase in longitudinal stress is given by

$$\sigma_2 \times \pi \times 150 \times 2{\cdot}5 + 0{\cdot}1 \times (\pi/4) \times 150^2 = 37{,}000 \quad \text{(Fig. 15.5)}$$

i.e. $\sigma_2 = 30\text{N/mm}^2$

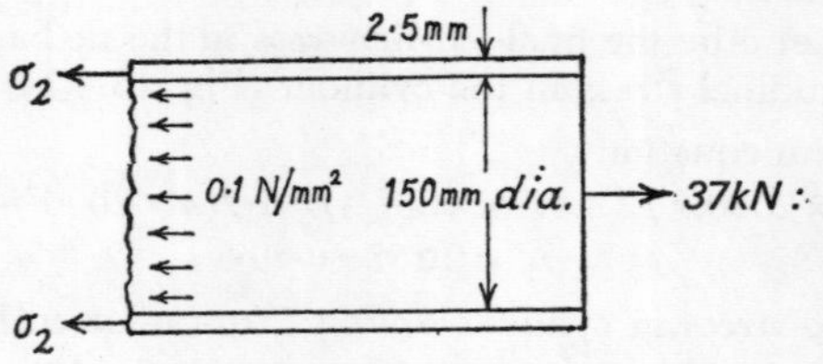

Fig. 15.5

Equating volumetric strains

$$p/K = (1/E)\ [2(-\sigma_1 - \nu\sigma_2) + (\sigma_2 + \nu\sigma_1)]$$

or $0{\cdot}1/2200 = (24 - 57\nu)/140{,}000$

From which $\nu = 17{\cdot}64/57$

$= 0{\cdot}31$

15.5. Tube under Combined Loading.

EXAMPLE 4. *A thin cylindrical tube 75 mm internal diameter, 5 mm thick is closed at the ends and subjected to an internal pressure of 5·5 N/mm². A torque of 500π Nm is also applied to the tube. Determine the maximum and minimum principal stresses and the maximum shearing stress.* (*U.L.*)

$$\text{Hoop stress} = (5{\cdot}5 \times 75)/(2 \times 5)$$
$$= 41{\cdot}2\ \text{N/mm}^2$$

$$\text{Longitudinal stress} = (5{\cdot}5 \times 75)/(4 \times 5)$$
$$= 20{\cdot}6\ \text{N/mm}^2$$

$$\text{Shear stress on transverse planes} = \frac{\text{Torque}}{(\text{Mean radius}) \times \text{Area}}$$
$$= \frac{500\pi \times 10^3}{40(\pi \times 80 \times 5)}$$

assuming stress is uniform

$$= 35{\cdot}7\ \text{N/mm}^2$$

Maximum and minimum principal stresses

$$= \tfrac{1}{2}(\sigma_x + \sigma_y) \pm \tfrac{1}{2}\sqrt{[(\sigma_x - \sigma_y)^2 + 4\tau^2]} \quad \text{(Chapter III)}$$
$$= \tfrac{1}{2} \times 61{\cdot}8 \pm \tfrac{1}{2}\sqrt{(20{\cdot}6^2 + 4 \times 35{\cdot}7^2)}$$
$$= 30{\cdot}9 \pm 37{\cdot}1$$
$$= 68 \quad \text{and} \quad -6{\cdot}2\ \text{N/mm}^2$$

$$\text{Maximum shear stress} = \tfrac{1}{2}\sqrt{[(\sigma_x - \sigma_y)^2 + 4\tau^2]}$$
$$= 37{\cdot}1\ \text{N/mm}^2$$

15.6 Wire Winding of Thin Cylinders. In order to strengthen the tube against the application of internal pressure it may first be wound with wire under tension, thus putting the wall in compression. When the pressure is applied the final hoop stress produced is much less than it would be without the wire reinforcement. The maximum stress will probably be that in the wire, which must be made of a high-tensile material.

The method of analysis can be broken down into a number of stages set out below. It is assumed that one layer of wire of diameter d is closely wound on the tube with an initial tension T (Fig. 15.6).

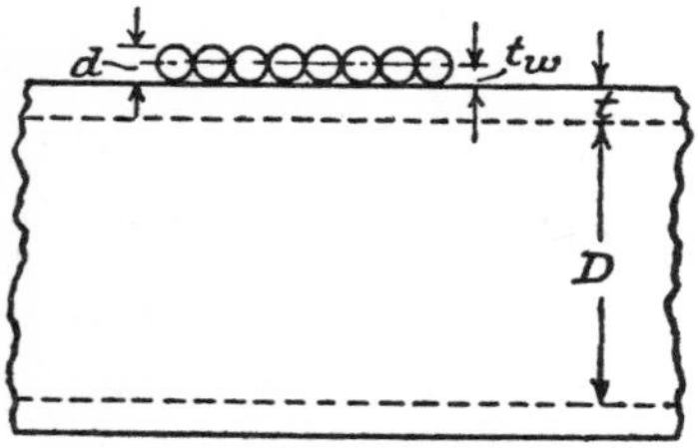

Fig. 15.6

(1) Replace the wire by an equivalent cylindrical shell, of thickness t_w, with the same cross-section in a longitudinal plane, i.e.

$$t_w \times d = \pi d^2/4$$
$$t_w = \pi d/4$$

(2) Initial tensile stress in wire

$$\sigma_w = 4T/\pi d^2$$

(3) Let σ_1 be the initial *compressive* hoop stress in the cylinder. Then for equilibrium (Fig. 15.7)

$$\sigma_1 . t = \sigma_w . t_w$$

(4) When an internal pressure p is applied, let the stresses be σ_w' tensile in the wire, and σ_1' *tensile* hoop stress in the cylinder.
For equilibrium (Fig. 15.8)

$$\sigma_1' . 2t + \sigma_w' . 2t_w = pD$$

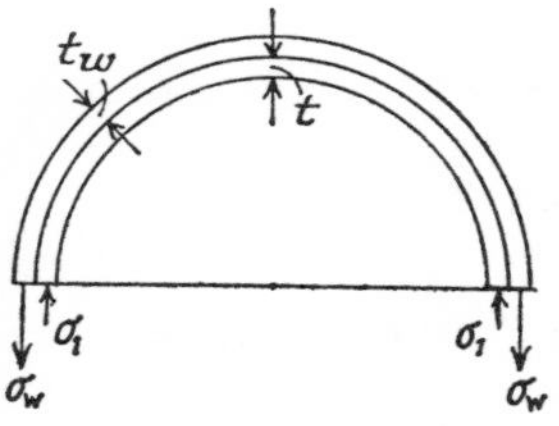

Fig. 15.7

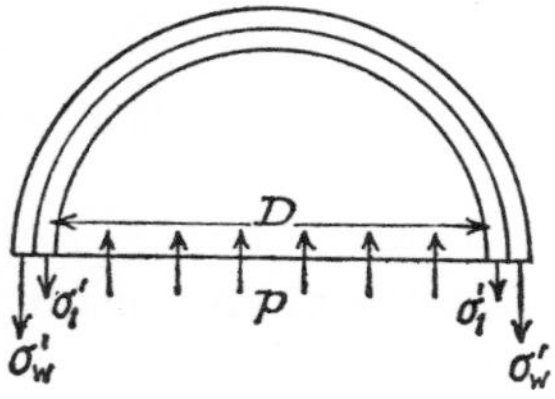

Fig. 15.8

(5) Final longitudinal stress in the cylinder is

$$\sigma_2 = pD/4t$$

or a smaller value for long tubes externally supported (see also Para. 15.1).

(6) Since the wire and cylinder remain in contact, the change of hoop strain due to the application of internal pressure must be the same for both, i.e.

$$(1/E)[(\sigma_1' - \nu\sigma_2) + \sigma_1] = (1/E_w)(\sigma_w' - \sigma_w)$$

Note that σ_1 is compressive, and that the wire is under stress in one direction only.

EXAMPLE 5. *A copper tube 38 mm external diameter, 35·5 mm internal diameter, is closely wound with steel wire 0·75 mm diameter. Stating clearly the assumptions made, estimate the tension at which the wire must have been wound if an internal pressure of 2N/mm² produces a tensile circumferential stress of 6·5 N/mm² in the tube.* $E_s = 1{\cdot}6 \times E_c$. (U.L.)

The references refer to the stages of analysis given above.

(1) Equivalent wire thickness

$$t_w = \pi d/4$$
$$= 0{\cdot}59 \text{ mm}$$

(3) If σ_w is the winding stress in wire, the initial hoop stress in the tube

$$\sigma_1 = (t_w/t) \, . \, \sigma_w$$
$$= 0{\cdot}472\sigma_w \text{ compression.}$$

(4) If the final stresses are σ_w' and σ_1', the equilibrium equation gives

$$\sigma_1' \times 2{\cdot}5 + \sigma_w' \times 1{\cdot}18 = 2 \times 35{\cdot}5$$

but $\sigma_1' = 6{\cdot}5$ N/mm²

$$\therefore \quad \sigma_w' = (71 - 16{\cdot}2)/1{\cdot}18$$
$$= 46{\cdot}5 \text{ N/mm}^2$$

(6) Equating change of hoop strain for wire and tube, and neglecting longitudinal stress in tube,

$$(46{\cdot}5 - \sigma_w)/E_s = (6{\cdot}5 + \sigma_1)/E_c$$

Substituting for σ_1 from (3), and noting $E_s/E_c = 1{\cdot}6$,

$$46{\cdot}5 - \sigma_w = 10{\cdot}4 + 1{\cdot}6 \times 0{\cdot}472\sigma_w$$

or

$$\sigma_w = 36{\cdot}1/1{\cdot}755$$
$$= 20{\cdot}5 \text{ N/mm}^2$$

(2)

$$\text{Winding tension} = 20{\cdot}5 \times \pi d^2/4$$
$$= 9 \text{ N}$$

15.7. Rotational Stresses in Thin Cylinders. Consider a cylinder of mean radius r and thickness t, rotating at an angular velocity ω about its axis.

The centrifugal force on the walls will produce a hoop stress σ which may be assumed constant.

If ρ is the density, the centrifugal force on an element (Fig. 15.9) of unit length axially

$$= (\rho r\delta\theta \, . \, t)r\omega^2$$

nd resolving radially

$$2\sigma t.\sin \tfrac{1}{2}\delta\theta = \rho r^2\omega^2.t\delta\theta$$

r $$\sigma = \rho r^2\omega^2 \text{ since } \sin \tfrac{1}{2}\delta\theta \to \tfrac{1}{2}\delta\theta$$

Consistent units are:

σ N/m² ω radn./sec.

ρ kg/m³

r m

The above analysis can also be applied pproximately to rim-type flywheels.

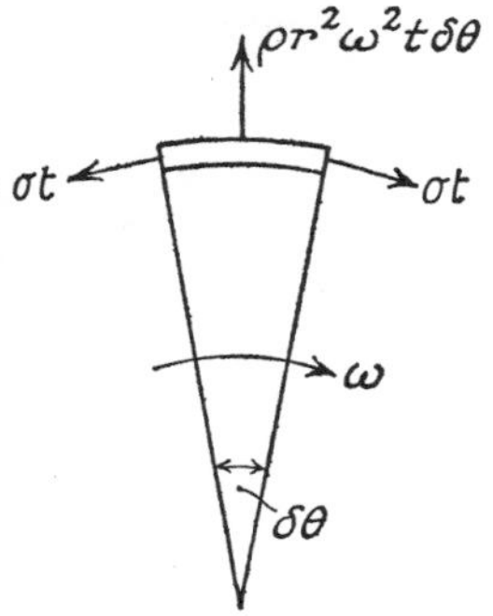

Fig. 15.9

EXAMPLE 6. *A flywheel is required with a noment of inertia of 250 kg m². It is to run at '50 r.p.m. and the maximum stress is not to xceed 4N/mm². Neglecting the inertia of the pokes, and assuming a width of 125 mm, find he thickness of the rim. Density 7200 kg/m³.*

The maximum radius is determined by the tress, i.e.

$$4 \times 10^6 = \rho r^2\omega^2$$

$$= 7200 \times r^2\left(\frac{250 \times \pi}{30}\right)^2$$

giving $$r^2 = 0{\cdot}813$$

or $$r = 0{\cdot}9 \text{ m}$$

For a first approximation assume a mean radius (and radius of gyration) of 0·85 m and let t m be the thickness.

Then $$\text{M.I.} = 250 = (0{\cdot}125 \times 2\pi \times 0{\cdot}85t \times 7200) \times (0{\cdot}85)^2$$

giving $$t = 0{\cdot}072 \text{ m}$$

Corrected values: mean radius 0·864 m

$$k^2 = (0{\cdot}9^2 + 0{\cdot}828^2)/2$$

$$= 0{\cdot}75 \text{ m}^2$$

Then $$250 = (0{\cdot}125 \times 2\pi \times 0{\cdot}864t \times 7200) \times 0{\cdot}75$$

or $$t = 0{\cdot}068 \text{ m} = 68 \text{ mm}$$

which approximately satisfies the assumption of 0·864 m mean radius and 0·9 m outside radius.

15.8. Thick Cylinders. Under the action of radial pressures at the surfaces, the three principal stresses will be p (*compressive*) radially, σ_1 (normally tensile) circumferentially, and σ_2 (normally tensile) longitudinally. These stresses may be expected to vary over any cross-section, and equations will be found to give their variation with radius r.

It may be assumed that the longitudinal strain ϵ is constant, which implies that cross-sections remain plane after straining, and this will b- true for sections remote from any end fixing.

Let u be the *radial shift* at a radius r; i.e. r becomes $r+u$ after straining, where u is small compare with r (Fig. 15.10). The circumferential, or hoop, strain

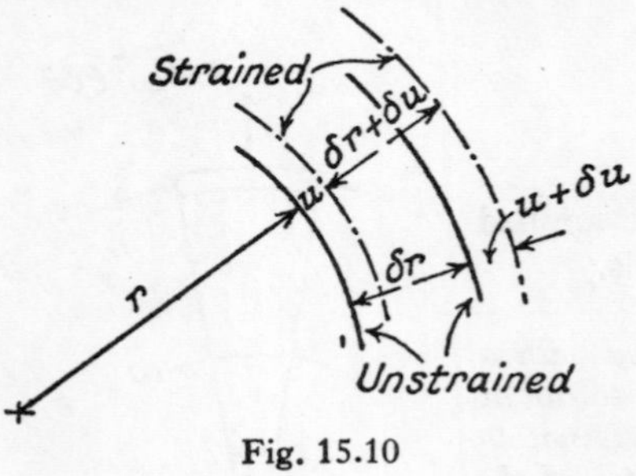

Fig. 15.10

$$= \frac{\text{Increase of circumference}}{\text{Original circumference}}$$

$$= [2\pi(r+u) - 2\pi r]/2\pi r$$

$$= u/r$$

The radial shift at an unstrained radius $r+\delta r$ will b- $u+\delta u$, and the radial strain

$$= (\text{Increase in } \delta r)/\delta r = du/dr \text{ in the limit.}$$

Stress-Strain equations (see Para. 3.14):

$$E\varepsilon = \sigma_2 - \nu\sigma_1 + \nu p \qquad (1)$$

$$E.u/r = \sigma_1 - \nu\sigma_2 + \nu p \qquad (2)$$

$$E.du/dr = -p - \nu\sigma_1 - \nu\sigma_2 \qquad (3)$$

First eliminate u from equations (2) and (3) by multiplying (2) by giving

$$Eu = r(\sigma_1 - \nu\sigma_2 + \nu p)$$

and differentiating

$$Edu/dr = \sigma_1 - \nu\sigma_2 + \nu p + r[d\sigma_1/dr - \nu(d\sigma_2/dr) + \nu(dp/dr)]$$

$$= -p - \nu\sigma_1 - \nu\sigma_2 \text{ from (3)}$$

Collecting terms

$$(p+\sigma_1)(1+\nu) + r.d\sigma_1/dr - \nu r(d\sigma_2/dr) + \nu r(dp/dr) = 0 \qquad (4)$$

From (1), since ε is constant

$$d\sigma_2/dr = \nu(d\sigma_1/dr - dp/dr)$$

and substituting this in (4)

$$(p+\sigma_1)(1+\nu) + r(1-\nu^2)(d\sigma_1/dr) + \nu r(1+\nu)(dp/dr) = 0$$

Reducing to

$$p + \sigma_1 + r(1-\nu)(d\sigma_1/dr) + \nu r(dp/dr) = 0 \qquad (5)$$

Equilibrium equation (radially) (Fig. 15.11):

$$2\sigma_1\delta r.\sin\tfrac{1}{2}\delta\theta + (p+\delta p)(r+\delta r)\delta\theta - pr\delta\theta = 0$$

In the limit $\sin\frac{1}{2}\delta\theta \to \frac{1}{2}\delta\theta$, and neglecting products of small quantities this equation reduces to

$$\sigma_1 + p + r.dp/dr = 0 \qquad (6)$$

Subtracting (6) from (5)

$$r(1-\nu)(d\sigma_1/dr)+\nu r(dp/dr)-r.(dp/dr)=0$$

which gives $\quad d\sigma_1/dr-dp/dr=0$

Integrating

$$\sigma_1-p=\text{constant}$$
$$=2a,\text{ say} \quad (7)$$

Subtracting (7) from (6)

$$2p+r.dp/dr=-2a$$

or

$$\frac{1}{r}.\frac{d(pr^2)}{dr}=-2a$$

i.e.

$$\frac{d(pr^2)}{dr}=-2ar$$

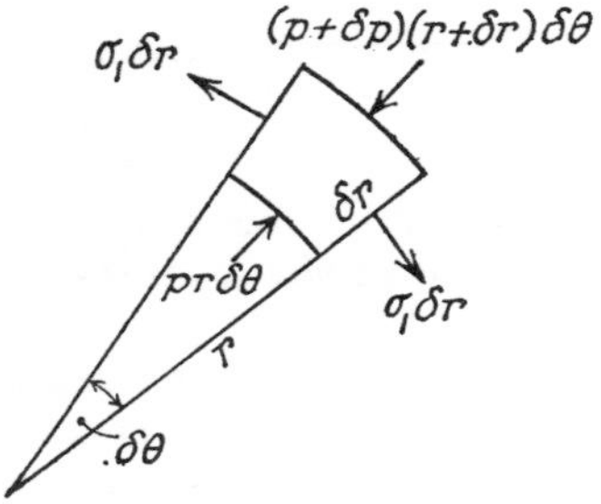

Fig. 15.11

Integrating

$$pr^2=-ar^2+B$$
$$p=-a+B/r^2$$
$$=-a+b/d^2 \quad (8)$$

where $d=2r$ and $b=4B$.

From (7)

$$\sigma_1=a+b/d^2 \quad (9)$$

where a and b are constants depending on the dimensions and the loading conditions.

It follows from equations (1) and (7), since ε is constant, that **σ_2 is constant** (i.e. independent of r). The analysis can be considerably shortened by making this assumption initially, when equation (1) reduces to

$$\sigma_1-p=\text{constant}$$

and the results are obtained by application of this and the equilibrium equation (6).

The majority of numerical problems are best solved directly from equations (8) and (9), but it may be of interest to put on record the general formulae for σ_1 and p in terms of the dimensions and the external pressures.

If the pressures are p_1 internally (diameter d_1), and p_2 externally (diameter d_2), then the radial stresses at these surfaces must be equal to the applied pressures, i.e.

$$p_1=-a+b/d_1^2$$

and

$$p_2=-a+b/d_2^2 \quad \text{from (8)}$$

Subtracting

$$b=[(p_1-p_2)d_1^2d_2^2]/(d_2^2-d_1^2)$$

By substitution

$$a=(p_1d_1^2-p_2d_2^2)/(d_2^2-d_1^2)$$

giving $\sigma_1=[p_1d_1^2-p_2d_2^2+(p_1-p_2)(d_1^2d_2^2/d^2)]/(d_2^2-d_1^2)$ from (9

and $p=[p_2d_2^2-p_1d_1^2+(p_1-p_2)(d_1^2d_2^2/d^2)]/(d_2^2-d_1^2)$ from (8

The maximum shear stress (half the stress difference, Para. 3.10)

$$=\tfrac{1}{2}(\sigma_1+p)$$
$$=(p_1-p_2)d_1^2d_2^2/(d_2^2-d_1^2)d^2.$$

It will be found that the **maximum principal stress an maximum shear stress occur at the inside surface.**

15.9. Internal Pressure Only. This is the most commonly occur ring case, and will be examined in detail.

If p_1 is the internal pressure at a diameter d_1, the external pressur being zero (atmospheric) at diameter d_2, then

$$p_1=-a+b/d_1^2$$

and $0=-a+b/d_2^2$ (Eq. (8), Para. 15.8)

Subtracting

$$b=[d_1^2d_2^2/(d_2^2-d_1^2)]p_1$$

and $a=b/d_2^2=[d_1^2/(d_2^2-d_1^2)]p_1$

The stresses at any diameter d are

Radial $p=-a+b/d^2$

$$=[d_1^2/(d_2^2-d_1^2)](-1+d_2^2/d^2)p_1$$
$$=\frac{(d_2^2-d^2)d_1^2}{(d_2^2-d_1^2)d^2}.p_1 \quad (1)$$

and Hoop $\sigma_1=a+b/d^2$

$$=\frac{(d_2^2+d^2)d_1^2}{(d_2^2-d_1^2)d^2}.p_1 \quad (2)$$

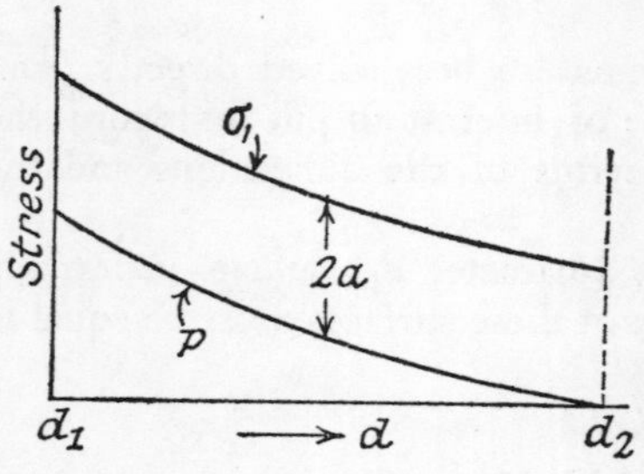

Fig. 15.12

The stress variation with diameter is shown in Fig. 15.12, the two curves being "parallel," since

$\sigma_1-p=2a$ (Eq. (7), Para. 15.8)

The maximum hoop stress is at $d=d_1$

$$\hat{\sigma}_1=[(d_2^2+d_1^2)/(d_2^2-d_1^2)]p_1 \quad (3)$$

Maximum shear stress

$$\tau=\tfrac{1}{2}(\hat{\sigma}_1+p_1)$$
$$=[d_2^2/(d_2^2-d_1^2)]p_1 \quad (4)$$

The longitudinal stress σ_2 has been shown to be constant (Para. 15.8), nd for a cylinder with closed ends is obtained from the equilibrium quation for any transverse section

$$\sigma_2 . (\pi/4)(d_2^2 - d_1^2) = p_1 . (\pi/4) d_1^2$$

r

$$\sigma_2 = [d_1^2/(d_2^2 - d_1^2)] p_1 \qquad (5)$$

Error in "thin cylinder" formula (Para. 15.1)

If the thickness is t, then write $d_2 = d_1 + 2t$ in (3) above, i.e.

$$\sigma_1 = \frac{(d_1 + 2t)^2 + d_1^2}{(d_1 + 2t)^2 - d_1^2} . p_1$$

$$= \frac{2(d_1/t)^2 + 4(d_1/t) + 4}{4(d_1/t) + 4} . p_1$$

If $d_1/t = 10$

$$\sigma_1 = (244/44) p_1$$
$$= 5{\cdot}55 p_1$$

which is 11% higher than the mean value given by $p_1 d_1/2t$

If $d_1/t = 20$

$$\sigma_1 = (884/84) p_1$$
$$= 10{\cdot}5 p_1$$

or 5% higher than $p_1 d_1/2t$

It should be noted that if the *mean* diameter is used in the thin cylinder formula the error is practically eliminated.

EXAMPLE 7. *The cylinder of a hydraulic ram is 6 cm internal diameter. Find the thickness required to withstand an internal pressure of 40 N/mm², if the maximum tensile stress is limited to 60 N/mm² and the maximum shear stress to 50 N/mm².*

If D cm is the external diameter, then the maximum tensile stress is the hoop stress at the inside, i.e.

$$60 = [(D^2 + 36)/(D^2 - 36)]40 \quad \text{from (3)}$$

or

$$3D^2 - 108 = 2D^2 + 72$$
$$D = \sqrt{180}$$
$$= 13{\cdot}43 \text{ cm}$$

The maximum shear stress is half the "stress difference" at the inside, i.e.

$$50 = [D^2/(D^2 - 36)]40 \quad \text{from (4)}$$

or

$$5D^2 - 180 = 4D^2$$
$$D = \sqrt{180}$$
$$= 13{\cdot}43 \text{ cm} \quad \text{as before}$$
$$\text{Thickness} = \tfrac{1}{2}(13{\cdot}43 - 6)$$
$$= 3{\cdot}72 \text{ cm}$$

EXAMPLE 8. ***Find the ratio of thickness to internal diameter for a tube***

subjected to internal pressure when the ratio of pressure to maximum circum ferential stress is 0·5.

Find the alteration of thickness of metal in such a tube 8 cm. interna diameter when the pressure is 50 N/mm². E=200,000 N/mm²; ν=0·304 (U.L.)

$$\hat{\sigma}_1 = [(d_2^2 + d_1^2)/(d_2^2 - d_1^2)]p_1 \quad \text{from (3)}$$

or $$(d_2^2 - d_1^2) = 0{\cdot}5(d_2^2 + d_1^2)$$

giving $$d_2/d_1 = \sqrt{3}$$

$$\text{Ratio} \quad \frac{\text{Thickness}}{\text{Internal diameter}} = \frac{d_2 - d_1}{2d_1} = \frac{\sqrt{3}-1}{2}$$
$$= 0{\cdot}366$$

$$d_1 = 80 \text{ mm} \quad d_2 = 80\sqrt{3} = 138{\cdot}6 \text{ mm}$$

At inside

$p = 50$ N/mm², $\sigma_1 = 100$ N/mm²

$\sigma_2 = pd_1^2/(d_2^2 - d_1^2) = 25$ N/mm²

$$\text{Hoop strain} = (100 + 0{\cdot}304 \times 50 - 0{\cdot}304 \times 25)/E$$
$$= 112{\cdot}6/E$$

$$\text{Increase in internal diameter} = (112{\cdot}6/E)80 \text{ mm}$$

At outside

$p = 0$, $\sigma_1 = 50$ N/mm² (since $\sigma_1 - p = \text{constant} = 50$)

$\sigma_2 = 25$ N/mm² as before.

$$\text{Hoop strain} = (50 - 0{\cdot}304 \times 25)/E$$
$$= 47{\cdot}4/E$$

$$\text{Increase in external diameter} = (47{\cdot}4/E)138{\cdot}6 \text{ mm}$$

$$\text{Decrease in thickness} = (112{\cdot}6 \times 80 - 47{\cdot}4 \times 138{\cdot}6)/(2 \times 200{,}000)$$
$$= 0{\cdot}006 \text{ mm}$$

EXAMPLE 9. *The maximum stress permitted in a thick cylinder, radii 8 cm and 12 cm, is 20 N/mm². The external pressure is 6 N/mm²; what interna pressure can be applied?*

Plot curves showing the variation of hoop and radial stresses through the material.

$$\text{External pressure } 600 = -a + b/576 \quad \text{N/cm}^2$$

$$\text{Maximum stress} = \text{hoop stress at inside}$$

i.e. $$2000 = a + b/256$$

Adding and solving

$$b = (2600 \times 256 \times 576)/832$$

and $$a = 2000 - b/256 = 200$$

$$\text{Internal pressure} = -a + b/256$$
$$= -200 + (2600 \times 576)/832$$
$$= 1600 \text{ N/cm}^2$$

The constant difference between the hoop and radial stresses = 400 N/cm².

At 10 cm radius

$$\sigma_1 = a + b/400$$
$$= 200 + (2600 \times 256 \times 576)/(832 \times 400)$$
$$= 1350 \text{ N/cm}^2$$

nd $$p = \sigma_1 - 400 = 950 \text{ N/cm}^2$$

See Fig. 15.13 for a graphical representation of the stress variation.

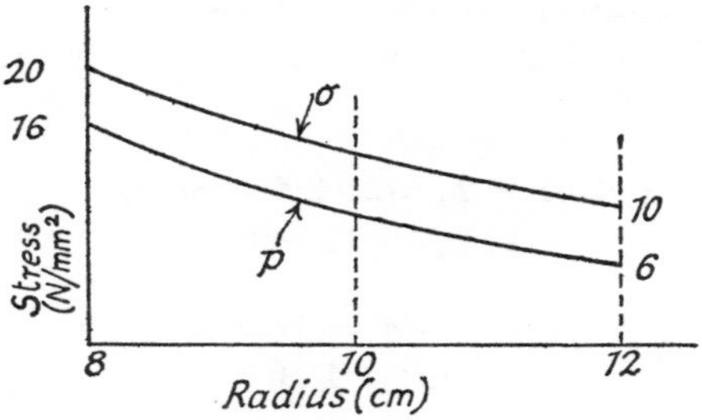

Fig. 15.13

Example 10. *Two thick steel cylinders A and B, closed at the ends, have he same dimensions, the outside diameter being 1·6 times the inside. A is subected to internal pressure only and B to external pressure only. Find the atio of these pressures (1) when the greatest circumferential stress has the ame numerical value, and (2) when the greatest circumferential strain has he same numerical value. Poisson's ratio = 0·304. (U.L.)*

Cylinder A

Internal pressure p_1.

Greatest circumferential stress

$$\hat{\sigma}_1 = [(d_2^2 + d_1^2)/(d_2^2 - d_1^2)]p_1 \quad \text{from (3)}$$
$$= (3{\cdot}56/1{\cdot}56)p_1 \text{ tensile.}$$

Longitudinal stress

$$\sigma_2 = p_1 d_1^2/(d_2^2 - d_1^2) \quad \text{from (5)}$$
$$= p_1/1{\cdot}56 \text{ tensile.}$$

Greatest circumferential strain

$$= (1/E)(\hat{\sigma}_1 + \nu p_1 - \nu\sigma_2)$$
$$= (p_1/E)(3{\cdot}56/1{\cdot}56 + 0{\cdot}304 - 0{\cdot}304/1{\cdot}56) \quad \text{from above}$$
$$= 2{\cdot}394 p_1/E$$

Cylinder B

External pressure $p_2 = -a + b/d_2^2$

Internal pressure $0 = -a + b/d_1^2$

$$\therefore \quad b = -[d_1^2 d_2^2/(d_2 - d_1^2)]p_2$$

and $$a = -[d_2^2/(d_2^2 - d_1^2)]p_2$$
$$\sigma_1 = a + b/d^2$$

and reaches its maximum *numerical* value at $d = d_1$, i.e.

$$\hat{\sigma}_1 = -[d_2^2/(d_2^2 - d_1^2)]p_2 - [d_2^2/(d_2^2 - d_1^2)]p_2$$
$$= -(2 \times 2{\cdot}56/1{\cdot}56)p_2$$

Longitudinal stress σ_2 is given by the equilibrium equation

$$\sigma_2(\pi/4)(d_2^2 - d_1^2) = p_2(\pi/4)d_2^2$$

i.e. $\sigma_2 = (2{\cdot}56/1{\cdot}56)p_2$ compressive

Greatest (numerical) circumferential strain

$$= (p_2/E)(-5{\cdot}12/1{\cdot}56 + 0{\cdot}304 \times 2{\cdot}56/1{\cdot}56), \quad \text{at the inside}$$
$$= -(2{\cdot}782/E)p_2$$

Case (1)

$$(3{\cdot}56/1{\cdot}56)p_1 = (2 \times 2{\cdot}56/1{\cdot}56)p_2$$

i.e. $p_1/p_2 = 5{\cdot}12/3{\cdot}56 = 1{\cdot}44$

Case (2)

$$2{\cdot}394p_1/E = 2{\cdot}782p_2/E$$

i.e. $p_1/p_2 = 1{\cdot}16$

15.10. Plastic Yielding of Thick Tubes. If the internal pressure is sufficiently increased, yielding will occur first at the internal surface and will spread outwards until the whole cross-section becomes plastic. Strains will not generally be excessive until this final state is reached since in the intermediate state there will be an outer ring of elastic material. If the pressure for complete plasticity can be estimated and used as the "collapse" pressure, the design pressure can be derived from it by dividing by a suitable "load factor", as in the plastic theory of bending (Chap. XII).

Another application is the "autofrettage" of gun tubes and pressure vessels, in which the tube is deliberately overstrained by internal pressure before being put into service, with the intention of producing residual compressive stresses in the inner layers (this has the same effect as shrinking one tube over another, Para. 15.11 below, the maximum hoop stress under the working pressure being thereby reduced).

Assumptions in theory of plastic yielding

(1) Yield takes place when the maximum stress difference (or shear stress) reaches the value corresponding to yield in simple tension (Tresca's criterion, Para. 3.21(2)). This is in good agreement with experiment for ductile materials.

(2) The material exhibits a constant yield stress σ_Y in tension, with no strain hardening (ideal elastic-plastic material, Fig. 12.1).

(3) The longitudinal stress in the tube is either zero, or lies algebraically between the hoop and radial stresses. From this it follows that the maximum stress difference is determined by the hoop and radial stresses only.

Hoop and Radial Stresses in the Plastic Zone

The equilibrium equation (6) of Para. 15.8 must apply,

$$\sigma_1 + p + r dp/dr = 0 \quad (1)$$

nd the yield criterion, by the assumptions stated above, is

$$\sigma_1 + p = \sigma_Y \quad (2)$$

provided σ_1 and p are stresses of opposite type). Subtracting these quations and integrating,

$$p = -\sigma_Y \log_e r + \text{constant}$$

f the radial stress is p_2 at the outer radius r_2 of the plastic zone, then ne constant $= p_2 + \sigma_Y \log_e r_2$, and hence the radial stress

$$p = \sigma_Y \log_e (r_2/r) + p_2 \quad (3)$$

rom (2), the hoop stress

$$\sigma_1 = \sigma_Y[1 - \log_e (r_2/r)] - p_2 \quad (4)$$

Partially Plastic Wall

Consider a thick tube of internal radius r_1 and external radius r_3, to which an internal pressure only, of magnitude p_1, is applied of such ntensity that the material at a radius below r_2 is in the plastic state i.e. r_2 is the radius at the boundary between the inner plastic region nd the outer elastic region).

If p_2 is the radial stress at r_2, it is given by elastic theory for internal pressure only (Para. 15.9, eqn. (4)), such that the maximum stress difference is σ_Y (i.e. just reaching the yield condition at r_2).

$$\sigma_Y = \sigma_1 + p \quad \text{at } r_2$$

$$= 2[r_3^2/(r_3^2 - r_2^2)]p_2$$

or

$$p_2 = [(r_3^2 - r_2^2)/2r_3^2]\sigma_Y \quad (5)$$

Substituting this value in (3) and (4) gives the variation of stresses in he plastic zone, i.e.

$$p = \sigma_Y[\log (r_2/r) + (r_3^2 - r_2^2)/2r_3^2] \quad (6)$$

and

$$\sigma_1 = \sigma_Y[(r_3^2 + r_2^2)/2r_3^2 - \log (r_2/r)] \quad (7)$$

The relation between internal pressure p_1 and radius of yield r_2 is given from (6) when $r = r_1$, i.e.

$$p_1 = \sigma_Y \, [\log (r_2/r_1) + (r_3^2 - r_2^2)/2r_3^2] \quad (8)$$

The pressure at initial yielding is found by putting $r_2 = r_1$, i.e.

$$p_1 = [(r_3^2 - r_1^2)/2r_3^2]\sigma_Y \quad (9)$$

and the pressure required for complete yielding through the wall given by $r_2 = r_3$, i.e.

$$p_1 = \sigma_Y \log_e (r_3/r_1) \quad (10)$$

Since $\sigma_1 + p = \sigma_Y$ in the plastic zone, the hoop stress at the inside in th fully plastic state is

$$\sigma_1 = \sigma_Y[1 - \log_e (r_3/r_1)] \quad (11)$$

If the longitudinal stress is zero, equations (10) and (11) can on apply for $r_3/r_1 < 2{\cdot}718$, since at this value $p_1 = \sigma_Y$ and $\sigma_1 = 0$, and th maximum stress difference becomes p_1. If the tube is thicker than thi and the internal pressure is raised to the value σ_y, there will be an inn zone in which the radial stress is constant and equal to σ_Y and the ho stress is $-\sigma_Y$ (to satisfy the equilibrium equation (1)), an intermedia zone in which equations (10) and (11) apply, and an outer elastic zon This argument can be modified to take account of any uniform long tudinal stress.

EXAMPLE 11. *A gun barrel of 100 mm bore and 75 mm thickness is subject to an internal pressure sufficient to cause yielding in two-thirds of the met Calculate this pressure and show the variation of stresses across the wall.*

What are the pressures required for initial yield and complete yield? Assu that yield occurs due to maximum shear stress, and neglect strain hardenin In simple tension $\sigma_Y = 400$ N/mm².

Equation (8) gives the pressure required to cause a given depth yielding, where $r_1 = 50$ mm, and $r_3 = 125$ mm. Then

$$p_1 = 400(\log_e 2 + 9/50)$$
$$= 350 \text{ N/mm}^2$$

From (5)

$$p_2 = (9/50)400$$
$$= 72 \text{ N/mm}^2$$
$$p_3 = 0$$

At r_1, hoop stress is given by (7)

$$\sigma_1 = 400(41/50 - \log_e 2)$$
$$= 50{\cdot}5 \text{ N/mm}^2$$

At r_2, from the plastic relation $\sigma_1 + p = \sigma_Y$,

$$\sigma_1 = \sigma_Y - p_2$$
$$= 328 \text{ N/mm}^2$$

In the elastic zone, using the conditions $p_2 = 72$ and $p_3 = 0$ for a tub of inner and outer radii 100 mm and 125 mm, it follows from Para. 15 that hoop stress

$$\sigma_1 = \frac{r_3^2 + r^2}{r_3^2 - r_2^2} \cdot \frac{r_2^2}{r^2} \cdot p_2$$

At $r = 100$ mm

$$\sigma_1 = (41/9)72 = 328 \text{ N/mm}^2$$

At $r = 125$ mm

$$\sigma_1 = (32/9)72 = 256 \text{ N/mm}^2$$

The variation of these stresses in the two zones is shown in Fig. 15.14.

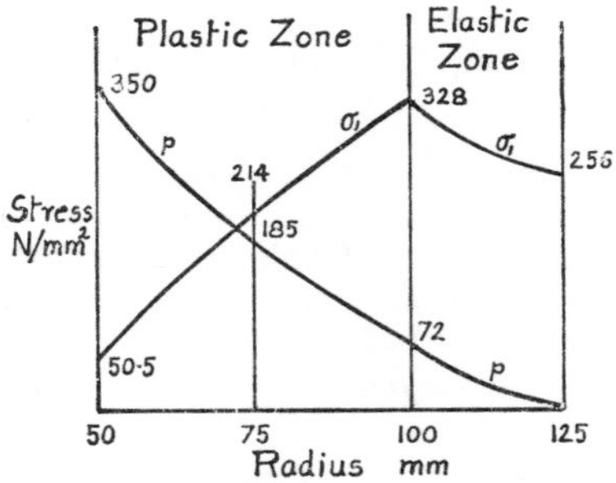

Fig. 15.14

The pressure for initial yield is given by (9)

$$p_1 = (21/50)400 = 168 \text{ N/mm}^2$$

and the pressure for complete yield by (10)

$$p_1 = 400 \log_e 2{\cdot}5 = 367 \text{ N/mm}^2$$

15.11. Compound Tubes. It can be seen from Fig. 15.12 that the hoop stress falls off appreciably as the radius increases, and that the material near the outside of the tube is not being stressed to its limit.

In order to even out the stresses the tube may be made in two parts, one part being shrunk on to the other (after heating). By this means the inner tube is put into compression and the outer tube is in tension. When an internal pressure is then applied it causes a tensile hoop stress to be superimposed on the "*shrinkage*" *stresses*, and the resultant stress is the algebraic sum of the two sets.

In general the procedure is first to calculate the stresses due to shrinkage in each component, from a knowledge of the radial pressure at the common surface. The stresses due to application of internal pressure are calculated in the normal way, and *the two tubes may be treated as one* (provided they are of the same material).

The radial pressure at the common surface due to shrinkage is related to the diametral "interference" before the tubes are fitted together. If σ_1 is the *compressive* hoop stress at the outside of the inner tube and σ_1'

the *tensile* hoop stress at the inside of the outer tube, then due t shrinkage: inner tube diameter is decreased by

$$(1/E)(\sigma_1 - \nu p) \times d$$

and the outer tube diameter is increased by

$$(1/E)(\sigma_1' + \nu p) \times d$$

where d is the common diameter.

The difference of diameters before shrinking

$$= \text{sum of these two changes}$$
$$= (1/E)(\sigma_1 + \sigma_1') \times d$$

EXAMPLE 12. *A tube 4 cm inside by 6 cm outside diameter is to be reinforce by shrinking on a second tube of 8 cm outside diameter. The compound tube to withstand an internal pressure of 50 N/mm² and the shrinkage allowance to be such that the final maximum stress in each tube is to be the same. Ca culate this stress and show on a diagram the variation of hoop stress in the tu tubes. What is the initial difference of diameters before shrinking on E = 207,000 N/mm².*

Let p_0 be the common radial pressure due to shrinkage.

For the inner tube:

At the outside $\quad p_0 = -a + b/36$

At the inside $\quad 0 = -a + b/16$

from the general equations (8), Para. 15.8.

Subtract and solve

$$b = -[(36 \times 16)/(36 - 16)]p_0 = -(144/5)p_0$$

and

$$a = b/16 = -(9/5)p_0$$

$$\text{Maximum hoop stress} = a + b/16 = -(18/5)p_0 \qquad \text{(i)}$$

$$\text{Hoop stress at 6 cm diameter} = a + b/36 = -(13/5)p_0 \qquad \text{(ii)}$$

For the outer tube:

At the inside $\quad p_0 = -a' + b'/36$

At the outside $\quad 0 = -a' + b'/64$

Subtract and solve

$$b' = [(64 \times 36)/(64 - 36)]p_0 = (576/7)p_0$$

and

$$a' = b'/64 = (9/7)p_0$$

$$\text{Maximum hoop stress} = a' + b'/36$$
$$= (25/7)p_0 \qquad \text{(iii)}$$

$$\text{Hoop stress at 8 cm diameter} = a' + b'/64$$
$$= (18/7)p_0 \qquad \text{(iv)}$$

The lines marked "shrinkage stresses" on Fig. 15.15 are sketched fro results (i) to (iv), the numerical value of p_0 being obtained later.

Stresses due to internal pressure:

At the inside $\quad 50 = -a'' + b''/16$

At the outside $\quad 0 = -a'' + b''/64$

Subtract and solve

$$b'' = [(64 \times 16)/(64 - 16)] \times 50 = (64/3) \times 50$$

d $$a'' = 50/3$$

Hoop stresses:

4 cm diameter $\sigma_1 = 50/3 + (64 \times 50)/(3 \times 16)$
$= 83{\cdot}3 \text{ N/mm}^2$ (v)

6 cm diameter $\sigma_1 = 50/3 + (64 \times 50)/(3 \times 36)$
$= 46{\cdot}4 \text{ N/mm}^2$ (vi)

8 cm diameter $\sigma_1 = 50/3 + (64 \times 50)/(3 \times 64)$
$= 33{\cdot}3 \text{ N/mm}^2$ (vii)

From results (v), (vi), and (vii) the line of "pressure" stresses is drawn ı Fig. 15.15. The final resultant hoop stress in each tube is obtained by king the algebraic sum of shrinkage and pressure stresses. It was pointed ut in Para. 15.8 that the maximum stress occurs at the inside surface. quating these values for the two tubes gives

$$\text{(i)} + \text{(v)} = \text{(iii)} + \text{(vi)}$$

e. $$-(18/5)p_0 + 83{\cdot}3 = (25/7)p_0 + 46{\cdot}4$$

r $$p_0 = 36{\cdot}9 \times 35/251$$
$$= 5{\cdot}15 \text{ N/mm}^2$$

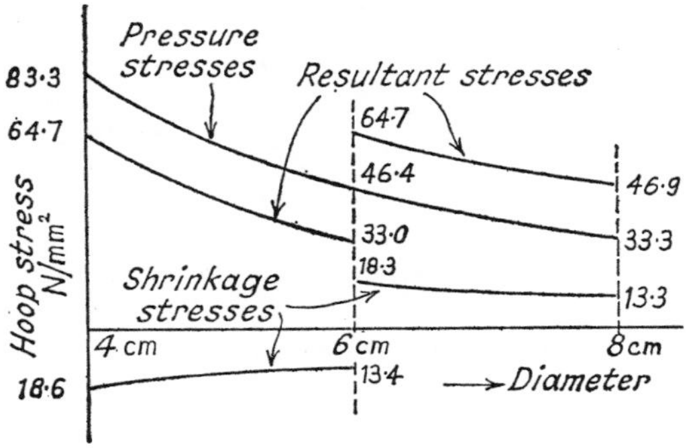

Fig. 15.15

Numerical value of maximum hoop stress

$$= \text{(iii)} + \text{(vi)} = 64{\cdot}7 \text{ N/mm}^2$$

he other values being shown in Fig. 15.15.

Initial difference of diameters at the common surface

= difference of hoop strains × diameter
= $(1/E)$(difference of hoop shrinkage stresses) × diameter
$= [(13{\cdot}4 + 18{\cdot}3)/(207{,}000)] \times 60$
$= 0{\cdot}0092$ mm

15.12. Hub Shrunk on Solid Shaft. The shaft will be subjected to n external pressure p_1, and if σ_1 and p are the hoop and radial stresses at a radius r, the equilibrium equation (6) of Para. 15.8 will be obtaine as for a "thick cylinder," i.e.

$$\sigma_1 + p + r \, . \, dp/dr = 0$$

The longitudinal stress is zero, and assuming the longitudinal strai to be constant, it follows from equation (1) of Para. 15.8 that

$$\sigma_1 - p = \text{constant}$$

These two equations are solved as before, giving

$$\sigma_1 = a + b/d^2$$

and

$$p = -a + b/d^2$$

But since the stresses cannot be infinite at the centre of the shaft (i. $d = 0$), then b must be zero, i.e.

$$\sigma_1 = a = -p$$

which means that the **hoop stress is compressive and equal t the radial stress** (and consequently the external pressure), bot stresses being constant throughout.

The hub or sleeve is subjected to an internal pressure p_1 and treated as a thick tube under internal pressure (Para. 15.9).

EXAMPLE 13. *A steel shaft 50 mm diameter is to be pressed into a cast-irc hub 150 mm external diameter and 100 mm long, so that no relative slip occu under a torque of 5 kNm. Find the necessary force fit allowance and the max mum circumferential stress in the hub. $E_s = 2 \times E_{ci}$. Poisson's ratio = 0·25 f both, and coefficient of friction between surfaces = 0·3.*

If, after assembly, the shaft is subjected to an axial compressive stress 80 N/mm², what is the resulting increase in the maximum circumferential h stress? $E_s = 207{,}000$ N/mm².

Let p_1 be the radial pressure at the common surface. Then

$$\text{Torque} = (\mu p_1 \times \text{surface area}) \times \text{radius}$$

i.e.

$$5 \times 10^6 = 0{\cdot}3 p_1 \times \pi \times 50 \times 100 \times 25 \text{ Nmm}$$

or

$$p_1 = 42{\cdot}5 \text{ N/mm}^2$$

For the shaft:

$$\text{Hoop stress} = p_1 = 42{\cdot}5 \text{ N/mm}^2 \text{ compressive,}$$

and

$$\text{Decrease of outside diameter} = \text{Hoop strain} \times \text{diameter}$$

$$= \frac{(42{\cdot}5 - 0{\cdot}25 \times 42{\cdot}5) \times 50}{207{,}000}$$

$$= 0{\cdot}0077 \text{ mm}$$

For the hub:

Hoop stress at inside (maximum) $= [(150^2 + 50^2)/(150^2 - 50^2)] \times 42{\cdot}5$ (Eq. (3), Para. 15.

$$= 53{\cdot}2 \text{ N/mm}^2$$

$$\text{Increase of inside diameter} = \frac{(53{\cdot}2 + 0{\cdot}25 \times 42{\cdot}5) \times 50}{103{,}500}$$
$$= 0{\cdot}0308 \text{ mm}$$
$$\therefore \quad \text{Force fit allowance} = 0{\cdot}0077 + 0{\cdot}0308$$
$$= 0{\cdot}0385 \text{ mm}$$

Let σ_1 be the increase in maximum hoop stress in the *hub* when an axial tress of 80 N/mm^2 is applied to shaft. Then the corresponding increase n radial pressure at the inside surface is determined by the dimensions of he hub, and

$$\sigma_1 = [(150^2 + 50^2)/(150^2 - 50^2)] \times \text{increase in pressure}$$

iving an increase in pressure $= 0{\cdot}8\ \sigma_1$.

The radial and hoop stresses in the *shaft* must also increase by $0{\cdot}8\sigma_1$ numerically, since they are both equal and compressive.

Increase in hoop strain at the outside of the shaft

$$= (1/E_s)(-0{\cdot}8\sigma_1 + 0{\cdot}25 \times 0{\cdot}8\sigma_1 + 0{\cdot}25 \times 80)$$
$$= \text{increase in hoop strain at inside of hub}$$
$$= (1/E_{ci})(\sigma_1 + 0{\cdot}25 \times 0{\cdot}8\sigma_1)$$

iving $\qquad -0{\cdot}6\sigma_1 + 20 = 2{\cdot}4\sigma_1 \quad (E_s = 2E_{ci})$

rom which $\qquad \sigma_1 = 6{\cdot}67$ N/mm^2

15.13. Thick Spherical Shells. At any radius r let the circumferential or hoop stress be σ tensile, and the radial stress be p compressive.

If u is the radial shift then it was shown in Para. 15.8 that the hoop strain is given by u/r, and the radial strain by du/dr. The stress-strain equations are

$$E.u/r = \sigma - \nu\sigma + \nu p \qquad (1)$$
$$E.du/dr = -p - 2\nu\sigma \qquad (2)$$

Multiplying (1) by r and differentiating

$$E.du/dr = \sigma - \nu\sigma + \nu p + r[d\sigma/dr - \nu(d\sigma/dr) + \nu(dp/dr)]$$
$$= -p - 2\nu\sigma \quad \text{from (2)}$$

or $\qquad (1+\nu)(\sigma + p) + r(1-\nu)(d\sigma/dr) + \nu r(dp/dr) = 0 \qquad (3)$

Considering the equilibrium of a hemisphere (Fig. 15.16)

$$\sigma.2\pi r.\delta r = p\pi r^2 - (p + \delta p)\pi(r + \delta r)^2$$

or $\sigma + p = -(r/2)(dp/dr)$ in the limit (4)

Substituting for $\sigma + p$ from (4) in (3)

$$-(r/2)(dp/dr)(1+\nu) + r(1-\nu)(d\sigma/dr) + \nu r(dp/dr) = 0$$

which reduces to

$$d\sigma/dr - \tfrac{1}{2}.dp/dr = 0$$

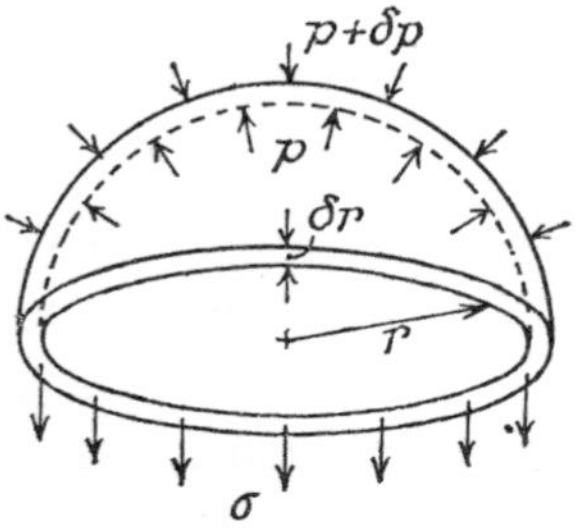

Fig. 15.16

Integrating

$$\sigma - p/2 = \text{constant}$$
$$= A, \text{ say} \qquad (5)$$

Substitute for σ from (5) in (4)

$$3p/2 + A = -(r/2)(dp/dr)$$

Rearranging

$$\frac{1}{r^2}\cdot\frac{d(pr^3)}{dr} = -2A$$

or

$$\frac{d(pr^3)}{dr} = -2Ar^2$$

Integrating

$$pr^3 = -2Ar^3/3 + B$$
$$p = -2A/3 + B/r^3$$
$$= -a + b/d^3 \qquad (6)$$

where $a = 2A/3$ and $b = 8B$.

From (5) $$\sigma = a + b/2d^3 \qquad (7)$$

If the inside and outside diameters are d_1 and d_2, and the pressure on these surfaces are p_1 and p_2 respectively

$$p_1 = -a + b/d_1^3$$

and

$$p_2 = -a + b/d_2^3$$

Subtracting and solving

$$b = [d_1^3 d_2^3/(d_2^3 - d_1^3)](p_1 - p_2)$$

and

$$a = b/d_1^3 - p_1$$
$$= (p_1 d_1^3 - p_2 d_2^3)/(d_2^3 - d_1^3)$$

From (6) and (7)

$$p = [p_2 d_2^3 - p_1 d_1^3 + (p_1 - p_2)d_1^3 d_2^3/d^3]/(d_2^3 - d_1^3)$$

and

$$\sigma = [p_1 d_1^3 - p_2 d_2^3 + (p_1 - p_2)d_1^3 d_2^3/2d^3]/(d_2^3 - d_1^3)$$

For *internal pressure only* ($p_2 = 0$)

$$p = p_1 d_1^3(d_2^3/d^3 - 1)/(d_2^3 - d_1^3)$$

and

$$\sigma = p_1 d_1^3(d_2^3/2d^3 + 1)/(d_2^3 - d_1^3)$$

The maximum stress is the value of σ at the inside: i.e.

$$\hat{\sigma} = p_1(d_2^3 + 2d_1^3)/2(d_2^3 - d_1^3)$$

and the maximum shear stress

$$= \tfrac{1}{2}(\hat{\sigma} + p_1)$$
$$= p_1 . 3d_2^3/4(d_2^3 - d_1^3)$$

SUMMARY

Thin Cylinders:

Hoop stress $\sigma_1 = pd/2t$.
Longitudinal stress $\sigma_2 = pd/4t$.
Increase in capacity = (2 × hoop strain + longitudinal strain) × volume.

Rotational stress $= \rho r^2 \omega^2$.

Thin Sphere:

Hoop stress $\sigma = pd/4t$.
Increase in capacity = (3 × hoop strain) × volume.

Thick Cylinders:

Hoop stress $\sigma_1 = a + b/d^2$.
Radial stress $p = -a + b/d^2$.
Internal pressure only: $\hat{\sigma} = [(d_2^2 + d_1^2)/(d_2^2 - d_1^2)]p_1$.
Longitudinal stress $\sigma_2 = [d_1^2/(d_2^2 - d_1^2)]p_1$ (closed ends).
Plastic yielding under constant stress difference.

Compound Tubes:

Resultant stress = algebraic sum of "shrinkage" + "pressure" stresses.
Shrinkage allowance = $(1/E)$(numerical sum of hoop stresses) × common diameter.

Hub on Shaft:

In shaft, hoop stress = radial stress = external pressure.

Thick Spheres:

Hoop stress $\sigma = a + b/2d^3$.
Radial stress $p = -a + b/d^3$.

PROBLEMS

1. A thin cylindrical shell, 1·5 m internal diameter, 2·4 m long, internal volume 4·23 m³, plates 25 mm thick, is under internal pressure of 1 N/mm². Assuming the end plates are rigid, find the changes in length, diameter, and volume. $E = 206{,}000$ N/mm²; $\nu = 0{\cdot}267$. (0·081 mm; 0·19 mm; 0·00124 m³.)

2. A thin spherical copper shell of diameter 0·3 m and thickness 1·6 mm is just full of water at atmospheric pressure. Find how much the internal pressure will be increased by pumping in 25,000 mm³ of water. $E = 100{,}000$ N/mm²: $\nu = 0{\cdot}286$; $K = 2200$ N/mm². (1·22 N/mm².)

3. A copper tube 25 mm bore and 2·5 mm thick is plugged at its ends and just filled with water at atmospheric pressure. If an axial compressive load of 5 kN is applied to the plugs, find by how much the water pressure will rise. Assume the

plugs are rigid and fixed to the tube, and neglect end effects. $E=103{,}000$ N/mm² $\nu=0\cdot35$; $K=2200$ N/mm². (131 kN/m²

4. A long straight tube, 144 mm bore and 3 mm wall thickness, is made steel which yields at 325 N/mm² in tension. If the ends of the tube are plugge and it is subjected to an internal fluid pressure find what pressure is required yielding is assumed to take place according to the following theories of elasti failure, (1) maximum principal stress, (2) maximum principal strain, (3) maxi mum shear stress, (4) maximum strain energy, (5) maximum shear strain energy $\nu=0\cdot3$. (I.Mech.E

(13·5, 16·2, 27, 13·9, 15·6 N/mm²

5. A cylindrical compressed-air drum is 1·9 m diameter with plates 12·7 mm thick. The efficiencies of longitudinal and circumferential joints are respectivel 85% and 45%. If the tensile stress in the plating is limited to 100 N/mm² fin the maximum safe air pressure. (U.L.) (1·14 N/mm²

6. A thin cylinder made of light alloy 200 mm internal diameter, 5 mm thick is wound with a single layer of steel tape, 1·25 mm, under a stress of 85 N/mm If the hoop stress in the cylinder is not to exceed 42·5 N/mm², find the maxi mum internal pressure and the stress in the tape. Poisson's ratio $=0\cdot25$; ratio elastic moduli 2·5. (U.L.) (4·8 N/mm²; 215 N/mm²

7. A copper tube 47·5 mm inside diameter, 50 mm outside diameter, is closel wound with steel wire 0·7 mm diameter. Find the winding tension on the tub if an internal pressure of 1·42 N/mm² is required before the copper is subjecte to tension, the tube being free to expand or contract axially. $E_s=210{,}000$ N mm²; $E_c=126{,}000$ N/mm². (U.L.) (13·7 N

8. A brass cylinder 100 mm outside diameter and 87·5 mm bore has a singl layer of steel wire 1·2 mm diameter wound on it under a constant tension 35 N/mm². If the cylinder is then subjected to an internal pressure of 14 N/mm and to a rise in temperature of 168° C, determine the final magnitude of (a) th tensile stress in the wire, (b) the radial pressure between the wire and cylinde and (c) the hoop stress in the cylinder wall. Assume the cylinder to be a thi shell with closed ends. For steel, $E=210{,}000$ N/mm², $\alpha=11\cdot8\times10^{-6}$ per °C For brass, $E=87{,}500$ N/mm², $\alpha=18\cdot6\times10^{6}$ per °C, $\nu=0\cdot3$. (U.L.)

(Add temperature strains to corresponding sides of (6), Para. 15.6. (a) 365 N mm², (b) 6·9 N/mm², (c) 47 N/mm².)

9. A bronze sleeve of 200 mm internal diameter and 6·4 mm thick is presse over a steel liner 200 mm external diameter and 16 mm thick, with a force-f allowance of 0·07 mm on diameter. Treating both as thin cylinders find (1) th radial pressure at the common surface, (2) the hoop stresses, (3) the percentage of the fit allowance met by the sleeve and liner. $E_b=117{,}000$ N/mm², $\nu_b=0\cdot33$ $E_s=207{,}000$ N/mm², $\nu_s=0\cdot304$. (U.L.)

(2·17 N/mm²; 34·7, 13·9 N/mm²; 82·5, 17·5%

10. A thick cylinder 200 mm internal diameter is subjected to an intern pressure of 3·55 N/mm². If the allowable stress is 24 N/mm², find the thicknes required. To strengthen the cylinder it is wire wound, and an internal pressur of 6·4 N/mm² can now be applied. What is the radial pressure caused by th wire? (16·2 mm; 2·5 N/mm²

11. A pressure vessel 0·3 m internal, 0·4 m external, diameter and 0·9 m long, ith closed ends, is to be subjected to a hydraulic test of 15 N/mm². Calculate ıe change of internal and external diameters. $E=210{,}000$ N/mm²; $\nu=0{\cdot}3$.

(0·074, 0·064 mm.)

12. A thick-walled steel cylinder having an inside diameter of 150 mm is to be ubjected to an internal pressure of 40 N/mm². Find to the nearest mm the outide diameter required if the hoop tension in the cylinder wall is not to exceed 25 N/mm².

Calculate the actual hoop stresses at the inner and outer surfaces of the cylinder nd plot a graph of the variation of hoop tension across the cylinder wall.

(210 mm; 124 N/mm²; 83·5 N/mm².)

13. A thick cylinder of uniform material is unstressed when at a uniform emperature. It is heated so that there is a temperature variation along any adius, the temperature being t at a radius r. If, due to heating, the radius r increases by a small increment u, show that

$$\frac{d}{dr}\left[\frac{1}{r}\cdot\frac{d(ru)}{dr}\right]=(1+\nu)\alpha\frac{dt}{dr}$$

vhere α is the coefficient of linear expansion. (U.L.)

(Assume $\sigma_2=0$ and add term $E\alpha t$ to right-hand side of equations (2) and (3) of Para. 15.8. Eliminate σ_1 and p between equations (2), (3) and (6). See also Para. 16.6.)

14. A steel cylinder 20 cm external diameter and 15 cm internal diameter has another cylinder, 25 cm external diameter, shrunk on to it. If the maximum tensile stress in the outer cylinder is 80 N/mm², find the radial compressive stress between the cylinders.

Determine the circumferential stresses at the inner and outer diameters of both cylinders, and calculate the shrinkage allowance at the common surface. $E=208{,}000$ N/mm²; $\nu=0{\cdot}304$.

(17·5 N/mm²; −80, −62·5 N/mm²; 80; 62 N/mm²; 0·14 mm.)

15. A compound cylinder is made by shrinking an outer tube, of 12 cm external diameter, on to an inner tube, of 6 cm internal diameter. Find the common diameter at the junction if the greatest circumferential stress in the inner tube is numerically $\frac{2}{3}$ of that in the outer. (9·74 cm.)

16. A compound tube 10 cm internal diameter and 20 cm external diameter is made by shrinking one tube on to another. After cooling a radial stress of 20 N/mm² is produced at the common surface, which is 15 cm diameter. If the tube is now subjected to an internal pressure of 60 N/mm², find the maximum hoop stress. (127 N/mm².)

17. A compound cylinder is to be made by shrinking one tube on to another so that the radial compressive stress at the junction is 28·5 N/mm². If the outside diameter is 26·5 cm, and the bore 12·5 cm, calculate the allowance for shrinkage at the common diameter, which is 20 cm. $E=210{,}000$ N/mm². (0·16 mm.)

18. A steel sleeve is pressed on to a solid steel shaft of 50 mm. diameter. The radial pressure between the shaft and sleeve is 17·5 N/mm² and the hoop stress at the inner surface of the sleeve is 42 N/mm². If an axial compressive load of

54 kN is now applied to the shaft, determine the change in radial pressu $\nu=0{\cdot}304$. (2·4 N/mm²

19. A steel cylinder 20 cm external dia. and 12·5 cm internal dia. is fitted wi a bronze liner which has an internal diameter of 10 cm. Assume that there is r stress in the compound cylinder due to fitting; regard the liner as a thin cylind and ignore longitudinal stress and strain.

Find the maximum direct stress and the maximum shear stress in eac material due to an internal pressure of 72 N/mm².

For steel, E = 207,000 N/mm², $\nu=0{\cdot}28$. For bronze, E = 112,000 N/mm $\nu=0{\cdot}30$ (U.L.)

(Steel, 107, 77 N/mm²; Bronze, 52, 62 N/mm²; Common Pressure = 47 N mm².)

20. A steel shaft 38 mm diameter is to be encased in a bronze sleeve, 57 mr outside diameter, which is to be forced into position and, before forcing on, th inside diameter of the sleeve is 0·05 mm smaller than the diameter of the shaf Find (a) the radial pressure between the shaft and sleeve, (b) the maximum hoo stress in the sleeve, (c) the change in outside diameter of the sleeve. E_s = 205,000 N/mm², $\nu_s=0{\cdot}29$; $E_b=123{,}000$ N/mm², $\nu_b=0{\cdot}34$. (U.L.)

(48 N/mm²; 125 N/mm²; 0·035 mm.

21. A bronze sleeve having an outside diameter 76 mm is forced onto a ste rod 57 mm diameter, the initial inside diameter of the sleeve being 0·064 mr smaller than the rod diameter. When in service the compound rod is subjecte to an external pressure of 19·5 N/mm² and at the same time to a rise in tempera ture of 100° C. Determine (a) the radial pressure between sleeve and rod, (b) th greatest circumferential stress in the sleeve. For steel, $E=205{,}000$ N/mm² $\nu=0{\cdot}3$, $\alpha=11\times10^{-6}$ per °C. For bronze, $E=104{,}000$ N/mm², $\nu=0{\cdot}33$, $\alpha=19\times$ 10^{-6} per °C. (U.L.)

(Apply compatibility equation to common diameter. (a) 28·5 N/mm² (b) 12·5 N/mm².)

22. Find the thickness of a spherical shell of 75 mm internal diameter, t withstand an internal pressure of 28 N/mm², if the permissible tensile stress i 63 N/mm² and shear stress 47 N/mm².

What is the change of thickness under pressure of such a shell. $E=210{,}000$ N mm²; $\nu=0{\cdot}3$. (8·8 mm; 0·0025 mm.

CHAPTER XVI

Rotating Discs and Cylinders

16.1. Disc of Uniform Thickness. It may be assumed, for a "thin" disc, that the stress in the axial direction is zero.

At a radius r from the axis of rotation, let the stresses be circumferentially σ_1 (hoop stress), and radially σ_2, *both tensile.* Then if u is the radial shift, the *stress-strain equations* are:

$$E.du/dr = \sigma_2 - \nu\sigma_1 \qquad (1)$$

$$E.u/r = \sigma_1 - \nu\sigma_2 \text{ (compare Para. 15.8)} \qquad (2)$$

Obtaining $E.du/dr$ from (2) and equating to (1) gives

$$(\sigma_1 - \sigma_2)(1+\nu) + r.d\sigma_1/dr - \nu r(d\sigma_2/dr) = 0 \qquad (3)$$

If the angular velocity of rotation is ω, and the density of the material is ρ, then for the element shown in Fig. 16.1, the centrifugal force

$$= (\rho r\delta\theta.\delta r)r\omega^2$$
$$= \rho r^2\omega^2\delta r.\delta\theta \text{ for unit thickness}$$

The *equilibrium equation* in the radial direction is

$$2\sigma_1.dr.\sin\tfrac{1}{2}\delta\theta + \sigma_2 r\delta\theta - (\sigma_2+\delta\sigma_2)(r+\delta r)\delta\theta = \rho r^2\omega^2\delta r.\delta\theta$$

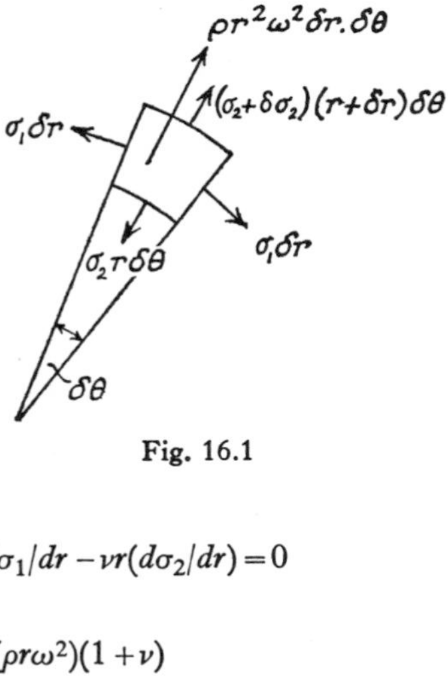

Fig. 16.1

In the limit this reduces to

$$\sigma_1 - \sigma_2 - r.d\sigma_2/dr = \rho r^2\omega^2 \qquad (4)$$

Substitute for $\sigma_1 - \sigma_2$ from (4) in (3)

$$(r.d\sigma_2/dr + \rho r^2\omega^2)(1+\nu) + r.d\sigma_1/dr - \nu r(d\sigma_2/dr) = 0$$

Rearranging

$$d\sigma_1/dr + d\sigma_2/dr = -(\rho r\omega^2)(1+\nu)$$

Integrating

$$\sigma_1 + \sigma_2 = -(\rho r^2\omega^2/2)(1+\nu) + 2A \qquad (5)$$

Subtract (4)

$$2\sigma_2 + r.d\sigma_2/dr = -(\rho r^2\omega^2/2)(3+\nu) + 2A$$

or

$$\frac{1}{r}\cdot\frac{d(\sigma_2 r^2)}{dr} = -\frac{\rho r^2\omega^2(3+\nu)}{2} + 2A$$

Integrating

$$\sigma_2 r^2 = -(\rho r^4\omega^2/8)(3+\nu) + Ar^2 - B$$

or

$$\boldsymbol{\sigma_2 = A - B/r^2 - (3+\nu)(\rho r^2\omega^2/8)} \qquad (6)$$

From (5)

$$\boldsymbol{\sigma_1 = A + B/r^2 - (1+3\nu)(\rho r^2\omega^2/8)} \qquad \mathbf{(7)}$$

16.2. Solid Disc. Since the stresses are not infinite at the centre $B=0$, from (6) and (7) of Para. 16.1.

If R is the outside radius, then

$$\sigma_2 = 0 = A - (3+\nu)(\rho R^2\omega^2/8) \text{ from (6)}$$

From which

$$\sigma_2 = (\rho\omega^2/8)(3+\nu)(R^2 - r^2)$$

and

$$\sigma_1 = (\rho\omega^2/8)[(3+\nu)R^2 - (1+3\nu)r^2]$$

At the centre, $r=0$, and $\sigma_2 = \sigma_1 = (3+\nu)(\rho\omega^2 R^2/8)$ and this is the maximum stress.

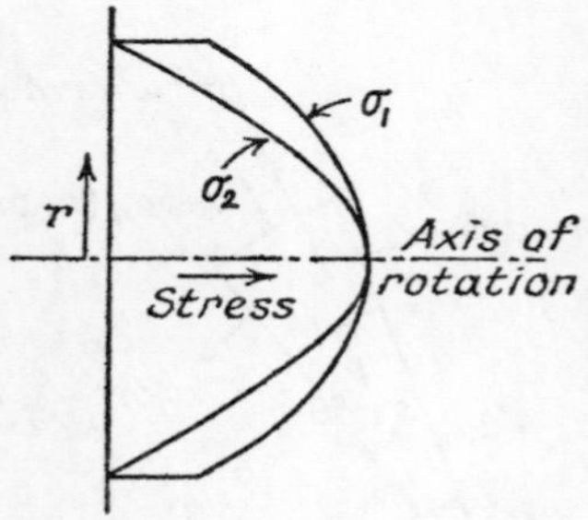

Fig. 16.2

At the outside

$$\sigma_1 = (1-\nu)(\rho\omega^2 R^2/4)$$

For a value of $\nu = 0{\cdot}3$

$$\hat{\sigma}_1 = (3{\cdot}3/8)(\rho\omega^2 R^2) = 0{\cdot}41\rho\omega^2 R^2 \quad \text{(at the centre)}$$

and at the outside

$$\sigma_1 = (0{\cdot}7/4)(\rho\omega^2 R^2) = 0{\cdot}425\hat{\sigma}_1$$

The variations of the hoop and radial stresses with radius are shown in Fig. 16.2.

16.3. Disc with Central Hole. If the inside and outside radii are R_1 and R_2 respectively, then the radial stress is zero at each of these values. From (6) of Para. 16.1

$$0 = A - B/R_1^2 - (3+\nu)(\rho R_1^2\omega^2/8)$$

and

$$0 = A - B/R_2^2 - (3+\nu)(\rho R_2^2\omega^2/8)$$

Solving

$$B = (3+\nu)(\rho\omega^2/8)(R_1^2 R_2^2)$$

and

$$A = (3+\nu)(\rho\omega^2/8)(R_1^2 + R^2)$$

Then

$$\sigma_2 = (3+\nu)(\rho\omega^2/8)(R_1^2 + R_2^2 - R_1^2R_2^2/r^2 - r^2)$$

and

$$\sigma_1 = (\rho\omega^2/8)[(3+\nu)(R_1^2 + R_2^2 + R_1^2R_2^2/r^2) - (1+3\nu)r^2] \qquad \text{from (7)}$$

σ_2 is a maximum when $r = \sqrt{R_1R_2}$, and

$$\hat{\sigma}_2 = (3+\nu)(\rho\omega^2/8)(R_2 - R_1)^2$$

$_1$ is a maximum at the inside, and

$$\hat{\sigma}_1 = (\rho\omega^2/4)[(1-\nu)R_1^2 + (3+\nu)R_2^2]$$

Note that if R_1 is very small, $\hat{\sigma}_1 \rightarrow (3+\nu)(\rho\omega^2 R_2^2/4)$, which is *twice he value for a solid disc* (Para. 16.2).

At the outside

$$\sigma_1 = (\rho\omega^2/4)[(3+\nu)R_1^2 + (1-\nu)R_2^2]$$

If $R_1 \rightarrow R_2 = R$, then

$$\hat{\sigma}_1 \rightarrow \rho\omega^2 R^2$$

as in the case of a thin rotating cylinder (Para. 15.7).

The variation of stresses is shown in Fig. 16.3.

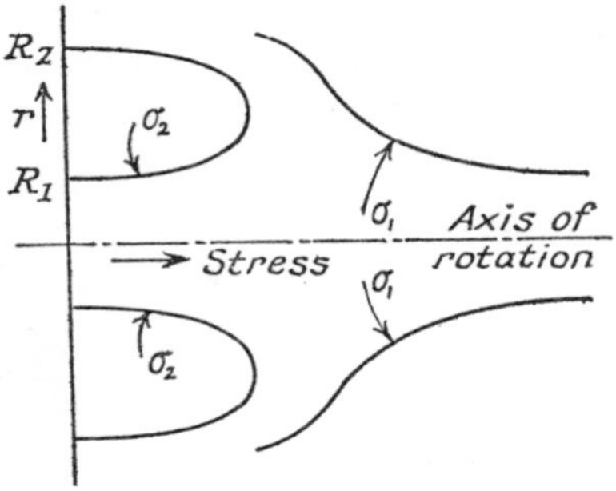

Fig. 16.3

EXAMPLE 1. *A thin uniform steel disc of 25 cm diameter, with a central hole of 5 cm diameter, runs at 10,000 r.p.m. Calculate the maximum principal stress and the maximum shearing stress in the disc.* $\nu = 0{\cdot}3$; *Density* $= 7700$ kg/m^3.

The maximum principal stress is

$$\hat{\sigma}_1 = (\rho\omega^2/4)[(1-\nu)R_1^2 + (3+\nu)R_2^2] \quad \text{from above}$$

$$= \frac{7700}{4}\left(\frac{10{,}000 \times 2\pi}{60}\right)^2 (0{\cdot}7 \times 0{\cdot}025^2 + 3{\cdot}3 \times 0{\cdot}125^2) \text{ N/m}^2$$

$$= 110 \text{ N/mm}^2$$

The maximum shearing stress at any radius

$$= \tfrac{1}{2}(\sigma_1 - \sigma_2)$$
$$= (\rho\omega^2/8)[(3+\nu)R_1^2 R_2^2/r^2 + (1-\nu)r^2]$$

It is clear from Fig. 16.3 that the greatest stress difference occurs at $r = R_1$.

Then maximum shearing stress

$$= \frac{7700}{8}\left(\frac{10{,}000 \times 2\pi}{60}\right)^2\left(3{\cdot}3 \times \frac{0{\cdot}025 \times 0{\cdot}125^2}{0{\cdot}025^2} + 0{\cdot}7 \times 0{\cdot}025^2\right) \text{ N/m}^2$$

$$= 55 \text{ N/mm}^2$$

16.4. Long Cylinder. Let the longitudinal stress be σ_l, and assume that the longitudinal strain ε is constant (i.e. cross-sections remain plane, which must be true away from the ends). Proceeding as in Para. 16.1, the strain equations are:

$$E\varepsilon = \sigma_l - \nu(\sigma_1 + \sigma_2) \quad (1)$$

$$E.du/dr = \sigma_2 - \nu(\sigma_1 + \sigma_l) \quad (2)$$

$$E.u/r = \sigma_1 - \nu(\sigma_2 + \sigma_l) \quad (3)$$

Eliminating du/dr between equations (2) and (3)

$$E.du/dr = \sigma_1 - \nu(\sigma_2 + \sigma_l) + r[d\sigma_1/dr - \nu(d\sigma_2/dr) - \nu(d\sigma_l/dr)] \quad \text{from (3}$$

$$= \sigma_2 - \nu(\sigma_1 + \sigma_l) \quad \text{from (2)}$$

giving $$(\sigma_1 - \sigma_2)(1+\nu) + r.d\sigma_1/dr - \nu r(d\sigma_2/dr) - \nu r(d\sigma_l/dr) = 0$$

Substituting $d\sigma_l/dr = \nu(d\sigma_1/dr + d\sigma_2/dr)$ from (1) gives

$$(\sigma_1 - \sigma_2)(1+\nu) + r(1-\nu^2)(d\sigma_1/dr) - \nu r(1+\nu)(d\sigma_2/dr) = 0$$

or $$\sigma_1 - \sigma_2 + r(1-\nu)(d\sigma_1/dr) - \nu r(d\sigma_2/dr) = 0 \tag{4}$$

The equilibrium equation is as before (Para. 16.1)

$$\sigma_1 - \sigma_2 - r.d\sigma_2/dr = \rho r^2\omega^2 \tag{5}$$

Subtracting (4)

$$-r(1-\nu)(d\sigma_1/dr) - r(1-\nu)(d\sigma_2/dr) = \rho r^2\omega^2$$

or $$\frac{d\sigma_1}{dr} + \frac{d\sigma_2}{dr} = -\frac{\rho r\omega^2}{(1-\nu)}$$

Integrating

$$\sigma_1 + \sigma_2 = -\frac{\rho r^2\omega^2}{2(1-\nu)} + 2A$$

Comparing this with equation (5) of Para. 16.1 it can be seen that the results for a long cylinder can be obtained from those for a thin disc by writing $\frac{1}{1-\nu}$ in place of $1+\nu$, i.e. substituting $\frac{\nu}{1-\nu}$ for ν.

Solid cylinder (obtained from Para. 16.2)

The maximum stress occurs at the centre, where σ_2 and σ_1 are equal, and

$$\hat{\sigma}_1 = \frac{3-2\nu}{1-\nu} \cdot \frac{\rho\omega^2 R^2}{8}$$

If $\nu = 0{\cdot}3$

$$\hat{\sigma}_1 = (2{\cdot}4/5{\cdot}6)(\rho\omega^2 R^2)$$
$$= 0{\cdot}43\rho\omega^2 R^2$$

(compare $0{\cdot}41\ p\omega^2R^2$ for a solid disc).

Hollow cylinder (from Para. 16.3)

$$\hat{\sigma}_2 = \left(\frac{3-2\nu}{1-\nu}\right)\frac{\rho\omega^2}{8}(R_2 - R_1)^2$$

and $$\hat{\sigma}_1 = \frac{\rho\omega^2}{4(1-\nu)}[(1-2\nu)R_1{}^2 + (3-2\nu)R_2{}^2]$$

which values again do not differ greatly from those for a thin disc.

16.5. Disc of uniform Strength. Consider the condition of equal stress at all radii, i.e. $\sigma_2 = \sigma_1 = \text{constant} = \sigma$, say.

Let t be the thickness at a radius r, and $t + \delta t$ at a radius $r + \delta r$.

The mass of the element (Fig. 16.4)

$$= \rho r \delta\theta . \delta r . t \text{ approx.}$$

and the centrifugal force

$$= \rho r^2 \omega^2 \delta\theta \cdot \delta r \cdot t$$

Hence the equilibrium equation is

$$2\sigma \delta r . t . \sin \tfrac{1}{2}\delta\theta + \sigma r \delta\theta . t = \sigma(r + \delta r)\delta\theta(t + \delta t) + \rho r^2 \omega^2 \delta\theta . \delta r . t$$

In the limit

$$\sigma t . dr = \sigma r . dt + \sigma t . dr + \rho r^2 \omega^2 t . dr$$

or $$dt/dr = -\rho r \omega^2 t/\sigma$$

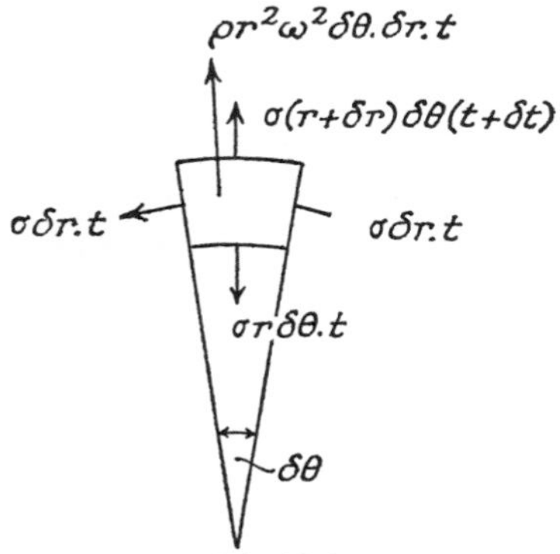

Fig.16.4

Integrating

$$\log t = -\rho r^2 \omega^2 / 2\sigma + \text{constant}$$

or $$t = A e^{-\rho r^2 \omega^2 / 2\sigma}$$

$$= t_0 e^{-\rho r^2 \omega^2 / 2\sigma}$$

where t_0 is the thickness at $r = 0$.

EXAMPLE 2. *A turbine rotor disc is 0·6 m diameter at the blade ring, and is keyed to a 50 mm diameter shaft. If the minimum thickness is 9·5 mm what should be the thickness at the shaft for a uniform stress of 200 N/mm² at 10,000 r.p.m.? Density 7700 kg/m³.*

$$t = A e^{-\rho r^2 \omega^2 / 2\sigma}$$

At $r = 0·3$ m

$$t = 9·5 = A e^{-\rho \omega^2 \times 0·09/2\sigma}$$

At $r = 0·025$ m

$$t = A e^{-\rho \omega^2 \times 0·0006/2\sigma};$$

$$= 9·5 e^{\rho \omega^2 \times 0·0894/2\sigma} \quad \text{from above,}$$

where $$\rho \omega^2 \times 0·0894/2\sigma = 7700(10{,}000\pi/30)^2 \times 0·0894/2 \times 200 \times 10^6$$

$$= 1·89$$

then $$t = 9·5 e^{1·89}$$

$$= 63 \text{ mm}$$

16.6. Temperature Stresses in Uniform Disc. Let T be the temperature rise above that of the unstressed state. Then, following the procedure of Para. 16.1, the *stress-strain* equations are

$$E du/dr = \sigma_2 - \nu\sigma_1 + E\alpha T \quad (1)$$

and

$$Eu/r = \sigma_1 - \nu\sigma_2 + E\alpha T \quad (2)$$

where α is the coefficient of linear expansion.

Eliminating u between (1) and (2) gives

$$(\sigma_1 - \sigma_2)(1+\nu) + r(d\sigma_1/dr) - \nu r(d\sigma_2/dr) + E\alpha r(dT/dr) = 0 \quad (3)$$

The *equilibrium* equation is unchanged,

$$\sigma_1 - \sigma_2 - r(d\sigma_2/dr) = -\rho r^2\omega^2 \quad (4)$$

Substituting for $\sigma_1 - \sigma_2$ from (4) in (3) and re-arranging

$$d\sigma_1/dr + d\sigma_2/dr = -(1+\nu)\rho r\omega^2 - E\alpha dT/dr$$

Integrating,

$$\sigma_1 + \sigma_2 = -(1+\nu)\rho r^2\omega^2/2 - E\alpha T + 2A \quad (5)$$

Subtracting (4), regrouping and integrating as in Para. 16.1.

$$\sigma_2 = A - B/r^2 - (3+\nu)\rho r^2\omega^2/8 - (E\alpha/r^2)\int Tr\,.\,dr \quad (6)$$

Then, from (5)

$$\sigma_1 = A + B/r^2 - (1+3\nu)\rho r^2\omega^2/8 - E\alpha T + (E\alpha/r^2)\int Tr\,.\,dr \quad (7)$$

EXAMPLE 3. *Suppose the disc of Ex. 1 has a linear variation of temperature of 45° C between the inner and outer (hotter) edges. Calculate the new value of maximum stress. $E = 205{,}000$ N/mm², $\alpha = 11 \times 10^{-6}$ per °C.*

The variation of temperature with radius may be written

$$T = 450(r - 0{\cdot}025)$$

Assuming no external radial pressure, the radial stress may be equated to zero at $r = 0{\cdot}025$ and $r = 0{\cdot}125$, i.e. from (6)

$$A - B/0{\cdot}025^2 - 7700\frac{3{\cdot}3 \times 0{\cdot}025^2}{8}\left(\frac{10{,}000 \times 2\pi}{60}\right)^2 = 0$$

or

$$A - 1600B = 2{\cdot}18 \times 10^6 \quad \text{(i)}$$

and

$$A - B/0{\cdot}0156 - 25 \times 2{\cdot}18 \times 10^6 - (205{,}000 \times 11/0{\cdot}0156)\left[450r^3/3 - 450 \times 0{\cdot}025r^2/2\right]_{0{\cdot}025}^{0{\cdot}125} = 0$$

or

$$A - 64B = 83{\cdot}4 \times 10^6 \quad \text{(ii)}$$

From (i) and (ii)

$$A = 86{\cdot}8 \times 10^6$$
$$B = 53 \times 10^3$$

The maximum stress again occurs at $r = 0{\cdot}025$ m

$$\sigma_1 = 86{\cdot}8 \times 10^6 + 85 \times 10^6 - 1{\cdot}26 \times 10^6 \text{ N/m}^2.$$
$$= 170 \text{ N/mm}^2.$$

16.7. Plastic Collapse of Rotating Discs. It has been seen that the centrifugal forces in a rotating disc set up a two-dimensional tensile stress system, and in all the cases considered the hoop stress is greater than or equal to the radial stress at a given radius, maximum values occurring at minimum radius. It follows that, as the speed is increased, ield will first occur in the circumferential direction when $\sigma_1 = \sigma_y$ the yield stress is tension). A state of collapse will be reached when this tress condition extends to the outer surface of the disc (assuming an deal elastic-plastic material, as Fig. 12.1).

Equilibrium equation (as 16.1 (4), with $\sigma_1 = \sigma_y$)

$$\sigma_y - \sigma_2 - r \, . \, d\sigma_2/dr = \rho r^2 \omega^2$$

Integrating,

$$\sigma_2 r = \sigma_y r - \rho r^3 \omega^2/3 + A$$

Solid disc. Since the stresses are not infinite at $r=0$, then $A=0$. At $r=R$, $\sigma_2 = 0 = \sigma_y - \rho R^2 \omega^2/3$ giving the collapse speed

$$\omega = \frac{1}{R}\sqrt{\frac{3\sigma_y}{\rho}}$$

Disc with central hole.

At $r=R_1$, $\sigma_2=0$, giving

$$A = (\rho R_1^2 \omega^2/3 - \sigma_y)R_1$$

At $r=R_2$, $\sigma_2 = 0 = \sigma_y - \rho R_2^2 \omega^2/3 + (\rho R_1^2 \omega^2/3 - \sigma_y)R_1/R_2$ giving the collapse speed

$$\omega = \sqrt{\left(\frac{3\sigma_y}{\rho} \cdot \frac{R_1 - R_2}{R_2^3 - R_1^3}\right)}$$

Substituting the values of Ex. 1 and assuming a yield stress of 280 N/mm² gives a collapse speed

$$= \sqrt{\frac{3 \times 280 \times 10^6 (0{\cdot}125 - 0{\cdot}025)}{7700 \quad (0{\cdot}125^3 - 0{\cdot}025^3)}}$$

$$= 2910 \text{ rad/sec. or } 27{,}700 \text{ rev/min}$$

SUMMARY

Uniform Disc. Solid: $\hat{\sigma}_1 = (3+\nu)(\rho\omega^2 R^2/8)$.

Hollow: $\hat{\sigma}_1 = (\rho\omega^2/4)[(1-\nu)R_1^2 + (3+\nu)R_2^2]$.

Long Cylinder. Solid: $\hat{\sigma}_1 = \dfrac{3-2\nu}{1-\nu} \cdot \dfrac{\rho\omega^2 R^2}{8}$.

Hollow: $\hat{\sigma}_1 = \dfrac{\rho\omega^2}{4(1-\nu)}[(1-2\nu)R_1^2 + (3-2\nu)R_2^2]$.

Disc of Uniform Strength: $t = t_0 e^{-\rho r^2 \omega^2/2\sigma}$.

Collapse Speed: $\omega = \sqrt{\left(\dfrac{3\sigma_y}{\rho} \cdot \dfrac{R_1 - R_2}{R_2^3 - R_1^3}\right)}$

REFERENCES

EDMUNDS, H. G., *Stress Concentration at Holes in Rotating Discs*. Engineer, Nov. 5, 1954.

HEYMAN J. *Plastic design of Rotating Discs*. I.Mech.E. Vol. 172, p. 14, 1958.

PROBLEMS

1. Determine the greatest values of radial and hoop stress for a rotating dis in which the outer and inner radii are 30 cm and 15 cm. $\omega = 150$ rad./sec. $\nu = 0{\cdot}304$; $\rho = 7700$ kg/m^3. (U.L.) (1·6 N/mm^2; 13·6N/mm^2

2. If a disc of inside and outside radii R_1 and R_2 is made up in two part which are shrunk together, the common radius being r, show that the hoo stresses at R_1 and R_2 will be equal at a rotational speed given by

$$\omega^2 = \frac{4pr^2}{\rho(1+\nu)(r^2 - R_1^2)(R_2^2 - r^2)},$$

where p is the pressure due to shrinkage at the common surface.

3. Calculate the maximum stress in a long cylinder 5 cm inside diameter an 25 cm outside diameter rotating at 3000 rev/min. $\nu = 0{\cdot}3$; $\rho = 7700$ kg/m^3. (10·3 N/mm^2

CHAPTER XVII

Circular Plates

17.1. Circular Plates Symmetrically Loaded

Consider a diametral section through the plate.

O is the centre of the plate and OX, OY the principal axes in the plane of Fig. 17.1. OZ is the axis perpendicular to the figure.

Let C be the centre of curvature of a section *ab* at a distance x from O. Then if the deflection y is small

$$dy/dx = \theta \qquad (1)$$

The radius of curvature in the plane XOY is given by

$$1/R_{XY} = d^2y/dx^2 \quad \text{approx.}$$
$$= d\theta/dx \quad \text{from (1)} \qquad (2)$$

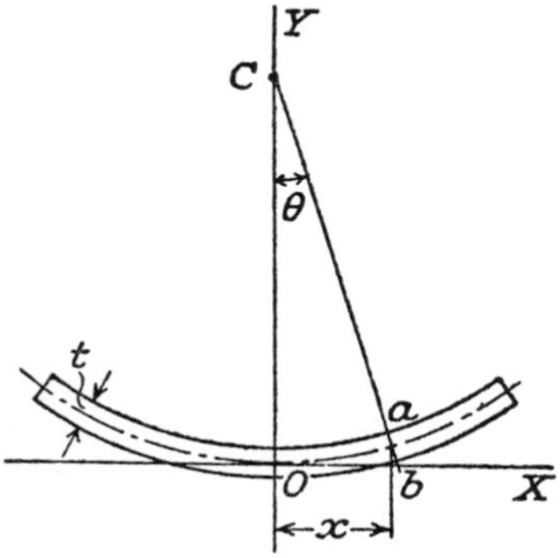

Fig. 17.1

Note that, on a circle of radius x and centre O, lines such as *ab* form part of a cone with C as apex. Hence C is the centre of curvature in the plane YOZ, and

$$1/R_{YZ} = \theta/x \quad \text{approx.} \qquad (3)$$

If u is the distance of any "fibre" from the neutral surface (assumed central), then, proceeding as for "pure bending" (Para. 6.1), in the planes XOY and YOZ, the linear strains are

$$\varepsilon_x = u/R_{XY} = (1/E)(\sigma_x - \nu\sigma_z) \qquad (4)$$

and

$$\varepsilon_z = u/R_{YZ} = (1/E)(\sigma_z - \nu\sigma_x) \qquad (5)$$

where σ_x and σ_z are the stresses in the directions OX and OZ, σ_y being zero.

Solving equations (4) and (5) for the stresses

$$\sigma_x = \frac{Eu}{1-\nu^2}\left(\frac{1}{R_{XY}} + \frac{\nu}{R_{YZ}}\right) = \frac{Eu}{1-\nu^2}\left(\frac{d\theta}{dx} + \frac{\nu\theta}{x}\right) \qquad (6)$$

and

$$\sigma_z = \frac{Eu}{1-\nu^2}\left(\frac{\nu}{R_{XY}} + \frac{1}{R_{YZ}}\right) = \frac{Eu}{1-\nu^2}\left(\nu\frac{d\theta}{dx} + \frac{\theta}{x}\right) \qquad (7)$$

from (2) and (3)

The bending moment per *unit length along* OZ, is M_{XY} given by

$$M_{XY}.dz = \int_{-t/2}^{t/2} \sigma_x . u dz . du$$

or

$$M_{XY} = D(d\theta/dx + \nu\theta/x) \tag{8}$$

by substitution from (6), where

$$D = \frac{Et^3}{12(1-\nu^2)}$$

Similarly, if M_{YZ} is the bending moment about OX per unit length

$$M_{YZ}.dx = \int_{-t/2}^{t/2} \sigma_z . u dx . du$$

or

$$M_{YZ} = D[\nu(d\theta/dx) + \theta/x] \quad \text{from (7)} \tag{9}$$

Note also that

$$\sigma_x = M_{XY} . 12u/t^3 \tag{10}$$

and

$$\sigma_z = M_{YZ} . 12u/t^3 \tag{11}$$

Fig. 17.2 shows the forces and moments per unit length acting on an element which subtends an angle $\delta\phi$ at the centre, F being the shearing force *per unit length* in the direction OZ.

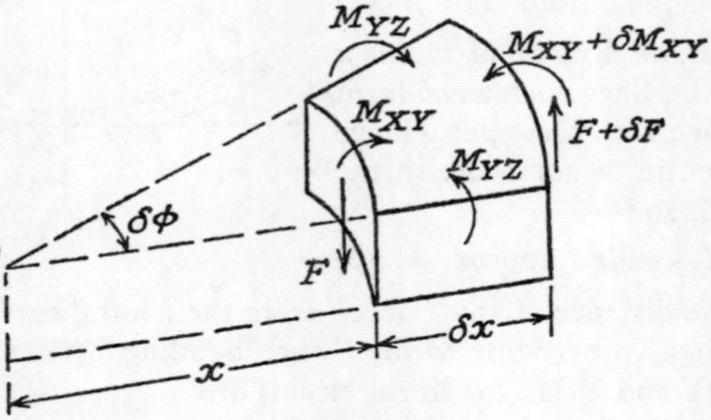

Fig. 17.2

Consider the equilibrium of the couples in the central radial plane, i.e.

$$(M_{XY}+\delta M_{XY})(x+\delta x)\delta\phi - M_{XY}x\delta\phi - 2M_{YZ}.\delta x . \sin \tfrac{1}{2}\delta\phi + Fx\delta\phi . \delta x = 0$$

In the limit

$$M_{XY} + x . dM_{XY}/dx - M_{YZ} + Fx = 0$$

Substituting from (8) and (9) gives

$$d^2\theta/dx^2 + (1/x)(d\theta/dx) - \theta/x^2 = -F/D \tag{12}$$

which can be written

$$(d/dx)[(1/x).d(x\theta)/dx] = -F/D \tag{13}$$

If F is known as a function of x this equation can be integrated to determine θ, and hence y. Bending moments and stresses can then be easily obtained. Particular cases will now be considered.

For a plate loaded with a *uniformly distributed load w per unit area and concentrated load P at the centre*, then

$$2\pi x . F = \pi x^2 . w + P$$

or

$$F = wx/2 + P/2\pi x$$

per unit length circumferentially (except at $x=0$).

Substituting in (13) and integrating

$$\theta = -wx^3/16D - (Px/8\pi D)(2 \log_e x - 1) + C_1 x/2 + C_2/x \quad (14)$$

$$y = \int \theta . dx + C_3 \quad \text{from (1)}$$
$$= -wx^4/64D - (Px^2/8\pi D)(\log_e x - 1) + C_1 x^2/4 + C_2 \log_e x + C_3 \quad (15)$$

17.2. Solid Circular Plate. Let R be the radius of the plate, and t the thickness. The references are to Para. 17.1.

(a) *Uniformly loaded, edge freely supported:*

$P=0$, and since θ and y cannot be infinite at the centre, $C_2 = 0$ from (14)

At $x=0$, $y=0$ $\therefore C_3=0$ from (15).

At $x=R$, $M_{XY}=0$, i.e.

$$-3wR^2/16D + C_1/2 - \nu wR^2/16D + \nu C_1/2 = 0 \quad \text{from (8) and (14)}$$

giving

$$C_1 = \frac{wR^2}{8D} \cdot \frac{3+\nu}{1+\nu}$$

Central deflection $= y$, at $x=R$

$$= -\frac{wR^4}{64D} + \frac{wR^4}{32D} \cdot \frac{3+\nu}{1+\nu} \quad \text{from (15)}$$

$$= \frac{wR^4}{64D}\left(\frac{5+\nu}{1+\nu}\right)$$

$$= (3wR^4/16Et^3)(5+\nu)(1-\nu)$$

From (6)

$$\sigma_x = \frac{Eu}{1-\nu^2}\left(-\frac{wx^2}{16D}(3+\nu) + \frac{wR^2}{16D}(3+\nu)\right)$$

and

$$\hat{\sigma}_x = \frac{E.t/2}{1-\nu^2} \cdot \frac{wR^2}{16D}(3+\nu), \quad \text{at } x=0$$

$$= \frac{3wR^2(3+\nu)}{8t^2}$$

From (7)

$$\sigma_z = \frac{Eu}{1-\nu^2}\left[\frac{-wx^2}{16D}(3\nu+1) + \frac{wR^2}{16D}(3+\nu)\right]$$

and hence $\hat{\sigma}_z = \hat{\sigma}_x$, and occurs at the centre.

(b) *Uniformly loaded, edge clamped:*

$P=0$ and $C_2=0$ as in case (a).

At $x=0$, $y=0$ $\therefore$ $C_3=0$ from (15).

At $x=R$, $dy/dx=\theta=0$, i.e.

$$-wR^3/16D+C_1R/2=0 \quad \text{from (14)}$$

giving

$$C_1=wR^2/8D$$

$$\text{Central deflection}=-wR^4/64D+wR^4/32D \quad \text{from (15)}$$
$$=wR^4/64D$$
$$=(3wR^4/16Et^3)(1-\nu^2)$$

$$\sigma_x=\frac{Eu}{1-\nu^2}\left(-\frac{wx^2}{16D}(3+\nu)+\frac{wR^2}{16D}(1+\nu)\right) \quad \text{from (6)}$$

This stress has its greatest numerical value when $x=R$ (at clamped edge), i.e.

$$\hat{\sigma}_x=\frac{E.t/2}{1-\nu^2}\cdot\frac{wR^2}{16D}\times 2$$
$$=3wR^2/4t^2$$

$$\sigma_z=\frac{Eu}{1-\nu^2}\left(\frac{-wx^2}{16D}(3\nu+1)+\frac{wR^2}{16D}(1+\nu)\right) \quad \text{from (7)}$$

and hence

$$\hat{\sigma}_z=\frac{E.t/2}{1-\nu^2}\cdot\frac{wR^2}{16D}(1+\nu) \quad \text{at the centre}$$
$$=\frac{3wR^2(1+\nu)}{8t^2}$$

(c) *Central load P, edge freely supported:*

$w=0$.

At $x=0$, $\theta=0$ $\therefore$ $C_2=0$ from (14), also $y=0$, $\therefore$ $C_3=0$ from (15). (Note that $Lt.(x\log_e x)=0$.)

At $x=R$, $M_{XY}=0$, i.e.

$$-(P/8\pi D)(2\log R-1)-(PR/8\pi D)(2/R)+C_1/2-(\nu P/8\pi D)(2\log R-1)+\nu C_1/2=0 \quad \text{from (8)}$$

giving

$$C_1=\frac{P}{4\pi D}\left(2\log R+\frac{1-\nu}{1+\nu}\right)$$

$$\text{Central deflection}=-\frac{PR^2}{8\pi D}(\log R-1)+\frac{PR^2}{16\pi D}\left(2\log R+\frac{1-\nu}{1+\nu}\right)$$
$$=\frac{PR^2}{16\pi D}\cdot\frac{(3+\nu)}{(1+\nu)}$$
$$=\frac{3PR^2}{4\pi Et^3}(3+\nu)(1-\nu)$$

From (6)

$$\sigma_x = \frac{Eu}{1-\nu^2} \cdot \frac{P}{4\pi D}(1+\nu) \log \frac{R}{x}$$

$$= (3P/2\pi t^2)(1+\nu) \log (R/x), \quad u = t/2$$

nd from (7)

$$\sigma_z = (3P/2\pi t^2)[(1+\nu) \log (R/x) + 1 - \nu]$$

These stresses appear to become infinite at the centre, but it must be ealised that the load cannot be applied at a point, but must extend over finite area. If this area can be estimated then the maximum stresses an be calculated.

(d) *Loaded round a circle, edge freely upported.* Supposing a total load P is istributed round a circle of radius r Fig. 17.3). It is necessary to divide the late into two regions, one for $x<r$, nd the other for $x>r$. At $x=r$, the alues of θ, y, and M_{XY} must be the ame in both regions.

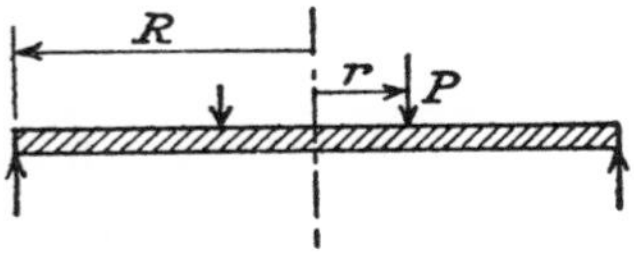

Fig. 17.3

$x<r$: $w=0$ and $P=0$.

Hence $\theta = C_1x/2 + C_2/x$ from (14)

nd $y = C_1x^2/4 + C_2 \log x + C_3$ from (15)

Since θ and y are not infinite at $x=0$, $C_2=0$, and since $y=0$ when $x=0$, $C_3=0$, and the above equations reduce to

$$\theta = C_1x/2$$

nd

$$y = C_1x^2/4$$

$x>r$: $w=0$, and

$$\theta = -(Px/8\pi D)(2 \log x - 1) + C_1'x/2 + C_2'/x \quad \text{from (14)}$$

$$y = -(Px^2/8\pi D)(\log x - 1) + C_1'x^2/4 + C_2' \log x + C_3' \quad \text{from (15)}$$

Equating the values of θ, y, and M_{XY} at $x=r$ gives the following equations:

$$-(Pr/8\pi D)(2 \log r - 1) + C_1'r/2 + C_2'/r = C_1r/2 \quad (16)$$

$$-(Pr^2/8\pi D)(\log r - 1) + C_1'r^2/4 + C_2' \log r + C_3' = C_1r^2/4 \quad (17)$$

nd

$$-(P/8\pi D)[(1+\nu)2 \log r + 1 - \nu] + (C_1'/2)(1+\nu) - (C_2'/r^2)(1-\nu) = (C_1/2)(1+\nu) \quad (18)$$

$M_{XY}=0$ at $x=R$ gives

$$-(P/8\pi D)[(1+\nu)2 \log R + 1 - \nu] + (C_1'/2)(1+\nu) - (C_2'/R^2)(1-\nu) = 0 \quad (19)$$

From equations (16) to (19) the constants are found to be:

$$C_1' = \frac{P}{4\pi D}\left[2 \log R + \frac{R^2 - r^2}{R^2}\left(\frac{1-\nu}{1+\nu}\right)\right]$$

$$C_2' = -Pr^2/8\pi D$$

and $$C_3' = (Pr^2/8\pi D)(\log r - 1)$$

The central deflection is given by the value of y at $x = R$, and by substitution in equation (15), reduces to

$$(P/8\pi D)[(R^2 - r^2)(3+\nu)/2(1+\nu) - r^2 \log R/r]$$

For $x > r$

$$M_{XY} = (P/8\pi)[(1+\nu)2 \log R/x + (1-\nu)r^2(1/x^2 - 1/R^2)]$$

which has a maximum value at $x = r$.

Hence

$$\hat{\sigma}_x = (6/t^2)M_{XY} \quad \text{from (10)}$$

$$= (3P/4\pi t^2)[(1+\nu)2 \log R/r + (1-\nu)(R^2 - r^2)/R^2]$$

Similarly

$$M_{YZ} = (P/8\pi)\{(1+\nu)2 \log R/x + (1-\nu)[(2R^2 - r^2)/R^2 - r^2/x^2]\}$$

and $$\hat{\sigma}_z = (3P/4\pi t^2)[(1+\nu)2 \log R/r + (1-\nu)(R^2 - r^2)/R^2]$$

$$= \hat{\sigma}_x$$

Fig. 17.4

17.3. Annular Ring, Loaded round Inner Edge. The ring is loaded with a total load P round the inner edge and freely supported round the outer edge (Fig. 17.4),

$M_{XY} = 0$ at $x = R$ and at $x = r$, giving

$$-(P/8\pi D)[(1+\nu)2 \log R + 1 - \nu] + (C_1/2)(1+\nu) - (C_2/R^2)(1-\nu) = 0 \quad \text{as Eq. (19), Para. 17.2(d)}$$

and $$-(P/8\pi D)[(1+\nu)2 \log r + 1 - \nu] + (C_1/2)(1+\nu) - (C_2/r^2)(1-\nu) = 0$$

Subtracting and solving

$$C_2 = \frac{P}{4\pi D} \cdot \frac{1+\nu}{1-\nu} \cdot \frac{R^2 r^2}{R^2 - r^2} \log \frac{R}{r}$$

and then $$C_1 = \frac{P}{4\pi D}\left[\frac{2(R^2 \log R - r^2 \log r)}{R^2 - r^2} + \frac{1-\nu}{1+\nu}\right]$$

Then $$M_{XY}/D = -(P/8\pi D)[(1+\nu)2 \log x + 1 - \nu] + (C_1/2)(1+\nu) - (C_2/x^2)(1-\nu)$$

and $$M_{YZ}/D = -(P/8\pi D)[(1+\nu)2 \log x - (1-\nu)] + (C_1/2)(1+\nu) + (C_2/x^2)(1-\nu)$$

The maximum bending moment is M_{YZ} at $x=r$, and hence

$$\hat{\sigma}_z=(6/t^2)M_{YZ}$$
$$=\frac{3P}{\pi t^2}\left[\frac{(1+\nu)R^2}{R^2-r^2}\log\frac{R}{r}+\frac{1-\nu}{2}\right]$$

REFERENCE

'IMOSHENKO, S., *Theory of Plates and Shells*. McGraw Hill. 1940.

PROBLEMS

1. Show that for a flat circular plate of radius R and thickness t, under the ction of a central load P, the deflection is $(3PR^2/4\pi Et^3)(1-\nu^2)$ when the dges are clamped, and that the maximum stress at the edge is $3P/2\pi t^2$.

2. A circular plate of radius R carries a total load P uniformly distributed over central area of radius r. Show that the maximum stress is

$$(3P/2\pi t^2)[(1+\nu)\log R/r+1-(1-\nu)(r^2/4R^2)]$$

3. Show that, for an annular ring of outside and inside radii R and r espectively, loaded round the inner edge and clamped at the outer edge, the naximum stress is given by $(3P/2\pi t^2)(R^2-r^2)/R^2$, where P is the total load.

4. A circular disc of uniform thickness t is firmly clamped round its outer eriphery at a radius of 3 cm, and at the centre is firmly held in a spindle of adius 1 cm. An axial force P is applied through the spindle to the disc. Show hat the bending moment per unit length of arc at any radius r cm is given by

$$M=(P/\pi)(0{\cdot}2163/r^2-0{\cdot}325\log_e r+0{\cdot}1517)$$

The plate may be assumed clamped at its inner edge, and M is measured in a adial plane. $\nu=0{\cdot}3$.) (U.L.)

CHAPTER XVIII

Vibrations and Critical Speeds

18.1 Linear Vibrations. Suppose a mass m to be carried on a elastic support, such as a spring, which has a stiffness k (force per uni extension). Then, if the mass is given a displacement x from its *equilib rium* position, the support will exert a *restoring* force equal to kx.

Neglecting the inertia of the support, the equation of motion of m i

$$m\ddot{x} = -kx \quad (\ddot{x} = d^2x/dt^2)$$

or

$$\ddot{x} + (k/m)x = 0$$

This represents simple harmonic motion, and if the zero of time i taken when $x = 0$, the solution is $x = A \sin\sqrt{(k/m)}t$.

The motion is periodic about the equilibrium position, A being th *amplitude*, or maximum displacement, which is independent of th period.

The *periodic time* is

$$t = 2\pi\sqrt{(m/k)}$$

since $\sin\sqrt{(k/m)}t$ "repeats" itself at intervals of 2π.

Note that the period can be written $t = 2\pi\sqrt{(\delta/g)}$, where δ is the "static" deflection caused by the force of gravity mg.

or $t = 2\pi\sqrt{(x/\ddot{x})}$

$= 2\pi\sqrt{(\text{Displacement}/\text{Acceleration})}$ from the equation o motion

Frequency (f) = number of oscillations per unit time

= 1/Period

or $f = 1/t = (1/2\pi)\sqrt{(g/\delta)}$

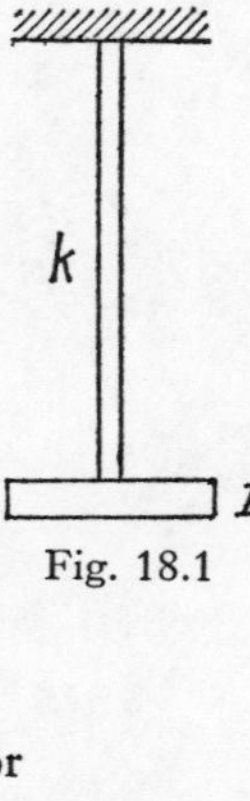

Fig. 18.1

18.2. Torsional Oscillations—Single Inertia. Consider the case of a shaft or wire fixed at one end and carrying an inertia I at the other end (Fig. 18.1).

If now the inertia is given an angular rotation θ from the equilibrium position there will be a torque set up in the wire equal to the $k\theta$ (k is stiffness – torque per radian twist), tending to reduce the value of θ. The equation of motion of I is

$$I\ddot{\theta} = -k\theta$$

or

$$\ddot{\theta} + (k/I)\theta = 0$$

'his is in simple harmonic motion as in Para. 18.1, and the period

$$t = 2\pi\sqrt{(\theta/\ddot{\theta})}$$
$$= 2\pi\sqrt{(I/k)}$$
$$\text{Frequency } f = (1/2\pi)\sqrt{(k/I)}$$

Note: $k = GJ/l$ Nm/rad (Para. 8.1), and $I = mK^2$ kgm². It will now e seen that the units of k/I are Nm/kgm² = Ns²/kgms², i.e. 1/s², since N = 1 kgm/s².

EXAMPLE 1. *A steel disc 0·3 m diameter, weighing 30 kg, is suspended from 'ıe end of a wire 2·5 mm diameter, 1·5 m long, which is clamped into a central ole in the disc. In torsional vibration the disc makes ten oscillations in 0 secs.*

Find the modulus of rigidity of the wire, and calculate the amplitude of scillation if the maximum permissible shearing stress in the wire is 140 N/ ım². (U.L.)

$$I = mK^2 = 30 \times 0{\cdot}3^2/8 = 0{\cdot}3375 \text{ kg. m}^2$$

$$\text{Period} = 8{\cdot}0 = 2\pi\sqrt{\frac{0{\cdot}3375}{k}} \quad \text{from above}$$

iving $$k = 0{\cdot}208 \text{ Nm/radn.}$$
$$= GJ/l$$
$$\therefore \quad G = \frac{0{\cdot}208 \times 1{\cdot}5 \times 32 \times 10^{12}}{\pi \times 2{\cdot}5^4}$$
$$= 8{\cdot}15 \times 10^{10} \text{ N/m}^2 = 81{,}500 \text{ N/mm}^2$$
$$\text{Direct stress } \sigma = \frac{30 \times 9{\cdot}81 \times 4}{\pi \times 2{\cdot}5^2} = 60 \text{ N/mm}^2$$

If τ is the permissible shear stress due to torsion

$$140 = \tfrac{1}{2}\sqrt{(\sigma^2 + 4\tau^2)} \quad \text{(Chapter III)}$$

;iving $$\tau = 137 \text{ N/mm}^2$$

$$\text{Corresponding amplitude } \theta = (2\tau/d)(l/G)$$
$$= 2{\cdot}02 \text{ radn.}$$
$$= 115^\circ$$

18.3. Torsional Oscillations—Two Inertias. It may be assumed and can be shown mathematically) that the two inertias will oscillate vith the same frequency, reaching their extreme positions at the same nstant. It follows that there will be a *node* (point of zero oscillation) n the shaft at a fixed point between the inertias.

Treating the node as a fixed end (Para. 18.2), the frequencies of each nertia individually are

$$(1/2\pi)\sqrt{(k_1/I_1)} \quad \text{and} \quad (1/2\pi)\sqrt{(k_2/I_2)}$$

where k_1 and k_2 are based on the length of shaft between the node an each inertia, i.e. for a uniform shaft

$$k_1 = GJ/l_1 \text{ and } k_2 = GJ/l_2$$

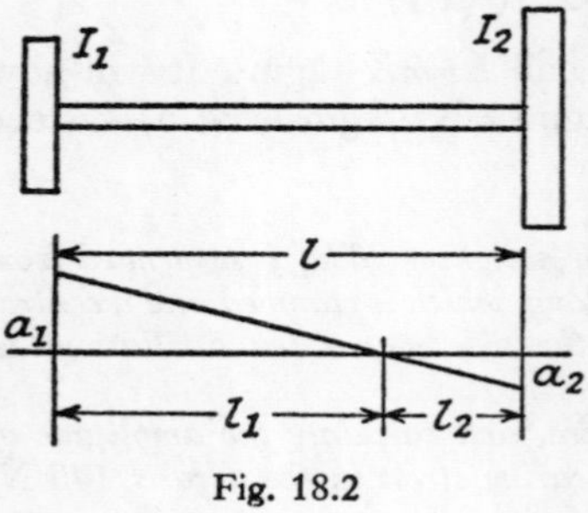

Fig. 18.2

(see Fig. 18.2).

Equating the frequencies gives

$$k_1/k_2 = I_1/I_2 \qquad (1)$$

or

$$l_2/l_1 = I_1/I_2$$

the node dividing the length inversel as the inertias at the ends.

Once the position of the node i established, the frequency can b calculated from either equatio above.

The amplitude ratio

$$a_1/a_2 = l_1/l_2 = I_2/I_1 \qquad (2)$$

Alternatively, if θ is the angle of twist of the shaft at any instan and T the torque transmitted

$$\theta = T/k_1 + T/k_2$$
$$= T(1/k_1 + 1/k_2)$$

so that the stiffness for the shaft *as a whole*

$$k = T/\theta = \frac{k_1 k_2}{k_1 + k_2}$$

and since $\quad k_1/k_2 = I_1/I_2 \quad$ from (1)

it can be shown that

$$k_1 = \frac{I_1 + I_2}{I_2} . k$$

Hence $\quad$ frequency $f = (1/2\pi)\sqrt{(k_1/I_1)}$

$$= \frac{1}{2\pi}\sqrt{\left(\frac{I_1 + I_2}{I_1 I_2} . k\right)} \qquad (3)$$

If the shaft is made up of parts of different stiffness per unit lengt (e.g. different diameters), it may be reduced to an *equivalent shaft c uniform stiffness* in the following manner.

If one part is of length l' and the other of length l'', the respectiv polar moments of inertia being J' and J'', then since stiffness $= GJ/l \propto J/$ the equivalent length of l'' reduced to a shaft of moment of inertia J is given by

$$J'/l_{\text{equiv.}}'' = J''/l'',$$

or

$$l_{\text{equiv.}}'' = l''(J'/J'')$$

The total length of shaft of uniform stiffness is then

$$l = l' + l''(J'/J'') \tag{4}$$

$$= l' + l''(d'/d'')^4 \tag{5}$$

r solid shafts, where d' and d'' are the corresponding diameters.

EXAMPLE 2. *The flywheel of an engine driving a dynamo has a mass of 80 kg and a radius of gyration of 0·3 m. The shaft at the flywheel end has an ffective length of 0·25 m and is 0mm diameter. The armature ass is 120 kg and its radius of yration is 0·225 m. The dynamo aft is 43 mm diameter and 0·2 m ffective length. Calculate the fre- uency of torsional oscillations and he position of the node. G= 3,000 N/mm². (U.L.)*

It has been shown that for niform shaft the node is nearer o the larger inertia (the fly- vheel), and it may be judged in his problem to lie in the engine haft. Consequently it is advis- ble to reduce the shaft to an quivalent length of 50 mm dia- neter (Fig. 18.3).

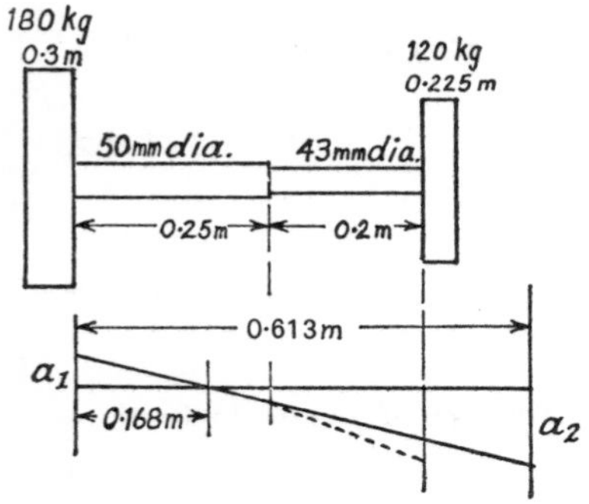

Fig. 18.3

Total equivalent length $= 0{\cdot}25 + 0{\cdot}2(50/43)^4$ from (5)

$= 0{\cdot}613$ m

The node divides this length in the inverse ratio of the inertias, i.e.

$(120 \times 0{\cdot}225^2)/(180 \times 0{\cdot}3^2) = 0{\cdot}376$ from (2)

Distance of node from flywheel $= (0{\cdot}376/1{\cdot}376)\, 0{\cdot}613 = 0{\cdot}168$ m

As this lies in the part of the shaft which is actually 50 mm diameter, no adjustment is necessary. Any distances which fell in the region of the 43 mm diameter shaft would have to be converted by the factor (diameter ratio)⁴.

The lower diagram in Fig. 18.3 shows the amplitude ratio a_1/a_2, which is 0·376 independent of the stiffness of shaft, and the slope of the dotted line indicates the angle of twist per unit length in the actual 43 mm shaft.

Frequency $= (1/2\pi)\sqrt{(k_1/I_1)}$, calculating for a single inertia with a fixed end at the node.

$$= \frac{1}{2\pi}\sqrt{\frac{83{,}000 \times 10^6 \times \pi \times 0{\cdot}050^4}{32 \times 0{\cdot}168 \times 180 \times 0{\cdot}3^2}}$$

$= 22{\cdot}1$/sec.

EXAMPLE 3. *In a radial engine the moving parts have a total moment of inertia of 1 kgm² and are concentrated in the plane of the single crank pin.*

The engine is directly connected to an air screw, of moment of inertia 18kgm by a hollow shaft having outer and inner diameters of 80 mm and 35 mm, an an effective length of 0·3 m. The stiffness of the crank throw alone is 2·5 10^6 Nm/radn.

Estimate the natural frequency of torsional vibrations of the system. Wh percentage error is involved if the air screw mass is assumed infinite? G 83,000 N/mm². (U.L.)

The stiffness of the crank throw may be reduced to an equivaler length of shaft of the same diameter as the engine shaft, but as the positio of the node is not required the expression for combined stiffne $k = k_1k_2/(k_1 + k_2)$ will be used.

$$\text{Stiffness of shaft} = \frac{83{,}000 \times \pi}{0{\cdot}3 \times 32 \times 10^6}(80^4 - 35^4)$$
$$= 1{\cdot}07 \times 10^6 \text{ Nm/radn.}$$

$$\text{Combined stiffness} = \frac{2{\cdot}5 \times 1{\cdot}07 \times 10^6}{2{\cdot}5 + 1{\cdot}07}$$
$$= 0{\cdot}75 \times 10^6 \text{ Nm/radn.}$$

Frequency of torsional vibrations

$$= \frac{1}{2\pi}\sqrt{\frac{k(I_1 + I_2)}{I_1 I_2}} \quad \text{from (3}$$

$$= \frac{1}{2\pi}\sqrt{\frac{0{\cdot}75 \times 10^6(1 + 18)}{1 \times 18}}$$

$$= 142/\text{sec.}$$

If the airscrew mass is assumed infinite, the frequency can be calculate from $(1/2\pi)\sqrt{(k/I_1)}$

$$= \frac{1}{2\pi}\sqrt{\frac{0{\cdot}75 \times 10^6}{1}}$$
$$= 138/\text{sec.}$$

$$\text{Percentage error} = 4/142 = 2{\cdot}8\%.$$

18.4. Torsional Oscillations of Spring. If a close-coiled helica spring carries an inertia I at its free end, then for an axial rotation θ fron the equilibrium position the spring exerts a restoring couple

$$EI_w\theta/l = (Ed^4/64Dn)\theta \quad \text{(see Para. 13.1)}$$

and the equation of motion for I is

$$I\ddot{\theta} + (Ed^4/64Dn)\theta = 0$$

$$\text{Period} = 2\pi\sqrt{(\theta/\ddot{\theta})}$$
$$= 2\pi\sqrt{(64DnI/Ed^4)}$$

EXAMPLE 4. *A close-coiled helical spring is fixed at its upper end and circular metal disc is fixed axially to the lower end. The times for vertical an gular oscillations are equal. Show that*

$$\frac{E}{G}=\left(\frac{\text{Diameter of disc}}{\text{Mean diameter of coils}}\right)^2$$

If the spring is made of wire 3 mm diameter, and has 50 turns of 45 mm ean diameter, find the mass of the disc, the time of oscillation being 1 second. eglect the mass of the spring. $G=83{,}000\ N/mm^2$. *(U.L.)*

Let m be the mass of the disc, and R its radius.

or a vertical displacement x the restoring force

$$=(Gd^4/8D^3n)x \quad \text{(Para. 13.1)}$$
$$=-m\ddot{x}$$
$$\text{Period}=2\pi\sqrt{(m\,.\,8D^3n/Gd^4)}$$

For angular oscillations

$$\text{Period}=2\pi\sqrt{(64DnI/Ed^4)},\ \text{above}$$
$$=2\pi\sqrt{(32DnmR^2/Ed^4)}$$

Equating the periods

$$8D^3n/Gd^4=32DnR^2/Ed^4$$
$$E/G=(2R/D)^2$$

Using the expression for vertical oscillations

$$\text{Period}=1=2\pi\sqrt{\frac{m\times 8\times 45^3\times 50}{83{,}000\times 3^4\times 10^3}}$$

rom which $m=4{\cdot}68$ kg.

18.5. Transverse Vibrations—Single Mass. If a single mass is arried on a beam and subjected to lateral vibrations, the case is similar the linear vibrations treated in Para. 18.1, the *inertia of the beam eing neglected.* Two particular loadings will be considered.

(1) *Mass m at end of cantilever.* For a lateral displacement y, the estoring force

$$=(3EI/l^3)y \quad \text{due to the stiffness of the beam (Chapter IX)}$$
$$=-m\ddot{y} \quad \text{when vibrating.}$$
$$\text{Frequency } f=(1/2\pi)\sqrt{(\ddot{y}/y)}$$
$$=(1/2\pi)\sqrt{(3EI/ml^3)}$$
$$=(1/2\pi)\sqrt{(g/\delta)}$$

where δ is the static deflection *at the load.*

It is clear that this form can always be applied to a single load carried on a beam, however supported.

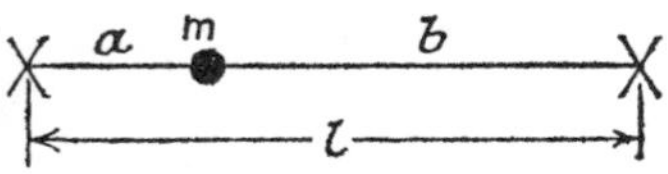

Fig. 18.4

(2) *Load on simply supported beam.*

Consider the case where the load is supported at a point which divides he length l into parts a and b (Fig. 18.4).

The deflection at the load

$$\delta = \text{mg}\ a^2b^2/3EIl \quad \text{(Para. 9.1)}$$

Hence, in lateral vibration

$$\text{Frequency } f = (1/2\pi)\sqrt{(g/\delta)}$$
$$= (1/2\pi)\sqrt{(3EIl/ma^2b^2)}$$

When the load is at the centre, this reduces to

$$f = (1/2\pi)\sqrt{(48EI/ml^3)}$$

EXAMPLE 5. *A small imperfectly balanced machine is mounted on a rig horizontal plate, supported on four vertical legs 28 mm outside diamete 25 mm inside diameter, and 0·9 m long, rigidly welded to the plate but havi their other extremities always position-fixed, but direction-fixed or not will. If the effective mass of the assembly is 45 kg, find the five lowest machi speeds which would give resonance corresponding to the five different fixi conditions of the legs. $E = 207{,}000\ N/mm^2$. (U.L.)*

If k is the composite stiffness of the four legs, then for a lateral di placement x, the equation of motion is

$$45\ddot{x} + kx = 0$$

Machine speed for resonance

$$= 60f \text{ r.p.m.}$$
$$= (60/2\pi)\sqrt{(\ddot{x}/x)} = (60/2\pi)\sqrt{(k/45)}$$
$$= (60/2\pi)\sqrt{(g/\delta)}$$

where δ is the lateral deflection which would be caused by gravitation pull on the mass if exerted in the direction of x.

Let the mass carried by a leg *not direction-fixed* be m_1. Then

$$\delta = m_1gl^3/3EI$$

or

$$m_1g = (3EI/l^3)\delta$$

Let the mass carried by a leg *direction-fixed* be m_2. Then

$$\delta = m_2gl^3/12EI \quad \text{(Ex. 5, Chap. X)}$$

or

$$m_2g = (12EI/l^3)\delta$$

(i) *None fixed*

$$45 = 4m_1 = (12EI/l^3).\delta/g$$
$$\delta = (45/12).(l^3/EI)g$$

$$\text{Machine speed} = \frac{60}{2\pi}\sqrt{\frac{12 \times 207{,}000 \times \pi(28^4 - 25^4)}{45 \times 0{\cdot}9^3 \times 64 \times 10^6}}$$
$$= 276 \text{ r.p.m.}$$

(ii) *One leg fixed*

$$45 = 3m_1 + m_2$$
$$= (EI/l^3)(9 + 12)\delta/g$$
$$\delta = (45/21)(l^3/EI)g$$

$$\text{Machine speed} = 276\sqrt{(21/12)} = 364 \text{ r.p.m.}$$

(iii) *Two legs fixed*

$$45 = 2m_1 + 2m_2$$
$$= (EI/l^3)(6+24)\delta/g$$
$$\delta = (45/30)(l^3/EI)g$$

Machine speed $= 435$ r.p.m.

(iv) *Three legs fixed*

$$\delta = (45/39)(l^3/EI)$$

Machine speed $= 496$ r.p.m.

(v) *All fixed*

$$\delta = (45/48)(l^3/EI)$$

Machine speed $= 550$ r.p.m.

18.6. Transverse Vibrations of Uniform Beam. If m is the ass per unit length, the rate of ertia loading at any point along e beam is $(m)(\partial^2 y/\partial t^2)$, its rection being opposite to that the acceleration (Fig. 18.5).

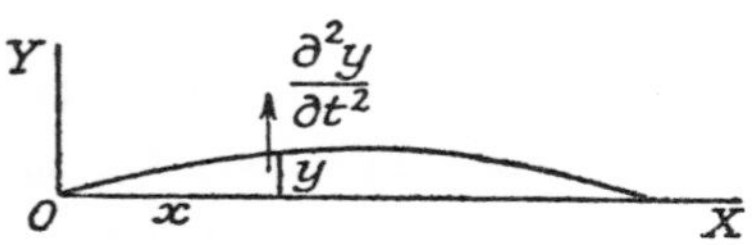

Fig. 18.5

Treating the vibration form as beam under the action of this ading (neglecting gravity effects)

$$EI.\partial^4 y/\partial x^4 = -m(\partial^2 y/\partial t^2) \quad \text{(Para. 9.3)}$$

$$\partial^4 y/\partial x^4 + (m/EI)(\partial^2 y/\partial t^2) = 0 \qquad (1)$$

Assuming a simple harmonic vibration, let

$$y = F(x).\sin 2\pi ft$$

here f is the frequency.

Equation (1) reduces to

$$\partial^4 F/\partial x^4 - (m/EI)4\pi^2 f^2.F(x) = 0 \qquad (2)$$

The solution can be written

$$F(x) = A\sin\alpha x + B\cos\alpha x + C\sinh\alpha x + D\cosh\alpha x$$

here $\alpha^2 = 2\pi f\sqrt{(m/EI)}$

(a) *Simply supported or pinned ends.* The conditions to be satisfied re:

$x = 0$, $y = 0$, $\therefore B + D = 0$.

$x = 0$, $\partial^2 y/\partial x^2 = 0$ (no bending moment), $\therefore -B + D = 0$.

$\therefore \quad B = D = 0.$

Also at $x = l$, $y = 0$, $\therefore A\sin\alpha l + C\sinh\alpha l = 0$.

and $x = l$, $\partial^2 y/\partial x^2 = 0$, $\therefore -A\sin\alpha l + C\sinh\alpha l = 0$.

Adding, $C = 0$ since $\sinh\alpha l \neq 0$

nd hence $A\sin\alpha l = 0$

The least solution is

$$\alpha = \pi/l$$

or
$$\alpha^2 = 2\pi f \sqrt{(m/EI)}$$
$$= \pi^2/l^2$$

giving
$$f = (\pi/2l^2)\sqrt{(EI/m)}$$
$$= \mathbf{(1{\cdot}57/l^2)\sqrt{(EI/m)}}$$

(b) *Cantilever*. Taking the origin at the fixed end:

At $x=0,\ y=0 \quad \therefore \quad B+D=0.$

i.e.
$$D = -B \tag{3}$$

also $\partial y/\partial x = 0 \quad \therefore \quad A + C = 0.$

i.e.
$$C = -A \tag{4}$$

At $x = l$, $\partial^2 y/\partial x^2 = 0$ (no bending moment)

$$\therefore \quad -A \sin \alpha l - B \cos \alpha l + C \sinh \alpha l + D \cosh \alpha l = 0$$

or $\quad A(\sin \alpha l + \sinh \alpha l) = -B(\cosh \alpha l + \cos \alpha l)$ from (3) and (4) (5)

also $\partial^3 y/\partial x^3 = 0$ (no shearing force)

$$\therefore \quad -A \cos \alpha l + B \sin \alpha l + C \cosh \alpha l + D \sinh \alpha l = 0$$

or
$$A(\cos \alpha l + \cosh \alpha l) = B(\sin \alpha l - \sinh \alpha l) \tag{6}$$

Eliminating A and B between (5) and (6)

$$(\sin \alpha l + \sinh \alpha l)(\sin \alpha l - \sinh \alpha l) = -(\cos \alpha l + \cosh \alpha l)^2$$

i.e.
$$\sin^2 \alpha l - \sinh^2 \alpha l = -\cos^2 \alpha l - \cosh^2 \alpha l - 2 \cos \alpha l . \cosh \alpha$$

or
$$\cos \alpha l . \cosh \alpha l = -1$$

The least solution is $\alpha l = 1{\cdot}875$, giving

$$f = (1{\cdot}875^2/2\pi l^2)\sqrt{(EI/m)}$$
$$= \mathbf{(0{\cdot}56/l^2)\sqrt{(EI/m)}}$$

(c) *Ends direction-fixed:*

At $x=0,\ y=0 \quad \therefore \quad B+D=0.$

i.e.
$$D = -B \tag{7}$$

and $\quad \partial y/\partial x = 0 \quad \therefore \quad A + C = 0.$

i.e.
$$C = -A \tag{8}$$

At $x = l,\ y = 0.$

$$\therefore \quad A \sin \alpha l + B \cos \alpha l + C \sinh \alpha l + D \cosh \alpha l = 0$$

or $\quad A(\sin \alpha l - \sinh \alpha l) = B(\cosh \alpha l - \cos \alpha l)$ from (7) and (8) (9)

also $\partial y/\partial x = 0$

$$\therefore \quad A \cos \alpha l - B \sin \alpha l + C \cosh \alpha l + D \sinh \alpha l = 0$$

or
$$A(\cos \alpha l - \cosh \alpha l) = B\ (\sin \alpha l + \sinh \alpha l) \tag{10}$$

Eliminating A and B between (9) and (10)

$$\text{sin } \alpha l - \sinh \alpha l)(\sin \alpha l + \sinh \alpha l) = (\cosh \alpha l - \cos \alpha l)(\cos \alpha l - \cosh \alpha l)$$

.e. $$\sin^2 \alpha l - \sinh^2 \alpha l = -\cosh^2 \alpha l - \cos^2 \alpha l + 2 \cos \alpha l . \cosh \alpha l$$

r $$\cos \alpha l . \cosh \alpha l = 1$$

The least solution is $\alpha l = 4{\cdot}73$, giving

$$f = (4{\cdot}73^2/2\pi l^2)\sqrt{(EI/m)}$$
$$= (3{\cdot}57/l^2)\sqrt{(EI/m)}$$

18.7. Transverse Vibrations—Combined Loading. In Paras. 18.5 nd 18.6 the frequency has been found for a single load treating the eam as "light," and for the beam under the action of its own inertia. To determine the frequency when a number of loads are carried on a 'heavy" beam, Dunkerley's empirical formula may be used. This tates

$$1/f^2 = 1/f_b^2 + 1/f_1^2 + 1/f_2^2 + 1/f_3^2 + \ldots$$

vhere f is the frequency under the combined loading, f_b the frequency lue to the beam inertia alone, and $f_1, f_2, f_3 \ldots$ the frequencies for each f the loads *acting alone* (neglecting the inertia of the beam).

18.8. Energy Method for Frequency. This is an approximate nethod, since it assumes the shape of the vibrating beam to be similar o that of the static deflection curve under the loads. However, Lord Rayleigh showed that the frequency was almost independent of the ibrating form assumed, so that very little error is involved.

(a) **Distributed load m.** Assume the vibrating form to be

$$y = kY \sin 2\pi ft$$

vhere $Y = F(x)$ is the static deflection form, and k is a constant.

In the extreme position ($\sin 2\pi ft = 1$), the energy is in the form of strain energy, and $y = kY$. The equivalent static load to deflect the beam nto this position $= kmg$, and hence the total strain energy

$$= \int_0^l \tfrac{1}{2}(kmg)kY . dx$$

$$= (k^2/2)\int_0^l mgY . dx \qquad (1)$$

In the mean position all the energy is kinetic, the velocity being given by

$$\partial y/\partial t = kY . 2\pi f \quad (\cos 2\pi ft = 1)$$

$$\text{Total kinetic energy} = \int_0^l \tfrac{1}{2}(m)(kY . 2\pi f)^2 . dx$$

$$= (4\pi^2 f^2 k^2/2)\int_0^l mY^2 . dx \qquad (2)$$

Equating (1) and (2) gives

$$4\pi^2 f^2 = g.\frac{\int mY dx}{\int mY^2 dx} \qquad (3)$$

EXAMPLE 6. *Obtain an expression for the natural frequency of transver vibrations of a simply supported beam of length l carrying a distributed load Assume the vibration deflection is of the same form as the static deflection.*

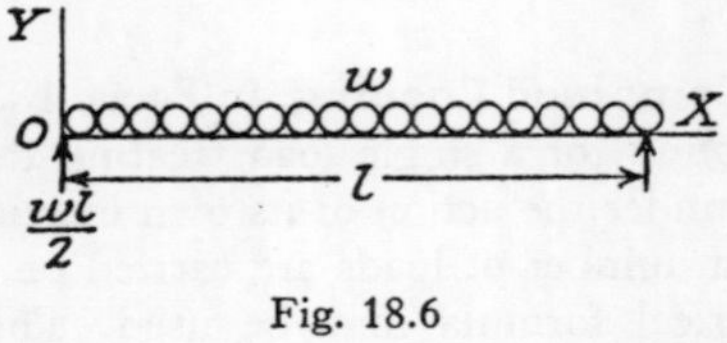

Fig. 18.6

Hence find the natural frequenc of a simply supported beam 6 m lor of moment of inertia 1·5 × 10⁸ mm carrying a uniformly distribute load of 1500 kg/m. E = 207,000 N mm². (U.L.)

Energy method. First obtain th equation of the static deflectio curve

$$EI.d^2y/dx^2 = (wl/2)x - wx^2/2 \quad \text{(Fig. 18.6)}$$

Integrating $\quad EI.y = wlx^3/12 - wx^4/24 + Ax + B$

When $x = 0,\ y = 0, \quad \therefore\ B = 0.$

When $x = l,\ y = 0, \quad \therefore\ A = -wl^3/24.$

Downward deflection under load $= -y$

$$= (w/24EI)(l^3x - 2lx^3 + x^4)$$

$$4\pi^2 f^2 = \frac{24EIg}{w}.\frac{\int_0^l (l^3x - 2lx^3 + x^4)dx}{\int_0^l (l^3x - 2lx^3 + x^4)^2 dx} \quad \text{from (3), with } w =$$

m

$$= \frac{24EIg}{w}.\frac{l^5(\frac{1}{2} - \frac{2}{4} + \frac{1}{5})}{\int_0^l (l^6x^2 - 4l^4x^4 + 2l^3x^5 + 4l^2x^6 - 4lx^7 + x^8)d}$$

$$= \frac{24EIg}{wl^4}.\frac{1}{5(\frac{1}{3} - \frac{4}{5} + \frac{2}{6} + \frac{4}{7} - \frac{4}{8} + \frac{1}{9})}$$

$$= (24EIg/wl^4)(126/31)$$

giving $\quad n = (1{\cdot}574/l^2)\sqrt{(EI/m)}$

This compares with a value of $(1{\cdot}57/l^2)\sqrt{(EI/m)}$ obtained by mathe matical analysis in Para. 18.6(a).

$$f = \frac{1{\cdot}574}{6^2}\sqrt{\frac{207{,}000 \times 1{\cdot}5 \times 10^8}{1500 \times 10^6}}$$

$$= 6{\cdot}29/\text{sec.}$$

(b) **Concentrated loads.** If a number of loads M_1, M_2, M_3 . . *acting together*, cause static deflections at their points of application c

$_1$, Y_2, $Y_3 \ldots$, assume the amplitudes of transverse vibration are Y_1, kY_2, kY_3, the equations of motion being $kY_1 \sin 2\pi ft$, $kY_2 \sin$ πft, $kY_3 \sin 2\pi ft \ldots$.

By similar arguments to those of case (a), the strain energy in the xtreme position is $\frac{1}{2}\Sigma k^2 MgY$, and the kinetic energy in the mean osition is $(1/2)\Sigma k^2 MY^2 . 4\pi^2 f^2$.

Equating, gives

$$4\pi^2 f^2 = g \cdot \frac{\Sigma MY}{\Sigma MY^2} \qquad (4)$$

EXAMPLE 7. *A beam of length 0 m carries two loads of 2000 kg t distances of 3 m from each end, gether with a central load of 000 kg. Calculate the frequency f transverse vibrations by (a) the iergy method, and (b) Dunkerley's rmula. Neglect the mass of the eam. $I = 10^9$ mm^4; $E = 205{,}000$ N/mm^2.*

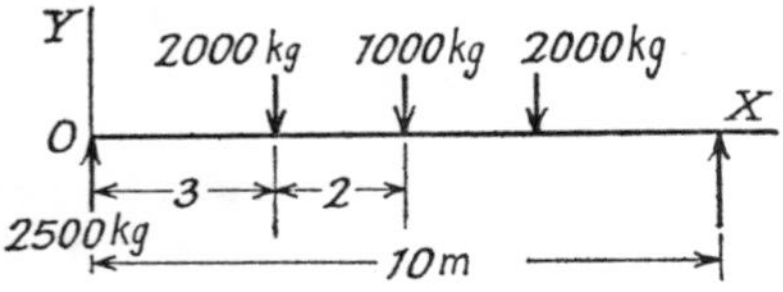

Fig. 18.7

(a) First find the deflection under each load (Fig. 18.7).

$$EI . d^2y/dx^2 = 2500x - 2000[x-3] \text{ kgm} \quad \text{for } x < 5$$

ntegrating $\quad EI . dy/dx = 1250x^2 - 1000[x-3]^2 + A$

nd $\quad EI . y = (1250/3)x^3 - (1000/3)[x-3]^3 + Ax + B$

When $x = 0$, $y = 0$, $\therefore \quad B = 0$.

When $x = 5$, $dy/dx = 0$, $\therefore \quad A = -27{,}250$.

At $x = 3$

$$y = \frac{(1250 \times 9 - 27{,}250 \times 3)}{205{,}000 \times 10^9} \times 9{\cdot}81 \times 10^9 \text{ mm}$$

$$= 3{\cdot}37 \text{ mm downwards}$$

At $x = 5$

$$y = \frac{-86{,}820 \times 9{\cdot}81}{205{,}000}$$

$$= 4{\cdot}15 \text{ mm downwards}$$

$$4\pi^2 f^2 = g\Sigma MY/\Sigma MY^2 \quad \text{from (4)}$$

$$= \frac{9{\cdot}81 \times 10^3(2000 \times 3{\cdot}37 + 1000 \times 4{\cdot}15 + 2000 \times 3{\cdot}37)}{2000 \times 3{\cdot}37^2 + 1000 \times 4{\cdot}15^2 + 2000 \times 3{\cdot}37^2}$$

$$= 2770$$

$$\therefore \quad f = 8{\cdot}38/\text{sec.}$$

(b) Referring to Para. 18.5, case (2), the frequency for each of the 2000-kg loads *acting alone*

$$= (1/2\pi)\sqrt{(3EIl/Ma^2b^2)}$$

$$= \frac{1}{2\pi}\sqrt{\frac{3 \times 205{,}000 \times 10^9 \times 10}{2000 \times 3^2 \times 7^2 \times 10^6}}$$

$$= 13{\cdot}3/\text{sec.}$$

The frequency for the central load alone

$$=(1/2\pi)\sqrt{(48EI/Ml^3)}$$

$$=\frac{1}{2\pi}\sqrt{\frac{48\times 205{,}000\times 10^9}{1000\times 10^3\times 10^6}}$$

$$=15{\cdot}8/\text{sec.}$$

The frequency for the combined loading is given by

$$1/f^2=1/13{\cdot}3^2+1/15{\cdot}8^2+1/13{\cdot}3^2 \quad \text{(Para. 18.7)}$$

from which $f=\dfrac{13{\cdot}1\times 15{\cdot}8}{\sqrt{(2\times 15{\cdot}8^2+13{\cdot}1^2)}}$

$$=7{\cdot}95/\text{sec.}$$

18.9. Whirling of Shafts. When a shaft running between bearin is rotated, it is kept rigid at low speeds by the stiffness of the sha acting as a "beam." As the speed is increased, a stage is reached which, if due to any imperfections the shaft is deflected from the ax of rotation, the centrifugal effect is equal to the restoring effect due shaft stiffness. Since both these forces are proportional to the deflectio the latter quantity becomes indeterminate at this speed, and the sha is said to "whirl." It is then in an unstable condition, and serio stresses and vibrations will be set up if it is allowed to run for long this speed. However, any further increase in speed will restore th stability of the shaft, and in practice many shafts are designed operate at speeds above the whirling speed.

(a) *Whirling of uniform shaft.* If m is the mass per unit length the shaft, and y the deflection at any point for an angular velocity ω, th rate of centrifugal loading $= -my\omega^2$.

When the shaft is whirling this is just balanced by the stiffness as beam, i.e. (neglecting gravity loading)

$$EI.d^4y/dx^4=my\omega^2 \quad \text{(Para. 9.3)}$$

or $$d^4y/dx^4-(m/EI)y\omega^2=0$$

This equation will be found to be the same as (2) of Para. 18.6, th whirling speed ω being equal to $2\pi f$. In fact *any problem of whirling ma be treated by the same methods as for transverse vibrations*, a conclusio which could also be deduced from the fact that a point moving wit simple harmonic motion along a straight line can be represented by point moving round a circle, with uniform velocity, based on th straight line as diameter.

The cases (a) and (c) of Para. 18.6 then correspond to:

"short" bearings, $\omega=(\pi^2/l^2)\sqrt{(EI/m)}$

$$=(9{\cdot}85/l^2)\sqrt{(EI/m)}$$

and "long" bearings, $\omega=(22{\cdot}4/l^2)\sqrt{(EI/m)}$

(b) *Whirling of single load* carried on a "light" shaft, the method f Para. 18.5 may be used giving

$$\omega = \sqrt{(g/\delta)}$$

(c) *Dunkerley's formula* (Para. 18.7) will give the whirling speed for combination of loads, taking into account the mass of the shaft,

$$1/\omega^2 = 1/\omega_s^2 + 1/\omega_1^2 + 1/\omega_2^2 + \ldots$$

(d) *The energy method* of Para. 18.8 may be applied, giving

$$\omega^2 = g\int mY\,dx / \int mY^2 dx \quad \text{for distributed loads}$$

nd

$$\omega^2 = g\Sigma MY/\Sigma MY^2 \quad \text{for concentrated loads}$$

EXAMPLE 8. *Calculate the lowest whirling speed of a steel shaft 50 mm 'iameter, 3 m long, carrying a wheel of mass 30 kg at 0·6 m from one end and ne of mass 20 kg at 0·9 m from the other end. The shaft may be considered imply supported in bearings at the ends. Density = 7800 kg/m³; E = '06,000 N/mm². (U.L.)*

For the shaft alone

$$\omega_s = (\pi^2/l^2)\sqrt{(EI/m)} \quad \text{by (a)}$$

$$= \frac{9{\cdot}85}{32}\sqrt{\frac{206{,}000 \times 4 \times \pi \times 50^4}{7800 \times \pi \times 50^2 \times 64}}$$

$$= 70{\cdot}3 \text{ radn./sec.}$$

For the 30 kg wheel alone

$$\omega_1 = \sqrt{(3EIl/Ma^2b^2)} \quad \text{by (b)}$$

$$= \sqrt{\frac{3 \times 206{,}000 \times \pi \times 50^4 \times 3}{30 \times 0{\cdot}6^2 \times 2{\cdot}4^2 \times 64 \times 10^6}}$$

$$= 95{\cdot}5 \text{ radn./sec.}$$

For the 20 kg wheel alone

$$\omega_2 = \sqrt{\frac{3 \times 206{,}000 \times \pi \times 50^4 \times 3}{20 \times 0{\cdot}9^2 \times 2{\cdot}1^2 \times 64 \times 10^6}}$$

$$= 89{\cdot}1 \text{ radn./sec.}$$

The combined whirling speed is given by Dunkerley's formula (c)

$$1/\omega^2 = 1/70{\cdot}3^2 + 1/95{\cdot}5^2 + 1/89{\cdot}1^2$$

or

$$\omega = 100/\sqrt{(2{\cdot}02 + 1{\cdot}10 + 1{\cdot}26)}$$

$$= 47{\cdot}8 \text{ radn./sec.}$$

$$= 457 \text{ r.p.m.}$$

18.10. Whirling of Eccentrically Mounted Mass. Consider a mass M, mounted on a shaft, with its centre of gravity eccentric by an amount e from the axis of rotation. When rotating, the centre of gravity, the axis of rotation, and the straight line between the bearings must lie in the same plane, but the centre of gravity may be "outside" or "inside" the axis of rotation (Fig. 18.8).

If k is the stiffness of the shaft (as a beam), defined as restoring forc per unit deflection at the load point, then for equilibrium when rotatin at an angular velocity ω

$$M(y \pm e)\omega^2 = ky$$

i.e.
$$\omega^2 = (k/M)y/(y \pm e) \quad (1)$$

or
$$y = \frac{\pm\omega^2}{k/M - \omega^2} \cdot e \quad (2)$$

Note that y tends to become infinite when $\omega = \sqrt{(k/M)} = \sqrt{(g/\delta)}$ which is the whirling speed independent of e.

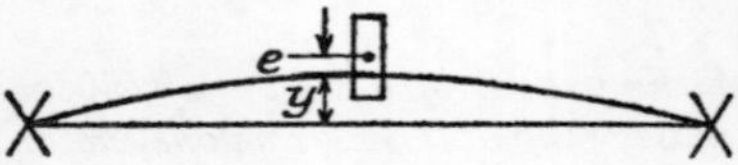

Fig. 18.8

When $\omega < \sqrt{(k/M)}$, the positiv sign is to be taken, i.e. the centre o gravity is now on the outside.

When $\omega > \sqrt{(k/M)}$ the negative sign is to be taken for e, showin that the centre of gravity is now on the inside. In fact when ω become very large $e \to -y$, the centre of gravity lying on the centre line betwee the bearings.

EXAMPLE 9. *A shaft 12 mm diameter rotates in spherical bearings with a span of 0·9 m, and carries a disc of mass 10 kg midway between bearings. Neglecting the mass of the shaft, determine its deflection in terms of the spee of rotation in radians per second if the mass centre of the disc is 0·25 mm ou of centre. E = 206,000 N/mm².*

If the stress in the shaft is not to exceed 100 N/mm² find the range of spee within which it is unsafe to run the shaft. (U.L.)

$$k = \frac{48EI}{l^3} = \frac{48 \times 206{,}000 \times \pi \times 12^4}{0{\cdot}9^3 \times 64 \times 10^6}$$

$$= 13{,}800 \text{ N/m}$$

$$y = \frac{\pm\omega^2}{13{,}800/10 - \omega^2} \times 0{\cdot}25 \text{ mm} \quad \text{from (2)}$$

$$= \frac{\pm 0{\cdot}25\omega^2}{1380 - \omega^2} \text{ mm}$$

A stress of 100 N/mm² would be caused by a *static* load o $100 \times (4/900) \times \pi \times 12^3/32$N, since the maximum bending moment i "$Wl/4$" and the section modulus "$\pi d^3/32$." Dividing by the stiffness, thi corresponds to a deflection

$$y = \frac{100 \times 4 \times \pi \times 12^3}{900 \times 32 \times 13{,}800} \text{ m}$$

$$= 4{\cdot}9 \text{ mm}$$

The range of speed is given by

$$\omega^2=(k/M)y/(y\pm e) \quad \text{from (1)}$$
$$=\frac{13{,}800}{10}\times\frac{4{\cdot}9}{4{\cdot}9\pm0{\cdot}25}$$
$$=1320 \quad \text{or} \quad 1460$$

i.e. ω between 36·4 radn./sec. and 38·2 radn. sec.

SUMMARY

Linear Vibrations: $t=2\pi\sqrt{(\delta/g)}$.
$f=1/t$.

Torsional Oscillations.

Single inertia: $2\pi f=\sqrt{(k/I)}$.

Two inertias: Node position $l_1/l_2=I_2/I_1$
$2\pi f=\sqrt{[k(I_1+I_2)/I_1I_2]}$.

Equivalent length of shaft of varying stiffness: $l=l'+l''\,(J'/J'')$.

Spring: $t=2\pi\sqrt{(64DnI/Ed^4)}$.

Transverse Vibrations.

Single mass: $2\pi f=\sqrt{(g/\delta)}$.

Uniform beam: $2\pi f=(\pi^2/l^2)\sqrt{(EI/m)}$ simple supported.

Dunkerley's formula: $1/f^2=1/f_b{}^2+1/f_1{}^2+1/f_2{}^2+\ldots$

Energy method: $4\pi^2f^2=g\int mY\,dx/\int mY^2dx$ for distributed load
$=g\Sigma MY/\Sigma MY^2$ for concentrated loads.

Whirling Speeds. Similar to transverse vibrations, with $\omega=2\pi f$.

PROBLEMS

1. A uniform vertical bar of steel of length l and cross-sectional area A, is fixed at the upper end and is extended a distance x by a load W at the lower end. If the rod is subjected to longitudinal vibrations, show that, at any instant when the additional extension is x, the change of potential energy measured from the rest position of the load is $\frac{1}{2}(AE/l)x^2$, and, from the energy equation, deduce the natural period of vibration. Find the length of bar to give a frequency of 100 vib./sec. when A is 640 mm²; $W=225$ kg; $E=208{,}000$ N/mm². (U.L.) (1·5 m.)

2. A mass of 5 kg is suspended from a spring of stiffness 1 kN/m. If it is set in motion with a maximum acceleration of 2·5 m/s², what are the amplitude and period of vibration? (12·5 mm; 0·444 s.)

3. A spring, fixed at its upper end, carries a mass of 1 kg at its lower end, which produces a static deflection of 38 mm. A further mass of 1 kg is suddenly applied to the original. Find the maximum elongation of the spring and show that the time of vertical oscillations is approximately $\frac{5}{9}$ sec. (114 mm.)

4. A vertical wire 3 mm diameter carries a heavy flywheel, radius of gyratio 168 mm, at its free end. The times of torsional and longitudinal vibrations ar 15 sec. and 0·06 sec. Find the value of Poisson's ratio. (0·2

5. The upper end of a vertical steel wire 2 mm diameter and 2 m long is hel securely. The other end is fixed centrally to a steel cylinder 75 mm diameter an of density 7700 kg/m^3, arranged with its axis horizontal. Find the length of th cylinder to give 0·6 torsional vibrations per second, and calculate the amplitud of vibrations when the maximum shear stress is 120 N/mm^2 G=80,000 N/mm^2 (U.L.) (104 mm 3 radn

6. A close-coiled helical steel spring is suspended vertically from one end. A uniform cylindrical bar of circular cross-section is fixed at its centre, with it axis horizontal, to the lower end of the spring, which has a mean coil diamete of 50 mm. If the longitudinal and angular oscillations have the same frequency find (a) the limiting length of bar of small diameter, and (b) the limiting diamete of bar of short length. G=81,000 N/mm^2; E=210,000 N/mm ^{2}. (U.L.) (99 mm; 114 mm

7. An engine shaft is directly coupled to the shaft of a dynamo. The engin shaft has a diameter of 56 mm and an effective length of 300 mm, while th dynamo shaft has a diameter of 50 mm and an effective length of 225 mm. Th flywheel mass is 225 kg and has a radius of gyration of 350 mm, and the armatur mass is 135 kg and its radius of gyration is 250 mm. Neglecting the inertia of th coupling and shafts, determine the position of the node and the frequency o torsional oscillations. Both shafts are steel, G=80,000 N/mm^2. (U.L.) (153 mm from engine; 21·6/sec.

8. The flywheel of an engine driving a dynamo has a mass of 136 kg and has a radius of gyration of 0·25 m. The armature has a mass of 100 kg and a radius o gyration of 0·2 m. The driving shaft has an effective length of 0·45 m and i 50 mm diameter, and a spring coupling is incorporated at one end, having a stiffness of 2·7 × 10^4 Nm/radn. Calculate the natural frequency of torsiona vibration of the system. What would be the frequency if the spring couplin were omitted? G=82,000 N/mm^2. (U.L.) (14·3/sec.; 32·3/sec.

9. The figures show (a) front elevation, and (b) side elevation, of a vibratin

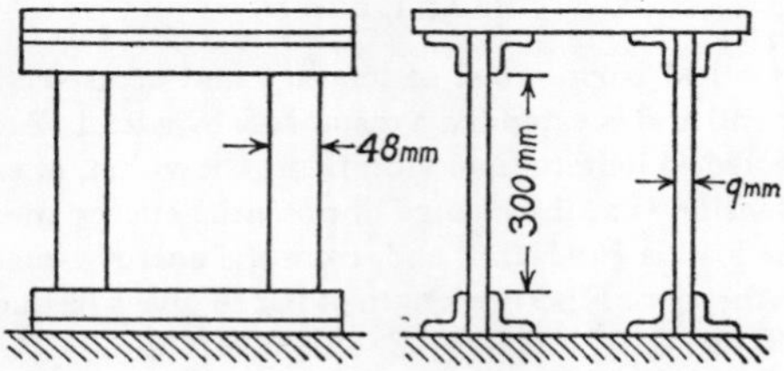

(a) (b)

table. Assume the ends of the supporting strips are rigidly fixed in direction and estimate the natural frequency of transverse vibration if the effective mass of the platform is 27 kg. E=207,000 N/mm^2. (U.L.) (31·4/sec.)

10. Obtain from first principles an expression for the fundamental natural frequency of transverse vibrations of a cantilever of length l and mass per unit

ngth m, assuming the vibration curve to be of the same form as the static eflection curve.

Hence find the natural frequency of transverse vibration of a steel turbine lade of uniform section 127 mm long, of mass 2 kg per metre length and least ıoment of inertia 2500 mm^4. Ignore centrifugal loading. $E = 208{,}000$ N/mm^2. U.L.) [$(0{\cdot}562/l^2)\sqrt{(EI/m)}$; 562/sec.]

11. A small turbine rotor has a shaft of uniform section, $EI = 1{\cdot}09 \times 10^6$ Nm^2 nd is freely supported in two bearings at 1 m centres. It carries three equal vheels, 350 kg each, at positions 0·25 m, 0·38 m and 0·5 m from one bearing. The tatic deflections at the wheels are 0·127 mm, 0·157 mm, and 0·162 mm respectvely. The maximum deflection occurs close to the third wheel, and is 0·165 mm. Compare the critical speeds as calculated by (a) Dunkerley method, (b) energy nethod, (c) use of rule.

Critical rev./minute $= 980/\sqrt{[\text{maximum static deflection (mm)}]}$ (U.L.)

(2420/min.; 2430/min.; 2420/min.)

12. A shaft 12·7 mm diameter rotates in "long" fixed bearings and a disc of 8 kg is secured to the shaft at the middle of its length. The span between bearngs is 0·61 m. The mass centre of the disc is 0·5 mm from the axis of the shaft. Neglecting the mass of the shaft, determine the central deflection in terms of the peed in r.p.m. $E = 206{,}000$ N/mm^2. If the bending stress in the shaft is not to xceed 120 N/mm^2, find the range of speed over which this stress would be xceeded. (U.L.) (910 r.p.m.; 1310 r.p.m.)

CHAPTER XIX

Material Testing and Experimental Methods

19.1. Tensile Tests. The behaviour of a ductile material, such a mild steel, when subjected to a simple tensile test, was described i Para. 1.7. It was shown that, up to a certain value of stress, strain i proportional to stress, and if the load is removed within this range ther will be no permanent strain (i.e. the material is stressed in the "elastic range). If the load is increased the material "yields," undergoing a larg "plastic" strain at a constant stress value. As the load is further in creased appreciable strain (mostly plastic) occurs up to the " ultimate stress value. At this stage the specimen begins to "neck" at som position along its length, the load falling off until fracture occurs. Mos engineering materials show these features to a varying degree, an definitions of the principal values will be found in Para. 1.7. It is pro posed to discuss some particular aspects of the tensile test and th significance of the results obtained.

(a) *The "working" portion* of the specimen is either circular or rec tangular in cross-section, and is enlarged at each end for a length suit able for the grips. The ends may be screwed into the grips, or they ma be provided with a shoulder through which the load is transmitted, o they may be held between wedge grips with roughened inside faces. Th latter method is the simplest and cheapest to employ, and is alway used for flat specimens, but it is limited to the "softer" steels an other metals. It is important that the grips should be self-centrin in order that the load shall be applied axially and evenly over th specimen (for a circular cross-section an eccentricity of $0{\cdot}01d$ in th load increases the maximum stress by 8%).

(b) *Testing machines* fall generally into two categories, one in whicl the load is applied manually, and the other in which hydraulic pressur is utilised, the choice depending largely on the capacity required. Ir either case the applied load is measured by a balance weight through system of levers. The latest types of hydraulically operated testin machines are self-indicating, the balancing mechanism being actuate by a piston working in a cylinder supplied with the same pressure a the main straining unit.

(c) In the elastic range strain is measured by an "*extensometer*" ttached to the gauge length. This is an instrument which can detect ery small changes in length, and various types in common use will be escribed later (Paras. 19.9 and 19.10). In the plastic region the much arger strains involved may be detected by means of a pair of dividers nd scale rule.

(d) *Effect of rate of loading*. It has been found that, except for hardened teels, the more rapid the test the higher the values of yield stress and ltimate stress, and the greater the elongation obtained.

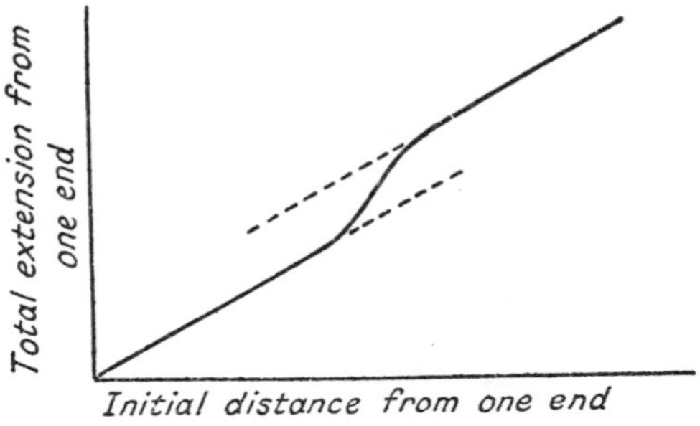

Fig. 19.1

(e) *Variation of elongation with gauge length and cross-sectional area.* If a specimen is marked off at a large number of intervals along its length and tested to destruction, the two pieces may be fitted together and the distance of each gauge mark from one end can be remeasured. Subtracting the initial distances gives total extension reckoned from one end, and when plotted against distance from that end will reveal a graph such as Fig. 19.1. This consists of two parallel straight lines, the sudden increase of extension taking place in the region of the neck at fracture. There is said to be a "*local*" *extension* at the fracture and a "*uniform*" *extension* along the remainder of the specimen. Let e be the extension over a gauge length l, chosen such that the fracture is approximately at the centre of the gauge length, then $e=a+bl$ expresses the form of the graph.

The percentage elongation $=100e/l=100a/l+100b$.

Unwin found that, for a given material, a was proportional to the square root of the original cross-sectional area A, and writing $100a= C\sqrt{A}$ and $100b=B$, the law becomes

$$100\frac{e}{l}=C\frac{\sqrt{A}}{l}+B$$

The following values are given for the constants B and C for mild steel: $B=20$, $C=70$. In order to eliminate any error in comparison of elongation figures it is recommended in B.S.18 that the gauge length should be $4\sqrt{A}$.

(f) *Overstrain—repeated loading*. If, in a tensile test on a steel specimen, the load is carried beyond the yield point and then gradually released, there will of course be considerable permanent set in the specimen. On reloading it will be found by careful observation that the steel appears to have lost its elasticity, i.e. it no longer obeys Hooke's law. In fact the unloading and reloading curves form a "hysteresis" loop which represents energy wasted in internal friction (Fig. 19.2). The yield point will be considerably raised, almost as high as the stress value at the end of the previous test, and the material is said to be work-hardened, as in cold drawing or rolling processes.

Repeated loadings will raise the yield point to a value approaching the ultimate stress. If continued until fracture, this will exhibit the characteristics of a hard steel, with only a small reduction in area and a much reduced elongation.

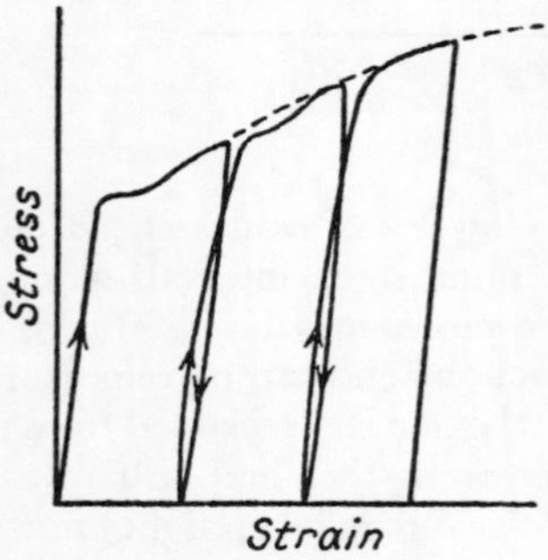

Fig. 19.2

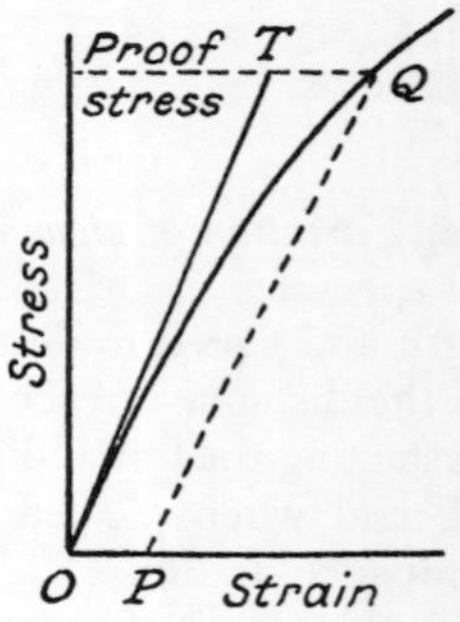

Fig. 19.3

Elasticity can be recovered by a long period of rest or by boiling in water for a few minutes. Annealing will return the steel to its original condition before overstraining, with the same yield point, etc.

(g) *Proof Stress*. Many materials, notably some alloy steels and light alloys of aluminium and magnesium, do not possess any definite limit of proportionality or yield point in a tensile test, the stress strain diagram being curved almost from the origin (Fig. 19.3).

If a tangent to the curve at the origin is drawn (OT) and a line PQ is drawn parallel to OT, cutting the curve at Q, such that $OP = 0{\cdot}1\%$, then the stress at Q is called the $0{\cdot}1\%$ proof stress. It is the stress at which the strain has departed by $0{\cdot}1\%$ of the gauge length from the line of proportionality OT.

19.2. Compression Tests. Specimens for compression tests on metals are usually circular, and for concrete square, in section. To prevent failure by buckling, the length should be of about the same order as the minimum width.

For a ductile material such as mild steel or copper lateral distortion takes place, and, due to the restraining influence of friction at the load faces, the cross-section becomes greatest at the centre, the test piece taking up a barrel shape. Failure finally occurs by cracks appearing on the surface and spreading inwards.

Brittle materials such as cast iron and cement usually fail by shearing along planes inclined at between 50° and 70° to the longitudinal axis.

19.3. Hardness Tests. Hardness represents the resistance of a material to indentation, and involves the measurement of plastic deformation caused when a loaded ball or diamond is applied to the surface of the material. Two of the principal commercial methods will be described below.

(a) *Brinell Method.* In this a hardened steel ball is pressed into the surface under a specified load which is held on for a fixed period and then released. A permanent impression is left in the surface, and the "Brinell Number" is defined as the ratio of the applied load in kilogrammes to the spherical area of the impression in square millimetres. In practice either the diameter or the depth of the impression is measured, and conversion tables used to determine the hardness number.

The application of the Brinell method is limited to materials with hardness numbers below 500, as above this value distortion of the steel ball appreciably affects the readings. For thin sheets the results are only reliable if the thickness is at least 10 times the depth of the impression (B.S.240, Pt. I).

(b) *Vickers Pyramid Diamond Method.* The method is basically similar to the Brinell, the indenter being a 136° pyramid diamond on a square base. Owing to the extreme hardness of the diamond it can be used over the whole range of material hardnesses, and there is a linear relationship between the depth of impression and the hardness number.

The calculation of the "Vickers Pyramid Number"(V.P.N.) is again based on the ratio of load to impressed area, the latter being obtained by measuring the length of a diagonal of the square impression at the surface of the material under test.

The limiting thickness of the test piece is $1\frac{1}{2}$ times the diagonal of the impression (B.S. 427).

The *Firth Hardometer* and the *Rockwell Hardness Tester* are similar in operation to the Brinell and Vickers diamond machines, though the Rockwell uses the *depth* of the impression as the criterion of hardness.

(c) *Shore Scleroscope Method.* A small weight, known as the hammer fitted with a diamond tip or a steel bar on its under surface, is dropped from a height of 25 cm. onto the surface under test. The height of the rebound is used as a measure of the hardness of the surface.

There is no direct relation between the Shore hardness and the Brinell and V.P.N., the ratio between the two varying for different materials. However, this method can be used as a standard of comparison, and in cases where an indentation is undesirable or the surface is inaccessible to the normal hardness testing machines.

(d) *Relation of hardness to tensile strength.* It is found that there is an approximate linear relation, such that

Ultimate tensile strength $(\text{N/mm}^2) = k \times$ Hardness number

For mild steel, $k = 3{\cdot}5$.

For alloy steel, $k = 3{\cdot}2$.

19.4. Impact Tests. Static tests are not satisfactory in determining the resistance to shock or impact loads such as automobile parts are subjected to, and in the impact test a notched specimen of the material is fractured by a single blow from a heavy hammer, the energy required being a measure of the resistance to impact.

Izod Impact Machine. This is the most commonly used type, and is illustrated diagrammatically in Fig. 19.4. The specimen (dimensions are

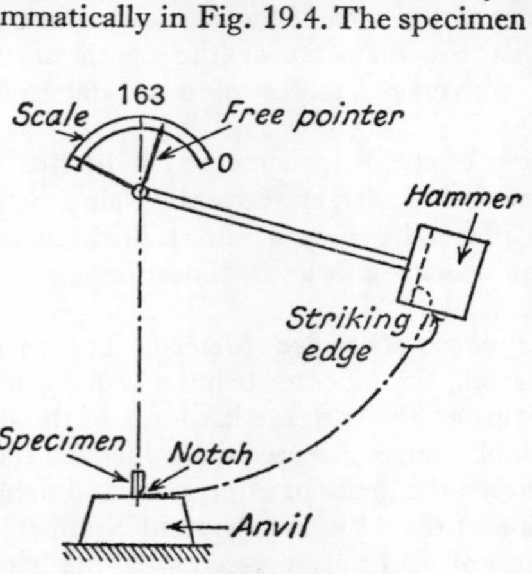

Fig. 19.4

laid down in B.S.131) is fixed in the anvil with the notch at the level of the top face and on the side of the falling hammer. The hammer is released from a fixed position (such that the total potential energy of fall is 163 Nm), strikes the specimen, which breaks, and continues for some distance on the other side. By means of a pointer which moves eely over a scale the energy absorbed in fracturing the test piece is corded.

The *Charpy* impact test is similar in principle to the *Izod*, but the tched specimen is supported at each end as a "beam", and struck the hammer in the centre.

The impact test has been found particularly valuable in revealing emper brittleness" in heat-treated nickel-chrome steels (see Para. .6), and also in revealing the resistance to fracture due to stress con- ntrations in a member. The notch sets up conditions of stress con- ntration from which cracks are liable to start, and for brittle materials ss energy is required to fracture the specimen than for ductile materials.

19.5. Effect of Carbon Content. The variation of mechanical operties in plain carbon steel in the annealed condition is shown in g. 19.5.

It will be seen that the ultimate strength and hardness values increase gether with increased carbon content, the elastic limit (and similarly e yield point) increasing at a reduced rate. At the same time there is marked falling off in ductility indicated by the decrease in values for ongation and reduction in area, steel containing more than about 6% carbon exhibiting a "brittle" type of fracture.

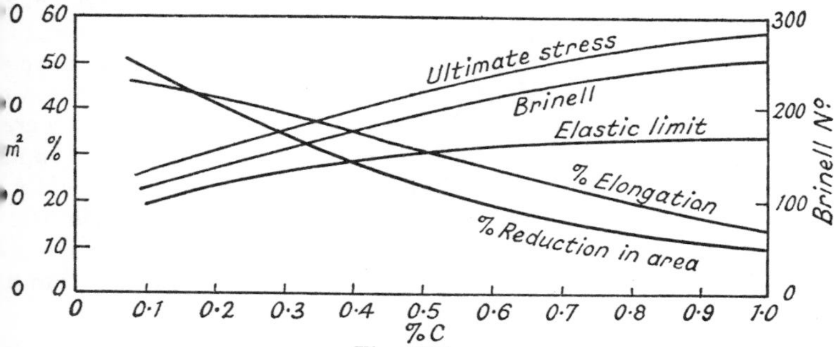

Fig. 19.5

19.6. Effect of Tempering. Nickel-chrome alloy steels are in wide e where a material possessing a high-tensile strength combined with fair measure of ductility is required. A typical heat treatment which ill bring out the best combination of mechanical properties is a rdening from about 850° C. (either by quenching in oil or cooling in r), followed by tempering at about 180° C. It will be seen from Fig. 19.6 at tempering reduces very slightly the ultimate strength, while raising e yield point from the fully hardened state. At the same time the ictility measured by reduction in area is increased, and a peak is ached on the curve of impact values.

Note the "temper brittleness" indicated by the impact values f temperatures between 200° C. and 400° C. referred to in Para. 19.4.

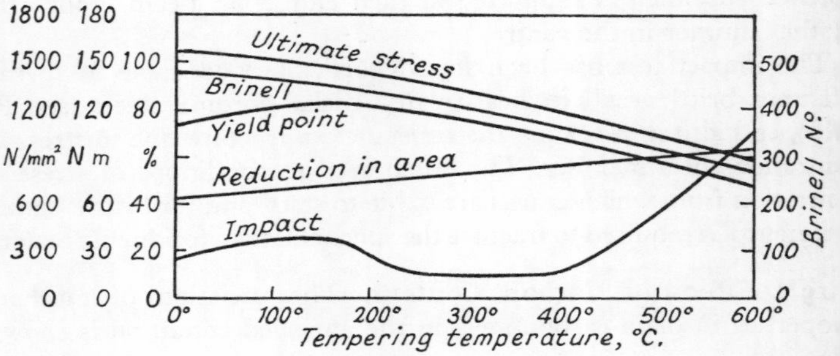

Fig. 19.6

19.7. Creep. It has been found that at elevated temperatures a me in tension will continue to elongate under a constant stress which m be much less than the ultimate tensile stress. This phenomenon called "creep," and is measured by the rate of strain per hour under certain stress at a given temperature.

If a "short time" tensile test is carried out on a metal specimen at specific temperature a fairly definite ultimate stress is obtained. T material may be made to fail by creep under a lower stress, howeve provided sufficient time is allowed, the rate of creep depending on t stress. At any temperature there is a limiting stress below which cre will not take place, i.e. the metal will not fracture if the stress is appli for an indefinite period. This limiting creep stress may frequently less than half the ultimate stress obtained in a normal tensile test that temperature. In designing any part which is stressed at high ter peratures it is clearly necessary to base the working stress on the limiti creep stress.

Special alloy steels containing small percentages of molybdenu vanadium, cobalt or tungsten, have been developed which are cree resisting, for applications such as gas-turbine blades and high-pressu steam fittings.

In practice a very lengthy investigation is involved to determine t limiting creep stress, since at stresses near to this value tests must extended over months or even years to determine the strain. It usual, therefore, to circumvent this difficulty by finding the stress which a definite very small rate of creep takes place after a short period of test. The creep rate is known to diminish with time and typical stress value obtained by a test of this nature is that which w cause a creep of 1 millionth per hour after 40 days. *Ludwig's* law giv

: creep rate at a stress σ as Ce^{σ}, where C and k are constants for a 'en material.

19.8. Fatigue. Many machine parts are subjected to fluctuating esses, taking place at relatively high frequencies, and under these con- :ions failure is found to occur at stress values much lower than would ply for static loading. The phenomenon is known as "fatigue" failure.

The *range of stress* (R) over which fluctuations occur is the algebraic ference between the maximum and minimum stresses, treating com- ession as negative. A *mean stress* M may be defined such that the niting stresses are $M \pm R/2$. Particular cases which frequently occur are:

(1) When the mean stress is zero and the fluctuations are of equal tension and compression (known as "*reversed stress*").

(2) When $M = R/2$, so that the stress ranges from zero to R (known as *repeated stress*).

Fluctuating stresses occur in practice under three main types of ading:

(a) direct stresses (tension and compression),
(b) bending stresses,
(c) torsional stresses.

Testing machines have been developed to reproduce each of these pes, and design stresses should be related to the conditions under hich the part is to operate.

Experiments show that, for a given mean stress, there is a limiting nge of stress below which fracture will not take place for an indefinite imber of cycles. This range is known as the *Endurance* or *Fatigue imit*, and may be quoted as a maximum and minimum stress or as a nge about a certain mean. The fatigue limit in reversed bending is und to be about 25% higher than in reversed tension and compression, obably due to the stress gradient. In reversed torsion the fatigue nit for shear stress is about 0·55 times the tensile fatigue limit.

In order to determine the fatigue limit at a given mean stress, it is ecessary to carry out a series of tests on specimens subjected to a adually decreasing range of stress. It will then be found that the imber of cycles of stress required to fracture each specimen increases, id as the fatigue limit is approached some hundreds of millions of versals may be withstood. From practical considerations it is fre- uently considered acceptable to use as the limit that stress range which ill not cause fracture after 10 million, or in some cases 100 million rcles.

The maximum stress corresponding to the fatigue limit (given by $I + R/2$) will be least under conditions of reversed stress (i.e. $M = 0$), id will be well within the elastic limit.

Factors of design which affect the fatigue strength are:

(1) Stress concentrations caused by sudden changes in cross-sectio and features such as screw threads and keyways. Fatigue failures a found to start from cracks at these points of stress concentration, ve little redistribution of stress being possible even in ductile materia However, the stress concentration factor under fatigue conditions found to be rather less than under static conditions.

(2) Surface treatment. Considerable improvement in the fatig strength of manufactured parts can be achieved by surface hardeni (e.g. carburising) or by work hardening processes. Cold rolling ar shot peening have been found to give increases of up to 20% in t endurance limit, due to surface hardening and to the residual com pressive stresses set up which resist the formation of fatigue cracks.

(3) Surface finish. The highest fatigue strength is obtained wit smooth ground surfaces, particularly in the case of high-tensile steel

(4) The frequency of stress reversals also influences the fatig limit, which is higher for increased frequency.

The most satisfactory empirical formula embodying the exper mental results for steels is due to Gerber, which may be written:

$$\sigma = R/2 + \sqrt{(\sigma_u^2 - nR\sigma_u)} \tag{1}$$

where σ is the maximum stress during each cycle at the fatigue limi
R is the stress range,
σ_u is the normal ultimate tensile stress,
and n is a constant for one material.

For mild steel, $n = 1{\cdot}5$, for high-tensile steel, $n = 2{\cdot}0$.

Applied to the particular cases previously mentioned:

(1) Reversed stresses

$$\sigma = R/2$$

and it can easily be shown that

$$\sigma = \sigma_u/2n = \sigma_u/3 \quad \text{for mild steel}$$

(2) Repeated stresses

$$\sigma = R$$

and solving the equation gives

$$\sigma = 0{\cdot}61\ \sigma_u \quad \text{for mild steel}$$

Noting that $\sigma - R/2 = M$, Gerber's formula can be re-arranged t give

$$R = \frac{\sigma_u}{n}\left(1 - \frac{M^2}{\sigma_u^2}\right) \tag{2}$$

and Goodman suggested a simpler straight line law relating the stre range and the mean stress, i.e.

$$R = \frac{\sigma_u}{n}\left(1 - \frac{M}{\sigma_u}\right) \tag{3}$$

ote that in both formulae σ_u/n is the stress range for reversed stress nditions (i.e. $M=0$) and Fig. 19.7 shows the variation of R with M

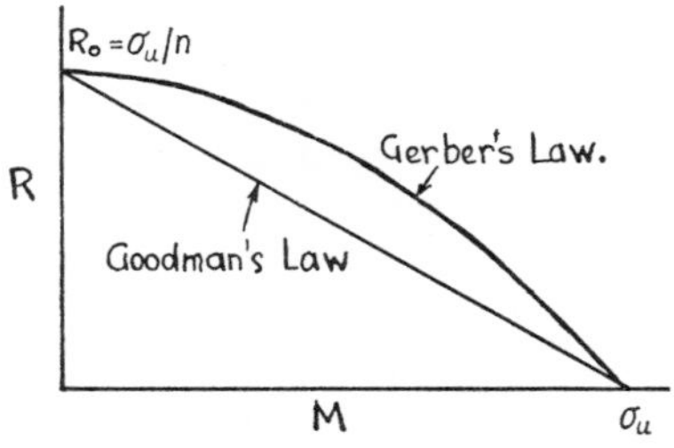

Fig. 19.7

:cording to Gerber and Goodman. In practice, if the values of σ_u and $_0$ $(=\sigma_u/n)$ for a given material are found by experiment, the fatigue mits under other conditions can be determined from this diagram.

EXAMPLE 1. *If the ultimate tensile strength of a material is 600 N/mm² and s endurance limit under reversed stress is ±180 N/mm², calculate the nstant n according to Gerber's law. What is the maximum stress at the tigue limit for repeated stress conditions (i.e. minimum stress zero), accord-g to Gerber's law and Goodman's law?*

Under reversed stress $M=0$, $\sigma=180$ N/mm² and $R=360$ N/mm². By erber's formula

$$n=\sigma_u/R$$
$$=600/360=5/3$$

Under repeated stress $R=\sigma$ and $M=\frac{1}{2}\sigma$

rom (2), $$\sigma=\tfrac{3}{5}.600(1-\sigma^2/4\times 600^2)$$

e. $$\sigma^2/4000+\sigma-360=0$$

iving $$\sigma=[-1+\sqrt{(1+9/25)}]2000$$
$$=335 \text{ N/mm}^2$$

rom (3), Goodman's law gives

$$\sigma=\tfrac{3}{5}.600(1-\sigma/2\times 600)$$

iving $$\sigma=360\times 10/13=277 \text{ N/mm}^2$$

If a machine part is run for a series of cycles n_1, n_2... at different tress levels, and the corresponding fatigue life at each level is N_1, N_2... cycles, Miner suggested that failure could be expected when $\Sigma n/N=1$. Experiments show variations in this factor from 0·6 to 1·5, he higher values being obtained for sequences of increasing loads.

For fatigue failures under combined bending and torsion, Gou showed that the ellipse

$$\frac{\sigma^2}{\sigma_0^{\,2}}+\frac{\tau^2}{\tau_0^{\,2}}=1$$

fitted the experimental results, where σ_0 and τ_0 are the direct and she stress fatigue limits under pure bending and pure torsion respectivel and σ and τ are the corresponding endurance limits under combin bending and torsion.

19.9. Extensometers. The strains involved within the elastic ran of stress in engineering materials do not exceed about 1 part in 100 and instruments used to measure such small linear movements a called extensometers or strain gauges. Magnification is usually achiev mechanically, as in types (1) and (3) below, or optically, as in (2), or a combination of both. Electrical resistance strain gauges are dealt wi separately in Para. 19.10.

The first two described are designed specifically for use with tensi test pieces, and work on a fixed gauge length, giving a reading of t mean extension along opposite sides. The third type measures surfa strain and can be fixed to any structure.

(1) *Cambridge Extensometer* (Fig. 19.8). This consists of two separa pieces clamped by means of conical pointed screws into gauge poin on the test specimen.

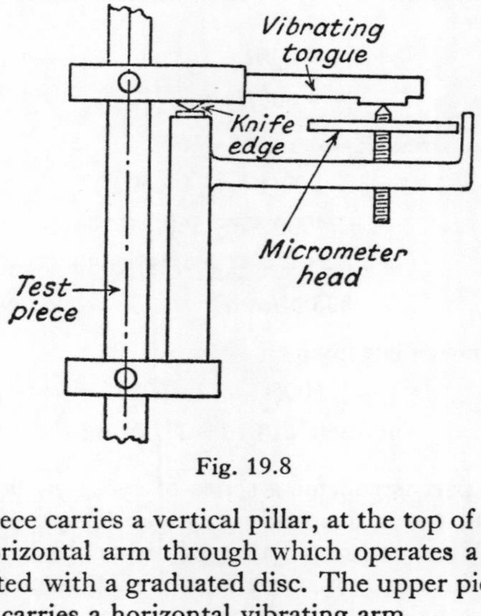

Fig. 19.8

The lower piece carries a vertical pillar, at the top of which is a kni edge, and a horizontal arm through which operates a vertical micr meter screw fitted with a graduated disc. The upper piece rests on t knife edge and carries a horizontal vibrating arm.

A reading is taken by setting the vibrating arm in motion and gradu-y bringing up the screw point until it just makes contact with the ıgue on the underside of the arm. The correct setting is indicated by ɛ noise and by the damping out of vibrations.

The relative distances of knife edge and micrometer screw from the is of the specimen produce a magnification of extension of five times, d the micrometer head is so divided that each division represents an tension of 0·002 mm on the test piece. Smaller intervals may be judged eye.

(2) *Ewing's Extensometer* (Fig. 19.9). The upper piece is fitted with an justable screw on one side, and at an equal distance on the other side ngs a small tube. At the lower end of the tube is a glass window on ıich is inscribed a fine horizontal line. This line is viewed by a micro-ope and focused on a scale in the eyepiece. The microscope is fixed the lower piece of the instrument, the two pieces turning about a vot joint between the ball end of the pillar extension of the lower ece and the conical seat in the end of the screw on the upper piece.

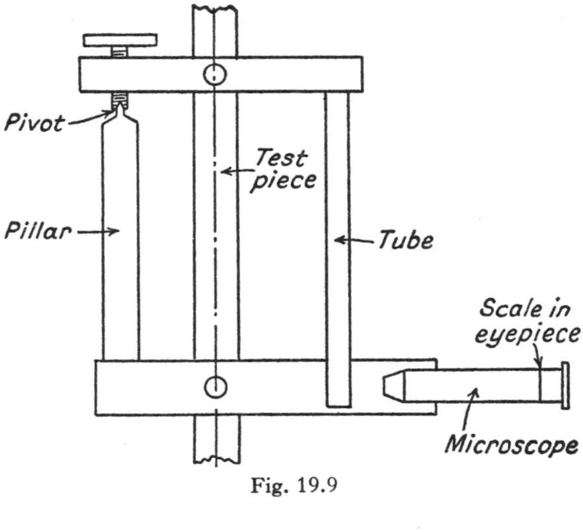

Fig. 19.9

The movement of the tube is twice the extension of the test piece, nd the optical magnification is such that an accuracy of 0·0005 mm xtension can be obtained. A considerable range can be obtained by ringing the scale back to zero by means of the adjustable screw, and ıis enables extensions beyond the elastic limit to be measured.

(3) *Huggenberger Extensometer*. A magnification of about 1000 times s obtained entirely mechanically by a double-lever system.

The pivots A and C (Fig. 19.10) are fixed to the frame, and B and D a movable. The rocker BD serves to transmit motion from the knife-ed arm to the pointer arm, and is held in position by a spring attached its other end to AB. The frame is held by a suitable clamp so that t knife edges press on to the surface, and the pointer may be set to ze by an adjustment not shown. The gauge length may be varied fitting extension pieces, and marked gauge points are necessary.

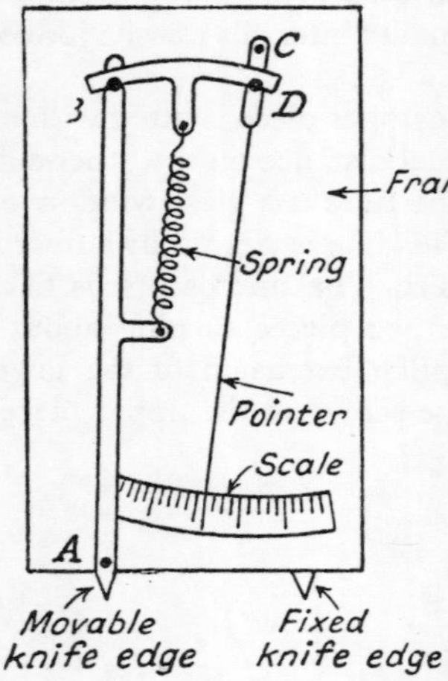

Fig. 19.10

Readings are taken directly off t scale, and converted into extensi or compression by dividing by t particular magnification factor. T smallest measurable movement about 0·0005 mm.

19.10. Electrical Resistan Strain Gauges. It was first d covered by Lord Kelvin in abo 1850 that if metal wires are stretch they undergo a change in electri resistance. This property has be made use of to develop a gauge f measuring the surface strain structures and machine parts.

The most commonly used materi are copper-nickel alloys, which have been found to possess a fai high sensitivity to change in resistance, and a low temperatu coefficient. In order to obtain an appreciable resistance from a sho length of wire, diameters of about 0·025 mm are employed. The wire wound on flat formers, and bonded between layers of resin-impre nated paper to form a flat grid as shown in Fig. 19·11. The total resi tance is usually in the region of 100 to 1000 ohms, and gauges vary size from 1 to 25 mm.

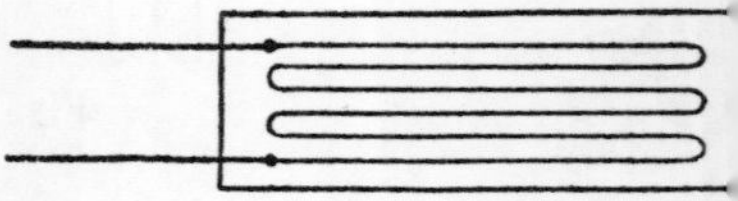

Fig. 19.11

The surface to which the gauge is to be attached is cleaned and grease is removed by washing with acetone or other chemical. It is then roughened by rubbing with fine emery, and the gauge is fixed by a suitable cement. Several days are necessary to ensure comple drying, unless moderate heat is used. When thoroughly dry the gau should be given a protective coating against atmospheric humidit which will cause corrosion of the wires.

Measurement of change in resistance is by means of a Wheatsto idge circuit (Fig. 19.12). Note that a "dummy" gauge is used to ance the active gauge. The dummy gauge is fixed to a piece of the ne material as the active gauge and kept in the same vicinity, so that ains (and hence changes of resistance) produced by change in nperature will be compensated for.

With no load on and the contact on the slide wire set at zero the mmy and active bridge arms are balanced by adjustment of the riable resistance. When the load is applied, stressing the active gauge, lance is restored by means of the slide re contact, which can be calibrated to ad change of resistance directly.

Change of resistance is converted into ain by means of the *gauge sensitivity ctor*, which is the ratio between fracnal change of resistance and strain. is factor is determined by calibration samples from a batch of similar gauges. accurate work a correction must be ade for the strain in a lateral direction, . the width of the gauge. The numerical lue of the gauge factor is approximately and depends not only on the actual anges of dimensions of the wire, but so on a change in specific resistance hich takes place under stress. Up to a niting strain value the factor is found to be constant.

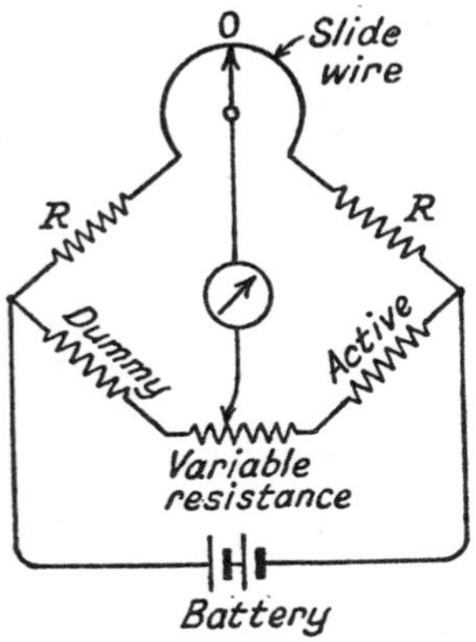

Fig. 19.12

Obvious advantages of the resistance strain gauge are that it can be ed in places which are inaccessible to normal types of extensometers, d that, with the use of a multi-channel bridge, up to 100 gauges can "read" in a short space of time. Once the gauges are fixed and procted against the atmosphere, tests can be extended over months or ars, which may be a useful asset in detecting changes of stress stribution.

If the directions of the principal stresses at the surface are not known, rain "rosettes," consisting of three gauges fixed at known relative gles, are used to determine them. Torsional stresses in shafts are easured by two gauges at right angles, placed with their axes at 45° to e shaft axis (see Para. 3.4), these gauges occupying the positions arked "dummy" and "active" in Fig. 19.12. Oscillatory stresses may e investigated by applying the fluctuations of voltage across the gauge a cathode-ray oscillograph or galvanometer recorder.

The methods of Para. 3.16 can be used to determine the principal resses from the measured strains in three directions at a point. The following results are quoted for reference. For the rectangular rose (gauge directions 0, 45° and 90°), the principal stresses are

$$\frac{E}{2}\left\{\frac{\varepsilon_0+\varepsilon_{90}}{1-\nu}\pm\frac{1}{1+\nu}\sqrt{[(\varepsilon_0-\varepsilon_{90})^2+(2\varepsilon_{45}-\varepsilon_0-\varepsilon_{90})^2]}\right\}$$

and for the delta rosette (gauge directions 0, 60°, and 120°), the princi stresses are

$$E\left\{\frac{\varepsilon_0+\varepsilon_{60}+\varepsilon_{120}}{3\,(1-\nu)}\pm\frac{1}{1+\nu}\sqrt{\left[(1-\nu^2)\left(\varepsilon_0-\frac{\varepsilon_0+\varepsilon_{60}+\varepsilon_{120}}{3}\right)^2+\frac{(\varepsilon_{60}-\varepsilon_{120})^2}{3}\right]}\right.$$

19.11. Photo-elastic Stress Analysis. This method is based the phenomenon of double refraction exhibited by transpare materials when subjected to stress. It was first discovered by Brews in 1816 when experimenting on glass, but it was not developed for abc a hundred years due to the difficulty of producing models from such brittle material. Coker and Filon were the pioneers of work on proble of stress analysis, using celluloid models. Since 1930 many other plas materials with suitable properties have been developed for this work

The method consists of observing a loaded model in a beam polarised light, and a simple arrangement is shown in Fig. 19.13. Mon chromatic light (either mercury or sodium vapour) is normally used, a a parallel beam is obtained by means of a condenser lens. The polaris and analyser are either natural crystals or "Polaroid" discs. T quarter-wave plates are of mica, their thickness being related to t wavelength of the light source. The model is carried in a loading fran and placed as shown. Light- and dark-coloured bands are produced the screen, and may be photographed for subsequent analysis. It is n proposed to discuss the theory of light waves, but an outline of t effects obtained and their interpretation is given below.

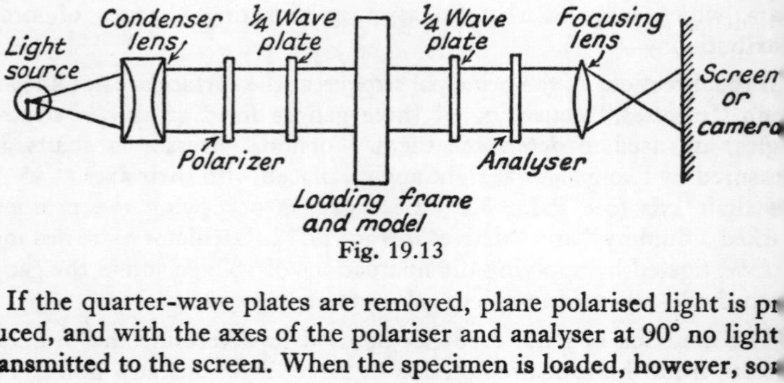

Fig. 19.13

If the quarter-wave plates are removed, plane polarised light is pr duced, and with the axes of the polariser and analyser at 90° no light transmitted to the screen. When the specimen is loaded, however, sor ht is passed through, except at points where the direction of one incipal stress is in the plane of polarisation. The result is a dark band ross the model indicating the locus of all points at which the principal esses are in the same directions. These bands are called *isoclinics*, d by rotating the polariser and analyser together a series of isoclinics n be obtained for various directions of principal stress.

The quarter-wave plates, placed with their axes at 45° to those of the lariser and analyser, produce circularly polarised light, and serve to t out the isoclinics. It can be shown that, under this arrangement, ;ht is extinguished on passing through the model and analyser at ints where the principal stress difference (or maximum shear stress) proportional to a value depending on the optical properties of the aterial and the thickness of the model. Consequently a series of dark nds are produced on the screen (*isochromatic* fringes), from which e values of stress difference can be determined. Calibration of the lue of stress represented by the fringes is carried out by a simple nsile or bending test on a piece of the same material.

At a free boundary the principal stresses must be parallel and per-endicular to the boundary, the latter being of zero value. Consequently e edge stresses can normally be determined directly from the fringes, id this may be sufficient indication of stress concentrations. If the dividual principal stresses are required for a more detailed analysis the llowing methods are available:

(1) Numerical integration along a line, starting from a free boundary.

(2) Numerical determination of values of the principal stress sum by relaxation methods, values at the free boundary being known.

(3) Experimental determination of the principal stress sum by use of lateral extensometer.

19.12. Brittle Lacquers. These are coatings which can be spread on ie surface to be tested, and when dry form a layer which will crack when he surface strain exceeds a certain value. They are particularly useful or indicating the weakest section of a complicated structure under oad (by watching where the cracks in the lacquer first appear), and or finding the directions of the principal stresses at the surface (the irection of the cracks being perpendicular to the maximum tensile tress).

Quantitative strain analysis must be carried out under carefully con-rolled conditions of temperature and humidity, which affect the esponse of the lacquer. The strain is then estimated by the spacing lensity of the cracks as compared with a calibration bar under known oading.

REFERENCES

CAZAUD, R., *Fatigue of Metals*. Chapman & Hall. 1953.

DOBIE, W. B., and ISAAC, P. C. G., *Electrical Resistance Strain Gauges*.E.U 1948.

DOVE, R. C., and ADAMS, P. H., *Experimental Stress Analysis and Mot Measurement*. Merrill Books. 1964.

FENNER, A. J., *Mechanical Testing of Materials*. Newnes. 1965.

FROCHT, M. M., *Photo-Elasticity*. J. Wiley. 1949.

GROVER, H. J., GORDON, S. A., JACKSON, L. P., *Fatigue of Metals and Structu* Thames & Hudson. 1956.

HEYWOOD, R. B., *Designing by Photo-Elasticity*. Chapman & Hall. 1952.

HEYWOOD, R. B., *Designing against Fatigue*. Chapman & Hall. 1962.

JESSOP, H. T., and HARRIS, F. C., *Photoelasticity*. Cleaver-Hume. 1949.

JUDGE, A. W., *Engineering Materials* (Vols. 1–3). Pitman.

LAMBLE, J. H., *Mechanical Testing and Inspection*. Cleaver-Hume. 1956.

LEE, G. H., *Experimental Stress Analysis*. J. Wiley. 1950.

LESSELLS, J. M., *Strength and Resistance of Metals*. J. Wiley. 1954.

MINISTRY OF SUPPLY (AERONAUTICAL RESEARCH COUNCIL). *Some Experiments the Resistance of Metals to Fatigue under Combined Stresses*. H.M.S.O. 19

PERRY, C. C., and LISSNER, H. R., *Strain Gage Primer*. McGraw-Hill. 1955.

SULLY, A. H., *Metallic Creep*. Butterworth. 1949.

TABOR, D., *The Hardness of Metals*. O.U.P. 1951.

TEED, P. L., *The Properties of Metallic Materials at Low Temperatures*. Chapm & Hall. 1950.

ZIENKIEWICZ, O. C., and HOLISTER, G. S., *Stress Analysis*. J. Wiley. 1965.

APPENDIX

Table of Elastic Constants

These values are only approximate, and in many cases vary considerably depending on the condition of the material (i.e. cast, forged, drawn, etc.) and its heat treatment.

Material	E N/mm²	G N/mm²	Elastic limit N/mm²	Ultimate tensile strength N/mm²	Elongation %
Brass	102,000	38,000	—	350	40
Bronze	116,000	45,000	210	310	20
Cast iron	96,000	41,000	—	210	8
Duralumin	72,000	26,000	280	380	18
Monel metal	180,000	70,000	410	550	20
Mild steel	202,000	80,000	280	480	25
Nickel-chrome steel	206,000	82,000	1200	1650	12
Timber	12,000	1,000	48	70	—

Index

Bars, compound, 14
—, curved, 195
Beams, bending stress in, 86
—, built-in, 178
—, composite, 100
—, continuous, 185
—, curved, 195
—, deflection of, 152, 174
—, on elastic foundations, 189
—, oscillation of, 307–314
—, reinforced concrete, 107
—, shear stress in, 117
Bending and direct stress, 95, 218
— and twisting, 139
— moment, 71
— —, graphical, 81
— —, maximum, 83
—, pure, 86
— strain energy, 152
—, unsymmetrical, 111
Built-in beams, 178
Bulk modulus, 65

Castigliano's theorem, 203
Centre of twist, 126
Circular plates, 295
Close-coiled springs, 225
Collapse load, 214
Compound bars, 14
— beams, 100
— shafts, 137
— stress, 34
— tubes, 277
Compression, 1
— test, 323
Concrete, reinforced, 107
Continuous beams, 185
Contraction, percentage, 5
Contraflexure, 73
Cottered joints, 27
Creep, 326
Curved bars, stresses in, 195
— —, deflection of, 201, 203
Cylinders, rotating, 289
—, thin, 259
—, thick, 267
—, wire-winding of, 265

Deflection coefficients, 175
Deflection of beams, 152
— — —, by calculus, 154
— — —, graphical method, 174
— — curved beams, 201, 203
Direct stress, 2
Discs, rotating, 287

Ductility, 5

Eccentric load, column, 95
— —, strut, 243
Elastic constants, 65, 337
— foundations, 189
— limit, 4
— packings, 17
Elongation, percentage, 5, 321
Euler theory, 238
Extensometers, 330

Factor of safety, 6, 7
Failure, theories of, 56
Fatigue, 327
Fixed beams, 178

Gerber's law, 329
Goodman's law, 329
Guest theory, 57

Haigh theory, 57
Hardness test, 323
Hooke's law, 3
Hub on shaft, 279

Impact, bending, 154
—, direct, 8
— test, 324
Inertia, moment of, 88, 109, 113
—, product of, 88, 109

Johnson's formula, 249
Joints, cottered, 27
—, riveted, 29, 122

Leaf springs, 230
Limit of proportionality, 4
Load, 1
—, concentrated, 74
—, distributed, 75
—, factor, 7, 209
—, impact, 8
—, proof, 232
—, suddenly applied, 8
—, type of, 6
—, varying distributed, 79

Macaulay's method, 156
Middle third rule, 99
— quarter rule, 100
Mises-Hencky theory, 57
Modulus, bulk, 65
— of elasticity, 3
— of rigidity, 26
— of section, 88

lulus, *Young's*, 3
ır's strain circle, 53
ır's stress circle, 42
nent, bending, 71
f resistance, 88
nent of inertia, 88, 109, 113
– —, equivalent, 101
– —, graphically, 91
– —, polar, 89
– —, principal, 109
nent-area method, 163

tral axis, 86
urface, 86

n-coiled springs, 228
illations, linear, 302
torsional, 302
transverse, 304
rstrain, 322

y-Robertson formula, 250
to-elasticity, 334
tic bending, 209
inge, 209
orsion, 139
ielding of tubes, 274
– — rotating discs, 293
es, circular, 295
son's ratio, 47
al frame, 192, 206, 220
cipal axis, 88
noments of inertia, 109
f superposition, 3
lanes, 38
train, 49
– theory, 57
tress, 39
– in beams, 121
– theory, 56
of load, 232
esilience, 7
tress, 322

kine theory, 57
kine-Gordon formula, 247
nforced concrete beams, 107
ilience, 7 (*see also* Strain energy)
proof, 7
idity, flexural, 152
modulus of, 26
eted joints, 29, 122
ating cylinders, 289
liscs, 287

Venant, principle of, 2
heory, 57
tion modulus, 88
fts, circular, 130
compound, 137
oscillation of, 301
rectangular, 142

Shafts, torsion of, 130
—, whirling of, 314
Shear centre, 126
—, deflection due to, 170
— strain, 26
— — theory, 57
— — energy, 26, 55
— stress, 24
— — complementary, 24
— —, in beams, 117
— —, maximum, 40
Shearing force, 71
— —, maximum, 83
Spherical shell, thick, 281
— —, thin, 260
Spiral springs, 234
Springs, close-coiled, 225
—, leaf, 230
—, open-coiled, 228
—, oscillations of, 302, 306
—, spiral, 234
Stiffness of beams, 175, 307
— of springs, 225
—, torsional, 131
Strain, direct, 3
— gauges, 332
—, principal, 49
—, shear, 26
—, volumetric, 54, 261
Strain circle, 53
— energy, 7
— — in bending, 152, 203
— — in torsion, 132
— —, shear, 26, 55
— — theory, 57
— —, volumetric, 55
Stress, 2
—, bending, 86
— circle, 42
— concentrations, bending, 95
—, compressive, 2
— —, tension, 19
— —, torsion, 135
—, direct, 2
—, principal, 39
—, proof, 322
—, shear, 24
—, temperature, 16, 105, 292
—, tensile, 2
—, working, 7
Struts, eccentric loading of, 243
—, *Euler* theory, 238
—, initially curved, 244
—, *Johnson's* formula for, 249
—, lateral loading of, 250
—, *Perry-Robertson* formula for, 250
—, *Rankine-Gordon* formula for, 247
—, varying cross-section, 254
Superposition, principle of, 3

Temperature stress, 16, 105, 292

Tensile test, 4, 322
— —, stress, 2
— —, ultimate, 5
Tension, 1
Testing, compression, 323
—, creep, 326
—, fatigue, 327
—, hardness, 323
—, impact, 324
—, tensile, 4, 322
Theories of failure, 56
Thick cylinders, 267
— spherical shells, 281
Thin cylinders, 259
— spherical shells, 260
Tie with lateral load, 253
Torsion beyond yield, 138
— of shafts, 130
— of thin tubular sections, 142
— — — cellular sections, 145
Torsion of thin rectangular memb
146
— — — open sections, 147
Tresca theory, 57
Tubes—*see* Cylinders
—, compound, 277

Unsymmetrical bending, 111

Volumetric strain, 54, 261
— — energy, 55
Vibrations, linear, 302
—, torsional, 302
—, transverse, 307

Wire-winding, 265
Whirling of shafts, 314

Young's modulus, 3
Yield point, 5

TO THE READER

Author and publisher would welcome suggestions towards future editions of this text, or the pointing out of any misprint or obscurity. Please write to the Technical Editor, The Macmillan Press Ltd, Houndmills, Basingstoke, Hampshire RG21 2XS